# MODERN OPTICS

Earle B. Brown

*Senior Engineering Staff*
*The Perkin-Elmer Corporation*

*New York*
REINHOLD PUBLISHING CORPORATION
*Chapman & Hall, Ltd., London*

*To my wife,*

MARY

# Preface

In 1945, when the author published his first book on optics, this field had been thrust out of the little-known workshops of two or three U. S. companies into an unaccustomed prominence by the demands of World War II. Precision optical instruments, for which we had depended heavily upon imports, were needed urgently and in quantity, and demands for different and better types were heavy. To meet these needs, the U. S. optical industry, beginning about 1940, expanded rapidly, both in capacity and in competence. This growth did not cease with the War. It has gone steadily on, and today it can be claimed that the United States is the world leader in this field.

Optics has come a long way in this period. In the area of lens design, for example, it was rather generally accepted in the thirties that lens designs were not likely to ever be significantly better than they were, and that it was unlikely there would be any really revolutionary developments in optics. Nothing could have been more premature than such a point of view.

At that time, optical design was carried out by hand computations with logarithms; a designer of a photographic lens might trace a dozen rays each at three or four field angles, and spend about a year in the process before committing his design to the optician. Early in the forties, the more forward-looking designers were beginning to experiment with optical computations carried out on desk calculators. Today, optical design is carried out on high-speed digital computers, and it is not unusual to trace a hundred rays each at a dozen different field angles, and to include skew ray computations as well (which is an almost hopeless task by hand), and yet complete an optical design in a week. Computers now design lenses by themselves, finding the best solution possible with a given set of parameters by reiterative computation. A modern computer used for optical design is equivalent to more than a thousand mathematicians operating desk calculators, and thus to perhaps five thousand using logarithms. And it can be operated 24 hours a day, if necessary.

The astronomical telescope used to be considered the ultimate in precision optical design and fabrication. Today, the astronomical telescope is a rather crude device in terms of optical performance. The Rayleigh limit was for decades an ultimate performance goal; today it is recognized as being a rather coarse criterion of quality.

It is not only in geometrical optics, however, that the field has grown in the last two decades. The whole field of infrared technology has developed in this period; electronic imaging devices, their development spurred in a large measure by the growth of television, have achieved most of their present status in this period; there have also been important developments in interferometry, metrology, spectroscopy and other fields whose exploitation depends heavily upon optical instrumentation. In many areas, optical instruments are no longer complete and independent entities; they have become parts of more complex opto-mechanical-electronic systems.

More generalized and more powerful methods of optical analysis have been developed, of which the application of communications theory is an example, which permit a more complete understanding of optical systems themselves and, more importantly, of optical systems as parts of more complex apparatus.

And, of course, in the last five years, the laser has opened completely new fields of exploration and exploitation.

As a result of the tremendous increase in the application of optical instruments and optical techniques throughout all types of industry and in all sorts of technologies, particularly in the defense and aerospace domain, more and more technical people whose primary specialization is in other fields—electronics, chemistry, mechanics, aerodynamics, and many others— have an interest and a need to understand the fundamental principles of optics, the domain of its technology, its possibilities and limitations, its language, its scope and its current status. It is for them that this book has been written.

Optics has added much to many fields of science and technology; its techniques and its apparatus have aided in providing deeper insight and more complete understanding in innumerable areas remote from optics itself. Much modern equipment owes its utility and capability to the combination of techniques and components from optics, electronics, mechanics and other technological domains; for example, we need only to mention television, missile guidance and many equipment developments in biology and medicine.

It has been the author's fortune to have spent most of his life working closely with technical people trained in disciplines other than optics; out of this experience has grown his own method of approach to the subject.

The guiding purpose of this book has been to give as broad a picture of optical technology as is possible within a reasonable bulk and to present the material at a technical level which will neither insult the intelligence of the intended reader nor burden him with unnecessary detail. A reasonable level of rigor has been attempted, but no attempt has been made to include proofs of many of the mathematical formulations. These have been done adequately by many authors, and references are included to such material for those who may wish to pursue a given subject further.

Problems have not been included. The book is not intended as a text for a classroom course in optics, but for self-study. In the case of the Fourier transform analysis of optical systems, in Chapter 9, a considerable mathematical development is given, primarily because, in the author's opinion, the conclusions are not readiy acceptable to the technical mind without this development.

The material on lasers is not extensive. In keeping with the purpose of the book, extensive material on theory is not pertinent, and in the field of applications, the technology is developing at such a rapid pace at the present time that anything but the most general discussion would be obsolete before the volume could reach the bookstore. A definitive volume on lasers and particularly on laser applications is three to five years away.

An effort has been made to include a comprehensive bibliography; individual readers will have specific interests in particular fields and will want to pursue these interests in greater depth. At the same time, the bibliography makes no pretense of being complete or authoritative.

There is very little in this book that is not discussed in greater detail and with greater rigor elsewhere; the primary aim has been scope rather than uniqueness of subject. The classification of optical instrument types is believed to be unique, as is the treatment of reflections and image rotations in mirrors and prisms. Both of these treatments have been developed over the years in the course of creating convincing methods of explaining these topics.

The author thanks his many associates at the Perkin-Elmer Corporation for stimulating discussions which have contributed significantly to the quality of this book. In particular, he wishes to thank Dr. Norman Adams for reviewing the material on lasers and Dr. Roland Shack for helpful discussions of the subjects covered in Chapter 9. He is especially indebted to his wife, not only for material assistance in preparation of the book, but also for the confidence and inspiration which alone could make such an undertaking possible.

EARLE B. BROWN

*Ridgefield, Conn.*
*September, 1965*

# Contents

# PART I

# Fundamentals

CHAPTER 1

# Nature and Properties of Light

## WAVES AND PARTICLES

**1.1. The Nature of Light.** There are two descriptions of the nature of light: the wave description and the particle description. The first is essential to the satisfactory explanation of phenomena such as interference and diffraction; the second is essential to the understanding of phenomena such as the photoelectric effect.

Historically, the two descriptions have been considered in opposition, and much intellectual labor has been expended in attempts to show that one was correct and the other wrong. "Modern" scientific concepts of light began with Newton and the particle theory; the wave theory, supported by Huygens,[1] gained ascendancy in the eighteenth century and was confirmed by the experiments of Young (1802)[2] and Fresnel (1814).[3] The introduction of the electromagnetic theory of Maxwell in 1856[4] provided a strong quantitative foundation for the existence of radiation in the form of waves, illustrated the equivalence of light and electromagnetic fields, and eliminated the problem of the ether, which had been thought necessary for the propagation of waves, but which experiments failed to detect.

In the early years of the twentieth century, it became evident that a particle description was necessary to explain certain phenomena, and the concept of the *photon* arose. Much effort has been devoted to considerations of a "unified" description, in which particles and waves might be combined as different aspects of a single entity, but this approach has been unsuccessful. It is now recognized that the concepts of both particles and waves are derived from our familiarity with the behavior of matter on a gross scale, and that on an atomic scale the behavior is quite different, and not describable in familiar terms. It is now sometimes neces-

3

sary to use a "wave" description in certain cases for electrons, protons, and other atomic "particles," and indeed for matter in general.

The current successful description of the behavior of matter on the atomic scale is embodied in quantum mechanics, which provides a sound *mathematical* basis for the discussion of this behavior, but does not help conceptual understanding.

**1.2. The Wave Character of Light.** Light is electromagnetic energy, traveling through space in the form of oscillating electric and magnetic fields. If one could measure directly the electric and magnetic fields associated with a beam of light (and thanks to the laser, this can now be done), it would be found that at a particular point in space the values of either the electric or the magnetic field would oscillate periodically, so that a plot of the values as a function of time would be a sine wave, like Figure 1.1.

Also, if one were to choose an instant of time, and measure the values of the fields as distributed in space, one would also get a sine wave like Figure 1.1. This is a picture of a *transverse* wave, in which the oscillating values are measured in a direction perpendicular to the way the energy is traveling. In a *longitudinal* wave, such as a sound wave, the pressure of the medium is the oscillating value, and this is measured in the direction of travel.

Transverse waves are completely defined by three parameters: velocity, amplitude ($\varepsilon$ in Figure 1.1) and either wavelength ($\lambda$ in Figure 1.1) or frequency (number of oscillations per unit of time). Velocity, wavelength and frequency are related by the equation

$$V = \lambda \nu \qquad (1.1)$$

where $V$ is the velocity, $\lambda$ the wavelength, and $\nu$ the frequency. Another

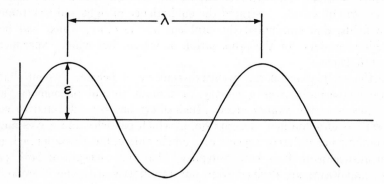

FIGURE 1.1. The sine wave.

quantity often used in discussions of light is the wave number, $N$, where $N = 1/\lambda$ is the number of waves per unit length (usually a centimeter). The velocity of light in vacuum is $3 \times 10^{10}$ cm/sec (see Section 1.19). That portion of the spectrum which falls under the nomenclature "light" is largely a matter of choice; for the application of the principles discussed in this book, the range of wavelengths may be considered to be from $10^{-5}$ to $10^{-2}$ cm ($10^3$ to $10^6$Å) or 0.1 to 100 microns ($\mu$). Therefore, the frequencies, from Equation (1.1) range from $3 \times 10^{12}$ to $3 \times 10^{15}$ cycles (from 3 teracycles to 3 kiloteracycles).[22] The wave numbers range from 100 to 100,000.

Light represents a small portion of the spectrum of electromagnetic radiation, which ranges from gamma rays with wavelengths as short as $10^{-14}$ cm to long wavelength radio waves, with wavelengths of thousands of meters, as shown in Figure 1.2. This spectrum includes X-rays, radar and radio waves, as well as the waves of visible light, flanked by the shorter wavelength ultraviolet on the one side and the infrared on the other. All of this radiation is exactly the same in nature as light, has the same parameters, and has the same fixed velocity in free space, usually denoted by the letter $c$, which seems to be a fundamental constant of Nature. Its constancy is the foundation of the laws of relativity. The other fundamental property of electromagnetic radiation is frequency. The wavelength is really a property of the medium in which the radiation is propagated, the determining equation being

$$\lambda' = \frac{c}{\nu\mu} \tag{1.2}$$

where $\mu$ is the *index of refraction* of the medium (for example, glass). When radiation travels in a medium other than vacuum, the velocity changes, so that $V = c/\mu$, and the frequency remains constant; consequently, the wavelength changes to $\lambda' = \lambda/\mu$.

In the regions of the spectrum where detection and measurement are by electrical means—in the radar and radio regions—it is customary to refer to radiation in terms of frequency, since this is the parameter which instruments measure directly. In the region of the spectrum which includes light, wavelength is the parameter which can be measured directly, and thus discussions are generally in these terms. In this book, we will follow the general custom.

**1.3. Interference and Diffraction.** It is in the phenomena of interference and diffraction that light most effectively reveals its wave character. If we consider a plane wave of light (Figure 1.3) impinging upon a barrier in which there are two tiny openings, it is readily seen that each

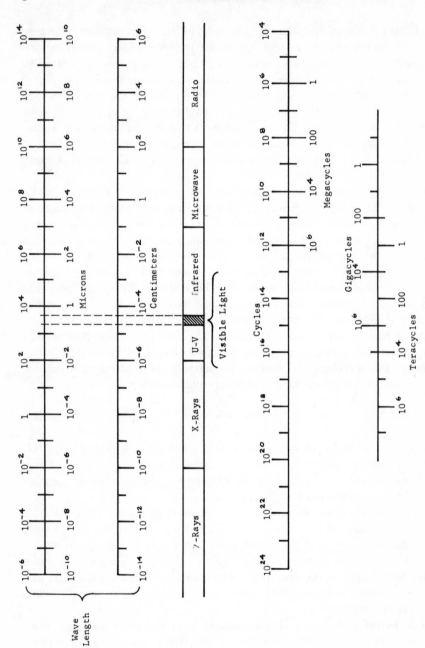

FIGURE 1.2. The electromagnetic spectrum.

of these openings will act as a new source of light waves, which will spread out in a circular pattern from each of the openings. In three dimensions, of course, the wave fronts from the openings would be spherical.

Now, since the conditions were defined so that a given plane wave front reached the two openings simultaneously, the two circular wave patterns are "in phase," that is, they oscillate together, so that they reach maxima and minima at the same time. If we now draw the remainder of Figure 1.3, it is seen that at a screen distant from the openings, light from the two separate openings combines, and that at a point a, whose distances from the two openings are equal, the two waves arrive in phase, whereas at a point b, the difference of whose distances from the two openings is ½ a wavelength, the two waves arrive exactly out of phase.

It is characteristic of wave motions that when separate motions occur at a point, the resultant is the sum of the separate disturbances. This is the rule of superposition, by which the amplitudes of the separate components are added. By this rule, the conditions of Figure 1.3 will give double amplitude at point a and zero at point b. Very simple experi-

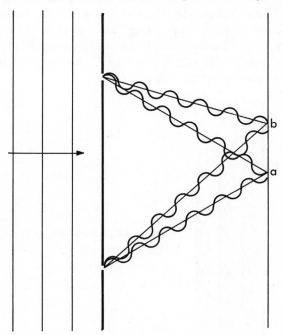

FIGURE 1.3. Interference from two pinholes.

ments clearly demonstrate that this is exactly what happens with light. Figure 1.3 is an illustration of the *interference* of light which results when two pinholes (or slits) are illuminated by a *coherent* beam of light.

When a beam of light passes through an aperture which is large with respect to the wavelength, there is a spreading of the beam at the edges of the aperture, so that the spot of light which might be projected upon a distant screen does not have completely sharp edges. The same is true of the shadows of opaque objects. This is the phenomenon of *diffraction*, and it is characteristic of wave motion.

Figure 1.4 illustrates Huygens' construction for the propagation of a beam of light. Each point on a wave front is considered to be a separate source of radiation, sending out a series of spherical wavelets. In the principal direction of propagation, these wavelets add, by superposition, to produce a wave front which is the envelope of the wavelets and which is a duplicate of the original wave front and parallel to it. When the original wave front is limited in extent, as when it is restricted by an aperture, as in Figure 1.4, the superposition of the wavelets in the region near the edges of the beam is more complex, and varies with the angle made with the principal direction of propagation. The result is that, close to the beam, there are interference maxima and minima; far from the beam, it can be shown, mathematically or graphically, the result of superposition of the wavelets leads to complete interference.

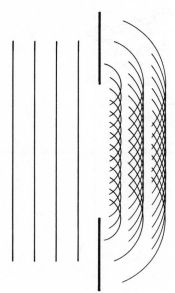

FIGURE 1.4. Huygens' construction for the propagation of light.

This is the wave theory explanation of the rectilinear propagation of light—that the propagation is really only roughly rectilinear. Actually, for apertures much larger than a wavelength, the spread of the beam is quite small, and not readily detectable; for a 1-mm aperture, the spread of a light beam is less than two minutes of arc. It becomes greater as the aperture becomes smaller, and when the size of the aperture is of the order of a wavelength, the interference phenomena take over completely, and the concept of rectilinear propagation no longer has validity. We will have much more to say about interference and diffraction later on.

**1.4. Maxwell.** In 1873, Maxwell's work[4] on electromagnetic theory was published. This work provided a unified mathematical structure which showed the interrelation of a number of empirical electrical laws which had been propounded by previous workers, and it related the electric and magnetic fields in a convincingly simple fashion. It showed that an oscillating electric charge gives rise to oscillating electric and magnetic fields and that these must travel outward in space at a fixed velocity equal to the observed velocity of light. Thus the major impediment to the acceptance of the wave theory of light—the need for an ether—was removed, and at the same time the electromagnetic nature of light was firmly established. Maxwell's mathematics showed clearly that the velocity of his electromagnetic waves would be

$$c = 1/\sqrt{\mu_0\epsilon_0} \tag{1.3}$$

where $\mu_0$ is the magnetic permeability and $\epsilon_0$ the electric permeability. When the measured values of these purely electrical constants are substituted in Equation (1.3), $c$ comes out to equal the known velocity of light within the limits of experimental error. This can hardly be a coincidence, and it makes obvious the fact that light is the electromagnetic radiation that Maxwell's equations predict.

If anything further were needed to prove the reality of this radiation, Hertz's (1887)[5] detection of electromagnetic radiation from an oscillating electric field provided it, and the wave theory was firmly established. Maxwell's work also made it clear that light represented only a small portion of an infinite possible spectrum of radiation, in which other then known radiation, such as the electrical waves detected by Hertz and heat radiation also had a place.

**1.5. Troubles with the Wave Theory.** Historically, the first difficulty with the wave theory, as unified by Maxwell's equations, arose about 1900, with attempts to explain blackbody radiation. When a material body is heated, it emits radiation; if its temperature becomes high enough, it emits radiation in the region of visible light. The existence of this radiation is readily explained in terms of the wave theory. If a radiation field is completely enclosed by matter at a given temperature, energy will be interchanged between the field and the matter, and a state of equilibrium will be reached wherein the field will contain a specific distribution of energy as a function of frequency or wavelength; this distribution is determined by the temperature only and not by the nature of the material. This radiation is called *blackbody* radiation because a perfectly radiating body is also a perfectly absorbing body and would, if cold, appear black. Any enclosed cavity in a material body contains blackbody radiation at the temperature of the body.

The methods of statistical mechanics suffice to show that this situation exists, but they do not provide information on the form of the distribution of energy with frequency.[5a] The electromagnetic theory provides the necessary relations to permit such a calculation, and it is readily carried out, based upon the number of degrees of freedom of oscillation available in the cavity, which is a function of the frequency and the size of the cavity. If such a computation is carried out, the result is

$$E_\nu \, d\nu = \frac{8\pi V}{c^3} kT\nu^2 \, d\nu \qquad (1.4)$$

The validity of the result can be tested by experiment. While it is not possible to observe in a completely enclosed cavity, one can come experimentally close enough to have a very small experimental error. When this is done, it becomes obvious that Equation (1.4) does not describe what is observed.

Equation (1.4) leads to the following conclusions with respect to the energy in a cavity:

(1) The total energy is infinite. This is not readily disproved experimentally, but it challenges reason.

(2) The radiation in the cavity has an infinite specific heat (it would require an infinite amount of energy to raise its temperature). This is definitely not true experimentally.

(3) The total energy is proportional to the temperature. This is not true, since it can be shown experimentally that the total energy is proportional to the fourth power of the temperature.

(4) The energy increases with frequency without limit. This is not true, since it can be shown experimentally that there is a definite maximum at a frequency which is a function of the temperature.

Planck[6] showed that this experimental contradiction can be removed if one adopts the assumption that each permitted frequency can exist only at such amplitudes that the energy is $nh\nu$, where $h$ is Planck's constant ($6.6 \times 10^{-27}$ erg-second), and that the probability that it has the energy $n_0h\nu$ is proportional to $e^{-(nh\nu/kT)}$. These assumptions lead to the energy distribution law

$$\rho(\nu) = \frac{8\pi h\nu^3}{c^3} \frac{1}{e^{(h\nu/kT)} - 1} \tag{1.5}$$

This result agrees with the observed distribution of blackbody radiation, hence the validity of Planck's assumptions and of his constant $h$ as a universal constant is assured, although in adopting it, he was concerned only with obtaining a correct mathematical result.

At about the same time, the photoelectric effect was being studied. When light is incident upon a clean metal plate in a vacuum, electrons are ejected. The effect occurs much more readily with some metals, such as cesium, than with others. When the phenomenon is carefully measured, the following facts are found:

(1) The kinetic energy of the electrons depends upon the *frequency* of the incident light, and obeys the relation $E = h\nu - \delta E$. The energy is completely independent of the *intensity* of the light.

(2) The number of electrons ejected in unit time is proportional to the *intensity* of the light.

(3) If the frequency of the light is lower than that required to make $h\nu = \delta E$ *no* electrons are emitted.

The $h$ in the relation above is Planck's constant.

Both the facts listed above and the assumptions needed to explain blackbody radiation show that the energy in the electromagnetic field is *quantized*—it comes in discrete packages. One might say at this point that it comes in packets of waves of finite extent. The electromagnetic theory itself makes no such restrictions, but it assumes that there can be a continuous variation of amplitudes and frequencies and that the waves consist of an infinite train.

Nothing yet points to specific particles. But if we again examine the photoelectric effect and allow the illumination on the metal plate to become very weak—so weak, in fact, that there can be only a few quanta per second, distributed over a very large area (say one cm²), it is found that a single electron can absorb all the energy from the entire area and be emitted with kinetic energy $h\nu - \delta E$. This effect points definitely to a particle, which can be effective at a point. Einstein adopted the term "photon" to describe this particle, and we use the term freely today. But what determines which electron is to absorb the photon?

One way out of the apparent dilemma is to say that the waves represent the probability distribution of the photons; in the phenomenon of interference, for example, the interference pattern is a probability distribution. Where there is a bright area, there is a high probability of finding the photon; where there is a dark area, the probability is low. This agrees with experiment. But an interference pattern is produced from two pinholes, widely separated in terms of atomic dimensions. The light pattern on a screen is completely different for two pinholes than for one. A photon, which is small enough in size to select a specific electron in the metal plate, presumably cannot go through *both* pinholes. But if it goes through only one, how does it know that the other exists, so that it can choose where to go on the screen? There are no satisfactory answers to questions like this, except to say that they imply we can describe these phenomena in terms of familiar things, and that this implication is not necessarily a valid one. Feynman gives an interesting discussion of this experiment.[7]

There are other phenomena which are not explainable in terms of the wave theory. One of the most important, since it points quite clearly to the interdependence of particles and waves, is the Compton effect. When light is scattered by electrons, some of the energy is absorbed by the electron, and the scattered light has less energy and is therefore of lower frequency, in accordance with

$$h\nu' = h\nu - x \tag{1.6}$$

where $x$ is the energy absorbed by the electron. It was shown by Compton,[8] for the scattering of X-rays, that the frequency of the scattered light was dependent upon the scattering angle, and that the phenomenon followed exactly what would be expected of an elastic collision of material particles. The relation of scattering angle and frequency can also be explained in terms of the wave theory, but the direction of recoil of the electron is different. In an elastic particle collision, the electron recoils at an angle to the incident photon, exactly as billiard balls recoil; in the case of absorption and reemission of a wave, the recoil is always in the direction of the incident light. Experiments in the cloud chamber have shown definitely that the phenomenon, in the Compton effect, follows the rules for the collision of material particles.

If the photon is a particle, then it must have a momentum. Now momentum is mass times velocity; the velocity of the photon is $c$. What is its mass? If Einstein's relation for the equivalence of mass and energy is invoked

$$E = mc^2 \tag{1.7}$$

we can write, for the photon

$$E = h\nu = mc^2 \tag{1.8}$$

hence the mass of the photon is

$$m = h\nu/c^2 \tag{1.9}$$

and its momentum is

$$P = h\nu/c = h/\lambda \tag{1.10}$$

This is exactly the momentum which Compton had to ascribe to the photon to obtain the observed results from the scattering experiments. The relation, however, has an even greater significance, as will be seen momentarily.

A small point may have caught the reader's attention. The velocity of a photon is always $c$, hence what of the fact that light travels more slowly in a material medium? As will be shown in later discussions, the velocity of light in a material medium is a *group* velocity, or velocity of a group of waves of varying frequency. The *photon velocity* is always $c$.

Before leaving the subject, one more lack in the electromagnetic theory should be noted—its failure to explain how an atom can maintain a stable energy level without radiating. Radiation from an atom can be explained by viewing it as a simple harmonic oscillator. But one would then expect it to lose energy rapidly by continuous radiation, which would cause a change in frequency and make it impossible to explain the existence of sharp spectral lines. The only explanation which fits the observed facts is that the atom, when shifting from one energy level to another, either absorbs or emits a photon, and the energy, $h\nu$, of the photon, is equivalent to the change in energy of the atom.

**1.6. The Wave Aspect of Matter.** In 1924, de Broglie[9] made the suggestion that the relationship expressed in Equation (1.10) applies to all matter; that with every free particle there is an associated wave aspect, whose wavelength is given by Equation (1.10), which may be written

$$\lambda = h/mv = h/P \tag{1.11}$$

This relation was experimentally verified in 1927 by Thomson, and also by Davison and Germer, by observation of the diffraction of electrons by crystals. It has subsequently been verified for atoms and molecules as well. The substance of the de Broglie relation is that all material bodies have a wave aspect; we have not noticed it before because for the bodies familiar to our experience the associated wavelength is so short as to be completely beyond observation.

**1.7. Complementarity and the Uncertainty Principle.** The very heart of the duality of character which light (and also other atomic particles, as has been shown) exhibits lies in the *uncertainty principle*, first stated by Heisenberg. This is the statement that it is impossible, *in principle*, to determine both the position and the momentum of a particle simultaneously to an accuracy better than

$$\Delta P \, \Delta y = h/2\pi \tag{1.12}$$

It is possible to find either the position *or* the momentum to any desired accuracy, but as precision in the one measurement is improved, accuracy in the other is sacrificed. It is important to note that this is a limitation *in principle;* it has nothing to do with the finesse of experimentation. Its significance is that we must accept the fact that the concepts of position and momentum, which seem to be separate and distinct properties, are not separable, and any questions directed to the simultaneous values of both of them *have no real meaning.*

Acceptance of this principle demands the acceptance of the dual character of energy and matter. There is a particle aspect of both light and matter, and there is a wave aspect. Depending upon the experiment which is being performed one or the other is predominant; but neither light nor matter can be completely described without taking account of both. This is the complementarity principle of Bohr[10] (1928)—that the wave and particle description are merely complementary ways of describing the same phenomenon, and both are equally valid.

This dual nature and the uncertainty principle are not limited to phenomena of atomic dimensions—they apply equally to the sizeable bodies dealt with in ordinary mechanics, but the wave aspect does not readily manifest itself here. It is only in the case of phenomena of atomic dimensions that the duality becomes evident.

**1.8. Quantum Mechanics.**[11] Initiation of a new mechanics, *quantum mechanics,* by Heisenberg and Schrödinger in 1926 provided the necessary tool for handling the apparently contradictory wave and particle aspects of radiation and matter. The underlying principle of quantum mechanics is a more general definition of momentum in terms of the de Broglie equation [Equation (1.11)] in place of the classical mechanics definition of momentum as $mv$.

Quantum mechanics is essential for the treatment of all atomic phenomena. It adequately explains all the complex features of atomic and molecular spectra, and the interaction of radiation and matter, so that the soundness of its fundamental assumptions have been adequately demonstrated. It breaks down only in attempts to apply it to the interior of the nucleus.

Once the electron is treated as a wave, as it is in quantum mechanics, the mystery of atomic spectra is immediately solved. The electron is confined to the atom by the attraction of its negative charge to the positively charged nucleus; it therefore assumes a pattern of standing waves. The number of possible patterns is quite restricted, and when they are worked out for a particular atom, as by Schrödinger for the hydrogen atom, it is found that the differences in energy between the various possible states agree exactly with the energy radiated in the line spectra of the atom. Thus the wave nature of the electron is shown to be fundamental in establishing the properties of matter, and the puzzling situation of a nonradiating atom is suddenly perfectly clear. The precision of the agreement with measured results from spectral analysis is almost magical. The success of the wave concept of the electron in explaining atomic structure ranks with the success of the electron-nucleus concept of the atom in explaining the periodic table.

**1.9. The Meaning of $h$.** It has become evident that Planck's constant $h$ has a deep physical significance. It provides the connecting link between the wave and particle aspects of light and matter. What is its meaning? Bohr has pointed out that it is the product of two variables, one of which is a quantity usually associated with a particle, the other one usually associated with a wave. This can be stated in two ways, from the relations given above

$$h = ET = P\lambda \qquad (1.13)$$

where $E$ is energy, $T$ is the period, or reciprocal of the frequency, $P$ is momentum and $\lambda$ is wavelength. $E$ and $P$ are quantities associated with particles; $T$ and $\lambda$ are associated with waves.

When the magnitudes of the particle-like properties are large with respect to those of the wave-like properties, the particle aspect prevails. This is the region of very short wavelengths, very high frequencies, where we find electrons, X-rays, and $\gamma$-rays. These behave very much like particles, and it requires refined experiments to demonstrate their wave aspect. At lower frequencies, longer wavelengths, the wave-like properties predominate. Here we find visible light, infrared and radio waves.

The location of the dividing line is determined by the value of $h$. Investigation of the electromagnetic spectrum has encompassed a range covering regions where both the particle and the wave aspects predominate, and we have thus been led to the need for understanding the duality. Were $h$ very much smaller than it is, the electromagnetic theory would be satisfactory for a long time to come, and quantum mechanics would be a concept far in the future. Were $h$ very much larger, quantum mechanics would have had to be invented in the eighteenth or nineteenth century, instead of the twentieth.

Is it a coincidence of Nature that the midpoint between wave and particle aspects is very near the region of visible light, where human senses operate?

## RELATIVITY

**1.10. Relation of Relativity to Optics.** For most optical problems, the theory of relativity is not a matter for concern, just as it is of no concern for most problems of mechanics. Most of the observable effects of relativity, however, are basically optical phenomena, and the concepts of relativity were born from experiments on light, so that one can hardly discuss the subject of modern optics without including the theory of relativity.

**1.11. Basis of the Theory of Relativity.** In 1887, Michelson and Morley[12] conducted their famous experiment on the velocity of light. This has been described in so much detail in so many places that it is summarized only briefly here. The wave concept of light was in its ascendancy, and the need for a medium in which the waves of light could be propagated had led to the concept of the "ether"—a medium which was required to be more rigid than steel and at the same time more tenuous than the best vacuum. Although Maxwell had shown, thirty years earlier, that a material medium was unnecessary for the propagation of electromagnetic radiation, the ether concept had not yet been entirely abandoned.

After rather inconclusive results by Fizeau, Airy and others on the velocity of light in moving media, Michelson and Morley carried out their now classic experiment. The experiment itself is nothing more than the measurement of the difference in the velocity of light in directions perpendicular to each other. Its unusual character lay in the degree of precision required to be certain of the results. The light was reflected in multiple paths along the two arms of a cross, which was floated in mercury and mounted on a concrete slab, and the difference in velocity, if any, would appear as a shift of interference fringes. The accuracy was such that a difference in velocity of three-thousandths of one per cent of the velocity of light could be detected.

Now, the earth is in motion through space, and hence through the ether, if there is an ether. In the first place, it revolves about the sun with a velocity that is a hundredth of a per cent of the velocity of light. In addition, the solar system is in motion within the galaxy, and the galaxy within the universe, and there may be other unknown motions. In particular, since the earth's path about the sun is a closed loop, it must be in motion with respect to the ether at some time during a year, at a rate at least ten times that detectable by the experiment.

The experiment showed no difference in velocity. Although repeated in many positions and at many different times of the year, and by other experimenters with more sensitive apparatus, it consistently gave a null result.

This surprising fact led to much theorizing, including the famous Lorentz-Fitzgerald contraction, which proposed that there is a contraction of length in the direction of velocity through the ether just sufficient to compensate for the variation in the velocity of light. This might be acceptable, were it not that other kinds of experiments were performed, also with null results, which would have required different laws of contraction to explain them.

Einstein furnished the explanation, in the form of the special theory of relativity, propounded in 1905.[13] The significance of the theory lies in its philosophical implications, in that it forced us to look more carefully into just what is meant by terms like "mass," "length" and "time." After the ancient Greeks, physics had developed from a contemplative to an experimental science; but the development had not gone far enough. We still labored under definitions which were created from intuition and not from experiment. Einstein's fundamental contribution was the proposition that the postulates and definitions of physics must rest upon measured results, and upon nothing else.

**1.12. Einstein's Hypotheses.** Einstein took the position that the results of the Michelson-Morley and other experiments were to be accepted as true, and he proceeded to determine what the result of their adoption would be on the basic concepts of dynamics. He adopted two hypotheses:

(1) The laws of physics are independent of the coordinate system in which they are observed to operate. This is the *principle of equivalence*.

(2) The velocity of light is the same for all observers.

The hypotheses are quite simple, but they have deep significance.

Every problem involving moving bodies is expressed in terms of a spatial coordinate system and a time reference. For example, consider a body in a rectangular three-dimensional coordinate system with coordinates $x,y,z$, at a time $t$, which is moving in the $X$-direction at a velocity $U$. Consider now a second coordinate system, parallel to the first, and moving in the $X$-direction with respect to the first system at a velocity $v$. What are the measured characteristics of the body in the second system? Assuming that the two $X$-axes coincide and that the origins were coincident at $t = t' = 0$, we can form the transformations from one coordinate system to the other

$$
\begin{aligned}
x' &= x - vt \\
y' &= y \\
z' &= z \\
t' &= t \\
U' &= U - v
\end{aligned}
\qquad (1.14)
$$

where $x',y',z'$ are the coordinates of the body in the second system, $t'$ is the time in the second system, and $U'$ is the velocity of the body in the second system. Other, more complicated transformations can be obtained —for example, for rotation of coordinate systems, but the above simple example will suffice.

The velocities of the body in the two systems are different, but the accelerations are the same, and laws like $F = m_a$ are unaffected by the transformation. These kinds of transformations are in accordance with ordinary mechanics, and they are in good agreement with experimental facts in the case of ordinary phenomena. But the Michelson-Morley experiment showed that, for light, the velocity equation does not hold, for it demonstrates that

$$c' = c \tag{1.15}$$

which is certainly not in agreement with Equation (1.14).

Using Einstein's two hypotheses, a set of transformation equations for the shift from one coordinate system to another can be derived[14] which makes Equation (1.15) true. These are

$$x' = \frac{x - vt}{\sqrt{1 - v^2/c^2}}$$

$$y' = y$$

$$z' = z$$

$$t' = \frac{t - \frac{v^2}{c^2}x}{\sqrt{1 - v^2/c^2}} \tag{1.16}$$

$$U' = \frac{U - v}{1 - \frac{v}{c^2}U}$$

This (Lorentz) transformation requires that new definitions be adopted for the concepts of measured length and measured time, which is the essence of the theory of relativity.

In the special theory of relativity, which Einstein published in 1905, and which we have been discussing above, he applied the principle of equivalence to systems in uniform motion with respect to each other, but not to systems with accelerated motion. This he did in the general theory, published in 1915. The principle of equivalence holds for both Newtonian and relativistic mechanics in the domain of the special theory; the only difference is the recognition of the constancy of the velocity of light.

**1.13. Consequences of the Special Theory.** There are seven consequences of the special theory of relativity which are of interest to consider in some detail.

(*a*) *The Relativity of Simultaneity.* Equations (1.16) show that two
events which are simultaneous in the first system are not simultaneous in
the second, if they occur in different places. For, let an event occur at $x_1$
and time $t_1$ in the first system, and another at $x_2$ and time $t_2$. Then, if $t_1$
$= t_2$, we have

$$t_1' = \frac{1}{\alpha}\left[t_1 - \frac{v}{c^2}x_1\right]$$

$$t_2' = \frac{1}{\alpha}\left[t_1 - \frac{v}{c^2}x_2\right]$$

(1.17)

where

$$\alpha = \sqrt{1 - v^2/c^2},$$

and it is seen that $t_1'$ and $t_2'$ are not equal if $x_1$ and $x_2$ are different.

(*b*) *The Dilation of Time.* In a similar way, it is seen that the interval
between two events occurring at the same place at different times is not
the same for the two systems. For, in the first system

$$\Delta t = t_1 - t_2$$

but, from Equation (1.17)

$$\Delta t' = t_1' - t_2' = \Delta t/\alpha$$

(1.18)

(*c*) *The Contraction of Space.* Lengths are measured fundamentally
by placing a measuring scale beside an object and observing the coordinates of the two ends *simultaneously*. Each observer must interpret the
word simultaneous with respect to his own system, and as we have seen,
these are not equivalent for two systems in motion with respect to each
other. Therefore, if an observer in the first system measures an object and
finds its length to be $x_2 - x_1$, an observer in the second system will measure
the same object and find its length to be

$$x_2' - x_1' = \alpha(x_2 - x_1)$$

(1.19)

(*d*) *Addition of Velocities.* It is seen from Equation (1.16) that the relativistic law for the addition of velocities is not the same as the Newtonian
law. The Newtonian law is derived on the assumption that time intervals in
the two systems are the same; it is seen in Equation (1.17) that this is an
invalid assumption if we accept the constancy of the velocity of light. The
best experimental evidence supports the constancy of the velocity of light,

and physics is concerned only with measured results, not with intuition. The equality of intervals in two systems which are in motion with respect to each other is inconsistent with a constant velocity of light.

It follows that a statement concerning a length or a time is not complete unless the frame of reference is stated, and all data in a given problem are referred to the same frame.

(*e*) *The Doppler Effect.* When light is emitted from a source in motion, classical theory would state that the frequency measured by a stationary observer will be higher than normal when the source is approaching, and lower than normal when its is receding. If the problem is worked out,[15] it will be seen that the relationship is slightly different depending upon whether the source is moving and the observer is at rest or the source is at rest and the observer moving. The results are as follows.

For moving source:

$$\nu' = \frac{\nu}{1 \pm \dfrac{v}{c}} + \text{ for receding source} \tag{1.20}$$

For moving observer:

$$\nu' = \nu \left( 1 \pm \frac{v}{c} \right) + \text{ for approaching source} \tag{1.21}$$

This is readily observed astronomically, and it is the basis for measuring the relative line of sight velocities of the earth and astronomical bodies. In practice, the difference between the two equations is too small to be detectable.

In relativistic mechanics, the equation for the Doppler effect is

$$\nu' = \frac{\nu \sqrt{1 - \dfrac{v^2}{c^2}}}{1 - \dfrac{v}{c}} \tag{1.22}$$

which gives a value intermediate between that of the two equations above.

(*f*) *The Aberration of Light.* Bradley,[16] in 1727, observed the effect known as the aberration of light. When light is received from an object which is at an angle to the direction of motion of the observer, the apparent direction of the light is the vector sum of the observer's velocity and the velocity of light, much as the apparent direction of a raindrop is changed when one is in motion. Bradley observed the effect on stars near the pole of the earth's orbit, which appeared to move in small parallactic ellipses as the earth pursued its orbital motion. He used it to determine the velocity of light. The diameter of the parallactic ellipse is about $41''$ of arc.

According to classical theory, the angle of aberration (the angle by which the incoming light is apparently deflected by the observer's motion) is

$$\tan \delta = v/c \qquad (1.23)$$

in relativistic mechanics, the angle is

$$\sin \delta = v/c \qquad (1.24)$$

For this small an angle, the difference between sine and tangent is far below the level of observational accuracy.

(g) *Reflection from a Moving Mirror.* Classical theory states the law of reflection from a plane mirror to be

$$I = -I' \qquad (1.25)$$

where $I$ is the angle of incidence and $I'$ the angle of reflection. In relativity theory, when the mirror is moving in the direction of its normal, and the source and observer are at rest, the law of reflection, stated in the observer's system, must be modified to[17]

$$\frac{\sin I}{1 + \dfrac{v}{c} \cos I} = - \frac{\sin I'}{1 - \dfrac{v}{c} \cos I'} \qquad (1.26)$$

**1.14. Significance of the Principle of Equivalence.** Explanation of the null results from the Michelson-Morley experiment in terms of the special theory of relativity has a deep philosophical significance. While the experiment was designed to detect the earth's motion through the ether, its real significance is that it is designed to detect a unique frame of reference. Whether this unique frame is the ether or the empty space in which Maxwell's electromagnetic waves can be propagated, the important point is that it is unique because it is the frame of reference in which the velocity of light is equal to $c$, and this velocity is different in all other systems which are moving with respect to it.

But the existence of any unique frame of reference is contrary to the principle of equivalence, which insists that all frames are equally valid for the derivation of physical laws, that there is no unique frame. If there were, then the concept of absolute rest and absolute motion would be meaningful, and *true* physical laws could only be derived by referring measurements to this special frame. The principle of equivalence, therefore, implies that the Michelson-Morley experiment, and all experiments designed to discover a unique frame of reference, must always give a null result. We can never detect absolute motion; indeed, the term has no meaning. The Doppler effect, for example, interpreted in classical theory, furnishes a tool for determining absolute motion; interpreted in relativity theory, it no longer becomes such a tool.

**1.15. The General Theory of Relativity.** In 1915 Einstein[18] published his general theory of relativity, which extended the concepts of the special theory to the case of accelerated systems. In the case of systems in uniform motion, it was noted that the principle of equivalence holds for such systems even in classical theory. In the case of accelerated systems, the principle of equivalence does not hold in classical theory; for example, according to classical theory, one can detect absolute acceleration. Detailed discussion of the general theory is beyond our scope, but we can call attention to three optical effects which are relevant to it.

(*a*) *Bending of Light in a Gravitational Field.* Classical theory predicts that a particle will be deflected in a gravitational field by a force equal to $m/r^2$, where $m$ is the mass of the particle and $r$ its distance from the center of the field. For waves, for which there is no mass, no deflection is predicted by classical theory.

The principle of equivalence of relativity theory predicts the deflection of a light ray in a gravitational field which is about twice that predicted for particles by the classical theory. Observation of stars near the limb of the sun during solar eclipses has verified the deflection predicted by relativity, which is about $1.75''$ of arc.

(*b*) *Increase in Wavelength in a Gravitational Field.* Relativity predicts that an atom in a gravitational field will emit light whose wavelength is increased by the factor $(1 + m/kr)$ compared to a similar atom in free space. The effect is only about two parts per million for an atom at the surface of the sun, but there is fairly strong evidence for the existence of the displacement; there is even stronger evidence for the existence in some white dwarf stars, such as the companion of Sirius. If the observed effect, which is definitely not a Doppler shift, is due to the action of the gravitational field, then the density of these stars is fantastically high. Evidence for the existence of stars of these densities, however, is available from cosmological theory.

(*c*) *The Nebular Red Shift.* It is observed that the light from distant galaxies is shifted toward the red with respect to light from nearby objects. It is a universal effect, and has been observed for distances up to several millions of light-years. The amount of the shift is linear with distance. This phenomenon is not in itself verification of the theory of relativity, but it has an important bearing on the theory of light and on cosmology, which are also involved in the general theory of relativity.

The exact cause of the red shift is not known. There are several possible explanations, choice among which must be based upon further understanding of the structure of the universe and of its evolutionary development. One possible cause is that the universe is expanding. A uniform expansion would explain the observed effect on the basis of a Doppler shift.

Another possibility is that, in traversing the extremely long paths in space, a photon may lose some of its energy at an extremely slow rate, which, for constant $h$, would lead to a decrease in the frequency and an increase in the wavelength. A third suggestion is that some or all of the fundamental physical constants, such as $h$, $E$, $m$ and $c$, are very slowly changing. A completely satisfactory explanation must await the future.

**1.16. Momentum and Energy.** Mass, as well as length and time, is a relative quantity. It is shown in discussions of relativity that the general methods of treating dynamical problems can be retained if mass is defined as

$$m = m_0/\alpha \tag{1.27}$$

where $m$ is the *relativistic* mass and $m_0$ is the *rest* mass, or mass of a body when it is at rest in the coordinate system in which it is being measured. Mass, then, varies with velocity. At velocities which are low compared with the velocity of light, the variation in mass is essentially undetectable; at velocities approaching the velocity of light, the increase of mass is significant. This increase of mass with velocity is readily observed in particle accelerators, providing one of the most potent confirmations of the theory of relativity.

The acceptance of this relativity of mass leads to the following expressions for the momentum $P$ and energy $E$ of a body

$$P = mv = m_0v/\alpha \tag{1.28}$$

$$E = mc^2 = m_0c^2/\alpha \tag{1.29}$$

Equation (1.29) is the famous equation of the equivalence of mass and energy. It has been shown with considerable reliability that the conversion of mass to energy in the interior of stars follows this law. When $v$ is small, Equation (1.29) may be written

$$E = m_0c^2 + \tfrac{1}{2}m_0v^2 = E_0 + \tfrac{1}{2}m_0v^2 \tag{1.30}$$

the last term being the familiar expression for kinetic energy. Thus the energy of a body consists of two parts—its kinetic energy and an energy corresponding to the mass of the body.

From Equations (1.28) and (1.29)

$$E^2 = m_0^2c^4 + c^2P^2 \tag{1.31}$$

For light, the energy of the photon, according to both theory and experiment, is

$$E = cP \tag{1.32}$$

which leads to the conclusion that, for the photon, $m_0 = 0$; that is, the photon has zero rest mass.

If we collect the equations

$$E = mc^2 = h\nu \tag{1.29}$$

$$P\lambda = h \tag{1.11}$$

$$E^2 = m_0^2 c^4 + c^2 P^2 \tag{1.31}$$

and note that they apply to material particles and to electromagnetic radiation as well, we see the reason why the photon seems sometimes to be a particle, and sometimes a wave. The photon is the limiting case of a particle—the particle which has zero rest mass. In order to observe a body, there must be a change in its energy. "Ordinary" bodies change their energy by changing their velocity, and in accordance with the law of conservation of momentum, there is a corresponding change in momentum. The photon cannot change its velocity, but must change its energy by changing its frequency.

All bodies tend to a minimum value of the energy which is represented by the rest mass; for a photon, this is zero. At low energies, changes in energy by changes in velocity are readily observed; at low energies the photon is very difficult to observe. At high energies (very high velocities), all bodies can readily change their energy by changing their (relativistic) mass, and hence very high energy particles behave very much like photons.

## THE VELOCITY OF LIGHT

**1.17. Early Measurements.** It appears that the velocity of light in free space is one of the fundamental constants of nature; thus the precise value of this velocity is important. Determinations have been made by many experimenters over the last two hundred years, yielding, as might be expected, more and more accurate results, until it is now felt to be known with a probable error of one part in a million.

One of the earliest recorded attempts to measure the velocity of light is attributed to Galileo, in the seventeenth century. With an assistant stationed a few miles away, he attempted to measure the time between the opening of a shutter on a lantern to receipt of a beam of light from a remote lantern, whose shutter was opened when the light from the scientist's lantern was observed by the assistant. Such a method, of course, was much too crude to yield a useful value; the speed of light being what it is, the assistant would have had to be about as far away as the moon to provide a value good to 10 per cent.

In 1666, Römer[19] attributed the variations in the successive eclipses of Jupiter's satellites as due to the finite velocity of light and thus obtained the first reliable value for this constant. He computed the value to be 3.5 × $10^{10}$ cm/sec. Some of Jupiter's moons revolve very rapidly, and thus the timing of their eclipse by the planet's shadow can be measured with high accuracy. Römer found that the periodicity of the eclipses was variable with the distance between the earth and Jupiter, the variations amounting to as much as 10 minutes, and he correctly attributed the effect to the finite velocity of light.

Römer's conclusions were not generally accepted until 1727, when Bradley[16] observed the phenomenon termed the *aberration of light*. The apparent direction of a star is the vector sum of the velocity of light in the true direction of the star and the earth's velocity vector in its orbital motion. The stars thus appear to have an annual periodic motion which is the projection of the earth's orbit. Stars near the pole of the orbit appear to move in circles—those near the orbital plane oscillate in a straight line. The maximum excursion is about 20.5 arc-seconds, which yields a value for the velocity of light of very nearly 3 × $10^{10}$ cm/sec, in good agreement with Römer's earlier result.

The first reliable direct measurements of the velocity of light were made by Fizeau (1849) and Foucault (1860), the former using a toothed wheel and the latter a rotating mirror. In the toothed wheel method, a beam of light is interrupted by a rotating toothed wheel, reflected back to the apparatus after traversing a relatively long path, and again interrupted by the wheel. For specific speeds of rotation of the wheel, the return beam is eclipsed because the wheel has rotated one, two or more teeth in the transit interval. In the rotating mirror method, the light beam is reflected from a rotating mirror, and the angle of rotation occurring during the transit time displaces the return image. Later experimenters, including Michelson, have used these methods with many refinements and improvements in apparatus and accordingly obtained more reliable results.

When Maxwell published his electromagnetic theory, he showed that the velocity of light was, by definition, equal to a simple function of the electromagnetic properties of free space (Equation 1.3). If this is accepted, then measurements of these electrical constants (the magnetic and electric permeability) constitutes a measure of the velocity of light. A number of experimenters especially Rosa and Dorsey (1906) have derived values by this means which are in good agreement with direct measurements on light.

**1.18. Modern Methods.** Many modern experimenters[20] have used refined versions of the earlier methods and obtained improved results. Two quite different methods however have become available. The first involves the modulation of a light beam, and the second involves direct experiments on frequency and wavelength of microwaves.

The Kerr cell and similar devices (see Section 3.32) provide a means for modulating a beam of light at a relatively high and precisely known frequency. The impression of an electrical voltage across the cell induces birefringence and thus creates an electro-optical shutter or modulator. If a modulated beam is sent out over a known path length and the return beam is compared with the outgoing beam, there will be a phase difference resulting from the finite transit time; this phase difference can be measured, and gives a value for the velocity of light. This method was used by Karolus and Mittelstadt in 1928 and by others including Bergstrand in 1951.

The experiment can be inverted, and if the velocity of light is known, the phase difference gives a measurement of the distance to the reflector. This is the basis of the Geodimeter, now being used as a precise survey instrument, and it is the basis of radar ranging systems, which reached a high state of development during and subsequent to World War II. Phase comparison is used in CW (continuous-wave) radar; pulsed radar systems measure the transit time for a very short pulse of microwave energy.

The limiting accuracy of the phase comparison method is the ability to measure phase shifts; this accuracy is improved by integrating the signals over relatively long time periods—as much as 30 seconds for the most precise measurements with the Geodimeter. In the pulse method, the limiting accuracy is the measurement of time periods.

It is worthy of note that, at least to a first approximation, the accuracy of measurement of transit times by either pulse or phase comparison is independent of the distance to the reflector. This represents a tremendous advantage of radar ranging over geometrical methods, which have errors proportional to the range.

It is not possible to measure the frequency of visible light directly, but this is possible with microwaves. A number of precise determinations of both frequency and wavelength have been made for microwaves by Mercier (1923), Essen and Gordon-Smith (1948), Hanson and Bol (1950), and others, using standing waves on transmission lines and in resonant cavities.[20]

**1.19. Values for the Velocity of Light.** Table 1.1 presents the results of a number of measurements of the velocity of light over the past century or more.

TABLE 1.1. MEASUREMENTS OF THE VELOCITY OF LIGHT

| Date | Experimenter | Method | Value (km/sec) | p.e. (km/sec) |
|------|------|------|------|------|
| 1876 | Cornu | Toothed wheel | 299,990 | 200 |
| 1880 | Michelson | Rotating mirror | 299,910 | 50 |
| 1883 | Newcomb | Rotating mirror | 299,860 | 30 |
| 1906 | Rosa and Dorsey | Electrical bridge | 299,781 | 10 |
| 1923 | Mercier | Microwave transmission line | 299,782 | 15 |
| 1926 | Michelson | Rotating mirror | 299,796 | 4 |
| 1928 | Karolus and Middelstadt | Kerr cell | 299,778 | 10 |
| 1940 | Huettel | Kerr cell | 299,768 | 10 |
| 1950 | Bergstrand | Kerr cell | 299,793 | 2 |
| 1950 | Essen | Microwave cavity | 299,792.5 | 3 |
| 1950 | Houstoun | Electro-optical crystal | 299,775 | 9 |
| 1950 | Hanson and Bol | Microwave cavity | 299,789.3 | 0.4 |
| 1951 | Aslakson | Shoran radar | 299,794.2 | 1.9 |
| 1952 | Froome | Microwave interferometer | 299,792.6 | 0.7 |
| 1954 | Plyler | Molecular spectra | 299,792 | 6 |

## SOURCES OF LIGHT

**1.20. Spectra.** Electromagnetic radiation is generated by oscillating electrical charges, as described by Maxwell's electromagnetic theory. Maxwell's theory includes the possibility of any frequency and any amplitude, which is known from quantum theory to be contrary to the facts. However, the principle of equivalence permits the treatment of light as a wave motion with full validity whenever it is convenient to do so, so the notion of simple harmonic oscillators is sufficient to describe the origin of electromagnetic radiation until one becomes concerned with the nature of the oscillator itself, which is not the subject of the moment.

Radio waves are generated by electrical charges oscillating in an antenna —at the frequencies included in the concept "light" the oscillating charges are the electrons in atoms and molecules. Normally, in the view of the quantum theory, these oscillations generate patterns of standing waves within the atom, and there is no external radiation. However, from time to time, due to one cause or another, an atom will change its pattern of standing waves by either the absorption or emission of radiation of a specific frequency, governed by Planck's relation $E = h\nu$, where $E$ is the difference in the energy of the atom before and after the event, and may be either positive, in the case of emission, or negative in the case of absorption. In the particle picture, the atom is said to emit or absorb a photon.

With some special exceptions, the interactions concern one photon for one atom.

Each atom has numerable possible energy states, so that it can absorb or emit photons of various energies. Which of the many possible changes in energy levels actually takes place in a given event is governed by statistical probabilities.

In the case of a large assemblage of atoms, these changes in energy levels give rise to *spectra*—a distribution of radiation with respect to frequency which is characteristic of the conditions which prevail.

**1.21. Classification of Spectra.** For the purposes of the present section, spectra may be classified as two general kinds—emission and absorption. Each kind has three different types: line spectra, band spectra, and continuous spectra. In a discussion of light *sources*, the concern is primarily with emission spectra of all three types.

**1.22. Line Spectra.** When the atoms giving rise to the spectra have relatively little physical interaction—that is, when they exist in the form of a gas at low pressure—the differences in energy levels are those dictated by the statistics of the quantum theory, and the photons corresponding to the same change in different atoms are almost precisely alike, so that the spectra consist of a finite number of specific frequencies. This is a line *spectrum*, since the product of a spectrograph is a series of images of its entrance slit, distributed according to frequency.

Even in this ideal case, the frequencies are not completely pure, for reasons which will be discussed later, so that the line in the spectrograph has a finite width (in excess of the slit width). A plot of intensity across a spectral line looks like Figure 1.5. For practical purposes, however, a line spectrum may be considered as being composed of a finite set of specific frequencies.

**1.23. Band Spectra.** Molecules, as contrasted with atoms, give rise to what are known as *band spectra*. These are really line spectra, except that there are a very large number of lines, and they crowd together toward the high frequencies to form characteristic "heads."

**1.24. Continuous Spectra.** When an assemblage of atoms are closely restrained, as in a liquid or solid, or high pressure gas, the energies associated with the various permitted standing wave patterns are affected by neighboring atoms, and hence are not so precisely defined as in the case of a low pressure gas. The same energy level transitions for different atoms do not give rise to photons of precisely the same energies, and the spectral lines are broadened to the point where they are completely indistinguishable from one another and blend into a *continuous spectrum*.

**1.25. Flame, Arc and Spark Spectra.** In an assemblage of atoms at

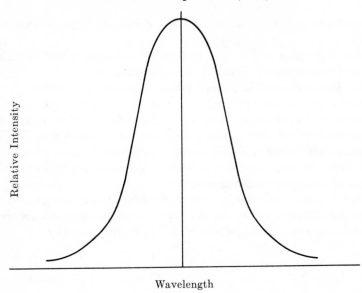

Wavelength

FIGURE 1.5. Light intensity distribution in a spectral line.

a given constant temperature, a state of equilibrium exists for the assemblage as a whole, but in the case of an individual atom, the actual energy level existing at a given moment is a statistical probability. The number of atoms in a given state at a particular moment is a statistical function of the temperature and the total number of atoms present. The observed spectrum will consist of lines corresponding to changes between the various levels.

At low temperatures, most of the atoms will be in the "ground" or lowest energy state, and most of the spectral lines observed will be those corresponding to changes from higher states to this ground state. At higher temperatures, a substantial number of the atoms may be maintained at an energy level higher than the ground state, and the spectra will be correspondingly different.

It is common to speak of *flame, arc* and *spark* spectra of various elements. Flame spectra are those obtained when the sample is held in a Bunsen flame (1800°C) and generally represent transitions to the ground state. Atoms at room temperature do not radiate to an observable degree, although energy level transitions do occur at a low rate.

If the sample material is placed in a carbon arc or (if a metal) is used as one of the electrodes of an arc, the effective temperature is of the order of 4000 to 7000°C and a different set of spectral lines appears, corresponding to transitions to levels higher than the ground state from even higher levels.

The electric spark may be used to generate still higher effective temperatures and hence another, different, set of spectral lines.

**1.26. Temperature Radiation.** When an assemblage of atoms is maintained at a specific temperature, a state of equilibrium is achieved in the absorption and emission of radiation, so that the radiation is maintained at a constant density which has a functional distribution with respect to frequency. In the case of a solid, the spectrum is continuous, and it can be shown that the frequency distribution of the radiation density is independent of the nature of the material.

It has been shown earlier in the chapter that attempts to arrive at this distribution formula led to the development of the quantum theory and the establishment of the function as that given by Planck[6]

$$\rho(\nu) = \frac{8\pi h \nu^3}{c^3} \frac{1}{e^{(h\nu/kT)} - 1} \tag{1.5}$$

where $h$ is Planck's constant ($6.623 \times 10^{-27}$ erg-second) and $k$ is Boltzmann's constant ($1.380 \times 10^{-16}$ erg/deg). Planck's equation may also be written as a function of wavelength:

$$\rho(\lambda) = \frac{8\pi}{\lambda^5} hc \frac{1}{e^{(h\nu/kT)} - 1} \tag{1.33}$$

$\rho(\lambda)$ being the energy density in watts per unit volume.

This equation is the energy density for *blackbody* radiation, which prevails in an internal cavity in a body at a given temperature, and would prevail for a body which is a perfect radiator. Radiation to the external world from a body at a given temperature is governed by Kirchhoff's radiation law,

$$W = \alpha W_b \tag{1.34}$$

in which $W$ is the radiant emittance of the body, $\alpha$ is its *absorptance* or *emissivity*, and $W_b$ is the radiant emittance of a blackbody. For a given body, Equation (1.34) holds at all frequencies, although the value of $\alpha$ varies with frequency.

Many solids at high temperature closely approach the radiation of a blackbody—for example, the sun. For a blackbody, of course, $\alpha = 1$.

The Planck equation is frequently written in the form

$$\rho(\lambda, T) = \frac{c_1}{\lambda^5 \{e^{(c_2/\lambda T)} - 1\}} \tag{1.33a}$$

where the constants are lumped into the constants $c_1$ and $c_2$, which are referred to as the first and second radiation constants, respectively.

**1.27. Derivations from Planck's Equation.** Earlier in this Chapter, it was pointed out that Planck's equation is based upon an assumption which makes the result agree with experiment—the assumption that the only permissible vibrational states are those which conform to the requirement $E = h\nu$. Prior to Planck's work, attempts had been made to derive equations representing the frequency distribution of radiation, both on empirical and theoretical bases. Those which were proposed are quite easily shown to be derivable from the Planck equation.

The key quantity in the Planck equation is the exponent $h\nu/kT$ or, in terms of wavelength, $hc/\lambda kT$. When this exponent has a value greater than about 5, Planck's equation gives, to a very close approximation

$$\rho(\lambda) = \frac{8\pi hc}{\lambda^5} e^{-(hc/\lambda kT)} \qquad (1.35)$$

which is the empirical *Wein's distribution law*.[20a] Of course, in the original presentation, $h$ was not separately identified. A value of 5 (actually 4.965) corresponds to the maximum of the distribution curve, so that Equation (1.35) agrees closely with the Planck expression for wavelengths shorter than the maximum, but begins to depart from it at the longer wavelengths.

When the exponent has a value less than unity, another asymptotic form of Planck's equation appears,

$$\rho(\lambda) = \frac{8\pi kT}{\lambda^4} \qquad (1.36)$$

which is the Rayleigh—Jean's distribution law,[20b] derived from consideration of atoms as classical oscillators. This curve goes to infinity at zero wavelength. It is not even approximately close to the Planck curve near the maximum and only approaches it at very long wavelengths (where the exponent is less than unity).

Planck's equation may be differentiated to find the wavelength of maximum energy, which gives *Wein's dsplacement law*[20a]

$$\lambda_m T = \frac{hc}{4.965k} \qquad (1.37)$$

It may also be integrated to give the total energy, in which case we obtain the *Stefan-Boltzmann law*[20]

$$W = \sigma T^4 \qquad (1.38)$$

where $\sigma$ ($5.67 \times 10^{-5}$ erg cm$^{-2}$ deg$^{-4}$ sec$^{-1}$) is the Stefan-Boltzmann constant.

**1.28. Blackbody Radiation.** When Planck's equation is plotted in the form of energy per unit wavelength interval versus wavelength, curves like those in Figure 1.6 are obtained. The total area under the curve corresponds to Equation (1.38); the wavelength at the maximum is proportional to the temperature, in accordance with Equation (1.37). The actual value of the energy for a given body is obtained by applying the *emissivity* factor α to the Planck curve. Most solids, especially at high temperatures, have an emissivity which is reasonably constant with wavelength, and they are called *gray bodies*. Their radiation curves are similar to the blackbody curve, except for the reduction by the constant factor α. In

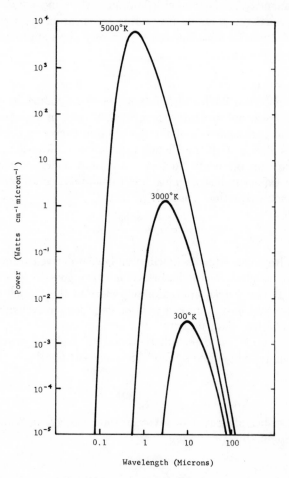

FIGURE 1.6. Blackbody radiation.

general, however, $\alpha$ is also a function of wavelength, and the true radiation curve is obtained as the product of these two functions of $\lambda$.

The color of natural objects is a consequence of the variation of $\alpha$ with wavelength. It follows from Kirchhoff's radiation law, Equation (1.34), that bodies are poor radiators in those spectral regions where they are poor absorbers (that is, where they reflect or transmit strongly). In these spectral regions, $\alpha$ is small.

The blackbody radiation curves are very useful in practical problems, since most common sources of radiation correspond very closely to them. One should note that the total radiation varies very rapidly with temperature ($T^4$) and that the radiation at any given wavelength is always greater for a greater temperature. At earth-level ambient temperature (about 300°K), the radiation peak is at about 10$\mu$. A body at 5000°K, whose peak is at 0.5$\mu$, will, however, provide more 10$\mu$ energy than the 300°K body.

Another point not always recognized is that changes in emissivity are nearly as effective in producing a change in total radiation as are changes in temperature. If we write the Stefan-Boltzmann equation for a gray body, including the emissivity as a constant factor,

$$E = \sigma\alpha T^4 \tag{1.39}$$

and then, if we differentiate it with respect to temperature to find the rate of change of total energy with temperature, we find

$$dE_T = 4\sigma\alpha T^3 dT \tag{1.40}$$

If the same equation is differentiated with respect to $\alpha$ to obtain the rate of change of total energy with emissivity, we have

$$dE_\alpha = \sigma T^4\, d\alpha \tag{1.41}$$

The ratio of these two is

$$\frac{dE_T}{dE_\alpha} = 4\,\frac{\alpha}{T}\,\frac{dT}{d\alpha} \tag{1.42}$$

which shows that, for equal percentage changes in $T$ or $\alpha$, the total radiation changes four times as much with temperature as with emissivity. But the range of $T$ in a practical case may be very large, whereas $\alpha$ ranges only from 0 to 1. For example, at ambient temperature (300°K), a change in emissivity of 1 per cent produces the same change in total radiation as a change in temperature of $\frac{3}{4}$°.

**1.29. Photometric and Radiometric Quantities.** The subject of photometry often creates an unnecessary amount of confusion at first exposure, largely because of a plethora of terminology. The physicist discusses the subject in one set of terms, the spectroscopist another, the optical engineer a third, and there are many special terminologies contributed by the illuminating engineer, the chemist, the photographer, and others. In this book we confine our usage to a very few number of terms which we can define precisely; those wishing to use a more extensive terminology may refer to any of the numerous handbooks which are available.

A distinction should be made between *photometry*, which applies to the area of visible light, and *radiometry*, which applies to the entire spectrum. *Radiometric* quantities may be computed from basic data [for example, Equation (1.38)] which, when $T$ is given in degrees Kelvin and $\sigma$ in ergs $cm^{-2}$ $deg^{-4}$ $sec^{-1}$, gives the total radiation in watts per square centimeter over the entire electromagnetic spectrum. To obtain the *photometric* radiation, we would have to consider only that portion of the total energy which lies within the visible spectrum, and then multiply this by a curve representing the spectral sensitivity of the eye, which is shown in Figure 1.7. *Photometry*, therefore, strictly interpreted, and by the definition of its units, refers to the *visible* effect of light, and excludes energy in the portions of the spectrum to which the eye is not sensitive. Its units are useful in photography, in spectroscopy, in optical design, and in other areas, but it must be remembered that they do not represent the actual quantity of energy present in radiation.

The units of radiometry are essentially electrical units, the quantity of radiation being given in *watts*. The fundamental photometric unit for quantity of radiation is the *lumen*, which is defined in terms of the standard *candle*, this being the average illumination of a group of standard carbon filament lamps preserved at the National Bureau of Standards, as measured by an apparatus which applies a correction for the sensitivity of the eye as a function of wavelength. This visibility curve is a standard curve and has a value of unity at its maximum ($0.556\mu$). The standard candle has been redefined as the *new candle*, which is defined as $1/60$ of the average luminous intensity of a blackbody radiator 1 $cm^2$ in area, at the solidification temperature of platinum ($2042°K$). A standard candle emits $4\pi$ lumens, or one lumen per steradian.

The lumen is a unit of luminous flux or power (energy per unit time). The corresponding radiometric unit is the watt. At the peak of the visibility curve ($0.556\mu$), 1 watt $=$ 680 lumens. At all other wavelengths, the ordinate of the visibility curve is less than unity, and the conversion factor is larger.

Table 5.1 in Chapter 5 lists certain important parameters and their names and units in both the radiometric and photometric terminology.

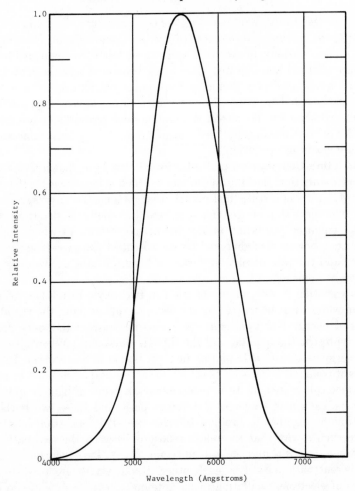

Wavelength (Angstroms)

FIGURE 1.7. Relative luminous efficiency of radiation. This curve, often referred to as the "visibility curve," is the relative sensitivity of the eye to light of the visible spectrum. The eye contains two receptors—rods and cones. Rod vision is called photopic and cone vision, which is color vision, is called scotopic. The above curve is for scotopic vision. The photopic curve is similar in shape, but has a peak at about 5100Å instead of at 5560Å.

For the most part, this book conforms to the terminology and symbolism set forth in the "Handbook of the American Institute of Physics" [21]— primarily to observe a more or less readily available and accepted standard. In the area of photometry, this source is not in conformance with the most recent practice in the field, and we therefore depart from it. In particular, the terms luminous emittance, luminance, and illuminance are not given; they are recommended by the Committee on Colorimetry of the Optical Society of America and are in fairly common use today. They are adopted here because they alone provide a natural conformity with the terms used in radiometry for similar phenomena.

The terms listed in Table 5.1 are sufficient for almost any problems encountered in optics. The use of the innumerable terms which are merely multiples or fractions of these terms seems to the author to be unnecessary and only leads to confusion.

**1.30. Time Distribution of Radiation.** It has been shown that radiation has a statistical distribution in space which is described by the wave theory. It also has a statistical distribution in time. The average rate at which photons are produced from a radiating body is determined by Planck's equation [Equation (1.5)]; the actual instants at which photons are emitted, however, is governed by the so-called *Einstein-Bose* statistical law, and the rate of photon flow in a beam of light is, therefore, not completely homogeneous.

This variation in rate manifests itself in two ways. In the case of phenomena which must be treated by the wave picture of light, the variations in rate of energy flow appear as variations in phase of the wave groups which represent the quanta, and the light is *incoherent*. When all of the light energy in a beam is in phase, the light is said to be *coherent*. In general, light from radiating sources is incoherent. Special pains must be taken to produce coherent light. In interferometers, a beam of light is split into two parts, each part traverses a different path, and these two parts are then brought together to produce interference. This operation has to be done in such a way that the phase relations between the two paths are maintained, else interference will not take place. Two such light beams are coherent with respect to each other. Radio waves are produced by streams of electrons oscillating in an antenna; these streams are so constrained by the electrical characteristics of the equipment as to oscillate in phase, thus the waves produced are coherent. In the laser, the conditions are such that the output is coherent, even in optical frequencies.

In the case of phenomena which must be treated by the particle picture of light, the variations in rate of energy flow appear as variations in the rate of arrival of photons; these variations may be treated as composed of superimposed periodic functions, and the energy therefore has a *noise spectrum*, represented by the distribution of the variations with respect to frequency. As will be seen, this noise is very nearly "white"—that is, its magnitude is independent of frequency. This noise frequency must not be confused with the frequency associated with the light in its wave aspect.

# REFERENCES

1. Chr. Huygens, "Traite de Lumiére," Leyden, 1690.
2. Th. Young, *Phil. Trans. Roy. Soc. London*, **92**, 12, 737 (1802).
3. A. Fresnel, *Ann. Chim. Phys.* **1**(2), 239 (1816).
4. J. Maxwell, "A Treatise on Electricity and Magnetism," 2 vols., Oxford, 1873.
5. H. Hertz, *Sitzb. Berl. Akad. Wiss.* (Feb. 2, 1888); *Wiedem. Ann.*, **34**, 551 (1888).
5a. R. Tolman, "Principles of Statistical Mechanics," London, Oxford University Press, 1953.
6. M. Planck, *Verh. Deutsch. Phys. Ges.*, **2**, 202, 237 (1900); *Ann. Physik*, **4**, 553 (1901).
7. See discussion in R. Feynman, R. Leighton and M. Sands, "The Feynman Lectures on Physics," pp. 16–23, Addison-Wesley, 1963.
8. A. Compton and S. Allison, "X-Rays in Theory and Experiment," 2nd ed., New York, D. Van Nostrand, 1935.
9. L. deBroglie, Thèse, Paris, 1924; *Ann. de Physique*, **3**(10), 22 (1925).
10. N. Bohr, *Nature*, **121**, 580 (1928).
11. The bases for quantum mechanics were laid in the following papers:

    W. Heisenberg, *Z. Physik*, **33**, 879 (1925).

    M. Born and P. Jordan, *Z. Physik*, **34**, 858 (1925).

    M. Born, W. Heisenberg and P. Jordan, *Z. Physik*, **35**, 557 (1926).

    E. Schrodinger, *Ann. Physik*, **79**(4), 361, 489, 734 (1926); **80**, 437 (1926); **81**, 109 (1926).

    P. Dirac, *Proc. Roy. Soc. Londer Ser. A*, **109**, 642 (1925); **110**, 194, 561 (1925).

    An up to date discussion of the subject is to be found in R. Dicke and J. Wittke, "Introduction to Quantum Mechanics," Addison-Wesley, 1960.
12. A. Michelson, *Am. J. Sci.*, **22**(3), 20 (1881).

    A. Michelson and E. Morley, *Am. J. Sci.*, **34**, 333 (1887); *Phil. Mag.*, **24**, 449 (1887).
13. A. Einstein, *Ann. Physik*, **17**(4), 891 (1905).
14. See discussion in reference 7, pp. 16–23.
15. See discussion in reference 7, pp. 34–37.
16. J. Bradley, *Phil. Trans.*, **35**, 637 (1728).
17. R. Ditchburn, "Light," 2nd ed., p. 437, New York, Interscience Publishers, 1963.
18. A. Einstein, *Phys. Berl. Sitz.*, 778, 799, 831, 844 (1915); *Ann. Physik*, **49**(4), 769 (1916).
19. O. Römer, *Mem. Acad. Sci. Paris*, **10**, 575 (1666–1699).
20. For a discussion of the various methods used in measuring the velocity of light, see E. Bergstrand, in (S. Flügge, Ed.) "Encyclopedia of Physics," Vol. 24, p. 1, Berlin, Springer, 1956.

    For an analysis of the results, see R. Birge, *Rept. Progr. Phys.*, **8**, 90 (1941).
20a. W. Wien, *Ann. Physik*, **58**, 662 (1896).
20b. Lord Rayleigh, *Phil. Mag.*, **49**, 539 (1900).
20c. J. Stefan, *Sitz. Ges. Wiss. Wien*, Part II, **79**, 391 (1879).

    L. Boltzmann, *Ann. Physik*, **22**, 31 (1884).
21. "Handbook of the American Institute of Physics," New York, McGraw-Hill Book Co., 1957.
22. The International Committee on Weights and Measures adopted the prefixes *tera* (for $10^{12}$) and *giga* (for $10^9$) in 1958. They also adopted the prefixes *nano* ($10^{-9}$) and *pico* ($10^{-12}$) at the same time. These are now officially added to the familiar list of prefixes: *deka* ($10^1$), *hecto* ($10^2$), *kilo* ($10^3$), *mega* ($10^6$), *deci* ($10^{-1}$), *centi* ($10^{-2}$), *milli* ($10^{-3}$), and *micro* ($10^{-6}$).

# CHAPTER 2

# Light as a Wave Motion

**2.1. The Wave Domain.** The principle of equivalence states that any phenomenon can be described by either the particle picture or the wave picture of light without loss of validity. It is therefore permissible to use whichever picture offers the most simple and direct means of explanation. Some phenomena, like reflection and refraction, could be discussed in accordance with either picture, but they are more easily described in terms of waves; other phenomena, like the action of thermal detectors, which could be described either way, are more readily treated in terms of particles. Then there are the phenomena, like interference and diffraction which can be explained only in terms of the wave picture, and other phenomena like the photoelectric effect, which can be understood only by thinking of photons.

We therefore discuss each phenomenon in terms of the picture most readily suited to it, and in order to avoid oscillating from one picture to the other, we will first discuss the topics which are conventionally treated by the wave theory, and we will defer those customarily involving the particle theory for a separate chapter.

**2.2. The Wave Equation.** Figure 1.1 (p. 4) presented a picture of a simple sine wave as representative of light. Such a curve is a plot of what the mathematicians call simple harmonic motion, a concept which is of common occurrence in science and engineering. Consider Figure 2.1 and its equation

$$y = \mathcal{E}_y \sin\,(\omega t - kx + \delta) \tag{2.1}$$

This equation has been deliberately complicated to make it completely general, and include in it all the essential parameters. The wave, as pictured in Figure 2.1, is in the $XY$-plane, and the equation gives $y$ as a function of $x$. $\mathcal{E}_y$ is the *amplitude*, or maximum value of $y$; $\omega$ is the *angular*

38

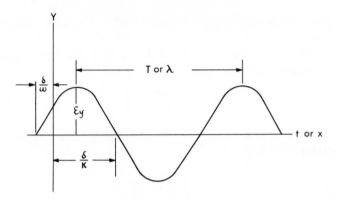

FIGURE 2.1. Parameters of a light wave.

frequency. Simple harmonic motion can be visualized as the motion, along a vertical line, of a perpendicular dropped from an arm which rotates at constant velocity, as shown in Figure 2.2. $\omega$ is the angular velocity of the arm in radians per unit of time; $k$ is called the *wavelength constant*, and is given by $k = 2\pi/\lambda$, where $\lambda$ is the *wavelength*, as shown in Figure 2.1.

The *phase angle*, or value of the angle when $t = 0$, is $(-kx + \delta)$. The reason for including the quantity $\delta$ will be seen presently.

This function may be considered as a function of $y$ with respect to time, $x$ being a constant, and the function is then *time periodic*. Its values repeat for successive values of $t$ equal to $2\pi N/\omega$. This time interval is the *period* $T$.

The function may also be considered as a function of $y$ with respect to $x$, $t$ being a constant, and the function is then *space periodic*. Its values

FIGURE 2.2. Generation of sine wave by a rotating vector. A perpendicular from the point of the arrow to the vertical axis generates continuous values of $y$ which, when plotted along a time axis, constitute a sine wave if the velocity of the arm is constant.

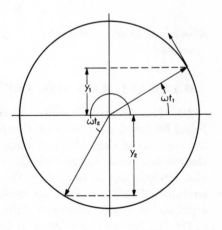

repeat for successive values of $x$ equal to $2\pi N/k$. This space interval is the *wavelength* $\lambda$.

The *velocity*, being distance/time, is $c = \lambda/T$. Using the values of these two quantities above,

$$\frac{\lambda}{T} = \frac{2\pi/k}{2\pi/\omega} = \frac{\omega}{k}$$

Now, the cyclical frequency, $\nu$ is $\omega/2\pi$, and by definition, $k = 2\pi/\lambda$. Making this substitution we have

$$c = \frac{2\pi\nu}{2\pi/\lambda} = \lambda\nu \tag{2.2}$$

The quantity $c$ indicates the velocity, because we are talking about light.

We frequently have to consider multiple waves which differ only in phase. This is the reason for introducing the term $\delta$. A series of waves, of the same amplitude, frequency and wavelength, but differing only in phase, will all have the Equation (2.1), except that the phase differences will be represented by values of $\delta = \delta_1$, $\delta_2$, $\delta_3$, etc.

The direction of propagation of the wave represented in Equation (2.1) is in the positive $X$-direction. A wave moving toward the negative $X$-direction will have the same equation, except that the sign of the term $kx$ will be positive.

For those familiar with the vector notation in terms of complex numbers, Equation (2.1) may be written more elegantly as

$$\mathbf{E} = \mathcal{E} \cdot e^{j(\omega t - kx + \delta)} \tag{2.3}$$

and an abbreviated version in common usage is

$$\mathbf{E} = \mathcal{E} e^{\delta\phi} \tag{2.4}$$

where it is understood that $\phi = (\omega t - kx + \delta)$ is a function of both space and time.

## MAXWELL AND THE ELECTROMAGNETIC THEORY

**2.3. The Electromagnetic Field Equations.** When Maxwell published his now famous work on electromagnetic theory, he not only unified the concepts of electricity and magnetism, but at the same time provided the mathematical background which supported the wave theory of light. His fundamental equations of the electromagnetic field predicted the existence of radiation from an oscillating electric field having a velocity equal to the known velocity of light, in that the wave equation discussed in the last section is a solution of the field equations. This mathematical background also dispensed with the need for the ether as a material medium and thus removed one of the primary stumbling blocks to the acceptance of a wave theory of light.

Maxwell's equations, expressed in their most concise manner as vector equations, are

$$\mathbf{D} = \epsilon\epsilon_v\mathbf{E} \tag{2.5}$$

$$\mathbf{B} = -\mu\mu_v\mathbf{H} \tag{2.6}$$

$$\text{div } \mathbf{D} = \rho \tag{2.7}$$

$$\text{div } \mathbf{B} = 0 \tag{2.8}$$

$$\text{curl } \mathbf{E} = -\mu\mu_v\frac{\partial \mathbf{H}}{\partial t} \tag{2.9}$$

$$\text{curl } \mathbf{H} = i_v + \epsilon\epsilon_v\frac{\partial \mathbf{E}}{\partial t} \tag{2.10}$$

The first equation states that an electric field $\mathbf{E}$ (volts/meter) produces an electric displacement (stress) $\mathbf{D}$ (coulombs/meter$^2$) in a medium. $\epsilon$ is the electric permittivity, or dielectric constant of the medium (farads/meter) and $\epsilon_v$ is the permittivity of free space ($8.85 \times 10^{-12}$).

The second equation expresses a similar relation between the magnetic field vector $\mathbf{H}$ (ampere-turns/meter) and the magnetic induction vector $\mathbf{B}$ (webers/meter$^2$), $\mu$ being the magnetic permeability of the medium and $\mu_v$ the permeability of free space (henrys/meter) ($4\pi \times 10^{-7}$).

The third and fourth equations are generalizations of Gauss' law for electric and magnetic fields respectively. They state merely that the total outward flux of lines of (electric or magnetic) force through a closed surface is proportional to the (electric or magnetic) charge enclosed by the surface; that is, the *divergence* of $\mathbf{D}$ equals $\rho$, the enclosed charge density (coulombs/meter$^3$), and the divergence of $\mathbf{B}$ is zero (since there is no isolated magnetic pole associated with an electric charge).

The fifth equation is a generalization of Faraday's law of induction "the electromotive force around any complete path is proportional to the rate of decrease of magnetic flux linked with that path." The electromotive force around the path is the *line integral* of the electric field vector, or curl $\mathbf{E}$, and the rate of decrease of magnetic flux is the negative time derivative of the magnetic intensity vector $\mathbf{H}$. Hence, the fifth Maxwell equation.

The sixth equation contains Maxwell's most significant contribution, the *displacement current*, expressed in the second term on the right. This represents a statement that a changing electric field produces the same effect as an electric current—a fact not observed at the time but abundantly demonstrated later. With this addition, the sixth equation is a statement of Ampere's law of magnetomotive force, "the magnetomotive force around any complete path is proportional to the current linked with that path." It is thus a statement for electric fields equivalent to the statement for magnetic fields expressed by the fifth equation.

The fifth and sixth equations express the reciprocal relation between the oscillating electric and magnetic fields which comprise light.

*The Equations in Differential Form.* Those unfamiliar with the conciseness of the vector notation will miss the significance of the Maxwell equations as predicting the existence of waves of electromagnetic radiation traveling at a velocity $c$, so it is well to restate them in the more pedestrian but much less concise form of differential equations. Here we must deal separately with the rectangular components of the vectors, using subscripts $x$, $y$ and $z$. The first equation becomes the set of three equations

$$D_x = \epsilon\epsilon_v E_x$$

$$D_y = \epsilon\epsilon_v E_y \tag{2.11}$$

$$D_z = \epsilon\epsilon_v E_z$$

and the second equation becomes

$$B_x = -\mu\mu_v H_x$$

$$B_y = -\mu\mu_v H_y \tag{2.12}$$

$$B_z = -\mu\mu_v H_z$$

The third equation is equivalent to

$$\frac{\partial E_x}{\partial_x} + \frac{\partial E_y}{\partial_y} + \frac{\partial E_z}{\partial_z} = \rho \tag{2.13}$$

and the fourth to

$$\frac{\partial H_x}{\partial x} + \frac{\partial H_y}{\partial y} + \frac{\partial H_z}{\partial z} = 0 \tag{2.14}$$

The fifth equation becomes the set

$$\frac{\partial E_z}{\partial y} - \frac{\partial E_y}{\partial z} = -\mu\mu_v \frac{\partial H_x}{\partial t}$$

$$\frac{\partial E_x}{\partial z} - \frac{\partial E_z}{\partial x} = -\mu\mu_v \frac{\partial H_y}{\partial t} \tag{2.15}$$

$$\frac{\partial E_y}{\partial x} - \frac{\partial E_x}{\partial y} = -\mu\mu_v \frac{\partial H_z}{\partial t}$$

and the last becomes a similar set

$$\frac{\partial H_z}{\partial y} - \frac{\partial H_y}{\partial z} = \epsilon\epsilon_v \frac{\partial E_x}{\partial t} + i_x$$

$$\frac{\partial H_x}{\partial z} - \frac{\partial H_z}{\partial x} = \epsilon\epsilon_v \frac{\partial E_y}{\partial t} + i_y \qquad (2.16)$$

$$\frac{\partial H_y}{\partial x} - \frac{\partial H_x}{\partial y} = \epsilon\epsilon_v \frac{\partial E_z}{\partial t} + i_z$$

In the differential form, Equations (2.15) and (2.16) show the interrelationship between the electric and magnetic fields—that an electric field which varies with time is associated with a magnetic field which varies in space [Equation (2.16)] and a magnetic field which varies in time is associated with an electric field which varies in space [Equation (2.15)]. This fact alone points to a wave motion as a solution of the equations. It can be shown[1] that Equation (2.1) is a solution to these equations in that it describes a wave traveling in the positive $X$-direction at velocity $c$.

When expressions such as Equation (2.1) are derived from the Maxwell equations, the value of the velocity comes out to be

$$c = \frac{1}{\sqrt{\epsilon_v \mu_v}} \qquad (2.17)$$

and when the measured values of $\epsilon_v$ and $\mu_v$ are introduced, one obtains

$$c = 2.99730 \times 10^8 \text{ meters/sec}$$

The agreement with the measured velocity of light given by using measurements of the two purely electrical quantities $\epsilon_v$ and $\mu_v$ could hardly be fortuitous, and it provided the crowning touch to prove the validity of Maxwell's theory.

**2.4. Characteristics of Electromagnetic Waves.** Maxwell's equations prescribe the characteristics of the waves which represent a solution. The waves are *transverse*, that is, the electric and magnetic vectors are perpendicular to the direction of propagation. The electric and magnetic vectors are also mutually perpendicular, in phase, and so oriented that, looking in the direction of propagation, the direction from **E** to **H** is clockwise.

Figure 2.3 shows this relation.

The flux in a light wave is proportional to the *square* of the amplitude. The rate of flow of energy is the velocity times the energy density. The energy flow is described by *Poynting's vector*

$$\Pi = \mathbf{E} \times \mathbf{H} \qquad (2.18)$$

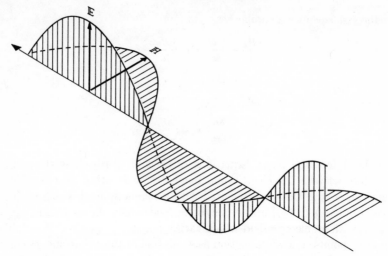

FIGURE 2.3. Relation of the electric and magnetic vectors in a light wave.

which indicates that the direction of flow of energy is in the direction of propagation. The time average of this vector is

$$I_{av} = c\epsilon_0 \mathcal{E}^2 \tag{2.19}$$

in free space. When $\mathcal{E}$ is given in volts/meter, the value of Equation (2.19) is

$$2.65 \times 10^{-3} \, \mathcal{E} \text{ watts/meter}^2$$

In free space, the values of the electric and magnetic fields have the relation

$$\mathbf{H} = \sqrt{\frac{\epsilon_0}{\mu_0}} \, \mathbf{E} \tag{2.20}$$

In a material medium, the ratio is multiplied by the *index of refraction*, $\mu$, so that

$$\mathbf{H} = \mu \sqrt{\frac{\epsilon_0}{\mu_0}} \, \mathbf{E} \tag{2.21}$$

where

$$\mu = \frac{1}{\sqrt{\epsilon}} = \frac{c}{V} \tag{2.22}$$

$V$ being the velocity of the wave in the medium.

**2.5. Boundary Conditions.** It is possible to derive the laws of reflection and refraction directly from the Maxwell equations, by imposing boundary conditions—namely, that the magnetic lines of force cross the boundary without any discontinuity, and that the tangential component of electric force and the normal component of electric displacement are continuous at the boundary—at a boundary where the value of the dielectric constant changes. One obtains

*Law of Reflection*

$$I' = -I \tag{2.23}$$

*Law of Refraction*

$$\mu \sin I = \mu' \sin I' \tag{2.24}$$

where $\mu$ and $\mu'$ are the refractive indices of the two media and $I$ and $I'$ are the angles of incidence and reflection or refraction, these angles being measured between a normal to the boundary surface and a normal to the wave front.

The law of reflection may be considered a special case of the law of refraction if we assume $\mu' = -\mu$.

The coefficients of reflection and refraction may also be derived from the equations. The coefficients of reflection for amplitude are

$$r_\pi = -\frac{\sin (I - I')}{\sin (I + I')} \tag{2.25}$$

for a wave in which the electric vector is perpendicular to the plane of incidence, and

$$r_\sigma = \frac{\tan (I - I')}{\tan (I + I')} \tag{2.26}$$

for a wave in which the electric vector is parallel to the plane of incidence.

The negative sign in Equation (2.25) indicates that the electric vector undergoes a change in phase upon reflection.

The average of the coefficients above is

$$r_a = \frac{\mu - 1}{\mu + 1} \tag{2.27}$$

These coefficients apply to the *amplitude* of the reflected or refracted waves. The energy flux is proportional to the square of the amplitude, so that the coefficients are squared if applied to the flux.

For waves which are oriented with the electric vector not parallel or perpendicular to the plane of incidence, the coefficients are applied to the components with respect to the plane of incidence. It will be apparent that we have just defined *polarization*, which will come in for considerably more discussion later.

**2.6. Brewster's Angle and the Critical Angle.** When $I + I' = \pi/2$, Equation (2.26) gives $r_\sigma = 0$; this is the "polarizing" or *Brewster's angle*, for which the reflected light is plane polarized with the electric vector perpendicular to the plane of incidence.

When $\mu > \mu'$ in Equation (2.24), the situation is that of light incident from a denser to a lighter medium (emerging from a lens or prism, for example). In this case, there will be a value of sin $I$ for which sin $I'$ is unity. For greater values of the angle of incidence, the law of refraction [Equation (2.24)] gives values of sin $I'$ greater than unity. When this occurs, the light cannot emerge from the denser medium. The value of $I$ for which sin $I' = 1.0$ is the *critical angle*. Its value, obviously is

$$\sin I_{\text{crit}} = \mu'/\mu \qquad (2.28)$$

For angles of incidence greater than the critical angle, *total internal reflection* occurs.

**2.7. The Index of Refraction.** Equation (2.22) defined the refractive index as the reciprocal of the square root of the dielectric constant of a medium. Experimentally, many materials demonstrate the validity of this equation, but many others show a wide departure from the rule. These latter materials have a high dielectric constant because of the induced orientation of polar molecules in the presence of an electric field, occurring at low frequencies. At light frequencies, this *polarization of the medium* is ineffective, because the molecules cannot orient themselves with sufficient speed. The dielectric constant is defined (at 0 frequency) in such a way that the effect influences the measured value. The measured value of $\mu$, however, is independent of this effect. In some substances, the polarization effect takes place at radio frequencies, and for these substances, the index of refraction for these frequencies follows Equation (2.22). Water is an example.

**2.8. The Electric and Magnetic Vectors.** Light waves comprise an electric and a magnetic vector, mutually perpendicular and in phase.* Mathematically, it makes no difference which vector we assume we are talking about. Which, then, is the dominant one? It can be shown that most experimental techniques measure the electric vector and that in most interactions between light and matter (for example, the effect of light on a photographic emulsion) it is the electric vector which is active. We may thus adopt the electric vector as the primary one in discussions of light.

---

* For anisotropic and absorbing media, this is no longer true.

**2.9. Note on Electrical Units.** The reader will find Maxwell's equations and derivations therefrom expressed with the constants introduced in different ways, sometimes associated with the velocity of light, $c$, and often with the factor $4\pi$. This apparent confusion arises because of the existence of different systems of electrical units, specifically the cgs system of electrostatic and electromagnetic units and the more recent *rationalized mks*, or Giorgi system (adopted by the International Electrotechnical Commission in 1935). The latter system is generally used in this book[2] (except where other units are specifically identified) and may therefore lead to some difficulty for those accustomed to the cgs definitions. For example, in Equations (2.5) and (2.6), the quantities $\epsilon_v$ and $\mu_v$ are introduced—these being the values of the quantities for free space. To obtain dimensional equality in these equations, the dimensions of these constants (farads/meter for $\epsilon$ and henrys/meter for $\mu$) must be applied only once where the products $\epsilon\epsilon_v$ and $\mu\mu_v$ appear.

## POLARIZATION OF LIGHT

**2.10. Definition and Descriptions.** In the wave equation [Equation (2.1)], the wave was described as having its vector in the $XY$-plane, and in the direction $Y$, $X$ being the direction of propagation. It is evident that the equation would be equally valid for any direction of this vector normal to the $Z$-axis, and also that the direction of the vector could easily be time variable. The term *polarization* of light refers to the direction of the vector. If the direction of this vector is constant in time, the light is *plane polarized;* if it rotates uniformly with time, the light is *circularly polarized;* if it rotates periodically but nonuniformly with time, the light is *elliptically polarized.* With ideally monochromatic light (the kind the fundamental equations describe) the phase relations are fixed and the light is, by definition, polarized. The general case is elliptical polarization—linear (plane) and circular polarization are special cases.

Real light beams are never perfectly monochromatic (this would imply infinitely long wave trains), and in practical cases, we have all degrees of mixtures of polarization. Two plane-polarized beams may be added to produce elliptical, circular or plane polarization, depending upon the phase difference; beams with various types of polarization may be added vectorially to produce various other types. The more usual case with real light beams, however, is *unpolarized* light—light in which the directions and phases of the vectors are randomly distributed—which explains why the effects of polarization and interference are not commonly observed in nature and are deemed unusual. States of *partial* polarization are often found, and thus it is necessary to distinguish the *degree* of polarization as well as the type.

It is customary to distinguish three *types* of polarization: linear, circular and elliptical. For linear polarization, the direction usually requires specification; for circular and elliptical polarization, a distinction between right- and left-handedness is required. Definition of the *plane of polarization* (the plane containing the vector and the direction of propagation) has led to confusion because some writers use the *electric* vector and some the *magnetic*. It makes no real difference, since they are always orthogonal, but there should be agreement on a definition. There would seem to be some justification for considering the electric vector the more important one (see Section 2.8), but the modern trend is to avoid use of the term plane of polarization entirely.

**2.11. Formalized Descriptions.** For detailed analysis of polarized light and the effects of polarizing devices, formalized mathematical descriptions are necessary; these are available in the form of the Stokes[3] parameters and the Jones parameters, and the Mueller and the Jones[4] calculus. Only the basic structure of these techniques is presented here; detailed discussions are available in the literature.

Poincaré devised the Poincaré sphere[5] (Figure 2.4) in 1892. The surface of this sphere is the collection of points which identify all possible types and combinations of types of polarization; the poles identify right- and left-hand circular polarization;* the equator identifies all orientations of linear polarization; the upper and lower hemispheres contain all possible orientations and ellipticities of elliptical polarization.

Any point on the Poincaré sphere may be identified in either spherical coordinates (longitude, $2\lambda$, and latitude, $2\omega$), or in Cartesian coordinates $(x,y,z)$. For the conventional representation of elliptically polarized light (Figure 2.5), where the measures are the orientation $(\alpha)$ and the ellipticity $(b/a)$, the Poincaré sphere provides

$$\alpha = \lambda$$
$$b/a = \tan |\omega|$$

(2.29)

Right- or left-handedness is identified by a positive or negative value of $2\omega$ respectively.

---

* Right- and left-handedness in circular and elliptically polarized light are most often described in terms of the apparent direction of rotation of the light vector as seen by an observer looking toward the source; right-handed being clockwise. This is opposite to the definition sometimes used comparing the advancing light vector to a right- or left-handed screw.

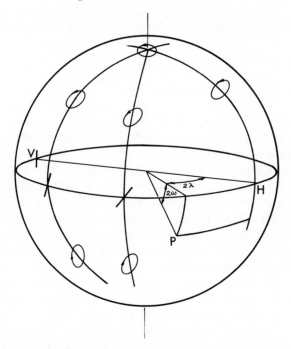

FIGURE 2.4. The Poincare sphere. The polarization of a beam of light may be identified by assigning it a point on the surface of the sphere. The poles represent circularity polarized light; the equator represents plane-polarized light in varying directions; points in the upper and lower hemispheres represent left- and right-handed elliptically polarized light.

FIGURE 2.5. The parameters of elliptically polarized light.

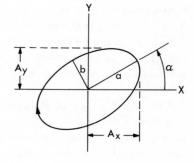

A point on the surface of the Poincaré sphere has the Cartesian coordinates

$$x = \cos 2\lambda \cos 2\omega \tag{2.30}$$

$$y = \cos 2\omega \sin 2\lambda \tag{2.31}$$

$$z = \sin 2\omega \tag{2.32}$$

These quantities are the *Stokes parameters*, although these were originally defined in quite a different way. The Stokes parameters, usually given the symbols $I$, $M$, $C$ and $S$ are respectively, the intensity of a beam of light, $I$; the proportion (in terms of intensity) of the beam which is polarized in the horizontal plane, $M$; the proportion polarized in the $+45°$ direction, $C$; and the proportion right circularly polarized, $S$. These quantities may be normalized by dividing each by the first quantity, $I$; when so normalized, $M$, $C$ and $S$ are identical to $x$, $y$ and $z$ of Equations (2.30) to (2.32). They may be written as a column vector

$$\begin{bmatrix} I \\ M \\ C \\ S \end{bmatrix} \tag{2.33}$$

In the Mueller calculus, polarizing devices may be described in terms of $4 \times 4$ matrices, and the effects of these devices on an incident beam of light are obtained by multiplication of these matrices by the Stokes vector.

The Jones calculus is similar in principle to the Mueller calculus, but achieves a more fundamental simplicity by utilizing complex quantities and thus operating with $2 \times 2$ instead of $4 \times 4$ matrices. The Jones vector for a beam of polarized light is the column vector

$$\begin{bmatrix} A_x e^{i(\epsilon_x + 2\pi\nu t)} \\ A_y e^{i(\epsilon_y + 2\pi\nu t)} \end{bmatrix} \tag{2.34}$$

Of which the two components (the Jones parameters) simply define the instantaneous value of the components of the electric vector along the $X$ and $Y$ axes. $\epsilon$ is the phase of the respective component at $t = 0$.

For complete treatment of all cases, the investigator needs both calculi; the Mueller calculus takes no account of phase relations and the Jones calculus takes no account of unpolarized components or of depolarization effects.

**2.12. Production of Polarized Light.** There are many ways in which polarized light can be produced. The wave train representing any one photon from an emitting atom is, by definition, polarized; any ordinary beam of light, however, contains innumerable photons which are, in general, polarized in random directions; in order for a beam of light of ordinary intensities to be polarized it must either be emitted from an assemblage of atoms so constrained as to emit in a single plane of polarization, or it must have been subjected to a sorting process, in which only the waves polarized in a particular fashion have been permitted to pass. The first condition is a little unusual, though not unknown, in Nature; it is the source of a number of "effects" which are discussed in Section 3.28 *et seq.*, such as the Stark effect, the Zeeman effect, etc. Certain unusual types of radiation such as Cerenkov radiation are polarized. For nearly all ordinary purposes, however, polarized light is observed after having been sorted out from a beam of unpolarized light by some type of polarizer, a polarizer being defined, in general, as a device or material which exhibits preferential properties with respect to the degree of polarization of a beam of incident light.

**2.13. Types of Polarizers.** Polarizers may be divided into three classes: dichroic polarizers, birefringence polarizers, and reflection polarizers. Dichroic polarizers show preferential absorption for light polarized in specific directions; birefringence polarizers have different refractive indices for light polarized in orthogonal planes; reflection polarizers depend upon the dependence of the coefficient of reflection on the polarization.

**2.14. Dichroic Polarizers.** The most widely known polarizers are the plastic sheets available under the trade names "Polaroid" and others. These are dichroic polarizers, and consist of a dichroic polarizing material embedded in a plastic sheet. A number of different types are available, some containing microcrystals, others molecular arrays; in all cases, the particles of material are aligned so that the crystals or the molecules are all pointed in the same direction; they thus act as would a single crystal of the material. These dichroic materials exhibit a high transmission coefficient for light polarized in a particular plane with respect to the axis of the crystal or molecule, and a high absorption coefficient for light polarized at right angles thereto. Their action on light polarized in an oblique plane is to treat it as if it were composed of two orthogonal components, to transmit one component and absorb the other.

As a result, when one of these polarizing sheets is exposed to a beam of unpolarized light, the light which is transmitted is found to be almost completely plane polarized and to have an intensity very nearly one-half that of the incident beam. When two polarizers are placed in series, and the second is rotated with respect to the first, it is found that when the two are "parallel"—that is, when the polarizing directions of both are the same—the light transmitted is plane polarized in this direction and that the second polarizer has not significantly reduced the intensity. When the second has its polarizing direction at right angles to the first—that is, when the two polarizers are "crossed," essentially no light is transmitted. For intermediate positions, the intensity of the transmitted light follows the *Law of Malus*[6]

$$H(\theta) = H_0 + (H_0 - H_{90}) \cos^2 \theta \qquad (2.35)$$

where $H(\theta)$ is the transmitted intensity, $H_0$ is the transmission of the second polarizer for light polarized in the transmission direction, and $H_{90}$ is its transmission for light polarized at right angles thereto. For an *ideal* polarizer, for which $H_0 = 0.5$ and $H_{90} = 0$, the Law of Malus reduces to

$$H(\theta) = \tfrac{1}{2} \cos^2 \theta \qquad (2.36)$$

Tourmaline is the most commonly known natural dichroic polarizer; its effect was discovered by Biot in 1815.[7]

Although sheet polarizers are highly efficient, they are far from ideal and are not adequate for careful quantitative work.

**2.15. Birefringence Polarizers.** Nearly all natural crystals are *birefringent*—that is, they show different properties for light polarized in mutually perpendicular planes. Glass, of course, is not a crystal, but a homogeneous solid. Cubic or regular crystals are not birefringent—all others are.

In general, crystalline dielectric materials have dielectric constants which are different in the three possible orthogonal spatial directions. This condition may be represented by the "dielectric ellipsoid" (Figure 2.6), an

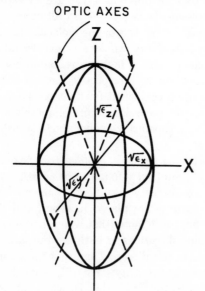

FIGURE 2.6. The dielectric ellipsoid.

ellipsoid in which the three semiaxes have the lengths $\sqrt{\epsilon_x}$, $\sqrt{\epsilon_y}$, $\sqrt{\epsilon_z}$, where $\epsilon_x$, $\epsilon_y$ and $\epsilon_z$ are the three dielectric constants. The lengths of the semiaxes are proportional to the three indices of refraction of the material, and the three corresponding velocities of light *rays* are

$$v_a = c/\sqrt{\epsilon_x} \tag{2.37}$$

$$v_b = c/\sqrt{\epsilon_y} \tag{2.38}$$

$$v_c = c/\sqrt{\epsilon_z} \tag{2.39}$$

These velocities are those for light polarized with its electric vector parallel to the corresponding axis, and traveling normal to that axis, as shown in Figure 2.7.

Maxwell's electromagnetic theory gives a complete explanation of this phenomenon if the three dielectric constants are used in Equations (2.5) and (2.11). The physical effect is that the polarization of the medium, described by the vector **D**, is different in the three different directions, which is quite logical when it is recognized that the crystalline structure of these materials is different in the three directions. Crystals which do not exhibit this difference in structure (cubic and regular crystals) do not exhibit birefringence.

As can be seen from Figure 2.7, there are two different velocities in any

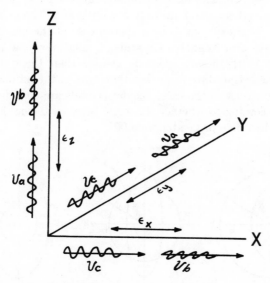

FIGURE 2.7. Velocities and polarizations in the three orthogonal directions.

given direction, and these give rise to two refracted rays, the *ordinary* ray and the *extraordinary* ray.

**2.16. Wave Surfaces for Biaxial Crystals.** The behavior of light in crystalline materials is best understood by the construction of wave surfaces by Huygens' principle. In the general case of a biaxial crystal, the Huygens' wavelets are double and are ellipsoids having semiaxes proportional to the velocities of the two rays in each of the three directions. Such three-dimensional surfaces are not readily shown in a diagram; Figure 2.8 shows the three orthogonal cross sections of a typical pair, the three semiaxes being shown. The relative magnitudes of the velocities are exaggerated for clarity.

The *optic axes* of a biaxial crystal are those directions where the velocities of the ordinary and the extraordinary ray are equal; this occurs for the directions where surfaces tangent to both the wave surfaces may be drawn. Such a surface is shown in Figure 2.9. In these directions, double refraction does not occur.

The optic axes are also the directions normal to which a cross section of the dielectric ellipsoid (Figure 2.6) is a circle; there are only two such directions.

When the dielectric constant is the same in two of the three directions in a crystal, the ordinary ray surface is a sphere, and there is only one direction in which both surfaces have a common tangent plane; this case is the *uniaxial* crystal—this crystal has only one optic axis. The uniaxial crystal may therefore be considered to be a special case of the biaxial crystal.

**2.17. Positive and Negative Crystals.** A uniaxial crystal is considered *positive* if the extraordinary index is greater than the ordinary index (velocity of the extraordinary ray less than that of the ordinary ray) and *negative* if the reverse is the case. Biaxial crystals are considered positive or negative according to whether the angle between the optic axes ($2\alpha$ in Figure 2.9) is less than or greater than 90°.

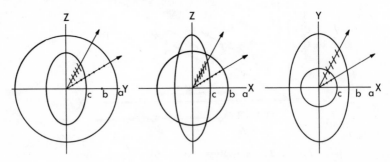

FIGURE 2.8. Wave surfaces in a biaxial crystal.

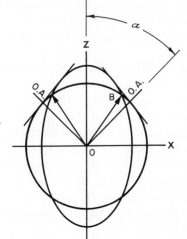

FIGURE 2.9. Optic axes of a biaxial crystal.

**2.18. Note on Snell's Law.** It will be noted that the Law of Refraction (Snell's Law) [Equation (2.24)] assumes a spherical Huygens' wavelet in the refracting medium; consequently, in the case of double refraction, the law is obeyed only for the ordinary ray in a uniaxial crystal.

**2.19. Calcite and Quartz.** The most common birefringent materials are calcite (Iceland Spar, calcium carbonate, $CaCO_3$) and quartz (silicon dioxide, $SiO_2$). Crystalline quartz is not to be confused with fused quartz, which is noncrystalline and not birefringent. Calcite crystallizes in rhombohedra and quartz in a complex form.

In calcite, which is a negative crystal, the two velocity surfaces are tangent along the optic axis, and the sperical ordinary velocity surface lies inside of the oblate spheriod which represents the extraordinary velocity surface. Along the optic axis, light is transmitted unpolarized; normal thereto, the two rays are plane polarized in orthogonal planes.

In quartz, which is a positive crystal, the prolate spheroid which is the extraordinary velocity surface lies entirely within the spherical ordinary velocity surface. In the direction of the optic axis, the two surfaces are parallel, but do not touch. In this direction, the ordinary and extraordinary rays are circularly polarized oppositely to each other; normal to this direction, the two rays are plane polarized in orthogonal planes. The circular polarization at the poles of the optic axis changes to elliptical polarization and then to plane polarization as the direction departs from the optic axis. There are two kinds of quartz, right- and left-handed, which give right- or left-circular polarization to the ordinary ray along the optic axis. The two kinds of crystal structures are mirror images.

The difference in refractive index is much greater for calcite $(-.172)$ than for quartz $(+.0091)$, and calcite is, therefore, a much more useful material for polarizing devices. These values are for $\lambda = 5893$Å, the sodium yellow line.

**2.20. Wave and Ray Surfaces.** The velocity surfaces described in Section 2.16 and illustrated in Figure 2.8 are *ray surfaces*. The *wave surfaces* are the tangent planes to these ellipsoids. Consequently, in general the ray direction is not normal to the wave front for the extraordinary rays. When the rays are not normal to the wave front, double refraction occurs, and the E-ray proceeds in a direction different from the O-ray, even though the two wave fronts may be parallel (as is the case whenever the light is incident normal to the surface of the crystal). In a uniaxial crystal, there are two directions (parallel and perpendicular to the optical axis) in which the rays are normal to the wave front, and hence do not give rise to double refraction.

**2.21. Conical Refraction.** In a biaxial crystal, there are no directions in which double refraction does not occur. There is, however, the phenomenon of conical refraction. Referring to Figures 2.8 and 2.9, it is seen that there are four directions in the biaxial crystal in which the ray velocities of the two rays are equal; these directions define the intersection of the two ray surfaces, at which points the combined surfaces exhibit a dimple. At this dimple, there are an infinite number of tangent planes to the surface, and the envelope of these tangent planes forms an obtuse cone. The normals to these surfaces form an acute cone.

If, now, a crystal is cut with its faces normal to the optic axis, and of thickness OM, as shown in Figure 2.10, and a ray is incident at O, the ordinary ray will pass through undeviated and emerge at $A_1$. For this particular direction of the incident ray, the E-ray is refracted to a hollow cone of rays with apex angle $\theta$, which is in turn refracted at the exit surface into a hollow cylinder of diameter $d$, as shown in the diagram. The directions of the electric vibrations at various points on the circumference of this cylinder are shown in the second diagram. This phenomenon is called *internal conical refraction*.[8]

The ray direction from the origin to the dimple (OB in Figure 2.9) is common to all of the external rays forming the cone of normals; consequently, if a cone of light of these dimensions is incident on a crystal, only a single internal ray will be generated from those components of the incident light which possess the proper planes of vibration. This is called *external conical refraction* (see Figure 2.11). Both internal and external conical refraction may be demonstrated experimentally with special arrangements, although they are not generally observed without these arrangements.

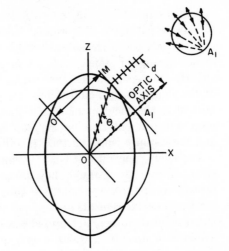

FIGURE 2.10. Internal conical refraction.

It should be noted that internal and external conical refraction are different phenomena. Internal conical refraction involves the optic axis for one of the rays; external conical refraction involves the ray axis for all of the rays.

**2.22. Double-refraction Polarizers.** Figure 2.12 illustrates a number of common types of double refraction polarizers. The best known double-refraction polarizer, historically, is the Nicol prism,[9] which is composed of two prisms of calcite, cut along cleavage planes to form the entrance and side faces. The incident light is oblique to the entrance face, and since this face is inclined to the optic axis (which lies as shown in the diagram), two rays are produced in the prism. The diagonal faces of the two prisms are cut at such an angle that the ordinary ray is totally reflected internally,

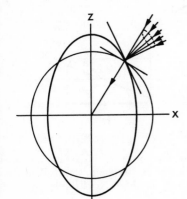

FIGURE 2.11. External conical refraction.

and the extraordinary ray is transmitted into the second prism, from which it emerges parallel to the original incident ray.

The Nicol prism has some disadvantages in that its acceptance angle is rather small, the emergent light is not strictly plane polarized, but is slightly elliptical, and astigmatism is introduced by the oblique entrance of the light. Some modifications are possible to make the entrance face normal to the incident light, but this prism has been largely replaced in normal instrumental use by the more compact arrangements of the Ahrens and Wollaston prisms and their modifications.

The Glan-Foucault and Glan-Thompson prisms also provide for a single emergent ray (the E-ray). They use an air gap instead of a cemented surface between the prisms and are thus useful in the ultraviolet, to which most practicable cements are opaque. The Glan-Thompson arrangement is larger than the other, but provides a larger acceptance angle (up to 40°). Taylor's modification, which uses a different direction for the optic axis, overcomes one of the principal objections of low transmission because of internal reflections in the air gap.

The Ahrens prism is very widely used, since it provides high efficiency

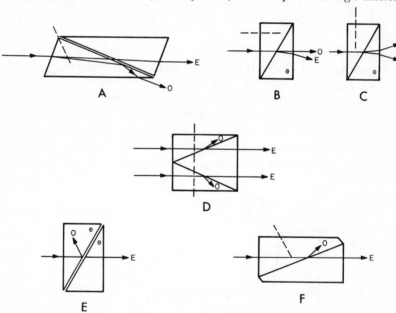

FIGURE 2.12. Double refraction polarizers. Directions of the optic axes are indicated by dotted lines and by dotted circles. A. Nicol prism. B. Rochon prism. C. Wollaston prism. D. Ahrens prism. E. Glan-Foucault prism. F. Modified Nicol prism.

with a compact and convenient form, a large angle of acceptance, and a perpendicular entrance face. It consists of three prisms of calcite.

The Wollaston and Rochon prisms, which are the same except for the optic axis direction, transmit both the E-ray and the O-ray, which emerge at a considerable angular separation.

Many other forms of polarizing prisms have been invented and used, but none as widely as those illustrated. The material for such prisms is almost invariably calcite, because this provides the highest difference in index of refraction of any readily available and easily worked material. All of the above prisms may, however, be made of various types of birefringent crystals, including biaxial types. Quartz is in reasonably common use, although its index difference is nearly 20 times less than that of calcite.

**2.23. Polarization by Reflection.** In Section 2.6, the laws of refraction and reflection were shown to be derivable from the electromagnetic theory by imposing certain boundary conditions at the surface joining two dielectrics, and these coefficients were presented in Equations (2.25) and (2.26) as functions of the refracted and reflected angles. It is apparent from Equation (2.26) that the reflected amplitude vanishes for the case where the angle between the refracted and reflected rays equals $\pi/2$, for light with its electric vector in the plane of incidence.

It is easy to see this qualitatively by considering Figure 2.13. If the dielectric is considered as composed of a cloud of harmonic oscillators set into vibration by the electric field of the incident light, then these oscillators give rise to the refracted and the reflected rays. Since light is a transverse wave, the oscillators can have no component of vibration in the direction of either the reflected or the refracted rays. When the angle between these rays is $\pi/2$, there is only one direction normal to both—the direction normal to the plane of incidence. Hence one of the rays must be plane polarized with its electric vector in this direction. Both theory and experiment indicate that it is the reflected ray which has this property.

It was shown [Section (2.28)] that, for a boundary between a vacuum and

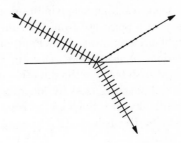

FIGURE 2.13. Polarization by reflection. For light polarized with the electric vector in the plane of the paper, this vector is parallel to the direction of propagation of the reflected ray when the angle between reflected and refracted rays is 90°. Hence light of this polarization cannot appear in the reflected beam.

a medium of index $\mu$, the reflected ray is completely polarized when

$$\tan I = \mu \qquad (2.40)$$

This angle is known as Brewster's angle or the polarizing angle.

A simple reflecting dielectric surface, therefore, set at the proper angle of incidence, provides an effective polarizer, in that it reflects only light in which the electric vector is normal to the plane of incidence. Unfortunately, the reflection coefficient for this light is rather low (about 4 per cent for ordinary glass) so that the efficiency of such a polarizer is quite low. However, it is readily seen that such a reflection removes some of the light polarized in this plane, and that a series of reflections will produce a cumulative effect. Thus, a pile of dielectric plates, tilted to the incident light at the polarizing angle, will produce partial polarization of the transmitted beam. Such polarizers are in common use, especially in the infrared region of the spectrum, where materials with a relatively high index of refraction, and consequently higher polarizing efficiency, are available. Even in the case of visible light, a pile of six plates gives a transmitted beam which is about 40 per cent polarized.

**2.24. Glare Reduction.** Even when the reflection from a dielectric is not at the polarizing angle, but is not too distant from it, the reflected light is highly polarized. This often occurs in nature in reflections from water or snow and ice, and therefore glare from such reflections is effectively reduced by polarizers, such as polarizing goggles so oriented as to be opaque to light with its electric vector in the horizontal plane.

**2.25. Polarization by Scattering.** Light scattered by particles of a size comparable to a wavelength is partially plane polarized. For single scattering, the degree of polarizaton is proportional to cos $\eta$, where $\eta$ is the scattering angle; for scattering at 90°, therefore, complete polarization is produced. This follows from the fact that the scattering cannot change the direction of vibration of the electric vector, which has no component in the direction of the incident beam. Hence, light scattered at 90° can have no component of vibration in the plane of scattering.

Sunlight scattered from the atmosphere is partially polarized for this reason, reaching a maximum degree of polarization of the order of 30 per cent at a point 90° from the sun. The polarization is not complete for sky-light because most of the light has been subjected to multiple scattering at various angles before reaching the observer. Instruments have been devised to determine the direction of the sun when it is below the horizon (as in the polar regions) by locating the direction of preferred polarization of zenith skylight. Such an instrument is a Polarizing Sky Compass.

**2.26. Retarders.** Referring to the discussion of Section 2.20, if a plate of a uniaxial crystal is cut parallel to the optic axis, and unpolarized light passed normally through it, there will be no double refraction, but the O-wave surface will have been retarded with respect to the E-wave surface by an amount depending upon the thickness of the plate and the difference of velocities of the two rays within it. For a plate of the proper thickness, this retardation may be made of any desired value.

It may also be seen (Figure 2.14) that, if a beam of plane-polarized light falls upon such a plate so that its plane of polarization makes an angle with respect to the optic axis, it may be considered to consist of two components, one with its plane of polarization parallel to the optic axis and the other with its plane of polarization orthogonal thereto. The transmitted light will have the same components, but with their phases displaced.

Such plates are known as *retarders*. Retarders may also be made with dichroic materials and with totally internally reflecting prisms. The most useful retarders are ¼-wave plates, ½-wave plates and full-wave plates.

A ¼-wave plate[10] produces circularly polarized light from an incident beam of unpolarized light, and elliptically polarized light from an incident beam of plane-polarized light, the ellipticity being determined by the angle between the optic axis and the plane of polarization of the incident beam.

A ½-wave plate has the effect of rotating the plane of polarization through the angle $2\theta$, where $\theta$ is the angle between the optic axis and the plane of polarization of the incident beam.

A full-wave plate, in combination with a polarizer, such as a Nicol prism, can produce two beams which interfere destructively to give zero transmission. The value of such a device is that the full-wave plate is, in general, a full-wave plate for only one wavelength of light; thus a highly colored beam is produced from incident white light. As the plane of polarization of the incident beam is rotated with respect to the optic axis of the plate, the wavelength for which the full-wave condition is satisfied changes, and the transmitted colors therefore change markedly. This is a very effective device for the analysis of polarized light.

**2.27. Compensators.** Babinet[11] introduced the device shown in Figure 2.15, known as the *Babinet Compensator*, which consists of two retardation

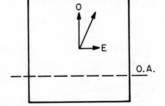

FIGURE 2.14. Resolution of plane-polarized light into orthogonal components.

plates, with their optic axes crossed, cut in the form of wedges. With this arrangement, the E-ray in the first prism becomes the O-ray in the second, so that the retardation of the two prisms is opposite in sign, and the net retardation in the combination is the difference of the two. Since this difference varies across the device, one prism becoming thicker and the other thinner, the phase retardation changes with distance across the device.

The *Soliel Compensator*[12] (Figure 2.16) is a Babinet Compensator with the upper prism divided into two wedges, which may be moved with respect to each other by a micrometer screw, and the lower prism in the form of a plane-parallel plate. With this device the amount of phase retardation is controllable by the screw, and is constant over the entire area of the plate.

**2.28. Rotatory Polarization.** In Section 2.19, it was pointed out that unpolarized light transmitted through crystal quartz parallel to the optic axis is emitted as circularly polarized light. If plane-polarized light is transmitted through crystal quartz parallel to the optic axis, plane-polarized light is emitted, but its plane of polarization will be found to have been rotated (22 deg/mm for 5893Å). This effect is found in many materials and is a result of the crystalline structure, the atoms being formed in helices. This is called *rotatory polarization,* or *optical activity,* and it provides a means for analysis of the concentration of many materials. One of its most common uses is in the analysis of sugar solutions, which is known as *Saccharimetry;* special instruments are available for this particular purpose. In some sugars, the direction of rotation is clockwise—these are known as *dextrarotarory;* in others, the rotation is counterclockwise, and these are *levorotatory.* Dextrose and levulose derive their names from this phenomenon. In fact, this is the only effective means of identifying these sugars.

**2.29. Dispersion of Birefringence and Optical Activity.** Both birefringence and optical activity are wavelength dependent, so that the

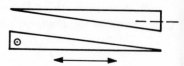

FIGURE 2.15. The Babinet compensator. Directions of the optic axes are indicated by the dotted line and the dotted circle.

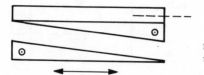

FIGURE 2.16. The Soliel compensator. Directions of the optic axes are indicated by the dotted line and the dotted circles.

phase retardation of a retarder and the rotational angle of an optically active material vary with the color of light. A number of sensitive measuring instruments have been constructed with elements based upon this principle, such as the Biquartz,[13] the Cornu-Jellett prism,[14] the Laurent plate,[15] and others. In such devices, the plane of polarization of a beam can be measured with high precision, because a small amount of rotation changes the colors of the transmitted light, and the human eye is quite sensitive to such changes.

**2.30. Interference of Polarized Light.** The rules for interference effects with polarized light are the Fresnel-Arago laws:[16]

(1) Two beams of light polarized in orthogonal planes do not produce interference.

(2) If the direction of vibration of one of the beams is brought into parallellism with that of the other beam by a suitable device, interference effects are observed, provided that the two beams are obtained from the same source.

In case (2), the interference effects are those which are produced by the phase retardation between the two beams by a retarding material, such as a crystal plate. Since, as has been pointed out, these effects vary with the wavelength of the light, the effects produced by an apparatus designed for this purpose show striking color effects. This is a powerful method for the study of crystalline materials, since the effects produced are characteristic of the materials and the manner in which they have been cut.

A well-known device for this type of examination is the polarizing microscope, in which a highly convergent beam of polarized light is permitted to pass through a sample, and the interference patterns produced in the focal plane by a rotating polarizer are studied under the eyepiece.

**2.31. Induced Birefringence and Optical Activity.** Birefringence and optical activity may be induced in otherwise homogeneous and inactive materials by the imposition of mechanical pressure, or strong electric and/or magnetic fields. The Faraday,[17] Kerr,[18] and Cotton-Mouton[19] effects, discussed elsewhere (see Section 3.32 *et seq.*) are polarizing effects induced by strong electric or magnetic fields. Mechanical pressure on glass or other normally isotropic material produces internal strains which are revealed by birefringence.

This induced birefringence may be studied by polarized light; a whole experimental domain of stress analysis has been constructed about this phenomenon. Models of mechanical structures constructed of homogeneous dielectric materials such as plastics are subjected to strains, and the effects produced are studied by polarized light. In this way, the internal distribution of stresses may be charted with ease. The name of *photoelasticity*[20] has been given to this study.

**2.32. Applications of Polarized Light.** Space does not permit more than the mere mention of a few of the dozens of applications which have been made of polarized light in science, industry and ordinary life. Glare reduction by removal of light polarized by reflection has been mentioned; it may also be reduced, or even eliminated in the case of controllable light sources, by polarizing the light at the source. Reduction of glare from automobile headlights by polarizing headlight lenses and windshields in orthogonal planes has received much discussion, and requires only agreements on the political and industrial level to be made effective.

Determining direction of the sun from the polarized skylight has been mentioned above; it is fairly well confirmed that many insects, particularly bees, use the polarization of skylight to find their way to and from the hive.

The use of polarized light as a coding method for stereoscopic motion pictures or stills is well known; the two images are superimposed on the same screen, but with light which is orthogonally polarized. The screen is suitably made to retain the polarization, and the observer wears spectacles in which the two lenses are orthogonally polarized. The two images are thus separated effectively for the two eyes.

Many interesting and useful effects may be achieved by exploiting the control over illumination and vision made possible through the use of polarizing devices.

## WAVE CONSTRUCTIONS

**2.33. Simple Harmonic Motion.** The wave equation [Equation (2.2)] is a solution of the general equation for simple harmonic motion

$$\ddot{q} = -\omega^2 q \tag{2.41}$$

This equation arises in connection with many physical phenomena, for example, the motions of a torsional pendulum and of a mass and spring, or the oscillations of an electric circuit.

The solution contains two arbitrary constants, and may be expressed in the forms

$$q = a \sin (\omega t + \delta) = a \sin \phi \tag{2.42}$$

or

$$q = -a \cos (\omega t + \delta') = -a \cos \phi' \tag{2.43}$$

or

$$q = A \sin t + B \cos t \tag{2.44}$$

the arbitrary constants being $a$ and $\delta$ or $a$ and $\delta'$ or $A$ and $B$, where $a$ is the amplitude and $\delta$ is the *phase* or *phase angle*.

The solutions may also be written in complex form, as shown in Equations (2.3) and (2.4).

The atom or molecule which is the source of an elementary wave train of light may therefore be thought of as a simple harmonic oscillator, and is often treated in this way. Consideration of the molecules of a medium in which light is propagated as simple harmonic oscillators which are forced into vibration by the electric and magnetic fields of the incident light leads to explanations of refraction and reflection and, when suitable properties of the medium are taken into account, of polarization and double refraction.

Ordinary oscillators, when excited to resonance, continue to oscillate at constantly decreasing amplitude or frequency until the energy expended through damping or friction losses has reduced the oscillation to zero. The emitters of light do not behave in this fashion, but exhibit a quantization of oscillation which it was left for quantum mechanics to explain.

**2.34. Huygens' Principle and Huygens' Construction.** Huygens' principle, or Huygens' construction,[21] describes in graphical form the progression of an electromagnetic wave in a medium. The construction has no real physical significance, but it is very useful in explaining various phenomena and provides a physical picture which mere mathematics cannot accomplish.

According to Huygens' construction, each point on a wavefront is considered to be the source of wavelets which expand (at the same velocity assigned to the major wavefront) into the space ahead of it, as shown in Figure 2.17. If these wavelets are drawn from each point on the wave front, their envelope constitutes a new wavefront. Actually, it is not necessary to draw more than a few of these wavelets to define the envelope, as is done in Figure 2.17. The wave front being considered can be of any form, and any surface of constant phase may be considered a wavefront. The construction does no more than to define the shape of the wavefront surface and identify its direction of advance.

The construction generates a new wavefront which, in an isotropic medium, is parallel to the original wavefront. In anisotropic media, the wavelets become ellipsoids, as has been explained in the previous section.

At the boundary of a dielectric, there is a change in the velocity, according to the relation

$$\frac{v'}{v} = \frac{\mu}{\mu'} \tag{2.45}$$

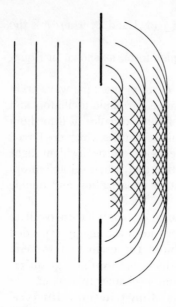

FIGURE 2.17. Huygens' construction for the propagation of light.

where $\mu$ and $\mu'$ are the indices of refraction of the two media, and when this difference in velocity is taken into account in the expansion of the wavelets, the bending of the light at the boundary is adequately explained.

To show the utility of Huygens' construction, it is interesting to derive the law of refraction by its means.

Given a dielectric boundary $A_1A_3$ (Figure 2.18) and a plane wavefront, $A_3W$ approaching the boundary at an angle of incidence $I$, the wavelet

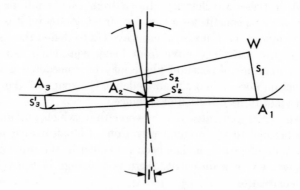

FIGURE 2.18. Derivation of the law of refraction by Huygens' construction of wave fronts. (see text, Section 2.34 for arguments).

from $W$ expands until it reaches the surface at $A_1$. In this same time interval, the wavelet expanding from $A_3$, in the second medium, will have expanded a distance $s_3'$, such that

$$\frac{s_3'}{s_1} = \frac{v'}{v} = \frac{\mu}{\mu'} \tag{2.46}$$

But

$$s_1 = A_1 A_3 \sin I$$

and

$$s_3' = A_1 A_3 \sin I'$$

Dividing

$$\frac{s_3'}{s_1} = \frac{\sin I'}{\sin I} = \frac{\mu}{\mu'}$$

Therefore

$$\mu' \sin I' = \mu \sin I \tag{2.47}$$

which is Snell's Law.[22]

Snell's Law was known from observation, so that Huygens' construction originally demonstrated that the law implied that the velocity of light became slower in a denser medium. Newton's corpuscular theory,[23] on the other hand, requires that the velocity of light increases in a denser medium. When Foucault[24] measured the speed of light in water and proved that it was less than in air, this was a convincing confirmation of the wave theory.

Huygens' construction explains the rectilinear propagation of light, which was at first considered to be inconsistent with the concept of it as a wave. He only considered the region where a common tangent can be drawn and, therefore, gave no account of the shadows of finite obstacles.

Fresnel expanded the concept,[25] and showed how the summation of the Huygens' wavelets in the shadow region gives rise to the fringes which are visible at the boundaries of shadows. This and additional modifications of Huygens' construction are necessary to give descriptions of interference and diffraction, which will be discussed later on.

**2.35. Curved Boundary Surfaces.** Huygens' construction may be used to show the form of the wavefronts generated by reflection from a plane surface (Figure 2.19) which prove the law of reflection ($I = -I'$) and those generated by reflection and refraction from spherical surfaces

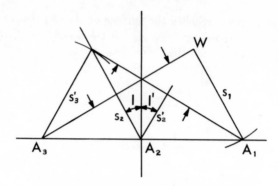

FIGURE 2.19. Derivation of the law of reflection by Huygens' construction of wave fronts.

The arguments may be developed by reasoning similar to that followed in Section 2.34.

(Figure 2.20). In this case, the formulas for first-order imaging

$$\text{for reflection: } \frac{1}{\ell'} + \frac{1}{\ell} = \frac{2}{r} = \frac{1}{f} = P \qquad (2.48)$$

$$\text{for refraction: } \frac{1}{\ell'} - \frac{1}{\ell} = \frac{\mu - 1}{r} = \frac{1}{f} = P \qquad (2.49)$$

may be derived, as shown. In the case of the spherical surface, it becomes evident that the wave generated in the second medium is not exactly spherical, and that the formulas derived above ignore this deviation.

To complete these first-order derivations, the formula for a simple lens, consisting of two spherical surfaces, is derived in Figure 2.21 and is

$$\frac{1}{\ell'} - \frac{1}{\ell} = (\mu - 1)\left[\frac{1}{r_1} - \frac{1}{r_2}\right] = \frac{1}{f} = P \qquad (2.50)$$

The thickness of the lens is ignored in the derivation, and this is therefore the formula for a "thin" lens. The quantity $P$ in all of the above equations is known as the *power* of the element; its units are reciprocal focal lengths, and if a focal length of one meter is taken as standard, the power is in *diopters*.

**2.36. Superposition of Waves.** The resultant of two or more simple harmonic waves is obtained by simple algebraic additions of their amplitudes. Thus, two waves of the same frequency

$$\xi_1 = \varepsilon_1 \sin (\omega t - kx + \delta_1)$$

and

$$\xi_2 = \varepsilon_1 \sin (\omega t - kx + \delta_2)$$

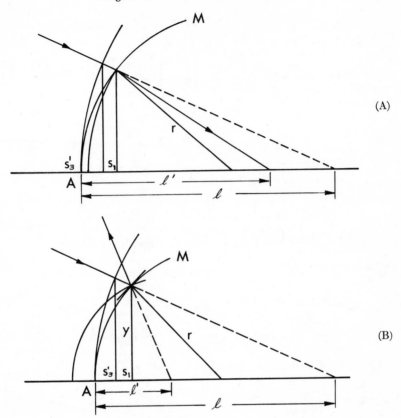

FIGURE 2.20. Construction of wave fronts generated by reflection and refraction at spherical surfaces.

By the arguments used in conjunction with Figures 2.18 and 2.19, the following analysis can be made:

For the refracting surface (a):

$$s_1 = t/\mu; \qquad s'_3 = t/\mu' \quad \therefore s'_3 = s_1(\mu/\mu')$$

But $s_1 = h^2/2r$ and $s_1 - s'_3 = h^2/2R$

$$\therefore \frac{1}{r} - \frac{\mu}{\mu' r} = \frac{1}{R} = \frac{\mu' - \mu}{\mu' r} \qquad \text{cf. Equation (4.45)}$$

For the reflecting surface (b):

$$s_1 = s'_3$$

But $s_1 = h^2/2r$ and $s_1 + s'_3 = h^2/2R$

$$\therefore \frac{1}{r} = \frac{1}{2R}; \qquad \frac{1}{R} = \frac{2}{r} \qquad \text{cf. Equation (4.67)}$$

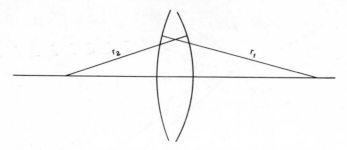

FIGURE 2.21. Derviation of the formula for a simple lens. For the second surface, from Equation (2.49)

$$\frac{1}{\ell_2'} = P_2 + \frac{1}{\ell_2}$$

But, if the lens thickness is assumed zero, $l_2 = l'_1$, hence

$$\frac{1}{\ell_2'} = P_1 + P_2 + \frac{1}{\ell_1}$$

And therefore

$$\frac{1}{\ell_2'} - \frac{1}{\ell_1} = P_1 + P_2 = \frac{\mu - 1}{r_1} + \frac{1 - \mu}{r_2} = (\mu - 1)\left[\frac{1}{r_1} - \frac{1}{r_2}\right]$$

which is Equation (2.50).

add to produce

$$\xi = \xi_1 + \xi_2 = (\varepsilon_1 \cos \delta_1 + \varepsilon_2 \cos \delta_2) \sin (\omega t - kx)$$
$$(\varepsilon_1 \sin \delta_1 + \varepsilon_2 \sin \delta_2) \cos (\omega t - kx)$$

$$(2.51)$$

In complex notation, the two waves are added vectorially.

**2.37. Superposition with Random Phase.**[26] The usual case in a light beam is the combination of many wave trains which have random phase distribution. For the superposition of $N$ waves, all of the same frequency and amplitude but with random phases, it is found that the resultant wave has an amplitude proportional to $\sqrt{N}$. The intensity, which is defined as the square of the amplitude, is therefore proportional to $N$. In other words, the intensity of the sum of a number of individual waves of random phase is equal to the sum of the individual intensities. One might have expected this result.

When a number of waves which are *in phase* are superimposed, however, the resultant intensity is $N^2$ times that of a single wave. This apparent violation of the conservation of energy is explained by the fact that when this occurs at a given point in space, there is always another point where the waves are exactly *out of phase*, and here the summation gives a zero resultant. When the intensity is summed over all points, the result is $N$.

Therefore, for waves with random phase, and individual intensities $\mathcal{E}_1^2$, the resultant intensity is $N\mathcal{E}_1^2$ everywhere; for waves which have a fixed phase relation, the resultant intensity is $N^2\mathcal{E}_1^2$ where the waves are *in phase* and zero where they are *out of phase*, the summation over all points becoming $N\mathcal{E}_1^2$.

**2.38. Stationary Waves.** When a wave is reflected from a surface, the reflected wave will combine with the incident wave by the principle of superposition, to form a resultant. If the reflecting surface is so located that $x = 0$ and $t = 0$ are the same for both the incident and reflected waves (taking into account any phase changes which occur upon reflection), a pattern of *standing waves* is formed, as shown in Figure 2.22.

Such a pattern is characterized by nodes and antinodes, the nodes being those points where the motion is zero. There is an energy density in the region of standing waves, but there is no energy flow. Two waves, an incident and a reflected wave, having the equations

$$\xi_1 = \mathcal{E} \sin (\omega t - kx)$$

and

$$\xi_2 = \mathcal{E} \sin (\omega t + kx)$$

for which the location of the reflecting surface satisfies the above condition, have the resultant

$$\xi = 2\mathcal{E} \cos kx \sin \omega t \qquad (2.52)$$

If the reflection is imperfect, the coefficient of reflection being $\rho$, then the resultant is

$$\xi = 2\mathcal{E}\rho^{1/2} \cos kx \sin \omega t + \mathcal{E}(1 - \rho^{1/2}) \sin (\omega t - kx) \qquad (2.52a)$$

This is a combination of standing and progressive waves.

Standing waves are well known in acoustics, as in the resonant cavities of organ pipes; resonant cavities which generate standing wave patterns are also common in microwave technology, and standing waves on trans-

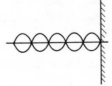

FIGURE 2.22. Standing waves.

mission lines and in wave guides are of frequent occurrence. Standing light waves were not commonly observed until the advent of the laser, although their existence was proven by Weiner,[27] who performed the experiment shown in Figure 2.23.

**2.39. Superposition of Waves at Right Angles.** The above discussion has implied that the plane of vibration of the waves being discussed was the same for all of the waves concerned. In general, the planes of vibration of individual waves will be oriented at random. In such cases, the components of each of the vibrations on a common pair of orthogonal planes may be taken, and these can be subjected independently to the principle of superposition to obtain resultant components.

When the phase relations of the waves are fixed, the resultant will have a specific direction of vibration which may be fixed or variable in time. For example, if two waves of equal amplitude and with their vibrations at right angles but $\frac{1}{4}$ λ out of phase are added, the resultant will have a plane of vibration which rotates uniformly with time and is of constant amplitude. This will be recognized as circularly polarized light. Other phase relations lead to elliptically polarized light.

**2.40. Irregular Waves.** When waves of different frequencies are added by the principle of superposition, waves of irregular form result. Fourier analysis provides a useful tool for the separation of irregular waves into simple harmonic components.

The concept of pure simple harmonic motion implies an infinite wave train. The wave trains from light sources, however, even in the case of single photons, are not infinite in duration, and cannot therefore be ideal simple harmonics. The radiation generated by a single photon is conceived as a finite wave train, consisting of a finite number of vibrations of a fixed frequency, as shown in Figure 2.24. For a typical photon, there may be 100,000 vibrations in the sequence, which will be about 3 cm long.

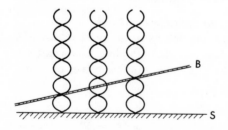

FIGURE 2.23. Weiner's experiment. A thin photosensitive plate (B) was placed at a slight angle to a pattern of standing waves generated by reflection at a surface. Nodes and antinodes alternate along the plate, and a series of light and dark lines are therefore recorded. The plate must be thin enough not to disturb the standing wave pattern significantly.

FIGURE 2.24. A finite wave train.

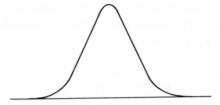

FIGURE 2.25. Frequency spectrum of a Gaussian wave group.

A Fourier analysis of such a finite wave train yields simple harmonic components, which comprise a fundamental, of the same frequency as the wave train vibrations and other components of slightly different frequency. The strength of these components diminishes on both sides of the fundamental. The rate at which these components diminish in amplitude is inversely proportional to the length of the original wave train. For a typical photon, the distribution is somewhat like that shown in Figure 2.25, which is the frequency spectrum of a Gaussian wave group.[28] Such a group is of the form

$$a(k) = A' e^{-\alpha(k-k_0)^2} \qquad (2.53)$$

or

$$\frac{I}{I_0} = e^{-(\lambda-\lambda_0)^2/\alpha^2} \qquad (2.54)$$

The *dispersion*, or spread of frequencies in the wave group, is often defined by the quantity $\lambda_0/\Delta\lambda$, where $\lambda_0$ is the wavelength of the fundamental, and $\Delta\lambda$ is the wavelength change for which the intensity is one-half that of the fundamental. For a typical atomic oscillator, $\lambda_0/\Delta\lambda$ has a value of the order of $10^6$.

**2.41. Coherence and Incoherence.** The term *coherence* is an important one in connection with interference and diffraction. It is defined as the temporal stability of phase, or degree of phase correlation between two wave trains. In order for interference phenomena to exist, the interfering wave trains must have a phase relation which persists for the period of observation.

In most interference experiments, light from a single source is divided into two beams, which later combine to form interference patterns. Two beams from separate sources have no fixed phase relations, and in general interference between them cannot take place. The division of the light from a single source is such that the individual wave trains are each divided and made to pursue separate paths. If these paths differ in length by more than the length of an individual wave train, coherence will not be preserved, and interference effects will not occur.

It has been shown that there is a reciprocal relation between the frequency dispersion of a wave train and its duration, thus

$$\Delta \nu \sim \frac{1}{\Delta t} \tag{2.55}$$

$\Delta t$ is defined as the *coherence time*.[29] From this definition, we may determine a *coherence length*,

$$\frac{\lambda^2}{\Delta \lambda} \tag{2.56}$$

which is the length of the wave train. It may also be shown that

$$\Delta t \, \Delta \nu \geq \frac{1}{4\pi} \tag{2.57}$$

which is a statement equivalent to the Uncertainty Principle of Heisenberg.

**2.42. Optical Path Length.** The optical path length is a concept of great usefulness. In a medium of refractive index $\mu$, the optical path length is defined as

$$opl = \mu t \tag{2.58}$$

where $t$ is the actual path length. Since the wave length varies with the refractive index, the optical path length is a measure of the number of waves in the distance $t$.

**2.43. Fermat's Principle.** In proceeding from one point to another, light will take a path such that the optical path length has a stationary value with respect to the optical path length for neighboring paths. This is *Fermat's principle*,[30] which is sometimes incorrectly stated. In some cases the path is a minimum and in some cases, a maximum.

Fermat's principle may be used to verify the laws of refraction and reflection,[31] and therefore the lens and mirror formulas given in Equations (2.48) through (2.50).

## THE INTERFERENCE OF LIGHT

**2.44. General.** The *interference* of light is a natural consequence of the superposition of separate wave trains, as was discussed in Section 2.36. Waves superimpose by the addition of amplitudes; where the waves happen to be *in phase*, the amplitudes are added, and where they are *out of phase*, the amplitudes subtract. At intermediate points, the phase difference determines the resultant amplitude.

**2.45. Conditions for Observable Interference.** Since every photon represents a separate and independent wave train, any ordinary situation involves a large number of these wave trains, and hence their superposition and consequent interference effects. As was pointed out, however, in Section 2.36, the usual case is that of a very large number of wave trains with randomly distributed phase, so that the interference effects taking place at a given point are random in nature and average out to a simple arithmetical sum of intensities. In order for interference effects to be *observable*, a relatively large number of wave trains must act in concord, and the effects must persist for a sufficient time to make the observation. This time, in general, is long enough for there to be a number of wavetrains arriving in succession.

This is another way of saying that in order to produce observable interference effects, the separate wavetrains producing it must be *coherent*, according to the definition of this term given above.

Usually, coherence between two beams of light can be obtained only if both beams arise from the same source and represent a single beam which has been divided and recombined at the point of observation after traveling different paths. This condition alone is not sufficient; since all sources are of finite size, it is also necessary that the phase differences produced at a given point be the same for all parts of the source in order for interference effects to be observable.

**2.46. Interference and Diffraction.** The term *interference* is usually reserved for the discussion of the production of light and dark fringes representing the near-doubling and near-cancellation of amplitudes; many effects which are actually cases of superposition of coherent or partially coherent light beams are discussed under separate topics. Thus, the production of circularly polarized light from the superposition of two coherent orthogonally plane-polarized beams out of phase by $\frac{1}{4}$ wavelength is really an interference phenomenon.

Interference bands are also produced at the edges of shadows and in the focal planes of optical systems as a result of the spatial limitations of wavefronts by apertures and obstacles; these effects are referred to as *diffraction*, and are discussed separately.

**2.47. Interference of Two Coherent Sources.** The basic phenomenon of interference is well illustrated by a consideration of Young's experiment,[32] which was the first to demonstrate the interference of light. In Figure 2.26, S is a monochromatic point source, and $s_1$ and $s_2$ are two pinholes in a screen which provide two mutually coherent secondary sources if the screen is perpendicular to a line joining the source with the point midway between the pinholes. The reason for restriction to point sources and monochromatic light will be made clear later.

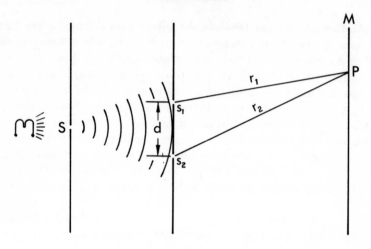

FIGURE 2.26. Geometry of Young's experiment.

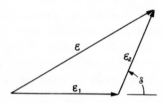

FIGURE 2.27. Vector addition of two waves.

The light beams spread out from the two pinholes and are intercepted by a screen, M. At a point P on the screen, the difference in the path lengths of the two beams is $r_2 - r_1 = s$. The path difference in wavelengths is $s/\lambda$, and the angular phase difference between the two wave trains is therefore $2\pi d/\lambda$, or to use previous nomenclature, if $\delta$ is the phase difference, then

$$\delta = ks \qquad (2.59)$$

The resultant of two superimposed waves with a phase difference $\delta$ is shown in vector form in Figure 2.27. The amplitude of the resultant is the vector sum of the amplitudes of the two components, or

$$\mathcal{E} = \mathcal{E}_1 + \mathcal{E}_2 \qquad (2.60)$$

or

$$\mathcal{E}^2 = \mathcal{E}_1{}^2 + \mathcal{E}_2{}^2 + 2\mathcal{E}_1\mathcal{E}_2 \cos \delta \qquad (2.61)$$

which is the law of cosines.

Since the intensity of light is proportional to the square of the amplitude, Equation (2.61) may also be written

$$I = I_1 + I_2 + 2 \sqrt{I_1 I_2} \cos \delta \qquad (2.62)$$

The first two terms represent merely the summation of intensities which takes place for incoherent light; the term $2\sqrt{I_1 I_2} \cos \delta$ is the *interference term*. When the phase difference is $2n\pi$, the interference term is $2\sqrt{I_1 I_2}$ and we have

$$I = (\sqrt{I_1} + \sqrt{I_2})^2 \qquad (2.63)$$

which, for $I_1 = I_2$ becomes

$$I = 4I_1 \qquad (2.64)$$

while when the phase difference is $(2n + 1)\pi$, the interference term has the negative sign and

$$I = (\sqrt{I_1} - \sqrt{I_2})^2 \qquad (2.65)$$

and for $I_1 = I_2$,

$$I = 0 \qquad (2.66)$$

In general, for $I_1 = I_2$,

$$I = 4I_1 \cos^2 \frac{\delta}{2} \qquad (2.67)$$

and the intensity varies from 0 to a maximum of $4I_1$ in the form of a cosine curve of the phase difference.

If the geometry of Figure 2.26 is analyzed, it can be shown that when $r \geq s \geq \lambda$, the conditions for maxima and minima on the screen are

$$\text{for a maximum } s \sin \theta = m\lambda \qquad (2.68)$$

$$\text{for a minimum } s \sin \theta = (2m + 1)\lambda/2 \qquad (2.69)$$

**2.48. Restrictions on Size and Monochromaticity.** In Equation (2.68), $m$ is known as the *order* of the interference band. It is clear from the equation that the value of $\theta$ for which the maximum occurs varies with $\lambda$, so that the maxima for different wavelengths do not coincide on the screen. Hence, unless the source used in this experiment is reasonably monochromatic, the overlapping of maxima of different wavelengths wipes out the fringes.

Although different portions of a source are incoherent with each other, corresponding parts of the two secondary sources in Young's experiment are mutually coherent; for a small source, the interference bands produced by the separate parts of the sources are coincident on the screen, so that fringes are visible. If the source is of significant size with respect to $s$, however, the maxima and minima produced by different parts are not formed at the same point on the screen, and the fringes are destroyed.

The sources may be extended in a direction perpendicular to the diagram,

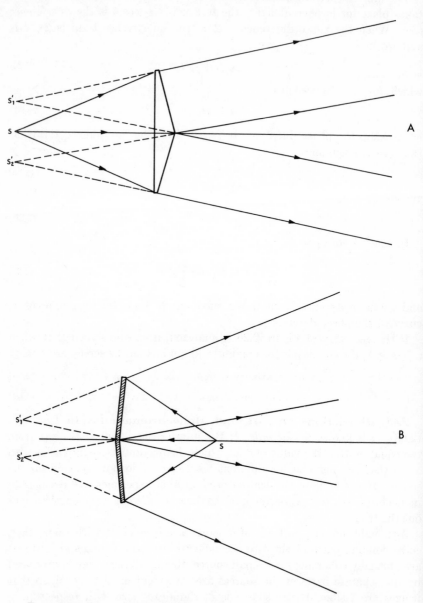

FIGURE 2.28. Methods for the division of wave front: (A) Fresnel's biprism, (B) Fresnel's mirrors, (C) Billet's split lens.

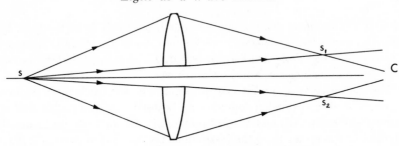

FIGURE 2.28—*Continued*

however, thereby becoming parallel slits; this is the usual experimental arrangement in order to obtain adequate illumination.

**2.49. Types of Interference.** Interference is commonly classified into two types, according to the method by which it is produced: *division of wavefront* and *division of amplitude*. Young's experiment is an example of division of wavefront, the wavefronts from the single source having been divided into two pieces, which then exhibit interference effects where they join.

Other examples of division of wavefront involve the Fresnel biprism, Fresnel's mirrors, and Billet's split lens (Figure 2.28), as well as others. This method is also utilized in phase microscopy, which is discussed in a later chapter.

An interesting technique is that of Lloyd, illustrated in Figure 2.29, because it demonstrates the phase change of a beam of light upon reflection. The interference is produced between a beam which falls directly upon the viewing plane and a beam which has been reflected from the mirror.

The viewing plane may be taken at M, in which case the point O at the surface of the mirror, corresponds to the 0th order *maximum*. Observation will show that this is at the center of a *dark* fringe, which is explicable only on the assumption that the reflected beam has undergone a phase change

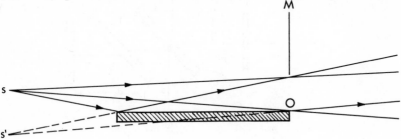

FIGURE 2.29. Lloyd's mirror.

of $\pi$. It will be remembered that theory indicated this to be the case. For Lloyd's mirror, then, the conditions for maxima and minima expressed in Equations (2.68) and (2.69) are reversed. In addition, this arrangement produces only one-half of a full set of fringes.

Methods involving the division of amplitude are much more common in practice, since extended sources may be used, and the problem of obtaining sufficient illumination does not exist. All methods involving the division of wavefront have the restrictions pointed out in Section 2.48.

**2.50. Division of Amplitude.** The methods involving division of amplitude are legion. In general, the division into two beams from a single source is accomplished through the use of a semitransparent surface. One beam is reflected from the surface and the other is transmitted; these two beams are later joined to produce interference fringes.

Descriptions and discussions of various types of interferometers are deferred for the sections on optical instruments; the method of division of amplitude, however, is most easily explained by describing an instrumental arrangement. For this purpose, the Michelson Interferometer[33] is an excellent example, as well as being a basic instrumental form, historically as well as physically.

**2.51. The Michelson Interferometer.** This instrument is illustrated in Figure 2.30. A beam of light from a source, S, falls upon a diagonal plane parallel glass plate $G_1$. This plate is usually partially silvered on its back surface, as indicated, so as to increase the intensity of the light transmitted through the instrument and to overcome the effects of light reflected from the first face of $G_1$. This silvering is of such density that the intensity of the reflected and transmitted beams are equal.

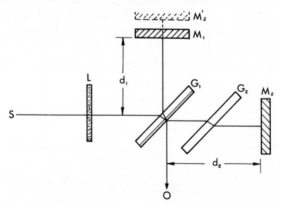

Figure 2.30. Schematic of the Michelson interferometer.

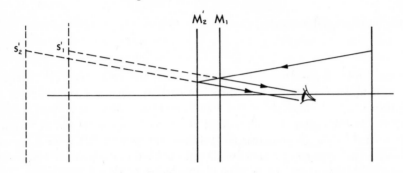

FIGURE 2.31. Principle of the Michelson interferometer for parallel mirrors.

The reflected beam from $G_1$ passes to the mirror $M_1$, and is there reflected back through $G_1$ to the observer; the transmitted beam passes to mirror $M_2$, and is there reflected back to $G_1$ and from it to the observer. The duplicate glass plate $G_2$ is included to make the optical paths *in glass* of the two legs equal; it is not essential for use of the interferometer with monochromatic light, but it is necessary when white light fringes are required.

It will be seen from examination of the diagram that the two paths are equivalent, in that they both contain the same number of reflections. The observer sees an image of the mirror $M_2$ in the reflector $G_1$, as indicated by the dotted line $M_2'$. If the distance $d_2$ is greater than $d_1$, this image will be more distant than the surface of $M_1$, as shown; if $d_2$ is less than $d_1$, the image will lie in front of $M_1$; and if the distances are equal, $M_2'$ will coincide with $M_1$.

If an extended source is used (usually provided by a ground glass plate, L), both mirrors will be filled with light, and the observer will see the entire field illuminated. If a point source is used, the observer merely sees its reflections, and since the fringes are only visible in the areas illuminated, no fringes are formed with a point source. A point source is usually used, however, for initial alignment of the instrument.

Two different types of interference effects are observable in the Michelson interferometer. When $M_2$ is adjusted so that its image $M_2'$ is parallel to $M_1$, but separated from it interference results from the phase difference introduced by this separation. It will be seen, from Figure 2.31, that, for every point in the source, the reflections from $M_1$ and $M_2'$ are seen by the observer in the same direction, so that the required conditions of coherence are met.

If $s$ is the difference $s_1 - s_2$, then the path difference between the two beams is

$$2s \cos \theta$$

and the phase difference is

$$\delta = 2ks \cos \theta \qquad (2.70)$$

A number of effects can be reasoned from the geometry. The fringes formed under the above conditions are circular, since a given value of $\delta$ corresponds to a circle about the line from the eye which is normal to the mirror. At the center, $\theta = 0$, so that we have, for a maximum, $2s = m\lambda$. In general, when this condition is fulfilled, the pattern has a *dark* center (because at $G_1$, one of the beams is reflected internally and the other externally, so that there is a relative phase change of $\pi$).

The order of interference decreases outward from the center (since $\cos \theta < 1$). When $M_1$ and $M_2'$ are coincident, $s = 0$ and the path difference is zero for all angles; thus there are no fringes or, in common terminology, there is only one fringe covering the entire mirror. Because of the phase change, the field is dark.

Beginning with the condition where $M_1$ is more distant than $M_2'$, a pattern of circular fringes is seen, coming closer together as their radius increases. As $M_1$ is moved closer to $M_2'$, the fringes move from the outer portions of the field toward the center, and the radii increase, so that the number of fringes in the field becomes smaller until, at coincidence, the central fringe has spread out to cover the field. As $M_1$ is brought in front of $M_2'$, the fringes reappear, welling up from the center and becoming more and more numerous.

These fringes are *fringes of equal inclination*, or *Haidinger fringes*. Since a new fringe appears for each movement of the mirror through a distance $\lambda/2$, counting fringes is a precise method for measuring length. Michelson used his interferometer[34] in this manner for measuring the number of wavelengths of the red cadmium line in the standard meter. This spectral line is now a primary standard in spectroscopy, and has the wavelength

$$\lambda_r = 6438.4696\text{Å}$$

With monochromatic light, such as the red line of cadmium, interference can be observed with this instrument over path differences which are limited only by the monochromaticity of the source—that is, the length of the individual wave trains. With the red cadmium line, this is about 50 cm. Observation of the *visibility* of the fringes is an excellent method for determining the degree of monochromaticity of a source, and was used by Michelson for this purpose. There are now more precise methods.

**2.52. Localized Fringes.** The Haidinger fringes discussed above are formed by the interference of rays which are parallel to each other, and hence are located at infinity. When the mirrors of the interferometer are not parallel, but are inclined to each other at a slight angle, a different type of fringe pattern is seen, which is localized near the mirror surfaces. In this case, which is diagrammed in Figure 2.32, the path differences are generated primarily by the wedge between the mirrors. When the mirrors intersect at the center, these fringes are straight and parallel to the edge of the wedge; when there is a separation between the mirrors at the center, the fringes are curved, convex to the thin edge of the wedge, because the mirror separation is now a factor in the path difference.

These fringes are known as *Fizeau* fringes. They are not seen with monochromatic light for path differences exceeding a few millimeters. The two rays which interfere appear to diverge from a virtual point behind the mirrors, and thus the eye must be focused at this distance to observe them. This is the meaning of fringe *localization*.

**2.53. White Light Fringes.** When the compensator plate $G_2$ is used, fringes may be formed in the interferometer with white light if the path difference does not exceed a few wavelengths. When the mirrors are co-incident at the center, the 0th order center fringe is seen, flanked by a few colored fringes. For path differences greater than a few wavelengths, however, the variation of path difference with wavelength washes them out.

**2.54. Interference in a Thin Plate.** Consider a beam of light incident on a thin plate at an angle of incidence $I$. Two beams will be reflected into the eye or an instrument located at O—one beam by direct reflection from the upper surface, and another beam by reflection from the lower surface. This is another case of division of amplitude, and the conditions of coherence are maintained, so that interference effects ensue.

The phase difference in the two beams is shown in Figure 2.33.

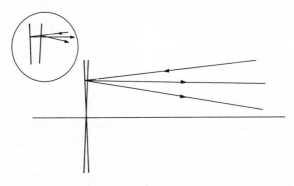

FIGURE 2.32. Principle of the Michelson interferometer for tilted mirrors.

*Fundamentals*

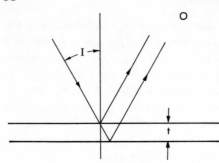

FIGURE 2.33. Interference in a thin plate. The ray which is reflected from the rear surface of the plate has a greater path length by the amount $2 \mu t \cos I'$, where $I'$ is the angle of refraction and is $\mu$ the index of the material. For a derivation, see reference 15, p. 133.

The optical path difference between the two beams is

$$\Delta d = \mu(AC + CD) - AB \qquad (2.71)$$

Now

$$AC = CD = \mu t/\cos I'$$

(using the *optical* path length)
and

$$AB = AD \sin I$$

But

$$AD = 2AC \sin I' = 2t \sin I'/\cos I'$$

and

$$\sin I = \mu \sin I'$$

$$AB = 2\mu t \sin^2 I'/\cos I'$$

Hence

$$\Delta d = 2\mu t \left[ \frac{1}{\cos I'} - \frac{\sin^2 I'}{\cos I'} \right] = 2\mu t \cos I' \qquad (2.72)$$

and the phase difference becomes

$$\delta = \frac{2\pi}{\lambda} \Delta d = \frac{4\pi\mu t}{\lambda} \cos I' \qquad (2.73)$$

In Equation (2.73) we see that there are three variables, whose variation may produce maxima and minima in the phase difference and, hence, interference fringes: the angle of inclination, I, the optical path difference $\mu t$, and the wavelength $\lambda$. These in turn lead to three different types of fringes:

(1) Haidinger fringes, or fringes of equal inclination, when the arrangement is such that the angle $I'$ dominates the situation—as in the Michelson interferometer with the mirrors parallel.

(2) Fizeau fringes, or fringes of equal thickness, when the path difference, $\mu t$, dominates—as in the Michelson interferometer when the mirrors are inclined to each other.

(3) Fringes of equal chromatic order (FECO fringes), when the wavelength variations dominate. Such fringes are usually not visible to the naked eye, but require a spectrometer, in which case they lead to the phenomenon known as the *channeled spectra*.[35]

**2.55. Haidinger Fringes.** These fringes have been analyzed in connection with the Michelson interferometer. They appear when the two reflecting surfaces are parallel. For plates of a thickness greater than a few wavelengths, monochromatic light is necessary. Viewed at normal incidence, they are circular, and become more crowded as the angle of inclination increases. The order number increases outward.

This type of fringe finds its greatest usefulness in application for measuring distances and wavelengths. They are much enhanced when the two surfaces involved have high reflecting power, and the fringes are produced by multiple reflections (see Section 2.57 *et seq.*).

**2.56. Fizeau Fringes.** These fringes of equal thickness find many applications in optical testing, since they reveal differences in optical path and may thus be utilized to indicate the departure of one optical surface from another, departures of a surface from flatness, variations in index of refraction, and similar phenomena.

The classic example of Fizeau fringes are Newton's rings, illustrated in Figure 2.34. These are seen when a surface of long radius of curvature is

FIGURE 2.34. Newton's rings. (*Courtesy Perkin-Elmer Corp.*)

placed upon a flat surface and illuminated from above. The plate which produces the fringes is in this case an air film immersed in glass. The central fringe is dark since one of the reflections undergoes a phase change of $\pi$ and the other does not. Successive circular dark fringes occur where the path difference is an integral number of full wavelengths or the air space is an integral number of half wavelengths.

With monochromatic or nearly monochromatic light, many rings are seen; with white light, interference can be observed for path differences of a few wavelengths, and the fringes are strongly colored.

Figure 2.35 shows a conventional method of testing optical surfaces for conformance to a test plate. When two surfaces of the same general curvature are used in this fashion to produce Fizeau fringes, the fringes indicate departures of the surfaces from exact conformity, and are interpreted exactly like the lines on a contour map. Usually, in testing flats, the master surface and the surface being tested will be set by the operator at a slight angle, so that if the test surface is also flat, the Fizeau fringes will be straight lines. By adjusting the angle of the wedge, any desired number of fringes may be produced. Then any curvature in the fringes indicates a variation in the piece being tested; by applying pressure and noticing the direction of movement of the fringes, one can determine whether the test surface is "high" or "low" with respect to the master.

When spherical surfaces are being tested against a master test plate, one usually adjusts them to give a minimum number of circular fringes; the number of fringes is often used as a tolerance criterion on radius of curvature. Departure of the fringes from a circular form indicates a departure from sphericity.

**2.57. Multiple Beam Fringes in a Plane-parallel Plate.** In the

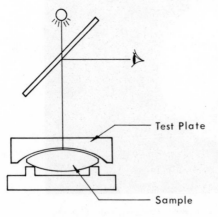

FIGURE 2.35. Testing of optical surfaces.

Test Plate

Sample

foregoing treatment, only two beams were considered—the beam reflected from the front surface and the beam reflected from the rear surface and passing twice through the thickness of the plate. In an actual case, some of the beam reflected at the rear surface will be re-reflected at the front surface, and again at the back surface, and will emerge parallel to the two beams already considered. It will have suffered a phase retardation of $2\delta$, and its amplitude is added to that of the other two beams. There are actually an infinite number of beams so generated, limited only by the aperture of the collecting means and the angle of incidence; at normal incidence, the number is infinite.

These multiple reflections can be ignored when the reflection coefficient is small, as for glass and similar dielectrics, because the intensity diminishes very rapidly. But when the reflection coefficient is significant, a rather surprising result occurs. The maxima for reflected light and the corresponding minima for transmitted light become very sharp as they are accentuated by the addition of multiple beams.

Figure 2.36 illustrates the geometry. A collecting lens is used to gather a large number of the reflected beams.

Let $\tau$ and $\rho$ be the transmission and reflection coefficients for the light *intensity* at each surface. If the plate is homogeneous and immersed in a homogeneous medium, $\tau$ and $\rho$ will be the same at both surfaces. The reflected and transmitted *amplitudes* will be proportional to $\tau^{1/2}$ and $\rho^{1/2}$ respectively.

Now, every beam is transmitted twice, and if the beams are numbered as shown, the number of reflections for a given beam will be $2(N-1)$, where $N$ is the number of the beam. Thus, if the amplitude of the incident beam is $\mathcal{E}$, the amplitude of beam $N$ is $\mathcal{E}\tau\rho^{(N-1)}$. Now, the phase retardation

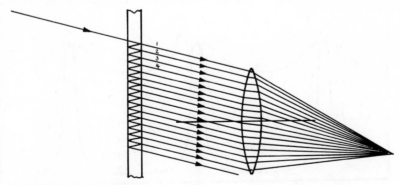

FIGURE 2.36. Multiple beams in a plane-parallel plate.

for beam $N$ is $(N - 1)\ \delta$. Using complex notation, one can see that
the several beams have the equations

$$E_1 = \mathcal{E}\tau e^{i\omega t}, \quad E_2 = \mathcal{E}\tau\rho e^{i(\omega t - \delta)}, \quad E_3 = \mathcal{E}\tau\rho^2 e^{i(\omega t - 2\delta)}, \text{ etc.} \tag{2.74}$$

Hence the sum of the superimposed waves has the equation

$$E = \mathcal{E}\tau e^{i\omega t}[1 + \rho e^{-i\delta} + \rho^2 e^{-2i\delta} + \rho^3 e^{-3i\delta} + \cdots + \rho^{N-1}e^{-(N-1)i\delta}] \tag{2.75}$$

which reduces to

$$E = \mathcal{E}\tau e^{i\omega t}\ \frac{1}{1 - \rho e^{-i\delta}} \quad \text{for } N \to \infty \tag{2.76}$$

Now, the *intensity* of the superimposed beam is the product of the complex conjugates, or

$$I = \frac{\mathcal{E}^2\tau^2}{1 + \rho^2 - 2\rho \cos \delta} \tag{2.77}$$

The maxima occur for $\cos \delta = 1$, and have an intensity

$$I_{\max} = \frac{\mathcal{E}^2\tau^2}{(1 - \rho)^2} \tag{2.78}$$

And the minima occur at $\cos \delta = -1$, and have an intensity

$$I_{\min} = \frac{\mathcal{E}^2\tau^2}{(1 + \rho)^2} \tag{2.79}$$

For the ideal case of no absorption in the medium, $\tau = 1 - \rho$ and the
maxima and minima have the intensities

$$I_{\max} = \mathcal{E}^2, \qquad I_{\min} = \mathcal{E}^2\ \frac{(1 - \rho)^2}{(1 + \rho)^2} \tag{2.80}$$

Figure 2.37 shows how the intensities of the transmitted maxima increase

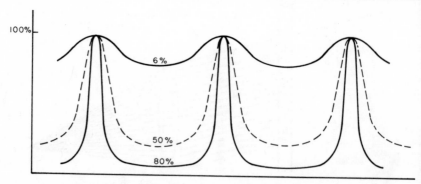

FIGURE 2.37. Intensities of transmitted beams in multiple-beam interference.

in sharpness as $\rho$ increases. The interferometer making use of this phenomenon is the Fabry-Perot interferometer, (see Section 8.49) and in this instrument, it is customary to use silvered or aluminized surfaces with a reflectivity of 90 per cent or greater.

If the reflected beams are subjected to the same analysis, it is found that for the case of no absorption, the equation is

$$I = \frac{2(1 - \cos \delta)\rho}{1 + \rho^2 - 2\rho \cos \delta} \tag{2.81}$$

There is a minimum for $\cos \delta = 1$, and a maximum for $\cos \delta = 0$, with the intensities

$$I_{\min} = 0, \qquad I_{\max} = \frac{2\rho}{1 + \rho^2} \tag{2.82}$$

If the transmitted and reflected intensities for each of the two cases, as given by Equations (2.80) and (2.82) are added, it is found that the sum is unity. It is interesting to note that even though the reflecting surfaces may be nearly opaque, at the maximum, *all* of the light is transmitted. For high reflectivities, the minimum in the transmitted light approaches zero.

The fringes which have been described are fringes of equal inclination, or Haidinger fringes; they are formed as concentric circles from extended sources.

**2.58. Surface Examination by Multiple-beam Interferometry.** For this type of fringe, the angle of inclination is more significant in producing successive fringes than are variations in the thickness of the plate. Multiple-beam Fizeau fringes may be formed when the thickness of the plate is of the order of a few wavelengths; surface variations take the form of shifts in the location of the fringes, just as with double-beam Fizeau fringes. Because of the sharpness of the multiple-beam fringes, however, it is possible to make much more precise measurements of small surface irregularities. Tolansky[36] has developed this technique extensively and has been able to measure surface contours to an accuracy of a few Angstroms. Similar techniques for examining the flatness of optical surfaces are used to make measurements to the order of 1/500 of a wavelength.

**2.59. Interference Filters.** When the two reflecting surfaces are parallel, and the angle of view is small, the principal variant in the phase difference [Equation (2.73)] is the wavelength, if a dielectric between the reflecting surfaces is assumed. If the thickness is only a few wavelengths, the maxima are widely separated.

This principle has been used to make *interference filters*, which transmit only a very narrow spectral region. With a sufficiently thin film, only one maximum occurs in the visible spectrum; with somewhat thicker films, the maxima are still widely enough separated that the unwanted ones may be suppressed by ordinary color filters.

This type of filter is usually constructed by evaporating successive coatings of silver, a dielectric and another silver layer on a glass substrate. It is usually cemented to another glass plate for purposes of protection.

**2.60. Reflection Controlling Films.** Thin dielectric films on the surfaces of optical elements can be used, by multiple beam interference, to control the reflections. For example, a coating of a low index material whose optical thickness is $\frac{1}{4}\lambda$ will minimize the reflections from a glass surface at the wavelength for which this thickness is optimum and will reduce the reflections at other wavelengths. In this case, since the two reflections are at different media boundaries, the reflection coefficients are not the same unless the index of the film is $\sqrt{\mu}$ where $\mu$ is the index of the glass. For most glasses, it is not possible to find a suitable material with an index low enough to satisfy this condition. The usual material is magnesium fluoride, whose index is 1.38; on crown glass, this treatment reduces the reflection for green light from about 4 per cent to less than 1 per cent. When applied to a large number of surfaces throughout an optical instrument, the cumulative effect can be significant.

Multiple-layer dielectric coatings can be used to enhance the reflectivity of metal surfaces; this technique has been developed by Turner and others, and it is now possible to produce mirrors with reflectivities of better than 99 per cent. Untreated silver or aluminum surfaces rarely have a reflectivity better than 90 per cent, except when freshly made.

**2.61. Achromatic Fringes.** In general, fringes can be produced with white light only when the path difference does not exceed a few wavelengths, for the reasons which have been explained above. If the path difference is the same for all wavelengths, then the phase difference is inversely proportional to the wavelength, and the maxima and minima for different wavelengths are not formed at the same points. In order to observe fringes in white light over large path differences, the *phase* difference must be constant for all wavelengths, which implies that the path difference be proportional to wavelength. Ordinary dielectrics have dispersion—variation of optical path with wavelength—but it is in the wrong direction, the index and therefore the optical path becoming greater for shorter wavelengths.

Achromatic fringes can be produced, however, by placing a dispersing medium, such as a spectroscope, in front of the wave-dividing means, so that by changing the angle of incidence, the necessary condition is closely achieved.

**2.62. Brewster's Fringes.** If two plane-parallel plates are inclined to each other at a slight angle, interference fringes can be formed by light which has been internally and externally reflected from both plates; these fringes are localized at infinity like Haidinger fringes, but are straight and parallel to the edge of the wedge, like Fizeau fringes. They are known as Brewster's fringes, and are used in the Jamin interferometer.[37]

There is a multiple beam form of Brewster's fringes, known as *fringes of superposition*, formed when the two plane-parallel plates have highly reflecting surfaces. The effect is to enhance certain maxima of the normal Fabry-Perot fringes and to minimize others.

**2.63. Interference in Radio Waves.** It is of interest to mention in passing, two phenomena in the radio region of the electromagnetic spectrum which are occasioned by the interaction of waves to produce interference. One is radio fading, caused when one beam passes directly to a receiver and another is reflected from some object and arrives at the receiver by a different path. This phenomenon was the cause of much concern before automatic volume controls were a common radio component.

The other point of interest is that the two-slit experiment of Young may be reversed to make a radio direction finder. If we consider the first order maximum, which is located on the normal bisector to the plane of the slits (see Figure 2.26), as a source of radio waves, it is apparent that the waves emitted from this point will be in phase at the two slits. If the plane of the slits is now rotated about an axis perpendicular to the paper, there will be a phase difference between the two slits.

If the two slits are replaced with two phase-sensitive receivers, the direction to the source can be determined by rotating the device until the two signals are in phase.

## DIFFRACTION

**2.64. Interference and Diffraction.** It is the nature of a wave to spread in all directions; therefore (as described in Section 1.3) when light passes the edge of an obstacle, it does not cast a geometrically sharp shadow. The edges of the shadow are characterized by a series of bands. These *diffraction* bands are easily observed but are not immediately apparent; their explanation in terms of a wave theory, by Fresnel,[38] did much to establish the wave theory of light in opposition to the particle theory. The particle concept of light has no satisfactory explanation for diffraction.

These bands are an interference phenomenon—they are the locations where maxima and minima occur in the superposition of the light waves. The term *diffraction* is reserved for those inteference phenomena which arise because of the spatial restriction of light beams, the term *interference* being used to describe phenomena which occur in the principal beam itself. Many effects are the result of a combination of interference and diffraction; the spectra which are formed by a diffraction grating are an example.

**2.65. Mathematics of Diffraction.** The rigorous mathematical treatment of diffraction is one of the most difficult areas of optics.[39] The analysis of diffraction is a straightforward boundary value problem in electromagnetic theory, but except for highly simplified situations, the mathematics becomes almost completely unmanageable, and only a very few special cases have actually been worked out. Fortunately, nearly all of the cases arising in instrumental optics can be adequately described with simplifying assumptions which make the mathematics tractable.

No attempt is made in this book to present a comprehensive mathematical treatment; for the interested reader, this has been done by many authors to almost any desired degree of rigor.

**2.66. Extension of Huygens' Principle.** Fresnel's analysis of diffraction involved the extension of Huygens' principle of secondary wavelets (see Section 1.3 and Figure 1.4). If light is presumed to pass through a restricted aperture, as shown in Figure 2.38, Huygens wavelets may be generated at the points in the plane of the aperture, and the integrated effect of these wavelets at an arbitrary point P beyond the aperture may be computed, if certain assumptions are made. By this type of reasoning, Fresnel generated an integral equation of the general form

$$U(\text{P}) = \frac{Ae^{ikr_0}}{r_0} \iint_S \frac{e^{iks}}{s} \text{K}(\chi)dS \tag{2.83}$$

where $U(\text{P})$ is the wave amplitude at P, the coefficient $Ae^{ikr_0}/r_0$ is the amplitude of the wave in the aperture, and $\text{K}(\chi)$ is an *obliquity* factor, which is a function of the change in direction of the light ray at the aper-

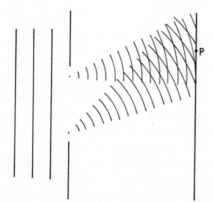

FIGURE 2.38. Interference effects in light passing through an aperture (diffraction).

ture in order to pass from the source to the point P. The correct form of $K(\chi)$ was not theoretically known, but assumptions were made concerning it to make the results of the integration agree with experiment.

For many cases of optics, this treatment is adequate to describe the form of diffraction patterns. When the aperture is large with respect to the wavelength of the light, but is small with respect to the distances $r_0$ and $s$, and the point P is not greatly distant from S', so that the obliquity factor may be taken as unity, this integral gives the diffraction *pattern* within experimental error.

Fresnel's integral, however, does not correctly predict the absolute intensity and phase at any point, and it does not explain the absence of any backward radiation. In fact, the Huygens' secondary wavelet principle makes the assumption that the energy always travels in the forward direction, although the idea of independent sources should include radiation into a spherical volume.

**2.67. Kirchhoff's Formulation.** Kirchhoff[40] was able to show that the diffraction integral could be obtained as a solution to the homogeneous wave equation

$$\nabla^2 E - \frac{\varepsilon\mu}{c^2}\ddot{E} = 0 \tag{2.84}$$

and expressed in the form

$$U(P) = \frac{iA}{2\lambda}\iint_A \frac{e^{ik(r+s)}}{rs}(\cos\alpha_1 - \cos\alpha_2)dA \tag{2.85}$$

in which the variables have the significances shown in Figure 2.39. This integral contains some simplifying assumptions which make it applicable

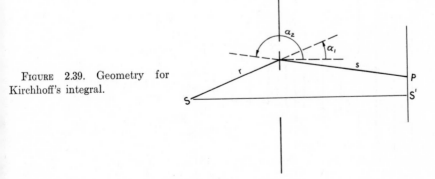

FIGURE 2.39. Geometry for Kirchhoff's integral.

only for apertures large with respect to a wavelength and for relatively large values of $r$ and $s$, but this integral removes the defects of Fresnel's integral in that it correctly predicts the amplitude and phase of the resultant. It also includes a value for the obliquity factor in the form

$$K(\chi) = -\frac{i}{2\lambda}(1 + \cos \chi) \tag{2.86}$$

**2.68. Classification of Diffraction.** The diffraction effects of apertures and obstacles are commonly classified as *Fraunhofer* and *Fresnel* diffraction. Fraunhofer diffraction represents the simplified case where the source and the point P are both removed to infinity. This case is of particular importance because it applies in optical systems when S and P are conjugate image points, and thus the diffraction seen at the focal points of optical instruments is Fraunhofer diffraction.

The distinction can more readily be seen in a subjective manner. In Figure 2.40, light passes through an aperture in an opaque screen. If a screen is placed at A, there will be a relatively sharp circular patch of light, which will be surrounded by very narrow bright bands caused by diffraction. This is *Fresnel*, or near-field, diffraction. If the screen is placed further away, at B, the geometrical projection of the aperture will be less distinct and the diffraction bands will be more prominent. If the screen is removed to infinity or, what is equivalent, if a lens is placed behind the aperture to focus the distant light source in a point, the diffraction effects in the vicinity of this point image represent *Fraunhofer* diffraction. There is actually no sharp transition from one form to the other. When the screen is relatively close to the aperture, the light pattern on the screen is a geometric projection of the aperture, surrounded by a region in which diffraction effects are observable. This is generally true in cases where

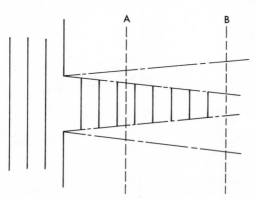

FIGURE 2.40. Diffraction regions of an aperture.

Fresnel diffraction applies. In the case of Fraunhofer diffraction, the geo-metrical projection of the aperture has disappeared, and the observed light pattern does not reproduce its shape—although, as will be seen, the pattern does depend upon the aperture shape, but not in a simple way.

Mathematically, the Fraunhofer condition is the case where, in the in-tegration over the aperture, terms in $r$ and $s$ higher than the first power can be ignored. In this case, the integral of Equation (2.85) reduces to

$$U(P) = C \iint_S e^{-ik(\alpha p+\beta q)} dp \, dq \tag{2.87}$$

where $p$ and $q$ are the coordinates in the aperture, and $\alpha$ and $\beta$ are the direction cosines of $s$ with respect to $r$. We have

$$C = \frac{1}{\lambda} \sqrt{\frac{E}{S}} \tag{2.88}$$

where $E$ is the total energy of the aperture and $S$ is its area.

In the following sections, a few cases of particular interest are discussed, to show the general nature of diffraction patterns.

**2.69. Fraunhofer Diffraction for a Rectangular Aperture.** Con-sider a rectangular aperture with dimensions $2x$ and $2y$.

The integral of Equation (2.87) becomes

$$U(P) = C \int_{-a}^{a} e^{-ik\alpha p} dp \int_{-b}^{b} e^{-ik\beta q} dq \tag{2.89}$$

This becomes

$$U(P) = CD \left( \frac{\sin k\alpha x}{k\alpha x} \right) \left( \frac{\sin k\beta y}{k\beta y} \right) \tag{2.90}$$

The intensity is

$$I(P) = |U(P)|^2 = I_0 \left( \frac{\sin k\alpha x}{k\alpha x} \right)^2 \left( \frac{\sin k\beta y}{k\beta y} \right)^2 \tag{2.91}$$

This function is the product of two functions of the form

$$u = \left( \frac{\sin z}{z} \right)^2 \tag{2.92}$$

which is plotted in Figure 2.41. It has a principal maximum $u = 1$ at $z = 0$, and zero minima at $z = \pm n\pi$. The maxima occur at $z = [(2m + 1)/2]\pi$.

The product of the two functions for the rectangular aperture gives a two dimensional pattern of maxima and minima, as shown in Figure 2.42. Note that the diffraction pattern is narrow in the direction in which

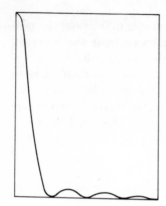

FIGURE 2.41. Fraunhofer diffraction from a slit.
The function $u = \left(\dfrac{\sin z}{z}\right)^2$.

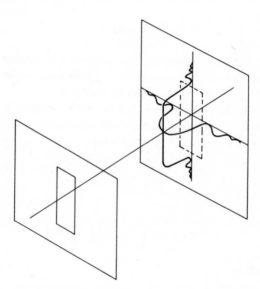

FIGURE 2.42. Diffraction pattern of a rectangular aperture.

the aperture is wide, and vice versa. Note also that the intensity diminishes very rapidly.

The coefficient $I_0$ of Equation (2.91) is the intensity at the center of the pattern:

$$I_0 = ED/\lambda^2$$

**2.70. Fraunhofer Diffraction Pattern for a Slit.** A single slit is a special case of a rectangular aperture, where one of the dimensions is assumed to extend indefinitely, and only the diffraction pattern in one direction is examined. We then have only one of the factors of Equation (2.90), and consequently the equation

$$U(P) = CD \left( \frac{\sin k\alpha x}{k\alpha x} \right) \tag{2.93}$$

and the intensity becomes

$$I(P) = |U(P)|^2 = I_0 \left( \frac{\sin k\alpha x}{k\alpha x} \right)^2 \tag{2.94}$$

The above mathematical procedure has not been shown in detail. For the interested reader, Born and Wolf[39] present a complete treatment, in accordance with the steps shown above; Andrews[41] develops the results in a less elegant but possibly more easily followed manner, directly from the geometry of the apertures concerned.

Minima occur at $\alpha = 0.5\lambda/a$, $\lambda/a$, etc.

**2.71. The Circular Aperture.** The circular aperture is one of particular interest, since it is the usual form of a lens. This case is more readily treated in polar coordinates.

If a point in the aperture has the coordinates $\rho,\theta$, and a point in the diffraction pattern has the coordinates $\omega,\psi$, then Equation (2.91) may be reconstructed to become

$$U(P) = C \int_0^a \int_0^{2\pi} e^{-ik\rho\omega \cos(\theta-\psi)} \rho \, d\rho d\theta \tag{2.95}$$

where $a$ is the radius of the aperture.

This may be evaluated in terms of Bessel functions[42] to give

$$U(P) = CD \left[ \frac{2J_1(kx\omega)}{kx\omega} \right] \tag{2.96}$$

for the amplitude and

$$I(P) = |U(P)|^2 = I_0 \left[ \frac{2J_1(kx\omega)}{kx\omega} \right]^2 \tag{2.97}$$

for the intensity, where $J_1$ is the Bessel function of order unity.

This function is plotted in Figure 2.43. It is very similar to the function shown in Figure 2.41, with the difference that the intensity falls off less rapidly than for the case of the slit or the rectangular aperture, and the maxima and minima are distributed in a slightly different way. The minima occur at $\omega = 0.61\lambda/x$, $1.116\lambda/x$, $1.619\lambda/x$, etc.

The fraction of the total energy contained within successive rings of the diffraction pattern is a matter of considerable interest. Figure 2.44 plots

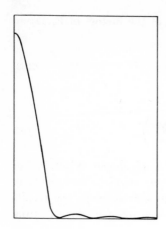

FIGURE 2.43. Diffraction by a circular aperture.

The function $u = \dfrac{2J_1(kx\omega)}{(kx\omega)}$

the cumulative energy as a function of the radius of the pattern. It is seen that more than 80 per cent of the energy is contained within the central core and more than 90 per cent within the circle formed by the second dark ring.

Note also that, as in the case of the rectangular aperture and the slit, the size of the diffraction pattern is inversely proportional to the size of the aperture.

**2.72. Fraunhofer Diffraction for Other Aperture Shapes.** The simplified situation which constitutes Fraunhofer diffraction makes it possible to analyze the diffraction patterns for other forms of aperture, particularly where the shape of the aperture can be simply expressed in some coordinate system.

The principle stated above relating to the reciprocal proportionality between the size of the aperture and that of the diffraction pattern may be extended in the case of other apertures to the statement that, if an aperture is uniformly extended in one direction, then its diffraction pattern is contracted uniformly in that direction by the equivalent ratio and the intensity of the pattern at the corresponding point is proportional to the square of that ratio.

The Fraunhofer diffraction patterns for multiple apertures is of particular interest, since this leads to the diffraction grating. Discussion of this is postponed until near-field, or Fresnel, diffraction has been briefly discussed.

**2.73. Fresnel Diffraction.** Diffraction patterns formed in the "near field"—that is, in regions not infinitely far from the aperture or obstruction—are generally called *Fresnel* diffraction patterns. The following discussion makes certain simplifying assumptions, such that the distances

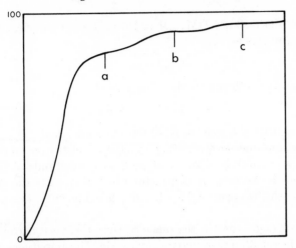

FIGURE 2.44. Plot of the cumulative energy in the diffraction image from a circular aperture; a, b, c are the successive dark rings.

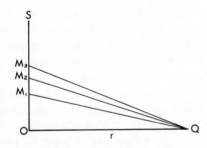

FIGURE 2.45. Fresnel's half-period zones.

involved are large with respect to a wavelength. Such simplifications are usually valid for most problems in optics, although the diffraction patterns in regions very close to the diffracting elements are of considerable interest in microwave problems.

**2.74. The Half-period Zones.** Consider a plane wave incident upon a plane surface S, as in Figure 2.45. Using Fresnel's approach, the plane S may be divided into a series of concentric circles, with radii $OM_1$, $OM_2$, $OM_3$, etc. The condition determining the value of each radius is that the distance $M_nQ = r_0 + n\lambda/2$. Thus the distance from $M_1$ to Q is $r_0 + \lambda/2$, the distance $M_2Q = r_0 + 2\lambda/2$, etc. Each successive zone, therefore, represents a distance from Q which is one-half a wavelength further than that of the preceding zone. Thus the terminology *half-period* zones.

For the $n$th circle

$$s_m^2 + r_0^2 = (r_0 + \tfrac{1}{2}n\lambda)^2 \qquad (2.98)$$

where $s_m$ is the distance $OM_n$. If $r_0 \gg n\lambda$, then a sufficiently close approximation to this is

$$s_m^2 = \lambda n r_0$$

The area of the $n$th zone is therefore given by

$$\sigma_n = \pi s_n^2 - \pi s_{n-1}^2 = \pi \lambda r_0 \qquad (2.99)$$

and it is seen that the areas of all of the zones are equal.

Now, the amplitude at Q resulting from the wavelets from an infinitesimal area of the wave front is $K\mathcal{E}dS/r$, where $\mathcal{E}$ is the amplitude of the incident wave and $dS$ is the area. K is a factor which represents the variation of amplitude with the angle OQM—its value is unknown at this point of the argument.

Consider a single zone in the plane S. Over this very narrow zone, the inclination factor K does not vary significantly. The amplitudes at Q due to each of the infinitesimal areas are therefore equal; they vary in phase over a range of $\pi$. Now the resultant of a set of disturbances of equal amplitude and uniformly varying phase may be computed by complex algebra or by vector diagram, and in the case where the variation in phase is $\pi$, the resultant is $2/\pi$ of that which would be the case were there no phase variation. The phase of the resultant is that corresponding to the center of the zone, and is therefore ½ wavelength behind the resultant from the preceding zone, hence the zones are referred to as *half-period zones*, or Fresnel zones.

The resultant at Q from an aperture in the plane S, is found by summing the resultants from all of the zones—in the case of a circular aperture centered on O, these resultants have vector amplitudes which alternately reverse in direction. Although the value of the inclination factor K is unknown, it can reasonably be assumed that it causes the amplitude to decrease as the angle OQM increases.

If there is no obstruction in the plane S, then there are an infinite number of zones, and the amplitude at Q is the sum of an infinite series whose terms alternate in sign but are of decreasing magnitude. If the decrease is a gradual one, the sum of such a series is very nearly one-half the value of the first term. Thus, for the unobstructed case, the amplitude at Q obtained from summing the effects of the zones is ½ × $2/\pi$ = $1/\pi$ times the amplitude resulting from the first zone. It is thus

$$\mathcal{E}_Q = \frac{1}{\pi} \int \frac{K\mathcal{E}\,dS}{r} \qquad (2.100)$$

the integral being taken over the first zone. The area of this zone, like that of all the others is $dS = \pi \lambda r_0$, and since for this zone, we may put $r = r_0$, we have, for the amplitude at Q

$$\mathcal{E}_Q = K\mathcal{E}\lambda \qquad (2.101)$$

But for an unobstructed plane at S, the amplitude at Q must be $\mathcal{E}$. Hence, $K = 1/\lambda$.

The phase at Q for the unobstructed case is the same as that for an unobstructed wave arriving directly from O. But the phase of the first half-period zone is $\frac{1}{4}$ wavelength behind this. Therefore, it is necessary to assume that the wavelets start one-quarter period in advance of the phase of the incident wave. This seems a little strange, but is supported both experimentally and theoretically, and arises from the fact that the Huygens' wavelets are only a convenient invention and do not really exist.

**2.75. Kirchhoff's Analysis.** Kirchhoff showed that the assumptions which were necessary in the above reasoning to give the correct amplitude and phase at Q were inherent in the results of a derivation from the wave equation. If the incident wave at S (see Figure 2.39) is given by

$$\xi = \frac{\mathcal{E}}{r} \exp i(\omega t - kr) \qquad (2.102)$$

then Kirchhoff's analysis, which will not be repeated here, shows that the amplitude at Q due to an element $dS$ at S is

$$du(Q) = \frac{i\mathcal{E}dS}{2\lambda rs} \{\cos \alpha_1 - \cos \alpha_2\} \exp [-ik(r + s)] \qquad (2.103)$$

where the quantities have the meanings shown in Figure 2.39.

Equation (2.103) contains a simplification which makes it valid only if the distances $r$ and $s$ are large compared to a wavelength; this is true for any ordinary optical problems. The trigonometric factor in brackets is the inclination factor; the factor $i$ introduces the $\frac{1}{4}$ wavelength phase advance.

When $\theta$ and $\beta$ are small, and the line $P_0P$ is normal to the diffracting plane, the approximation $\cos \theta - \cos \beta = 2 \cos \delta = 2$, may be made, and the equation becomes

$$du(Q) = \frac{\mathcal{E}i}{\lambda rs} e^{ik(r+s)} dS \qquad (2.104)$$

and if the surface over which integration is taken is a wavefront, $\mathcal{E}e^{ikr}/r = \mathcal{E}$, and therefore

$$du(Q) = \frac{i\mathcal{E}}{\lambda s} e^{iks} dS = \frac{i\mathcal{E}}{\lambda s} e^{iks} dx \, dy \qquad (2.105)$$

If the coordinates of a point on the screen S are $(x_0, y_0, z_0)$ and the coordinates of a point near Q are $(x_1, y_1, z_1)$, where $z_1 = r$ then

$$s^2 = z_1{}^2 + (x_1 - x_0)^2 + (y_1 - y_0)^2$$

and the approximation

$$s = z_1 + (x_1 - x_0)/2z_1 + (y_1 - y_0)^2/2z_1$$

may be made. Now, the $s$ in the denominator represents the variation in amplitude as a result of the variation in the distance $s$. If $s$ is large compared to a wavelength, it will not vary significantly over the aperture to be integrated, hence this $s$ may be treated as a constant. The $s$ in the complex term, however, represents the variation in phase over the aperture, and this is significant, so that the approximation given above must be used here.

To express the *relative* amplitudes, the constant factors in the equation may be lumped together, and this gives (expressing the integration over the aperture)

$$U(Q) = C \iint_s \exp -(ik/2z_1)[(x_1 - x_0)^2 + (y_1 - y_0)^2]dx_0dy_0 \qquad (2.106)$$

If a new variable, $v = (x - x_0)\sqrt{2/\lambda z_1}$ is introduced, the equation becomes

$$U(Q) = C \int_{v_1}^{v_2} \exp [-(i\pi/2)v^2]dv \qquad (2.107)$$

for the integration in the $x$-direction only. This may be written

$$\begin{aligned} U(Q) &= C \int_{v_1}^{v_2} \left[ \cos \frac{\pi}{2} v^2 - i \sin \frac{\pi}{2} v^2 \right] dv \\ &= \int_{v_1}^{v_2} \cos \frac{\pi}{2} v^2 dv - i \int_{v_1}^{v_2} \sin \frac{\pi}{2} v^2 dv \end{aligned} \qquad (2.108)$$

The *intensity* is

$$I = |U(Q)|^2 = \left[ \int_{v_1}^{v_2} \cos \frac{\pi}{2} v^2 dv \right]^2 + \left[ \int_{v_1}^{v_2} \sin \frac{\pi}{2} v^2 dv \right]^2 \qquad (2.109)$$

These two integrals are known as *Fresnel's* integrals.[43]

This problem has been developed above in some detail, partly because the results are valid for a wide variety of optical problems, and are used repeatedly for computational purposes, and partly to illustrate the kinds of simplification which must be adopted in order to make the equations tractable.

When the limits of integration are $\pm\infty$, the value of either integral is $\pm\frac{1}{2}$; this corresponds to the case of no obstruction in the diffraction

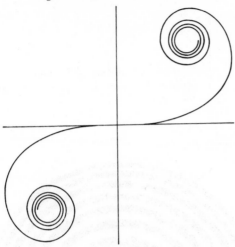

FIGURE 2.46. Cornu's spiral.

plane, and gives, as is to be expected, an intensity and amplitude factor of unity. For integration between finite limits, special techniques are required.

**2.76. Cornu's Spiral.** A graphical method of solution was given by Cornu.[44] If $v$ is used as a parameter to plot a curve whose ordinate and abscissa are the values of the two integrals, then the square of the length of a line joining two points on the curve whose values are $v_1$ and $v_2$ is equal to the sum of the squares of the integrals, and therefore to the intensity in the direction corresponding to the values of $v_1$ and $v_2$. The direction of this line also gives the phase of the resulting vibration. The spiral is shown in Figure 2.46. The two arms of the curve approach the asymptotic points $+\frac{1}{2}, +\frac{1}{2}$ and $-\frac{1}{2}, -\frac{1}{2}$, which correspond to $v = \pm \infty$.

**2.77. Diffraction at a Slit.** As an exercise in the use of Cornu's spiral, the reader may follow the following discussion. Assume a slit with edges at $x_0 = \pm a$. We consider variations in the $X$-direction only, which assumes that the slit is very long in the $Y$-direction. The limits of integration for a point in the $P$-plane are

$$v_1 = \sqrt{\frac{2}{\lambda z_1}}\,(x_1 + a)$$

and

$$v_2 = \sqrt{\frac{2}{\lambda z_1}}\,(x_1 - a)$$

The difference $v_1 - v_2$ is $\sqrt{8a^2/\lambda z_1}$ and is independent of $x_1$.

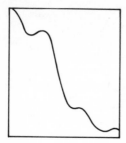

FIGURE 2.47. Fresnel diffraction by a slit. Intensity as a function of distance from the axis, computed by the use of the Cornu spiral.

FIGURE 2.48. The Fresnel zone plate.

The intensity as a function of $x_1$ is given by the square of the length of a line joining the ends of a segment of the curve of constant length (measured along the curve) as it slides along the curve to represent variations in the value of $x_1$, the point in the $P$-plane whose intensity is being considered. The result is shown in Figure 2.47.

**2.78. The Fresnel Zone Plate.** The concept of half-period zones in a circular aperture, in which alternate zones are in phase with each other, leads to the concept of a circular plate marked off in accordance with these zones, with the zones alternately transparent and opaque, as shown in Figure 2.48. It can readily be shown that on such a plate, the radii are proportional to the square root of the integers.

At the distance from the plate corresponding to a $\frac{1}{2}$ wavelength path difference between adjoining zones, such a plate will form a bright image on its axis if illuminated by a plane or a spherical wave. If the alternate zones, instead of being made opaque, are cut to such a thickness that they introduce a $\frac{1}{2}$ wavelength retardation of the light, then all of the zones are active in producing the bright image, and its intensity is much increased. As was seen in the preceding analysis, for the conventional zone plate, the intensity of this image is $\frac{1}{2}$ that due to the light transmitted by the first zone.

**2.79. Fresnel Diffraction by a Circular Aperture.** In accordance with the preceding analysis, it is a simple matter to determine the diffraction from a circular aperture for points along the axis. As one proceeds along the axis, the condition that the amplitude is $\frac{1}{2}$ that due to the first zone (for an infinite number of zones) and that the phase is the same as that of the first zone is applicable, so that there are minima and maxima along the axis.

The situation at points away from the axis is a different matter; the mathematics is very difficult and is rarely discussed in texts on optics. It has been investigated, however, both theoretically and experimentally.[45] A series of circular rings is produced; whether the central spot is bright or dark depends upon the position along the axis at which the analysis is made.

**2.80. Diffraction by a Circular Obstacle.** It is easily seen that the analysis by half-period zones leads to the conclusion that a circular obstacle will produce a bright spot on the axis. For, in the alternating series which represents the resultant amplitude, if the first N terms are omitted, the sum of the series still is $\frac{1}{2}$ the first term. It was once contended that this "ridiculous" result disproved the entire Fresnel concept, until experimental verification was made.

A circular obstacle produces a series of bright rings in the same manner as does a circular aperture; inide the geometrical shadow of the obstacle, these rings are very dim and fade rapidly.

**2.81. Diffraction by Slit and Straight Edge.** Fresnel diffraction by a slit and by a straight edge are easily analyzed, especially with the help of the Cornu spiral. As might be expected, both cases show bright bands near the edges of the geometrical shadow, which fade rapidly in brightness as one proceeds away from that edge. For wide slits, there are also bright bands within the shadow. For a straight edge, there are no bands within the shadow; the illumination fades continuously and rapidly from the first bright band which is located slightly outside the geometrical shadow line.

**2.82. Application of Diffraction.** The principles and details of diffraction have many applications in practical optics, some of which will be discussed later on. The diffraction grating, which is the indispensable tool of wavelength analysis, displays the Fraunhofer diffraction pattern for many regularly spaced slits; the Fraunhofer diffraction pattern of an optical aperture sets limits on the resolving power of optical instruments; diffraction by apertures illuminated with coherent light plays a major role in the design and operating principles of microscopes; diffraction sets limits upon the accuracy of optical measurements; and modern optical design leans heavily upon analyses of diffraction.

**2.83. Babinet's Principle.** A principle of considerable utility, which would appear at first glance to be obvious, is *Babinet's principle*,[46] which states that the sum of the resultants of two complementary diffracting screens at a given point is equal to the resultant of an undiffracted wave. Complementary screens are defined as a pair such that where one screen is transparent, the other is opaque, and vice versa.

**2.84. Wave and Ray Optics.** Geometrical optics treats *rays* of light; until recently, geometrical optics was the universal basis for the design of lenses and instruments, and it is still extensively used. Treatment of rays makes the problems those of pure geometry, and accordingly achieves much mathematical simplification. *Rays* are defined as the paths of energy flow, which are defined by Poynting's vector [Equation (2.18)]; in isotropic media, they are the normals to the wavefronts. In anisotropic media, as has been seen, this is no longer true, and the rays are defined in a different way.

Diffraction is seen to describe the manner in which a restricted wavefront fails to conform to this simplified geometrical picture, and hence describes the manner in which the principle of the rectilinear propagation of light does not hold. It arises whenever we consider the finite wavelength of light and its phase aspects. The deviations are, for the most part, of second order and are not readily apparent.

Geometrical optics and the principle of rectilinear propagation may be said to represent the limiting condition for light when the wavelength approaches zero.

### REFERENCES

1. See R. Ditchburn, "Light," 2nd ed., p. 511, New York, Interscience Publishers, 1963.
2. For a comprehensive discussion of the rationalized mks (Giorgi) system, see G. Di Francia, "Electromagnetic Waves," Ch. 1, New York, Interscience Publishers, 1955.
   In this book, we have attempted to use this system, but there are many cases where convention seems to make it unwise; for example, Planck's constant $h$

is always expressed in erg-seconds—to express it in joule-seconds and change the numerical value accordingly would confuse many readers.

3. G. Stokes, *Trans. Cambridge Phil. Soc.*, **9**, 399 (1852).
4. R. Jones, *J. Opt. Soc. Am.*, **31**, 488 (1941).
   H. Hurwitz and R. Jones, *J. Opt. Soc. Am.*, **31**, 493 (1941).
   H. Mueller, Rep. No. 2, OSRD, OEM-sr-576, Nov. 15, 1946.
5. H. Poincaré, "Thèorie Mathematique de la Lumière," Vol. 2, Ch. 12, Paris, Georges Corré, 1892.
6. E. Malus, *Nouveau Bull. Sci. Soc. Philomatique*, **1**, 266 (1809); *Mem. Soc. d'Arcueil*, **2** (1809).
7. J. Biot, *Bull. Soc. Philomatique, Paris*, **6**, 26 (1815).
8. H. Lloyd, *Trans. Roy. Irish Acad.*, **17**, 145 (1833).
9. W. Nicol, *Edinburgh New Phil. J.*, **6**, 83 (1829).
10. G. Airy, *Trans. Cambridge Phil. Soc.*, **4**, 313 (1833).
11. J. Babinet, *C. R. Acad. Sci., Paris*, **29**, 514 (1849).
12. H. Soleil, *C. R. Acad. Sci., Paris*, **21**, 426 (1845); **24**, 973 (1847); **28**, 162 (1848).
13. Cf. reference 1, p. 493.
14. See J. Strong, "Concepts in Classical Optics," p. 148, W. H. Freeman Co., 1958.
15. See R. Longhurst, "Geometrical and Physical Optics," p. 487, New York, Longmans, Green, 1957.
16. A. Fresnel, "Oeuvres," Vol. 1, pp. 89, 129; Vol. 2, pp. 261, 479, 1816.
17. See F. Joos, "Theoretical Physics," p. 2119, Blackie,
18. J. Kerr, *Phil. Mag.*, **50**(4)**, 337 (1875).
19. See M. Born, "Optik," p. 360, Berlin, Springer.
20. D. Brewster, *Phil. Trans.*, 60 (1815); 156 (1816); *Trans. Roy. Soc. Edinburgh*, **8**, 369 (1818).
21. Chr. Huygens, "Traite de Lumiere," Leyden, 1690.
22. W. Snell, in (R. Descartes) "Dioptrique," Meteores Leyden, 1637 (source not acknowledged by Descartes).
23. I. Newton, *Phil. Trans.*, No. 80, 3075 (Feb., 1672).
24. L. Foucault, *Compt. Rend. Acad. Sci., Paris*, **30**, 551 (1850).
   H. Fizeau and L. Breguet, *Compt. Rend. Acad. Sci., Paris*, **30**, 562, 771 (1850).
25. A. Fresnel, *Ann. Chim. Phys.*, **1**(2), 239 (1816); "Oeuvres," Vol. 1, pp. 89, 129; Vol. 2, pp. 261, 479 (1816).
26. Cf. reference 14, p. 31.
27. O. Weiner, *Ann. Physik*, **40**, 203 (1890).
28. Cf. reference 1, pp. 84, 91.
29. For a comprehensive discussion of coherence, see M. Born and E. Wolf, "Principles of Optics," pp. 318, 319, New York, Pergamon Press, 1959.
30. P. Fermat, "Oeuvres de Fermat," pp. 2, 354, Paris, 1891.
31. R. Feynman *et al.*, "Lectures on Physics," pp. 26–34, Addison-Wesley, 1963.
32. T. Young, *Phil. Trans. Roy Soc., London*, **92**, 12, 737 (1802).
33. A. Michelson, *Am. J. Sci.*, **22**(3), 120 (1881); *Phil. Mag.*, **13**(5), 236 (1882).
34. A. Michelson and J. Benoit, *Trav. Mem. Bur. Int. Poids Mes.*, **11**, 1 (1895).
   J. Benoit, C. Fabry and A. Perot, *Trav. Mem. Bur. Int. Poids Mes.*, **15**, 1 (1913).
   For discussions of the measurements, see H. Barrell, *Proc. Roy. Soc., London Ser. A*, **186**, 164 (1946).
   For discussions of techniques, see J. Sears and H. Barrell, *Phil. Trans. Roy. Soc., London Ser. A*, **231**, 75 (1932); **233**, 143 (1934); J. Sears, *ibid.*, **186**, 152 (1946).

35. Cf. reference 14, p. 232.
36. S. Tolansky, "Multiple Beam Interferometry of Surfaces and Films," Oxford, Clarendon Press, 1948.
37. J. Jamin, *C. R. Acad. Sci., Paris*, **42,** 482 (1856).
38. Cf. reference 25.
39. Born and Wolf (reference 29, p. 553) give an extensive discussion of rigorous diffraction theory for certain special cases.
40. G. Kirchhoff, *Berl. Ber.*, 641 (1882); *Ann. Physik,* **18**(2), 663 (1883); *Ges. Abhandl. Nachtr.,* **22**.
41. C. Andrews, "Optics of the Electromagnetic Spectrum," Ch. 9, Englewood Cliffs, N.J., Prentice-Hall, 1960.
42. G. Watson, "A Treatise on the Theory of Bessel Functions," 2nd ed., Cambridge, Cambridge University Press, 1946.
43. T. Pearcey, "Tables of Fresnel Integrals," Cambridge, Cambridge University Press, 1956.
44. A. Cornu, *J. Phys.*, **3,** 5, 44 (1874).
45. G. Mie, *Ann. Physik,* **35**(4), 377 (1908).
    A. Sommerfeld, *Math. Ann.*, **47,** 317 (1896).
    For reviews and references, see J. Miles, *J. Appl. Phys.*, **20,** 760 (1949); C. Bouwkamp, *Rept. Progr. Phys.*, **17,** 35 (1954). Cf. also reference 29, and reference 41, Ch. 11.
46. A. Babinet, *Compt. Rend.*, **4,** 638 (1837).

# CHAPTER 3

# The Interaction of Light and Matter

**3.1. General.** In the view of modern physics, light and matter are simply different forms of energy; in the interaction of light and matter, there is a complex array of phenomena with respect to some of which there are still gaps in our understanding. The association of light and matter is a dynamic, not a passive one; when light encounters opaque matter, it is absorbed; its energy disappears as light energy and reappears in other forms, such as kinetic energy of material particles; when light is said to be transmitted by a transparent material, it does not just pass through—there is a complicated interaction with the material.

**3.2. Harmonic Oscillators.** Matter may be thought of as a cloud of tiny harmonic oscillators. In the early days of the wave theory, the "elastic solid" theory of matter served to explain many phenomena; with the advent of electromagnetic theory, the elastic solid became a cloud of electrical dipoles, each possessing certain characteristic resonant frequencies; in quantum theory, the resonant conditions become transition probabilities. The general picture is not greatly altered by the details: matter consists of an assemblage of atoms or molecules—arranged in regular arrays in crystals, bound closely together but more or less in disarray in noncrystalline solids, loosely coupled in liquids, and randomly and independently distributed in gases. These particles are electrical in nature and respond to the electric and magnetic fields existing in a beam of light. This response is a discontinuous function of frequency—the particles are particularly susceptible at their many "resonant" frequencies and at these frequencies they may even spontaneously emit light.

The response of the particles to the light depends upon the particular kinds of particles involved, on their arrangement and binding forces, and on the conditions of their environment. These responses are all completely explainable in general terms, and in most cases they are also explainable

109

in detail. There are still, however, some gaps in our detailed knowledge which must be filled in—in particular, the optical properties of metals are not as predictable as they might be, and the quantum theory does not yet give as clear-cut an explanation of a phenomenon like dispersion as it has of radiation.

**3.3. Polarization of the Medium.** In Section 2.7, the concept of polarization of a material medium acted upon by light was mentioned. The polarization is described by stating Maxwell's first equation [Equation (2–5)] in the form

$$\mathbf{D} = \mathbf{E} + 4\pi\mathbf{P} \tag{3.1}$$

where $4\pi\mathbf{P}$ is the *polarization* of the medium. (There is an analogous magnetic polarization given by $\mathbf{B} = \mathbf{H} + 4\pi\mathbf{M}$).

The polarization describes the field which is generated in the material by the action of the electric and magnetic fields of the light. It was also shown that the electromagnetic theory requires that the index of refraction be equivalent to the square root of the dielectric constant, and it was pointed out that experimentally this turns out in general not to be true for light, but that it is reasonably true at lower frequencies.

Before the advent of the laser, the fields which could be experimentally produced by light were very weak, and the polarization has conventionally been treated as a linear effect.[1]

The actual situation, however, is much more complex than Equation (3.1) indicates. It can be shown, both experimentally and theoretically, that the condition described in Equation (3.1) and the square root relationship of the index of refraction and the dielectric constant hold for *steady* fields. But the fields of a light beam are high-frequency fields (of the order of $10^{14}$ cycles/sec), and the situation is different. The polarization can be represented by the sum of a series of many terms[2]

$$\mathbf{P} = a_1\mathbf{E} + a_2\mathbf{E}^2 + \cdots + a_r\mathbf{E}\nabla\mathbf{E} + \cdots + a_s\dot{\mathbf{E}}\mathbf{B} + \text{etc.} \tag{3.2}$$

involving the powers of the electric and magnetic fields and their time and space derivatives.

In most ordinary situations, the strength of the fields of a beam of light are so small that only the linear effect is observable, but nonlinear effects appear when the field of the light beam is supplemented by external electric and/or magnetic fields, and effects such as the Faraday (see Section 3.35) and the Kerr (see Section 3.32) effects are created. When the fields of the light beam are sufficiently strong, as in the light of high intensity lasers, these secondary effects may appear strongly from the effects of the light alone, and a whole new array of phenomena, including harmonic generation, heterodyning, etc., are open to investigation. Work in this area is just beginning.

**3.4. Classification of Interaction Phenomena.** The interaction phenomena are often closely interdependent so that a clearcut classification is not possible. The nomenclature for various specific phenomena are, however, in common use, and must be clearly understood to follow the literature.

All of the phenomena involving the interaction of light and matter are usually discussed under one of the three categories: absorption, dispersion and scattering. Phenomena observed in the past only when external electric and/or magnetic fields were applied, such as the Faraday effect and the Kerr effect, have been classified in the literature under the titles of "electro-optics" and "magneto-optics"; in order to discuss matters in some kind of a sequence, this classification is retained in this book, although with the advent of the laser, and the production of these phenomena without the introduction of external fields, the distinction is now an artificial one.

In a certain sense, diffraction, which has already been discussed, is an interaction of light with matter, but we exclude it from this Chapter since it deserves separate treatment.

In the following discussions, the light is looked upon sometimes as a particle (photon) and sometimes as a wave, and no excuses are presented in switching from one concept to the other. This is permissible by the principle of complementarity, and the reader should learn as soon as possible to adopt whichever view offers the most lucid explanation of a phenomenon.

Consider a photon incident upon a material substance; what different sorts of interaction may occur? An event takes place only if the photon encounters a particle of the material substance. When this occurs, there are three types of interaction which may take place. (1) The photon retains its original energy, as does the material particle, and the photon continues on, possibly in a new direction. (2) The photon gives up part of its energy to the particle, and proceeds onward, usually in a new direction, with less energy, and hence with lower frequency and longer wavelength. (3) The photon is completely absorbed—it gives up all of its energy to the particle.

Case (1) is easy to understand on a particle concept—the photon merely bounces off the material particle and continues on, undisturbed as to energy, but perhaps changed in direction. To account for the phenomenon on a wave basis, it is necessary to assume that the energy is absorbed and reemitted at the same frequency, considering the material particle as a harmonic oscillator. Under this case, we have *scattering* of light—if the scattering particles are small with respect to a wavelength, it is *Rayleigh scattering;* if they are large, it is *Mie scattering.* This phenomenon also accounts for *dispersion,* and for the *index of refraction* of material media, as will be seen later.

In Case (2), part of the energy of the photon is given up to the material particle, and the remainder becomes a new photon of lower energy. If the energy is given up to produce an increase in the kinetic energy of the particle, the particle does not change its quantum state, and we have *Compton* scattering. If the particle absorbs its part of the energy by undergoing a change in state, we have *Raman* scattering.

In Case (3), the particle absorbs all of the energy of the incident photon and undergoes a change in state. This takes place only when the energy of the photon corresponds to the energy required for specific changes to take place; in other words, this phenomenon occurs only in specific frequency bands of the incident light.

After absorption of the photon, it may be reemitted at the same frequency almost immediately, in which case we have *resonance radiation;* it may be emitted at a different frequency, as the particle spontaneously reverts to a lower energy level, in which case we have *fluorescence;* it may be emitted at a different frequency after a long interval (say $10^{-8}$ seconds), in which case we have *phosphorescence;* or the energy absorbed may be sufficient to ionize the atom, and eject an electron, which then takes up the excess energy in the form of kinetic energy, in which case we have *photoelectric emission.*

One other rather rare event may take place; the incident photon may be annihilated and converted to a positron-electron pair. This is referred to as *pair production.*

## SCATTERING WITHOUT CHANGE IN ENERGY

**3.5. Rayleigh Scattering.** When the scattering particles are considerably smaller than a wavelength of the incident light, and are randomly distributed, the scattering follows a function of the form

$$I/I_0 = kV^2\lambda^{-4} \tag{3.3}$$

which expresses Lord Rayleigh's famous $\lambda^{-4}$ law of scattering.[3] $k$ is a constant, and $V$ is the volume of the scattering particles. For the intensity of the scattering in a specified direction, Monk[4] gives

$$I = I_0 \frac{2\mu^2(\mu - 1)^2}{N\lambda^4} (1 + \cos^2 \eta) \tag{3.4}$$

which holds only for *unpolarized* incident light.

In view of the restriction to particles smaller than the wavelength, Rayleigh's law holds for scattering by molecules and atoms; it is responsible, for example, for the blue color of the daylight sky and the red color of the sun near the horizon. The law generally applies to scattering by gases at relatively low pressures. In high pressure gases, liquids and solids, the particles can no longer said to be randomly distributed, and the interaction between them must be taken into account. The $\lambda^{-4}$ rule holds, however, even in liquids and solids.

**3.6. Mie Scattering.** Mie,[5] in an exhaustive mathematical treatment, derived the scattering functions for particles of any size, based upon electromagnetic theory. These functions have been computed, for many types of particles and particle distributions, and are available in the form of tables.[6] The scattering depends upon the nature of the particles, their size and distribution. In general, for particles large with respect to a wavelength, the scattering is independent of wavelength.

The problem of scattering is really a problem of diffraction; Mie scattering is simply a combination of diffraction and diffuse reflection. It is an interesting point of the theory that the scattering cross section of a large body (the fraction of the incident energy which it extracts from a plane-parallel light beam) is twice its geometrical cross section.[7]

**3.7. Dispersion.** When a beam of light traverses a transparent liquid or solid, it is observed that the velocity is a function of the wavelength, or frequency; usually the velocity is reduced for the higher frequencies. This means that the index of refraction varies with wavelength, usually becoming greater as the wavelength becomes shorter. This phenomenon is called *dispersion*, since in optical devices it leads to the gradual separation of wavelengths in the direction of propagation.

When a large portion of the electromagnetic spectrum is considered, it is found that all materials have specific absorption bands, which represent those frequencies where the atoms or molecules of the material absorb light quanta and undergo a change in state. As the wavelength of the incident light approaches these points, it is observed that the index of refraction undergoes an apparent discontinuity, rising sharply on the low-frequency side of the absorption frequency, and then appearing on the high-frequency side at a much lower value (often less than unity) and rising more slowly until the next absorption band is reached.

Figure 3.1 shows a typical index of refraction curve for a material substance, with the shape described above. The location of the specific absorption frequencies depends, of course, upon the substance in question.

Measurements of the index of refraction are difficult in the region of an absorption band since the light becomes almost completely absorbed, but

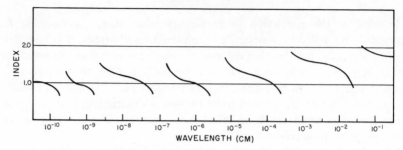

FIGURE 3.1. Extended plot of refractive index for a typical dielectric. The curve is schematic only, and does not represent any specific substance.

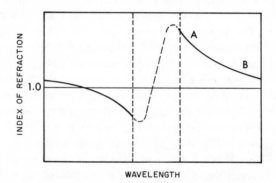

WAVELENGTH

FIGURE 3.2. Actual form of refractive index curve through an absorption line. The region enclosed between dotted lines is observable only with great difficulty because essentially all of the incident light is absorbed in this region.

this has been accomplished in many instances, and it is found that there is actually a continuous variation, as shown in Figure 3.2.

Most of the mathematical relationships for the treatment of dispersion have been developed empirically, from measurements on the index of refraction. Cauchy's formula[8]

$$\mu = A + \frac{B}{\lambda^2} + \frac{C}{\lambda^4} + \cdots \tag{3.5}$$

represents a reasonable fit in the region AB shown in Figure 3.2. This was developed to fit observed values.

The behavior of the curves in the vicinity of absorption points is referred to as *anomalous dispersion*, because it does not correspond to relations like the Cauchy formula. It has been known for a long time, however, that there is nothing abnormal about it.

**3.8. Theoretical Dispersion Formulas.** One of the first attempts at a theoretical treatment of dispersion was that of Sellmeier, who considered frictionless vibrators in an elastic solid and arrived at the equation

$$\mu^2 - 1 = \sum_{j}^{m} \frac{A_j \lambda^2}{\lambda^2 - \lambda_j^2} \tag{3.6}$$

where the $A_j$'s and $\lambda_j$'s are constants and wavelengths associated with resonant points. The constants are selected to fit the observed values of the index.

This formula fits the experimental curves much better than Cauchy's formula and, in particular, shows a good fit near absorption points. It has the defect, however, that it goes to infinity at a resonant (absorption) point.

The reason that Equation (3.6) fails in the region of absorption is that it takes no account of the subtraction of energy from the incident wave by the oscillator. Helmholtz derived an equation taking this factor into account, and obtained

$$\mu^2 - \kappa_0^2 = 1 + \sum_{j}^{m} \frac{A_j \lambda^2}{(\lambda^2 - \lambda_j^2) + g_j \lambda^2/(\lambda^2 - \lambda_j^2)} \tag{3.7}$$

which gives the curve completely through an absorption point. $\kappa_0$ is the *extinction coefficient*, defined as

$$\kappa_0 = \frac{\alpha \lambda}{4\pi}$$

where $\alpha$ is the *absorption coefficient* (see Section 1.26)

This was prior to the advent of the electromagnetic theory.

From the electromagnetic theory (using the relation $\mu = \sqrt{\epsilon}$) the following expression can be derived[9]

$$\vec{\mu}^2 - 1 = \sum_{j}^{M} \frac{N_j e^2}{\epsilon_0 m_j} \frac{1}{(\omega_j^2 - \omega^2) + jg\omega_j\omega} \tag{3.8}$$

where the dielectric is assumed to have dipoles with $M$ natural frequencies, $\omega_j$ ; $N$ is the number of dipoles per unit volume; $e$ is the dipole charge; $m_j$ is its mass; $\omega$ is the frequency of the incident wave; $g$ is the friction constant, and $\epsilon_0$ is the permittivity of free space (see Section 2.3).

This expression shows that the index of refraction is a complex quantity, in general, and it can be expressed as

$$\vec{\mu} = \mu(1 - j\kappa) \tag{3.9}$$

where $\kappa$ turns out to be the extinction coefficient, as defined above. In an *absorbing* medium, therefore, the index of refraction is complex, and the imaginary term represents the effect of the absorption. In transparent media, the absorption may be neglected for most purposes, and the index of refraction then becomes real.

In a region far from an absorption point, the imaginary part of the index may be dropped, and Equation (3.9) reduces to

$$\mu^2 - 1 = \sum_{j}^{m} \frac{A_j \omega_j^2}{\omega_j^2 - \omega^2}$$

where

$$A_j = \frac{N_j e^2}{\epsilon_0 m_j \omega_j^2}$$

(3.10)

and, when expressed in terms of wavelength, rather than frequency, this is identical with Sellmeier's equation [Equation (3.6)].

In the region of absorption, the complex index must be retained. The extinction coefficient $\kappa$ has the significance that the intensity falls to $1/e^{4\pi\kappa}$ of its incident value in a distance of one wavelength.

**3.9. Dispersion as the Result of Scattering.** If an oscillator is acted upon by an incident vibration, its behavior will depend upon its natural resonant frequency and the frequency of the input disturbance. If the disturbance is far from a resonant point, the oscillator will merely pass it on without absorption of energy, but with a difference in phase. As the resonant frequency is approached, the oscillator begins to absorb some of the energy, until at resonance, it absorbs it completely. As the frequency of the disturbance passes to the other side of the resonant point,[1] there is a 180° change in phase in the secondary disturbance passed on, and a decrease in the absorption.

This is exactly the mechanism involved in scattering from a cloud of oscillators, as discussed above. Furthermore, it may be shown that the superposition of the secondary, phase-shifted waves from the oscillator with the incident vibration, introduces a phase change in the resultant, which effectively modifies its phase velocity.

In a liquid or a solid, it may also be shown that in directions other than the direction of propagation of the incident disturbance, the effect of the superposition of the secondary waves is to create essentially completely destructive interference.

The phase velocity of the resultant of the secondary waves and the incident radiation represents the dispersion of the medium, and it can be shown that the results from such an analysis agree quantitatively with the results from experiment and from electromagnetic theory. On one side of the resonant frequency (absorption point), the phase of the secondary wave is shifted in one direction, and on the other side it is shifted in the other direction, so that the index of refraction jumps from a value which has been rapidly increasing to a value very much below the average value on the other side of the resonant point; this is a result of the 180° phase shift of the oscillator at the resonant point.

On the high-frequency side of the absorption points, the index of refraction is less than unity—this implies a velocity in the medium greater than the velocity in vacuum, $c$. At first, this would appear to violate the principle of relativity that velocities greater than $c$ cannot exist. The velocity in question, however, is a *phase* velocity; the velocity at which energy is propagated is always less than $c$.[10]

**3.10. Dispersion in Quantum Theory.** Quantum theory retains the same general equations as those given above, with some redefinition of terms. The resonant points become transitions in energy states, and the numbers of oscillators become transition probabilities. Otherwise, the mathematics is essentially the same. Quantum theory provides the means for computing the values of the transition probabilities and the locations of the resonant points, which electromagnetic theory could not do for its corresponding resonances.

It was found, in earlier experimental work that in equations like Sellmeier's, where the $A_j$'s represented in part the number of oscillators, values less than unity were necessary to make the equations fit the facts. Their interpretation in terms of transition probabilities makes this much easier to understand.

## SCATTERING WITH A CHANGE IN WAVELENGTH

**3.11. Compton Scattering.** The Compton effect has been mentioned previously (Section 1.5) as a demonstration of the particle aspect of light. It is observed in the X-ray region. Incident photons, colliding with light particles, may be scattered with a decrease in energy, this energy difference showing up in kinetic energy of an electron which is removed from the particle by the collision. The Compton effect is different from the photoelectric effect in that there is a definite relation in the former between the direction of the scattered radiation and the energy loss.

**3.12. Raman Scattering.** Raman scattering[10a] was first observed as a series of weak scattered frequencies slightly lower than the frequency of the incident light. It is incoherent with the incident light (whereas Rayleigh scattering is coherent therewith), and the change in frequency from that of the incident light is characteristic of the substance doing the scattering but independent of the incident frequency.

In this effect, the scattering particles absorb *part* of the energy of the incident quantum to produce a change in state; the remainder is reradiated as a lower-frequency quantum.

When the scattering medium is maintained at a high temperature, Raman frequencies higher than that of the incident light sometimes appear. These "anti-Stokes" lines correspond to reradiation to an energy level lower than that at which the energy was absorbed, and they can only occur when the absorbing particle is in an excited state due to the temperature.

## ABSORPTION

**3.13. General Absorption.** All substances absorb light to a greater or a lesser degree. Even those substances which we term "transparent" have a measurable absorption in large path lengths. Absorption is the removal of energy from a beam of light; this may take place in several ways. Scattering has already been discussed; the absorption of specific quanta from the light beam to produce changes in state of the particles of a medium is discussed under spectra. This is generally termed *absorptance*, and takes place, for the most part, in the case of solids and liquids, at the surface. In passing through a finite thickness of material, however, a light beam will suffer a general attenuation which is termed *body absorption*.

This body absorption may be independent of wavelength, or it may be highly dependent upon wavelength. Those materials which show *selective absorption*, or absorption dependent upon wavelength, are those bodies which appear to us to be colored. In the case of many materials, certain spectral regions are selectively reflected, and the remainder of the visible spectrum is absorbed; these materials appear to have the color of the reflected light. Examples are ordinary pigments. These materials, when provided in a layer which is thin enough to transmit some of the light, appear to be of the same color in both transmitted and reflected light; the light which is reflected or transmitted is subjected to multiple reflections between small particles of the material until all of the light lying in the absorbed wavelengths is subtracted from the beam.

Other materials, such as colored metals like copper and gold, and many dyes, absorb in the same spectral regions which they reflect strongly; these materials, when viewed by transmission in the form of thin films, appear to have a color complementary to that shown by reflected light.

All metals absorb strongly, so strongly in fact that in thicknesses of the order of a few wavelengths, they are completely opaque. Most metals absorb throughout the visible spectrum, and appear gray.

**3.14. The Absorption Coefficient.** If $I_0$ is the intensity of a beam of light incident on an absorbing medium, and $I$ the intensity transmitted through a thickness $t$, then

$$I = I_0 e^{-at} \tag{3.11}$$

which is *Lambert's Law*.

It should be noted that $I_0$ is the intensity of the light actually entering the medium, after correction for any reflection loss at the surface. $a$ as a measured value includes any attenuation from scattering, so that, if $a_m$ is the measured value, and $a_s$ and $a_a$ the attenuation coefficients from scattering and from true absorption, we have

$$a_m = a_s + a_a \tag{3.12}$$

**3.15. The Extinction Coefficient.** It is often convenient to use the extinction coefficient, $\kappa$, which has been previously defined:

$$\kappa = a\lambda_m/4\pi \tag{3.13}$$

in which case, Lambert's Law becomes

$$I = I_0 \exp -\frac{4\pi}{\lambda_m} \kappa t \tag{3.14}$$

which expresses the *intensity* of the transmitted light. $\lambda_m$ is the wavelength in the medium. For the *amplitude* of the transmitted light, we have

$$\mathcal{E} = \mathcal{E}_0 \exp -\frac{2\pi}{\lambda_m} \kappa t \tag{3.15}$$

and, expressed in terms of the wavelength in vacuum

$$\mathcal{E} = \mathcal{E}_0 \exp -\frac{2\pi}{\lambda} \mu\kappa t \tag{3.16}$$

where $\mu\kappa$ is known as the *absorption index*.

**3.16. Dichromatism.** In materials where there are two regions of absorption, and in which the absorption coefficient is different for the two regions, the color of the material will vary with thickness. This effect is known as *dichromatism*—not to be confused with the same term applied to a visual condition in which a mixture of two primary colors is sufficient for complete color vision.

**3.17. Reflectivity and Absorption.** It is a general rule that materials reflect strongly at just those wavelengths at which they absorb strongly. This follows from Kirchhoff's radiation law [Equation (1.34)]. From the electromagnetic theory, it may be shown that the reflectivity of an absorbing medium is given by

$$I_p = \mathcal{E}_p{}^2 \frac{(\mu - \sec i)^2 + \kappa_0{}^2}{(\mu + \sec i)^2 + \kappa_0{}^2} \tag{3.17}$$

$$I_s = \mathcal{E}_s{}^2 \frac{(\mu - \cos i)^2 + \kappa_0{}^2}{(\mu + \cos i)^2 + \kappa_0{}^2} \tag{3.18}$$

where $I_p$, $I_s$ are the reflected *intensities* for the electric vector parallel and perpendicular to the plane of incidence; $\mathcal{E}_p$, $\mathcal{E}_s$ are the incident *amplitudes;* $\mu$ is the index of refraction (which becomes real when the intensities are concerned); $\kappa_0$ is the extinction coefficient; $i$ is the angle of incidence.

At normal incidence, $i = 0$ and Equations (3.17) and (3.18) become identical and reduce to

$$r = \mathcal{E}^2 \frac{(\mu - 1)^2 + \kappa_0{}^2}{(\mu + 1)^2 + \kappa_0{}^2} \tag{3.19}$$

For most dielectrics, the extinction coefficient is small and may be neglected, in which case the equation reduces to the equation previously given for reflection at the surface of a dielectric [Equation (2.27)]. For metals and other highly absorbing materials, $\kappa_0$ cannot be neglected.

For most metals at most wavelengths, $\mu$ is no greater than a small integer; $\kappa_0$ however, is usually a moderately large integer, so that Equation (3.19) gives reflectivities approaching unity. For highly absorbing materials, $\kappa_0$ predominates over the index of refraction in determining the reflectivity.

It may also be noted that neither Equation (3.17) nor Equation (3.18) vanishes for any angle of incidence, as was the case for a dielectric for $r_p$ at Brewster's angle.

**3.18. Penetration on Reflection.** As in the case of total internal reflection in a dielectric, there is a small penetration of the medium upon reflection from an absorbing material, but there is no case of total reflection.

**3.19. Disposition of the Energy.** When the photons are not absorbed by the particles of the medium so as to produce changes in energy states, the energy is taken up in kinetic energy of the particles and produces heat—the final destination of all energy. In metals, there are free electrons as well as atoms and molecules available for the absorption of energy; these lighter particles are much more readily affected by the photons, and this explains the high absorption coefficient for these materials. Dielectrics show high absorption only in the regions of "resonant" points, where the light quanta are absorbed to produce energy state changes.

**3.20. Resonance Radiation.** In gases, the rule of high reflectivity at those wavelengths most strongly absorbed does not usually have an opportunity to operate. Light which is not absorbed in energy state changes is transmitted through the gas. This is true even for metals in the gaseous state, since the free electrons which exist in the solid material are no longer present at the high temperatures necessary to maintain the gaseous state.

It is possible, however, to observe strong reflectance at the wavelengths at which changes of state are produced, as was shown by Wood for sodium vapor; when the vapor density reaches a sufficiently high level, strong reflection from a very thin layer of the vapor is observed (which appears visually like a mirror) at the sodium absorption lines (5896Å). The same effect has been observed with other materials. It is termed *resonance radiation*.

**3.21. Reststrahlen.**[10b] It is possible to demonstrate this strong reflection in the neighborhood of an absorption point for materials such as crystals. If light is reflected successively from the same material, it is found to exhibit maximum intensity at certain specified frequencies, which are the absorption frequencies of the material. These residual rays are sometimes known as the *reststrahlen*.

**3.22. Fluorescence.** A large class of materials, including many minerals, exhibits the phenomenon known as *fluorescence*. When irradiated with light—usually in the ultraviolet spectrum—they reradiate at visible frequencies. This phenomenon is the basis for the identification of many minerals and is also the source of many spectacular visual effects; materials such as the cornea of the human eye and the enamel of teeth exhibit this effect.

The high-frequency light is absorbed to produce a change of energy state in the atoms of the material, which leap several energy levels. They reradiate by dropping to intermediate levels, for which the energy difference is less than that which was absorbed, and therefore the radiated light is at a lower frequency. This is exactly what happens in the laser in a much more spectacular manner.

Stokes investigated the phenomena of fluorescence exhaustively, and the normal fluorescence lines of a substance are known as Stokes lines. He propounded the rule that the reradiation was always at a lower frequency than the absorbed radiation. This is not necessarily true when the absorbing material is at a high temperature so that the atoms are maintained in an excited state. In this case, the atom, after absorbing radiation to produce an even higher state, may return to a state lower than that which prevailed at the time of absorption, and thus give rise to radiation of higher frequency. Such lines are known as *anti-Stokes* lines. In ordinary fluorescence, these are rare; they are often observed, however, in the Raman effect [Section (3.12)] which is nearly identical to fluorescence.

**3.23. Phosphorescence.** *Phosphorescence* is identical in principle to fluorescence and is the result of exactly the same physical action. The difference is associated with the time interval between absorption and reradiation. In fluorescence, the time interval is short (or the order of $10^{-8}$ seconds); in phosphorescence, the time interval may be long—perhaps hours. Phosphorescence resulting from the absorption of light is not too commonly observed, but phosphorescence resulting from the creation of excited states by other means, such as electron bombardment, is a very common phenomenon, being the basis for the displays on oscilloscopes and television picture tubes. The materials used for coating these tubes are known as *phosphors*.

Another phosphorescence phenomenon is that of induced phosphorescence. A phosphor, excited by some means such as electron bombardment or irradiation by a radioactive material, can sometimes be caused to discharge its energy by low-frequency light such as infrared radiation, and this energy is emitted in the visible region. This phenomenon was the basis for the first infrared gunsights, developed early in World War II and known as *metascopes*. These have been replaced by more sensitive dynamic devices.

**3.24. The Photoelectric Effect.**[10c] When the energy in a photon is greater than that required to excite the receiving atom to any stable energy level, the quantum may be absorbed to produce *ionization* and the ejection of an electron, which takes up the excess energy in the form of kinetic energy. This *photoelectric effect* is one of the most significant in demonstrating failure of the wave theory of light to explain all phenomena.

It is found that for suitable *photosensitive* materials, whenever the energy of the photon exceeds a specific threshold value, which is the value required for ionization, electrons begin to be ejected from the material. For frequencies less than this threshold value, no photoelectric effect is observed.

If the intensity of the incident light is increased, the rate of electron production increases, but there is no change in the kinetic energy of the electrons. If the frequency of the incident light is increased, the kinetic energy of the electrons increases.

**3.25. The Inverse Photoelectric Effect.** Electrons emitted by the photoelectric effect from a material may be caused, in suitable apparatus, to transfer their kinetic energy to other electrons in a second material; this has been called the inverse photoelectric effect, although it is not really the inverse. This transfer of energy is utilized in photomultiplier and similar amplifying devices, in which the emitted electrons are accelerated by an electric field and caused to eject multiple electrons from the second material. With a number of successive stages, amplifications of several million with a very low noise contribution can be produced.

The actual inverse of the photoelectric effect is really the phosphorescence produced by a bombarding electron beam on the phosphor of an oscilloscope tube.

**3.26. Photoconductivity.** Although it will come in for more comprehensive discussion later, the basis of the photoconductive effect should be mentioned here for completeness. Certain materials, notably impurity semiconductors, but also some pure materials like selenium, cesium and tellurium, can absorb photons and create an excited state, the existence of which changes the resistivity of the material. In most cases, this comes about by a type of photoelectric effect in which the ejected electrons, instead of being emitted from the surface, are retained in the material as free electrons, and thus increase the conductivity.

The same phenomenon, produced by the injection of electrons into the material, is the basis for the transistor.

**3.27. Other Absorption Effects.** A number of other interesting phenomena are produced as a result of the absorption of photons by solid materials to produce changes in state; these are discussed in later chapters. Among these are light amplification, the photoelectromagnetic effect, the photovoltaic effect, and others.

General absorption, raising the temperature of an absorbing flake, is the basis for the radiation thermocouple and bolometer. The temperature difference caused by the absorption of light energy causes detectable changes in a coupled electrical circuit. These devices are sufficiently sensitive to detect the rise in temperature caused by the absorption of the order of $10^7$ photons/sec or $10^{-13}$ watts of energy.

## OPTICAL EFFECTS OF ELECTRIC AND MAGNETIC FIELDS

**3.28. Optical Activity.** Optical activity, or rotatory polarization, was discussed briefly in Section (2.29), and in Section (2.33) the existence of induced optical activity was mentioned. To understand the nature of this induced optical activity, it is convenient to adopt the concept of plane-polarized light as the resultant of two circularly polarized components, rotating in opposite directions. Their phase difference defines the plane of polarization of the resultant.

**3.29. The Zeeman and Stark Effects.** When the emission of light from atoms takes place in an electric or a magnetic field, each characteristic wavelength is split into several components, with slightly different wavelengths (energies) and each with a specific polarization. The effect in a magnetic field is the *Zeeman effect;* in an electric field, it is the *Stark effect.*

It can be shown by classical theory that the light emitted by an atom in a magnetic field should be divided into several components; two components when viewed parallel to the magnetic field (longitudinal Zeeman effect), right- and left-circularly polarized, and three components perpendicular to the field (transverse Zeeman effect), all plane-polarized. The actual frequency difference is calculable from classical theory. Such splitting of spectral lines is observed for many substances.

Under stronger fields and with the advantage of higher spectral dispersion, it is found that the pairs and the triplets are themselves often split into multiples, for which classical theory has no explanation. In terms of the quantum theory, these are explainable, however, as resulting from the existence of several quantum energy states whose energies are the same in the absence of a magnetic field, but become different when the field is present.

The Stark effect is a similar effect in the presence of an electric field. This also shows a difference when viewed parallel to the field (longitudinal Stark effect) or perpendicular to the field (transverse Stark effect). Parallel to the field, the components are plane-polarized, in the direction normal to the field; perpendicular to the field, the components are also plane-polarized—some parallel to, and some normal to, the field.

**3.30. The Inverse Zeeman and Stark Effects.** When light is absorbed to produce changes in energy states by a material under the influence of a strong magnetic or electric field, the *inverse Zeeman or Stark effects* are observed. The light is absorbed at the same multiple frequencies that prevail for emission.

**3.31. Induced Birefringence.** When placed in strong fields, isotropic substances become birefringent. This effect, when produced in an electric field, is the *Kerr electro-optic effect* or the *Pockels effect;* when produced in a magnetic field, it is known as the *Cotton-Mouton effect* in liquids, and the *Voight effect* in gases.

**3.32. The Kerr Electro-optic Effect or Pockels Effect.** This effect[11] is of particular interest, because it has been used in recent years as the principle of extremely fast optical shutters and as a means for modulating a light beam at high frequencies for communication, distance measuring, and other purposes. When it occurs in a liquid, it is referred to as the *Kerr electro-optic effect;* in solids as the *Pockels effect.*

Birefringence is a difference in the index of refraction for light which is plane-polarized in orthogonal planes. When an isotropic medium is subjected to an electric field, birefringence is created according to the relations

$$(\mu_p - \mu_s) = \lambda B \mathcal{E}^2 \qquad \text{(Kerr's Law)} \qquad (3.20)$$

$$(\mu_p - \mu) = 2(\mu_s - \mu) \qquad \text{(Havelock's Law)} \qquad (3.21)$$

In this effect, most substances become uniaxial crystals, with their optic axis along the electric lines of force. $B$ is *Kerr's constant;* at a wavelength of 5890Å, its value in electrostatic units is

| | |
|---|---|
| for $CO_2$ | $.25 \times 10^{-10}$ |
| for $H_2O$ | $4.7 \times 10^{-7}$ |
| for $CHCl_3$ | $-3.46 \times 10^{-7}$ |
| for glass | $2.9 \times 10^{-9}$ to $1.5 \times 10^{-8}$ |

The effect is proportional to the square of the impressed field and hence is independent of its direction. As can be seen from the above values, some substances become positive crystals, others negative.

The time required for the effect to become established varies markedly with different materials; for glass it is several seconds; for polar liquids, it is about $10^{-8}$ seconds, and for nonpolar liquids, it is less than $10^{-11}$ seconds. It is the latter materials which are used in the *Kerr cell* or *Kerr shutter* [see Section (10.43)]. The *Kerr cell*, because of this very fast response time, can be operated as a modulator at frequencies up to $10^9$ or even $10^{10}$ cycles/sec.

**3.33. The Cotton-Mouton and Voight Effects.** An effect similar to the Kerr electro-optic effect occurs in the presence of a magnetic field, and is called the *Cotton-Mouton effect*[12] or the *Voight effect*, according to its appearance in liquids or in vapors. The mathematical relation is the same as for the Kerr electro-optic effect [Equations (3.20) and (3.21)].

The numerical value of the constants are much smaller than for the Kerr electro-optic effect, being of the order of $10^{-14}$. The effect is difficult to observe because it must be observed for light traversing the substance exactly perpendicular to the magnetic lines of force in order to eliminate the much stronger Faraday effect (see below).

**3.34. Electric Double Refraction.** An effect very similar to the Pockels effect occurs in the vicinity of the absorption frequencies of an isotropic material under the influence of an impressed electric field. This effect is termed *electric double refraction*, and it occurs as a result of the inverse Stark effect. The latter shifts the frequency of the absorption lines as a function of the polarization; thus, in the immediate vicinity of these lines, the index of refraction changes as a function of the polarization.

**3.35. The Faraday Effect.** Another effect which in recent years has been utilized in instrumentation is the *Faraday effect*,[13] which is *induced optical activity*. It occurs in the presence of a magnetic field—there is no analogous effect for an electric field.

Optical activity is the rotation of the plane of polarization of an incident light beam. This is proportional to the length of the path, the strength of the field, and a constant known as Verdet's constant:

$$\theta_r = CH_p\, t \tag{3.22}$$

It occurs only for light traveling in the direction of the lines of force, or having a component parallel thereto, and can thus be separated from the Cotton-Mouton effect. In general, the sign of Verdet's constant is positive for diamagnetic materials and negative for paramagnetic and ferromagnetic materials.

The amount of rotation varies widely for different materials; for water, the rotation is $2°10'$ per cm for an applied field of $10^4$ oersteds; for iron (which, of course, can be used only in extremely thin films), it is $130°$ for a path length of $10^{-3}$ cm. In flint glass, it is about $5°$ per cm.

The direction of rotation of the plane of polarization of the incident light is in the direction of current flow in the encompassing coil. Thus, the direction of rotation is the same when the path of the light is reversed, and in an instrument, the rotation can be multiplied by causing the light to pass back and forth in the material, as in multiple-path interference. This is different from the effect of naturally optically active crystals, in which a reversal of the light path cancels the rotation.

**3.36. The Kerr Magneto-optic Effect.** Kerr observed that when plane-polarized light is reflected from the polished end of a magnet pole, a rotation of the plane of polarization takes place. The effect produces elliptically polarized light except when the light is incident normally or when the plane of polarization is perpendicular to the plane of incidence. The effect is known as the *Kerr magneto-optic effect*.

**3.37. The Cotton Effect.** One other effect should be mentioned—the *Cotton effect*. This is the unequal absorption of right- and left-handed circularly polarized light by some substances, just as some substances show unequal absorption for different orientations of plane-polarized light (*dichroism*). This effect has an accompanying anomalous rotatory dispersion in the region of absorption lines.

# SPECTRA

**3.38. General.** The outstanding example of the interaction of light and matter is in the absorption and emission spectra of atoms and molecules. Some brief references have been made to this phenomenon in the prior pages, where it was pointed out that when in a low pressure gaseous state, the atoms of a material will absorb and emit light only at specified frequencies which are characteristic of the material. At higher pressures, the influences of neighboring particles cause these frequencies to become broadened, and at sufficiently high pressure, or in the liquid and solid states, these characteristic "lines" degenerate into a *continuous* spectrum, whose form is given by Planck's law (Section 1.5) and which is a function of the temperature and is the same for all materials.

The nature of the *line spectrum* is the key to the structure of the atom, and was the medium which led to the formulation of the Quantum Theory. Its story is really a part of atomic physics and not of optics, but reference to spectra and spectral lines is necessarily so frequent in any discussion of optics that some explanation is required. The analysis of spectra is the subject matter of *spectroscopy*, which is treated in this book only from an instrumental standpoint.

**3.39. The Spectroscope.** The term *spectral line*, which is used frequently in this and any other book on optics, is derived from the nature of the fundamental instrument for the analysis of spectra—the *spectroscope*, or *spectrograph*, depending upon whether it is used visually or with a recording medium, such as photographic film. Figure 3.3 shows a schematic representation of a spectroscope; a more detailed discussion of the instrument itself is given in Chapter 8. The instrument has six essential elements—a source slit, a collimator, a dispersing means, a viewing objective, a focal plane and an eyepiece.

The dispersing component may be either a prism or a grating—in either case, it has the property of deviating the light through an angle which is a function of the frequency; thus in an incident beam of light with more than one frequency present, the position in the focal plane will be a function of frequency.

The collimator collects light from the source slit and provides a large diameter beam to the dispersing component; the viewing objective merely forms an image of the slit in the focal plane. But when the incident light has more than a single frequency component, there will be more than one image of the slit, and these multiple images will be spread out in the

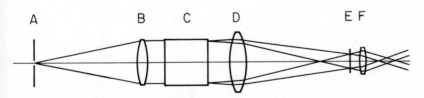

FIGURE 3.3. Schematic diagram of a spectroscope. The six major components are identified as follows: A. entrance slit, B. collimator, C. dispersing element, D. viewing objective, E. focal plane, F. eyepiece.

focal plane to produce a *spectrum*. The slit is made as narrow as possible (consistent with obtaining adequate illumination) so that the multiple images will not run together, and can be separately identified—it is a slit rather than a point because a slit admits more light, and the dispersion is only in one plane (normal to the slit).

The position in the focal plane of a given image of the slit is a function of the wavelength or frequency of the light which produced it, thus the spectroscope is an instrument for the determination of wavelength or frequency.

**3.40. Spectra and Spectral Lines.** It is seen that the *spectrum*, in that it is a strip of discrete or overlapping images of the source slit in which position is a function of frequency, is produced by the instrument. The term is often used in this sense, although rigorously the term spectrum refers to the frequency distribution of the radiation.

The term *spectral line* is derived solely from the instrument itself. A specific frequency component appears in the focal plane as a line—the image of the source slit; its width is determined by the purity of the frequency component involved and the width of the entrance slit. The term spectral line is used almost universally as meaning "frequency component," and terms such as *line width, line broadening, double line,* etc., meaning *frequency spread, dispersion of frequency, two distinct frequencies close together,* respectively, as well as other terms derived from the spectroscope, are frequently used. Usually there is no confusion if one recognizes that the source of the terminology is in the characteristics of the instrument.

**3.41. Line Series.** One of the earliest noted facts concerning the spectra of atoms—at least in the case of the simple ones—was that they occurred in series, with the characteristics shown in Figure 3.4. In each series, the lines occurred closer and closer together as the frequency increased, and

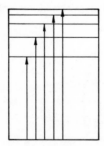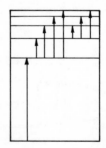

FIGURE 3.4. Spectral line series. The wave numbers of spectral lines may be represented by the distances indicated by the arrows.

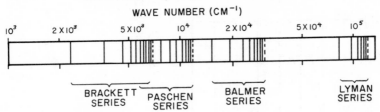

FIGURE 3.5. The principal line series of hydrogen.

usually fainter and fainter, and there was a definite limit to the series on the high-frequency side.

In the case of hydrogen, the simplest atom, four distinct series are found, two in the infrared region of the spectrum, one in the visible, and one in the ultraviolet. These are shown in Figure 3.5.

It was soon shown that the *wave numbers* of the lines could be accurately given by an equation of the form

$$N = R \left[ \frac{1}{n_0^2} - \frac{1}{n_1^2} \right] \tag{3.23}$$

where $R = 109,737.31$ cm$^{-1}$. For the Lyman series, $n_0 = 1$, for the Balmer series, $n_0 = 2$, for the Paschen series, $n_0 = 3$, and for the Brackett series, $n_0 = 4$. In each series, $n_1$ takes all the integral values from $n_0$ up, and the series limit is given for $n_0 = \infty$.

**3.42. Energy Levels.** This regularity in atomic spectra, together with the known quantization of radiation as shown by Planck's law, led first to the development of the Bohr-Rutherford atom[13a] and finally to the quantum theory. In the Bohr-Rutherford atom, the electrons were considered to be in orbital motion about the nucleus, and only orbits with angular momenta which differed by $h$ were assumed to be possible.

This planetary atom has been superseded by the atom described by the quantum mechanics, in which the different orbital configurations are replaced by patterns of standing waves, but spectroscopy still talks in terms of the Bohr atom and of electron orbits. The general features of spectra are equally well discussed in terms of either model.

The principal feature of interest is that the atom has a number of *stationary states, or energy levels,* in which it does not radiate. Absorption or emission of radiation takes place when the atom undergoes a transition from one energy level to another; if the transition is to a higher energy level, the atom absorbs energy; if it is to a lower energy level, the atom radiates. This absorption and emission take place only in discrete steps, and the energy involved in any given step is an integral multiple of $h$.

**3.43. The Term Diagram.** Each term of Equation (3.23) represents

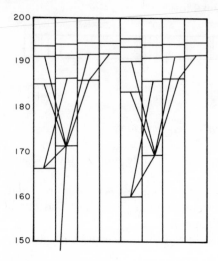

FɪɢᴜʀE 3.6. Term diagram for helium I.

an energy level of the hydrogen atom. The state of lowest energy corresponds to the term $n = 1$. Transitions from this state to states of higher energy, for which $n > 1$, involve the absorption of a photon of the proper frequency, and Equation (3.23) gives the wave number, or reciprocal frequency, for each such transition. The atom will remain in this *excited* state for only a brief interval, and then will spontaneously return to the ground state with the emission of a photon of the same frequency it absorbed. Transitions from and to the ground state ($n = 1$) from various other energy levels ($n = m$) give rise to the Lyman series of lines.

At relatively high temperatures, a significant number of atoms will remain more or less permanently in states of higher energy, and transitions to and from these higher levels may be observed. These transitions give rise to the other series, for which $n_0 = 2, 3$, etc.

The energy levels and the transitions between them are usually represented in a diagram known as a *term diagram*, illustrated for helium in Figure 3.6.

**3.44. Atoms with Higher Atomic Number.** Hydrogen is a very simple atom, consisting of a single proton as the nucleus and one electron. It would normally have a relatively simple array of energy levels. Atoms with more complex nuclei, and with more electrons, would be expected to have more complex spectra. This is indeed the case, but the spectra are much simpler, for the most part, than might at first be expected.

The presence of more than one electron does not in general increase the number of possible energy levels; rather it insures that, for $m$ electrons, $m$ energy levels are simultaneously occupied, and therefore only transitions to and from unoccupied levels become possible.

Further, the energy levels form groups, referred to as *shells*,[14] such that, when a shell is full of electrons, the spectra are nearly identical in form to that of simpler atoms. For example, lithium, with three electrons, gives spectra very similar to those of hydrogen, with one electron, because the first two electrons of lithium form a closed shell, so that to a first approximation at least, lithium behaves like a one-electron atom. The actual wave numbers for lithium, of course, are quite different from those of hydrogen, but correspond to a formula like Equation (3.23), in which the constant $R$ is replaced by $Z^2 R$, where $Z$ is the atomic number (3 for lithium), this being the charge on the nucleus.

The first complete shell consists of two electrons, the next shell consists of eight, the third of eight, the fourth of eighteen, and so on.

**3.45. The Periodic Table.** This shell configuration is the key to the structure of the periodic table of the elements (Figure 3.7). The groupings in the periodic table correspond to the electron shells. Electrons outside of closed shells are referred to as *valence* electrons, because they represent the chemical valence, which determines the behavior of the elements in forming chemical compounds. Elements with a similar number of valence electrons have similar physical and chemical properties, and they also have similar types of spectra.

The so-called rare earths, which form an anomalous group, are elements in which electrons are missing from internal shells, although external shells may be complete.

The inert gases, He, Ne, Kr, A, Xe, are the elements which have completed shells and no valence electrons; they consequently enter into chemical compounds only with great difficulty.

Similarly, elements in which the shells are more than half complete have *negative* valences, representing the number of electrons missing from a complete shell. Elements of this type readily combine with elements having positive valences to form ionic compounds.

**3.46. Ionization.** When an incident photon does not have the proper energy (frequency) to correspond with a specific transition from a lower to a higher energy level, the atom cannot absorb the photon, since there is no place for the excess energy to go; the result is an elastic collision (scattering). However, when the energy of the photon is greater than that required to raise the atom to the energy level represented by the limit of the line series, the atom may absorb the photon and emit an electron, thus becoming *ionized*. The excess of energy over that required to produce the ionization appears as kinetic energy of the ejected electron. This is the photoelectric effect (Section 3.24).

A singly ionized atom is spectroscopically similar to an atom one step lower in the periodic table, with the exception that the nuclear charge is

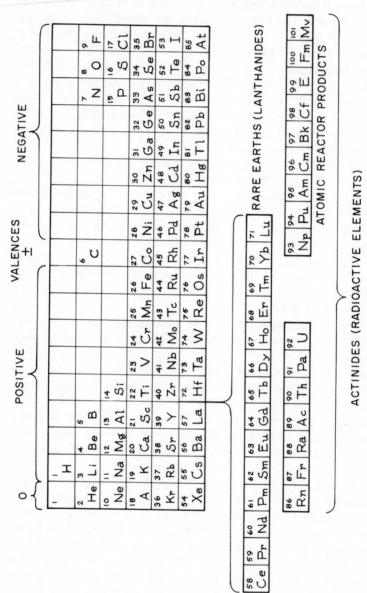

FIGURE 3.7. The periodic table of the elements. The valences are zero for complete shells. For light elements, as valence electrons are added, the valence is positive and increases incrementally. When the shell is half full, the valence is positive or negative ($C = \pm 4$). Beyond this point, the valences become negative and decrease numerically. After element 25, this simple pattern no longer dominates.

one unit greater, which fact appears in the actual value of the transition frequencies. Thus, He, which has two valence electrons, when it loses one electron by ionization, gives a spectrum similar to Li, which has one valence electron. The ionized atom is represented by the symbol Be$^+$. Atoms may become multiply ionized up to the number of valence electrons available, thus Be$^{++}$, Al$^{+++}$, etc. Electrons may even be ejected from completed shells, although the energy requirements are greater than for valence electrons. Elements with negative valences may become negative ions by temporarily taking up excess electrons.

**3.47. Electron Spin and Multiple Levels.** Many of the spectral lines of atoms are actually doublets, triplets, or multiplets when observed with instruments of high resolution. The strong doublet line of Na at 5890 and 5896Å is a typical case. This doubling, which is common to the alkali metals, is interpreted in terms of a spinning electron, in the concept of the Bohr atom. This spin has two possible values, $\pm\frac{1}{2}$, and adds to or subtracts from the angular momentum, thus producing two spectral lines slightly different in energy. In atoms with several electrons, the various combinations of electron spin which may exist give rise to multiple lines.

There are also energy levels which are equal in energy in an atom which is free of external fields, but which become separated in energy when magnetic or electric fields are imposed; this condition leads to effects such as the Zeeman and Stark effects, described in previous sections, and to the so-called *hyperfine structure* of spectral lines.

**3.48. Boltzmann's Law.** If an assemblage of atoms is in thermodynamic equilibrium at a temperature $T$, then *Boltzmann's law* states that the numbers of atoms in various energy states are related to the energies of those states by the proportion

$$n_1 : n_2 : n_3 : \cdots n_m = e^{-W_1/kT} : e^{-W_2/kT} : e^{-W_3/kT} \cdots e^{-W_m kT} \qquad (3.24)$$

where $n_m$ is the number of atoms in state $m$, $W_m$ is the energy of state $m$, and $k$ is Boltzmann's constant ($1.38 \times 10^{-16}$ erg deg$^{-1}$).

In some cases, there are several states of equal energy; in these cases, the terms on the right have coefficients $g_m$ where $g_m$ is the number of states having energy $W_m$. The $n$'s then represent the total number of atoms in states having the corresponding energy.

**3.49. Energy Levels and Temperature Radiation.** It was shown in Section 1.26 that in a cavity in thermodynamic equilibrium at a temperature $T$, the radiation has a frequency distribution given by Planck's equation

$$\rho(\nu) = \frac{8\pi h\nu^3}{c^3} \cdot \frac{1}{e^{h\nu/kT} - 1} \qquad (1.5)$$

Now, in such a situation, the number of atoms shifting from state 1 to state 2 in unit time by the absorption of radiation will be proportional to the number of atoms in state 1, to the energy of radiation at the proper frequency, and to a constant of proportionality, $B_{12}$. Thus the number is $\rho(\nu_{12})B_{12}N_1$. Also, in unit time, some atoms will be transferred from state 2 to state 1 by spontaneous emission (independently of the presence of the radiation field). This number will be proportional to the number of atoms in state 2 and to a constant of proportionality, or *probability of transition*, $A_{21}$. The number will therefore be $A_{21}N_2$. Equilibrium will be maintained only if

$$\rho(\nu_{12})B_{12}N_1 = A_{21}N_2 \tag{3.25}$$

or

$$\rho(\nu_{12}) = \frac{A_{21}}{B_{12}}\frac{N_2}{N_1} \tag{3.26}$$

But, from Boltzmann's law [Equation (3-24)] we have

$$\frac{N_2}{N_1} e^{-h\nu_{12}/kT} \tag{3.27}$$

since $W_2 - W_1 = h\nu_{12}$. Therefore,

$$\rho(\nu_{12}) = \frac{A_{21}}{B_{12}} e^{-h\nu_{12}/kT} \tag{3.28}$$

This is not in agreement with Planck's law [Equation (1.5)], which is supported by experimental proof. It can be made so if it is assumed that in addition to the spontaneous emission which is given by the right-hand side of Equation (3.25), there is induced emission resulting from the presence of the radiation field. This will be proportional to the radiation, to the number of atoms in state 2 and to a proportionality constant, $B_{21}$. Then Equation (3.25) becomes

$$\rho(\nu_{12})B_{12}N_1 = A_{21}N_2 + \rho(\nu_{12})B_{21}N_2 \tag{3.29}$$

and this leads to

$$\rho(\nu_{12}) = \frac{A_{21}}{B_{12}e^{-h\nu_{12}/kT} - B_{21}} \tag{3.30}$$

This agrees with Planck's Law if

$$B_{12} = B_{21}$$

and

$$A_{21} = \frac{8\pi h \nu_{12}{}^3}{c^3} B_{21}$$

$A_{12}$, $B_{12}$ and $B_{21}$ are the *Einstein coefficients*, the above theory being due to Einstein. $A_{21}$ is also the *transition probability*.

**3.50. The Life of an Excited Atom.** From Equation (3.25) the number of atoms leaving state 2 in time $dt$ is

$$d(N_2) = A_{21} N_2 \, dt \tag{3.31}$$

where $N_2$ is a function of time. It follows that

$$N_2 = (N_2)_0 \, e^{-A_{21} t} = (N_2)_0 \, e^{-t/\tau} \tag{3.32}$$

where $(N_2)_0$ is the number of atoms in state 2 at time $t = 0$. The quantity

$$\tau = 1/A_{21} \tag{3.33}$$

is the lifetime of the atom in state 2. The number of atoms in this state decreases by the factor $e$ in time $\tau$.

A typical value of $\tau$ for a normal transition is $10^{-8}$ seconds. There are many transitions, however, for which the lifetime is much longer, and which therefore do not show up in spectra except very faintly. Lines due to such transitions are often called *forbidden* lines. The values of the transition probabilities can be calculated from atomic constants by means of quantum mechanics, and for many transitions, these probabilities turn out to be zero or very low; these transitions correspond with the so-called *forbidden* lines. Atoms in energy levels from which the transition probabilities are nearly zero are said to be in *metastable* states. Only under special conditions do they lose their energy by spontaneous radiation; they may lose it by collision or by induced transitions.

In general, the transition probabilities for adjacent energy levels are much higher than those for levels further apart.

It is not necessary for atoms to absorb photons to reach higher energy levels from which they may revert to lower levels by radiation. The excitation may be produced by collisions with other particles or with the walls of an enclosing chamber. Atoms may also lose energy by collisions and revert to a lower state without radiation.

**3.51. Width of Spectral Lines.** When an atom emits a photon in undergoing a transition, a wave train of finite length is generated. It has been seen that the narrower the line (the purer the frequency), the longer must this wave train be. Hence, it cannot be the case that the radiation is emitted by the atom instantaneously. The radiation resembles that which comes from a damped oscillator, and it requires a finite time for emission. Therefore, the frequency cannot be absolutely pure, and there is a distribution of energy over a frequency band. The spectral line will, therefore, have a finite width.

It is sufficient to account for the experimental facts to assume an amplitude of the atomic oscillator proportional to $e^{-A_{21}t}$. It can be shown[15] that the frequency distribution around a resonance frequency $\nu_0$ will be

$$f(\nu) = \frac{A_{21}}{4\pi^2} \cdot \frac{1}{(\nu - \nu_0)^2 + \frac{1}{2}A_{21}{}^2} \tag{3.34}$$

which corresponds to a line with maximum at $\nu_0$ and with its intensity $\frac{1}{2}$ of the maximum at $\nu = \nu_0 \pm \frac{1}{2}A_{21} = \nu_0 \pm (1/2\tau)$.

This is the *natural width* of a spectral line, and it is seen to be determined by the transition probability. This width applies also to absorption lines. Spectral lines are also broadened by the Doppler effect (see Section 1.13) resulting from the random velocities of the atoms, and from collisions.

**3.52. Molecular Spectra.** There are also energy levels in molecules, corresponding to various possible structural patterns; transitions between these patterns may take place through radiative interchange. There are, therefore, spectra of molecules, which usually appear as spectral *bands*, since the frequency spread is rather large, and the various lines in a series will overlap. These bands, however, show the phenomenon of a distinct limit at the high-frequency end, corresponding to molecular dissociation.

### REFERENCES

1. See, for example, R. Ditchburn, "Light," 2d ed., New York, Interscience, 1963.
2. J. Armstrong, N. Blooembergen, J. Ducuing and P. Pershan, *Phys. Rev.*, **127**, 1918 (1962).
   N. Blooembergen and P. Pershan, *Phys. Rev.*, **128**, 606 (1962).
   J. Kleinman, *Phys. Rev.*, **128**, 1761 (1962).
   N. Blooembergen, *Proc. IEEE*, **51**, 124 (1963).
   P. Franken and J. Ward, *Rev. Mod. Phys.*, **35**, 23 (1963).
3. Lord Rayleigh, *Phil. Mag.*, **41**(4), 274, 447 (1871); **48**(5), 375 (1899).
4. G. Monk, "Light," 2d ed., p. 287, Dover, 1963.
5. G. Mie, *Ann. Physik*, **25**(4), 377 (1908).
6. National Bureau of Standards, Washington, D.C., Applied Mathematics Series, Vol. 4, "Tables of Scattering Functions for Spherical Particles."
7. M. Born and E. Wolf, "Principles of Optics," p. 656, New York, Pergamon Press, 1959.
8. L. Cauchy, *Bull. Sc. Math.*, **14**, 9 (1830).
9. Cf. reference 1, p. 562.
10. See F. Jenkins and H. White, "Fundamentals of Optics," 2d ed., New York, McGraw-Hill Book Co., 1950.
10a. G. Herzberg, "Infrared and Raman Spectroscopy," Princeton, N.J., D. Van Nostrand, 1944.

10b. H. Rubens and E. Nichols, *Ann. Physik.*, **3,** 418 (1897); *Ann. Phys. Chem.*, No. 60 (1897).

    E. Nichols, *Phys. Rev.*, **4,** 314 (1897).

    R. Porter, *Astrophys. J.*, **22,** 229 (1905).

10c. H. Hertz, *Ann. Physik.*, **31,** 421 (1887).

11. J. Kerr, *Phil. Mag.*, **50**(4)**,** 337 (1875).

12. See M. Born, "Optik," p. 360, Berlin, Springer.

13. See F. Joos, "Theoretical Physics," p. 2119, Blackie.

13a. E. Rutherford, *Phil. Mag.*, **26,** 669 (1913).

    N. Bohr, *Phil. Mag.*, **26,** 6857 (1913).

14. M. Mayer, *Science*, **145,** 999 (1964).

15. Cf. reference 1, p. 113.

# CHAPTER 4

# Geometrical Optics

**4.1. Definitions.** In the equations in the previous chapters concerning the propagation of light, when the wavelength is assumed to be zero, then the phenomena of diffraction and interference disappear, and the equations take on exactly the same form they would have for particles. This is the special case which defines the domain of *geometrical optics*. Phase relations do not exist; the paths of energy flow, by definition normal to the wave fronts (except in anisotropic media), are the *rays;* geometrical optics is concerned with the paths of these rays as they pass through media of different refractive indices. The problems then become simply problems of geometry, and while they are sometimes hopelessly complex in detail, they remain fundamentally simple in concept.

Geometrical optics is the fundamental tool of optical instrument design; not very long ago, the optical designer never ventured beyond its boundaries, but recently he has come to make more and more use of wave optics, as opposed to ray optics, for his more precise computations. Diffraction theory has become a tool of lens design since the electronic digital computer arrived to take over the burden of much more complex calculations, but using diffraction theory from the outset to design an optical instrument is still a little like using quantum mechanics to design a bridge.

The basic concepts of geometrical optics are the *ray*, defined as the path of energy flow, and the geometrical form of the boundaries between different media which comprise an optical system.

Its ruling principle is the law of refraction

$$\mu' \sin I' = \mu \sin I \tag{4.1}$$

where $\mu$ and $I$ are the index of refraction and the angle of incidence at the boundary in one medium, and $\mu'$ and $I'$ are the corresponding values in the

138

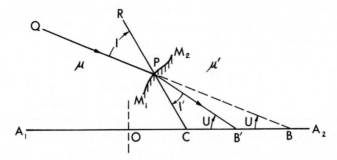

FIGURE 4.1. Fundamental construction.

other medium. This is all there is to geometrical optics. The complexities which can grow from this simple beginning are almost unbelievable.

**4.2. Fundamental Construction.** Figure 4.1 shows the fundamental construction of geometrical optics, which is almost universally accepted. The nomenclature may vary somewhat from individual to individual. $A_1A_2$ is a reference *axis;* QPB is an *incident* light *ray,* which meets the boundary $M_1M_2$ between two media of refractive indices $\mu$ and $\mu'$ at P. RPC is the *normal* to the surface at the point of intersection. By refraction at the surface, the incident ray becomes the *refracted ray,* PB'. When $\mu' > \mu$, the diagram shows the direction of deviation. The angles $I$ and $I'$ are the *angles of incidence and refraction,* respectively, and $U$ and $U'$ are the *convergence angles* of the incident and refracted rays, respectively. *Intersection lengths* of incident and refracted rays on the axis are measured from some coordinate center O, and are OB and OB' respectively.

More generally, a three-axis coordinate system is used, with the $Z$-axis being the axis shown in Figure 4.1, the $Y$-axis vertical, and the $X$-axis extending out of the paper. The intersections are then defined with reference to a plane parallel to the $XY$-plane. For the discussions of this chapter, a two-dimensional representation will be adequate for most purposes.

Algebraic signs are a never-ending source of annoyance in optical computations, and a rigorous and carefully adhered to sign convention is a necessity. It is customary to consider the light as incident from the left and to measure lengths positive and negative from the coordinate center, in common with the conventions of coordinate geometry. With respect to angles, however, most workers adopt a clockwise convention, opposite to the counterclockwise convention of coordinate geometry. In this convention, the angles $I$ and $I'$ are drawn from the ray to the respective normal, and the angles $U$ and $U'$ from the axis to the ray. In the diagram of Figure 4.1, all of the angles are positive.

This convention is not universal; any convention which yields the correct results and gives the proper signs to the computed data is satisfactory, provided it is rigidly adhered to.

When the sign conventions have been appropriately defined, the law of refraction can be used in place of the law of reflection by putting $\mu' = -\mu$, and thus the same computations can apply to both reflecting and refracting surfaces, which is a great convenience in computation.

**4.3. Purpose of an Optical System.** The purpose of an optical system is to form images, and an understanding of optical systems will benefit from some general consideration of images and the means for producing them prior to the discussion of details of optical components and systems. An image is formed by collecting light emitted by or reflected from an object and bringing it together so that an image of the object is formed, usually at a different place and often of a different size. By definition, a perfect image cannot be distinguished from the object itself except by reference to something other than the light used to form it. Images formed by actual optical systems are of course, never quite perfect, and it is with considerations of these imperfections that optical scientists and engineers spend most of their time. The understanding of optical instruments is most readily achieved, however, by temporarily neglecting these imperfections.

**4.4. Types of Images.** If an optical image is observed with the eye or with an optical system of some kind, it cannot, in general, be distinguished from the actual object which it depicts. In an optical instrument, images formed by some optical components become objects for others, and these in turn form new images, until the original intent of the system has been accomplished.

Two general types of images are definable—*real* images and *virtual* images. In a real image, the light which is collected from the object is physically brought together at the image, so that the image can be detected at that point, as by a photographic plate, or made visible to the eye from an angle by interposing a diffusing screen. In the case of a virtual image, the light does not actually come together at the image, but merely appears to do so; such an image is that seen in an ordinary mirror, or with a simple magnifier. It cannot be registered by a photographic plate or focused on a screen without additional optical components.

**4.5. The Point Concept.** In geometrical optics, every object and image is considered to be made up of an infinite array of points, each point constituting a source of light rays. The rays may in some cases be confined to a cone of some specified vertex angle, but there are an infinite number of rays from each point. Each point is independent of the other points; each object point has its corresponding (*conjugate*) image point, and each is treated independently.

Therefore, an optical system, in order to form a perfect image, has to accomplish two feats—it must bring all of the light collected from each independent object point together into an image point, and it must also arrange these image points in an array which is geometrically similar to the object point array.

This concept of object points as sources of rays spreading in accordance with the inverse square law assumes that the light is incoherent—coherence has no meaning in geometrical optics. There will be occasion to discuss imaging with coherent light later on, but this is not a topic of geometrical optics.

The discriminating reader will immediately see the fundamental limitation of geometrical optics. The location and perfection of the image points may be specified and computed to as minute dimensions as desired—it means only more decimal places in the computation. But the discussion of diffraction has shown that in dimensions which are not large with respect to the wavelength, light does not behave geometrically. The imaging of real optical systems, therefore, is limited by diffraction, and when the structure of images to a precision of the order of a few wavelengths is desired, recourse must be had to wave optics, and the predictions of geometrical optics in these dimensions are not valid.

**4.6. Magnification.** Magnification refers to the relative dimensions of object and image in an optical system. Three kinds of magnification are recognized: linear (or lateral) magnification, longitudinal magnification, and angular magnification. In situations where both object and image are at finite distances from the optical system (for example, in the case of the projection of a slide), they can be compared as to size. The ratio of linear size of an image, or portion of an image, to the size of the corresponding object is called the *linear magnification*. The definition applies only to dimensions measured in planes normal to the optical axis.

The ratio of size of image and object in the direction of the axis is called the *longitudinal magnification*. Although images are often thought of as two-dimensional entities, they are really three-dimensional.

When either object or image is very far away, for example, in the case of a telescope, one cannot compare linear sizes. Yet the image seen in the telescope appears larger than the object viewed with the unaided eye. A similar situation occurs in the microscope. In such cases, the magnification is defined as the *angular magnification*, which is the ratio of the apparent angular subtense of image and object, usually from a single specified point.

**4.7. The Perfect Optical Instrument.** For every *object point*, an optical system has a corresponding *image point*—these are referred to as *conjugate points*. More generally, for an *object plane*, normal to the optical axis, there is a conjugate *image plane*, although real systems do not completely conform to this concept, as will be seen.

If an optical system forms an image of any object, at an arbitrary location, which is geometrically similar to it and in which all of the object points are precisely rendered as image points (in the geometrical optics sense), it is defined as a *perfect* (or *absolute*) *optical system*. It is readily shown that this is not possible in a three-dimensional sense because the lateral and longitudinal magnifications are not linearly related. A less restrictive requirement for a perfect optical system is that it image any two-dimensional object in a plane at right angles to the optical axis as a geometrically similar figure in an image plane also at right angles to the optical axis and with perfect convergence of the rays at all points in the image. It was proven by Maxwell[1] that if this condition is met for two different object planes, then it is met for all object planes. Hence, to show whether a perfect optical instrument according to this definition is consistent with the laws of reflection and refraction, it is only necessary to show whether it can be achieved in principle for two different object planes and their conjugate image planes.

In Figure 4.2, let $O_1$ and $O_2$ be the two object planes, and $O_1'$, $O_2'$ their conjugate image planes, and consider a ray which crosses the axis in object plane $O_1$ at $P_1$ at an angle $U$, and intersects object plane $O_2$ at a point $P_2$ whose height above the axis is $h_1$. This ray, after traversing the optical system S, will pass through the conjugate image points $P_1'$ and $P_2'$. $P_1'$, being the conjugate of an axial object point is, by definition, on the optical axis. $P_2'$ will be in the conjugate image plane $O_2'$, at a height $h_1'$ above the axis. The angle of the image ray with the axis is $U'$. If the distances between the object planes is $b$ and that between the image planes is $b'$, then, from Figure 4.2,

$$\tan U = h_1/b \qquad \tan U' = h_1'/b'$$

If the linear magnification between $O_1$ and $O_1'$ is $M_1$ and that between $O_2$ and $O_2'$ is $M_2$, then the image in $O_2'$ will be geometrically similar to its object only if

$$h_1' = M_2 h_1 \qquad\qquad (4.2)$$

Substituting this in the expression for $\tan U'$, and taking the ratio of the tangents gives

$$\frac{\tan U}{\tan U'} = \frac{b'}{b} \frac{1}{M_2} \qquad\qquad (4.3)$$

From equations developed later in the chapter, the ratio $b'/b$ can be expressed as

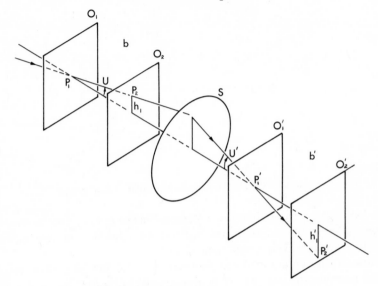

FIGURE 4.2. Imagery in an optical instrument.

$$b'/b = \frac{\mu}{\mu'} M_1 M_2 \qquad (4.4)$$

and thus Equation (4.3) becomes

$$\frac{\tan U}{\tan U'} = \frac{\mu}{\mu'} M_1 \qquad (4.5)$$

Now, a necessary condition for a point object to be imaged as a geometrical point is the *Optical Sine Condition*, discussed later in the chapter, and this condition requires that the convergence angles $U$ and $U'$ for an object and image ray have the relation

$$\frac{\sin U}{\sin U'} = \frac{\mu}{\mu'} M \qquad (4.6)$$

which is clearly inconsistent with the condition expressed in Equation (4.5), and it is therefore to be concluded that the required condition for a perfect optical instrument cannot be fulfilled, at least not for the general case.

Equations (4.5) and (4.6) do, however, indicate that the fulfillment of the condition, and therefore the existence of a perfect optical instrument, is possible subject to a restriction on the values of the angles $U$ and $U'$ to those where the sine and the tangent are essentially equal—that is, the unavoidable departure from perfection occurs only to the degree to which $\tan U \neq \sin U$ and $\tan U' \neq \sin U'$. This departure becomes significant

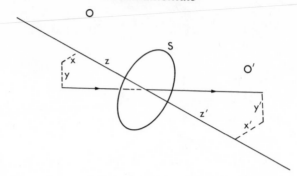

FIGURE 4.3. Projective transformation in an optical system.

only for angles greater than a few degrees; hence optical instruments can approach perfection in the sense defined for relatively narrow fields of view (and for relatively small diameters).

There is nothing in the above discussion to indicate that perfect imagery is not possible for *one pair* of conjugate planes, and since most optical instruments are intended to operate for a particular pair of conjugates, the above proof that an absolutely perfect optical instrument is not possible is largely academic.

**4.8. The Projective Transformation.** While the geometrical characteristics of an optical system may be derived trigonometrically from the data given in Figure 4.1, as is done later in the chapter, they are arrived at more directly and perhaps with greater significance, by considering the optical system as producing a projective transformation from object to image.[2] When the requirement for geometrical similarity of object and image is met, the situation is, by definition, a projective transformation. This is achieved in an *ideal* (as distinguished from a *perfect*) optical instrument; while real instruments do not in general achieve it completely, they do so very closely when the restrictions on aperture and field are met, and it is always the intent of an optical design to achieve this condition as closely as the requirements for the use of the instrument dictate.

In Figure 4.3, S is an optical system, separating an object space, O, from an image space O'; $x,y,z$ is a point in object space, and $x',y',z'$ is its projective transformation to image space. In a projective transformation, the two points are related by expressions of the form

$$x' = F_1/F_0 \quad y' = F_2/F_0 \quad z' = F_3/F_0 \tag{4.7}$$

$$x = F_1'/F_0' \quad y = F_2'/F_0' \quad z = F_3'/F_0' \tag{4.8}$$

where

$$F_i = a_i x + b_i y + c_i z + d_i$$
$$F_i' = a_i' x' + b_i' y' + c_i' z' + d_i' \tag{4.9}$$

For an object point such that $F_0 = 0$, Equation (4.7) gives

$$x' = y' = z' = \infty \tag{4.10}$$

and similarly, for an image-point such that $F_0' = 0$, Equation (4.8) gives

$$x = y = z = \infty \tag{4.11}$$

$F_0$ and $F_0'$, from Equation (4.9) are the equations of planes; the planes $F_0 = 0$ and $F_0' = 0$ are defined as the *focal planes*.

Except in very unusual cases, an optical system is a *centered* one (all of its elements lie on a common axis), and its elements are symmetrical about this axis, so that very little generality will be lost by making this assumption, and dealing only with the $YZ$ plane of Figure 4.3. With this restriction to a two-dimensional case, Equation (4.7), in combination with Equation (4.9), becomes

$$y' = \frac{b_2 y + c_2 z + d_2}{b_0 y + c_0 z + d_0} \qquad z' = \frac{b_3 y + c_3 z + d_3}{b_0 y + c_0 z + d_0} \tag{4.12}$$

Moreover, the condition of symmetry about the Z-axis requires that, when $y = -y$, $z' = z'$ and $y' = -y'$. This can be true only if $b_0 = b_3 = 0$, and $c_2 = d_2 = 0$; hence Equation (4.12) reduces to

$$y' = \frac{b_2 y}{c_0 z + d_0} \qquad z' = \frac{c_3 z + d_3}{c_0 z + d_0} \tag{4.13}$$

Solving Equation (4.13) for $y$ and $z$ gives

$$y = \frac{c_0 d_3 - c_3 d_0}{b_2} \frac{y'}{c_0 z' - c_3}$$

$$z = \frac{-d_0 z' + d_3}{c_0 z' - c_3} \tag{4.14}$$

From the definition of the focal planes given above, these are the object plane for which $y' = z' = \infty$, and the image plane for which $y = z = \infty$, or

$$F_0 = c_0 z + d_0 = 0$$
$$F_0' = c_0 z' - c_3 = 0 \tag{4.15}$$

These equations define planes perpendicular to the Z-axis and intersecting at the points

$$z_f = -d_0/c_0 \qquad z'_{f'} = c_3/c_0 \qquad (4.16)$$

These points are defined as the *principal foci*.

**4.9. Newton's Equation.** It is convenient to define two new coordinate systems, centered on the principal foci. If the coordinates of the object point in its new coordinate system are $Y, Z$, and those of the image point in its new coordinate system are $Y', Z'$, then

$$
\begin{aligned}
Y &= y & Z &= z + d_0/c_0 \\
Y' &= y' & Z' &= z' - c_3/c_0
\end{aligned}
\qquad (4.17)
$$

From Equation (4.13) we obtain, in terms of the new coordinate systems

$$Y' = \frac{b_2 Y}{c_0 Z} \qquad Z' = \frac{c_0 d_3 - c_3 d_0}{c_0^2 Z} \qquad (4.18)$$

and if we make the substitution of new constants

$$f = b_2/c_0 \qquad f' = \frac{c_0 d_3 - c_3 d_0}{b_2 c_0} \qquad (4.19)$$

we obtain

$$\frac{Y'}{Y} = \frac{f}{Z} = \frac{Z'}{f'} \qquad (4.20)$$

which is known as *Newton's Equation*. It is most often written in the form

$$ZZ' = ff' \qquad (4.20a)$$

**4.10. Magnification and the Cardinal Points.** The lateral magnification is defined by $dY'/dY$, and therefore

$$M_{\text{lat}} = \frac{dY'}{dY} = \frac{Y'}{Y} = \frac{f}{Z} = \frac{Z'}{f'} \qquad (4.21)$$

for a constant $Z$.

The linear magnification is unity when $Z = f$ and $Z' = f'$. These planes are known as the *principal* planes of the optical system, and their intersections with the $Z$-axis are the *principal points*.

The longitudinal magnification is defined by $dZ'/dZ$, and therefore

$$M_{\text{long.}} = \frac{dZ'}{dZ} = -\frac{Z'}{Z} = -\frac{ff'}{Z^2} = -\frac{Z'^2}{ff'} \qquad (4.22)$$

and also

$$M_{\text{long.}} = \frac{dZ'}{dZ} = -\frac{f'}{f}\left(\frac{dY'}{dY}\right)^2 \qquad (4.23)$$

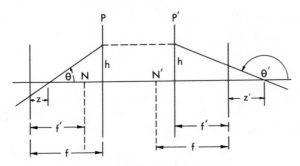

FIGURE 4.4. Angular magnification.

The linear magnification is independent of $Y$, which indicates that there is geometrical similarity between object and image.

Consider Figure 4.4. If a ray intersecting the axis at $Z$ pierces the first principal plane at height $h$, its inclination to the axis is given by $\tan \theta = h/(f - Z)$. Since the magnification in the principal planes is unity, the ray, after traversing the optical system, will leave the second principal plane at height $h$, also, and will pass through the axial point $Z'$, which is the conjugate of $Z$. The inclination of this ray is given by $\tan \theta' = h/(f' - Z')$. The ratio of these two inclinations is

$$\frac{\tan \theta'}{\tan \theta} = \frac{f - Z}{f' - Z'} = -\frac{Z}{f'} = -\frac{f}{Z'} = M_{\text{ang}}. \tag{4.24}$$

which is the *angular magnification*. It is also a restatement of the condition expressed in Equation (4.5).

The angular magnification is unity when $Z = -f'$ and $Z' = -f$. These planes are known as the *nodal planes* of the optical system, and their intersections with the $Z$-axis are the *nodal points*.

The distance between the nodal points is equal to the distance between the principal points. When the indices of refraction of the object space and image space are the same, as is the case for most complete instruments, then $f' = -f$, and the principal planes and nodal planes coincide.

**4.11. The Image Equation.** If object and image points are measured from the principal planes, then we have, by translation of coordinates

$$\ell = Z - f \quad \ell' = Z' - f' \tag{4.25}$$

and Newton's Equation (4.20) becomes

$$\frac{f}{\ell + f} = \frac{\ell' + f'}{f'}$$

which converts to

$$\frac{f'}{\ell'} + \frac{f}{\ell} = -1 \tag{4.26}$$

which is a generalized form of the image equation derived in Section 4.16.

**4.12. The Telescope.** A special case of some importance is that of the telescope, for which $f = f' = \infty$. From Equation (4.19) therefore, $c_0 = 0$, and Equation (4.13) becomes

$$y' = \frac{b_2}{d_0} y \qquad z' = \frac{c_3 z + d_3}{d_0} \tag{4.27}$$

If we translate coordinates according to the relations

$$Y = y \qquad Z = z$$

$$Y' = y' \qquad Z' = z' - \frac{d_3}{d_0} \tag{4.28}$$

then, from Equation (4.27) we obtain

$$Y' = \frac{b_2}{d_0} Y \qquad Z' = \frac{c_3}{d_0} Z \tag{4.29}$$

and for this case it is seen that the linear and longitudinal magnifications are constant, since

$$M_{\text{lat.}} = Y'/Y = b_2/d_0 = \alpha \tag{4.30}$$

and

$$M_{\text{long.}} = Z'/Z = c_3/d_0 = \beta \tag{4.31}$$

The angular magnification is also constant, as may be seen by taking a ray through an axial object point $Z$ at inclination $\theta$. This ray will pass through the image-point $Z'$ at inclination $\theta'$. The equations of the two rays are

$$Y = Z \tan \theta \quad \text{and} \quad Y' = Z' \tan \theta' \tag{4.32}$$

and the angular magnification is

$$M_{\text{ang.}} = \tan \theta'/\tan \theta = Y'Z/YZ' = \alpha/\beta = b_2/c_3 \tag{4.33}$$

Although both $f$ and $f'$ are infinite, their ratio must be considered finite. From Equation (4.19)

$$\frac{f'}{f} = \frac{c_0 d_3 - c_3 d_0}{b_2{}^2} \tag{4.34}$$

and, as $c_0 \to 0$, we have

$$\frac{f'}{f} \to -\frac{c_3 d_0}{b_2{}^2} \to -\frac{\beta}{\alpha^2} \qquad (4.35)$$

## COMPUTATIONS FOR REAL OPTICAL COMPONENTS

**4.13. General.** The above discussion is informative in that it brings out the significant properties of an optical system considered from the point of view of a projective transformation. The conclusions are valid *to the extent that a real optical system produces a projective transformation.* In real optical systems of limited field and aperture, and in well-designed optical systems of extended field and aperture, this condition is sufficient closely achieved that the deviations from it may be considered as the direct objects of separate investigation.

An optical system is first ordered and arranged as if it were an ideal system; the locations and sizes of components are chosen on this basis. Then the departures from ideal for the particular choices which have been made are computed. The design then proceeds by the process of small adjustments in parameters until a sufficiently good result has been achieved. The changes which have to be made to minimize the departures from ideal performance are usually of a minor nature, and it is rarely necessary to make any major change in the original arrangement, especially if it has been adopted on the basis of good prior experience.

The departures from ideal performance are called *aberrations*, and these will come in for some detailed discussion later on in this chapter. At this point, it is necessary to develop the parameters which have been discussed above in terms of real optical components. The discussion of parameters as they relate to ideal projective transformations was carried out in terms of some undefined constants, and tells nothing which will permit the computation of these parameters from the data of real optical components, which are indices of refraction, surface curvatures, thicknesses and diameters.

**4.14. General Equations for a Ray.** The exact geometrical performance of an optical system is determined, in the final analysis, only by precise computation of the passage of selected rays of light from an object point through the system to an image point, applying the law of refraction or reflection at each optical surface in the system. This is termed *ray tracing.* It is possible to go quite a way in optical design by the application of analytical formulas, but it is eventually necessary to trace rays through the

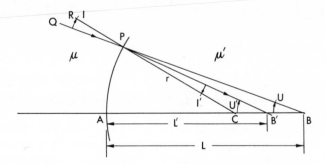

FIGURE 4.5. Refraction at a spherical surface—fundamental geometry.

system and compare the results with the theoretical predictions; usually this leads to the requirement for small corrections and repeated ray traces, so that the final solution is achieved by a reiteration method.

The basic trigonometric equations used for computation may be expressed in many different ways, and optical designers have developed many ingenious methods of expression which are convenient for their computation procedures, which now involve the participation of electronic digital computers. Quite frequently, computations in terms of optical path differences rather than conventional trigonometry are used, but this does not alter the basic concept, which is that of precise computation of specific paths through the optical system, which alone can determine the actual performance. It must be remembered that while the computation can be carried out to any desired degree of precision, merely by adding more decimal points, the computation is valid only to the limits on point imagery imposed by diffraction.

The equations developed below are archaic from the standpoint of actual optical design—they were used when optical computation was carried out with pencil, paper, and tables of logarithms. They are used here because the purpose of this book is to give a basic understanding of, and not to teach, optical design. This direct trigonometric approach, together with the diagrams that support it, gives the best general understanding of the geometry involved.

Figure 4.5 shows the refraction of a ray of light at an optical surface; the nomenclature will be recognized as that of Figure 4.1. The optical surface is shown as a spherical surface of radius $r$, and its pole at A is the origin of coordinates for the equations given below. The computation is restricted to the *meridional plane*—the plane of the paper. Generalization to three-dimensional coordinates is a straightforward matter, but adds nothing to the clarity of the explanation. In cases where the optical surface is not spherical, the equations must, of course, be modified to take account of this—again, nothing would be gained here by an attempt to be completely general.

The incident ray is QPB, intersecting the surface at P. RPC is the normal to the surface at the point of incidence, and since the surface is spherical, PC $= r =$ AC. The incident ray meets the axis at convergence angle $U$, and its angle of incidence is $I$.

At the surface, the ray is refracted according to the law of refraction, the refracted ray being PB′, at angle of refraction $I'$, and meeting the axis at B′ at convergence angle $U'$.

The known data are the radius of curvature of the surface, $r$, the indices of refraction of the two media, $\mu$ and $\mu'$, the intersection length of the incident ray, AB $= L$, and the angle of convergence $U$. The data required from the computation are the data for the refracted ray: the intersection length AB′ $= L'$ and the convergence angle $U'$. This provides the necessary input data for the next succeeding surface, and the computation can proceed through the optical system, surface by surface.

By dropping a perpendicular from the incident ray to the center of curvature, C, the expression for the angle of incidence is found to be

$$\sin I = \frac{(L - r) \sin U}{r} \tag{4.36}$$

The law of refraction gives the angle of refraction

$$\mu' \sin I' = \mu \sin I \tag{4.37}$$

The convergence angle $U'$ is the external angle of the oblique triangle BPB′, of which the internal angles are $U$ and $I - I'$, hence

$$U' = U + I - I' \tag{4.38}$$

and finally, a perpendicular dropped from the refracted ray to the center of curvature, C, gives

$$L' - r = \frac{r \sin I'}{\sin U'} \tag{4.39}$$

The intersection length of the incident ray for the next surface in the system will be $L_2 = L_1' - t$, where $t$ is the distance between the surfaces. And, of course, $U_2 = U_1'$. These equations are in the optimum form for the surface-to-surface computation of a system, using logarithms or tables of trigonometric functions. In actual calculations, using computers, it is

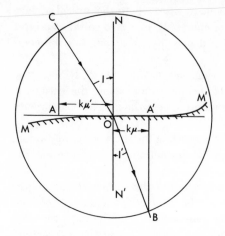

FIGURE 4.6. Graphical ray tracing for a refracting surface.

generally the custom to use equations based upon a three-dimensional coordinate system and the methods of direction cosines.

One is naturally tempted to try to develop a single equation for several surfaces in series. This is of course possible, but it leads to a hopelessly complicated expression. Even to attempt to reduce Equations (4.36) through (4.39) to a smaller set leads to completely unwieldy expressions. This difficulty is involved entirely in the fact that sin $x \neq x$. For small angles $U$ and $I$, where this equality can be adopted, very great simplification can be attained, as will be seen below.

**4.15. Graphical Ray Tracing for a Refracting Surface.** It is often convenient to trace a ray through a refracting surface by a graphical rather than a computational method. This may be done by the method illustrated in Figure 4.6.

MOM′ is the refracting surface, which may be of any form, and NON′ is its normal, constructed by whatever method is appropriate to the surface under consideration. CO is the incident ray, and the angle of incidence, $I$, is assumed known. Distances proportional to $\mu$ and $\mu'$ are laid out along the tangent to the surface at the incident point (AOA′). $\mu'$ is the index of refraction of the refracting medium, and is laid out under the *incident* ray; $\mu$ is the index of the medium in which the incident ray lies, and is laid out on the opposite side of the normal.

A perpendicular is erected from A to the incident ray, and with O as a center, a circle is drawn through the intersection C. A perpendicular is dropped from A′ to meet this circle at B. The refracted ray is then drawn from O through B.

**4.16. The Paraxial Case.** The approximations sin $x = x$, cos $x = 1$ can be made for cases where the angles involved are of the order of 10° or less. In many optical systems, this limit is not exceeded; in others, computations for the restricted case yield all of the parameters of an *ideal* system. When computations are carried out for finite angles $U$ and $I$, the differences between these results and the results for the restricted case are termed *aberrations*, and minor adjustments can be made to bring these under control which do not materially affect the established system parameters.

The case where the angle approximations can be made is termed the paraxial case. The performance of real optical systems approaches that of the paraxial case when the system aperture and field approach zero. The simplified case is of more utility than might at first be supposed, and it is only in rather extreme systems that the aberrations become significant with respect to the principal parameters.

If Equations (4.36) to (4.39) are rewritten with the angle approximation adopted, we obtain, using lower case symbols to indicate the paraxial case,

$$i = (\ell - r)u/r \qquad (4.40)$$

$$\mu'i' = \mu i \qquad (4.41)$$

$$u = u + i - i' \qquad (4.42)$$

$$\ell' - r = ri'/u' \qquad (4.43)$$

It is now easy to make substitutions in Equation (4.43) from the other equations and, after some algebraic manipulation, to arrive at the expression

$$\frac{\mu'}{\ell'} - \frac{\mu}{\ell} = \frac{\mu' - \mu}{r} \qquad (4.44)$$

By definition, the focal points are the image point for an infinitely distant object and the object point for an infinitely distant image. When $\ell = \infty$, we have

$$\frac{\mu'}{\ell'} = \frac{\mu' - \mu}{r}$$

or

$$1/\ell' = (\mu' - \mu)/\mu'r = 1/f' \qquad (4.45)$$

and, when $\ell' = \infty$,

$$\frac{\mu}{\ell} = -\frac{\mu' - \mu}{r}$$

or

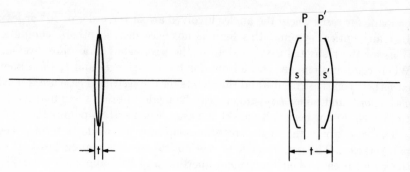

FIGURE 4.7. The thin lens and the thick lens.

$$1/\ell = -(\mu' - \mu)/\mu r = 1/f \tag{4.46}$$

From these definitions of the focal points, it is easy to write Equation (4.26).

Equation (4.44) is called the *image equation*. In this form it applies to a single refracting surface, and if we use the *relative index of refraction* between the two media, and put $\mu'/\mu = \mu_0$, we can write the equation

$$\frac{\mu_0}{\ell'} - \frac{1}{\ell} = \frac{\mu_0 - 1}{r} \tag{4.47}$$

**4.17 The Thin Lens.** Consider a lens, as in Figure 4.7, consisting of two refracting surfaces, separated by a distance $t$, immersed in a medium of refractive index $\mu$, the index of the lens material being $\mu'$. Equation (4.44) for the first surface gives

$$\frac{\mu'}{\ell'_1} - \frac{\mu}{\ell_1} = \frac{\mu' - \mu}{r_1} \tag{4.48}$$

and for the second surface

$$\frac{\mu}{\ell'_2} - \frac{\mu'}{\ell_2} = \frac{\mu - \mu'}{r_2} \tag{4.49}$$

If the assumption is made that $t = 0$, then $\ell_2 = \ell'_1$, and the two equations can be combined to eliminate $\ell'_1$ and yield

$$\frac{1}{\ell'_2} - \frac{1}{\ell_1} = \frac{\mu' - \mu}{\mu r_1} - \frac{\mu' - \mu}{\mu r_2} = \frac{1}{f'_2} - \frac{1}{f_1} = \frac{1}{f'} \tag{4.50}$$

Now, when $\ell'_1 = \infty$, we have

$$\frac{1}{\ell'_2} = \frac{\mu' - \mu}{\mu} \left( \frac{1}{r_1} - \frac{1}{r_2} \right) = \frac{1}{f'_2} - \frac{1}{f_1} = \frac{1}{f'} \tag{4.51}$$

and when $\ell_2' = \infty$,

$$\frac{1}{\ell_1} = -\frac{\mu' - \mu}{\mu}\left(\frac{1}{r_1} - \frac{1}{r_2}\right) = \frac{1}{f_1} - \frac{1}{f_2'} = \frac{1}{f} \tag{4.52}$$

where $f'$ and $f$ are the focal points for the complete lens.

Combining Equations (4.50) and (4.51) gives

$$\frac{1}{f'} = -\frac{1}{f} = \frac{\mu' - \mu}{\mu}\left(\frac{1}{r_1} - \frac{1}{r_2}\right) \tag{4.53}$$

This condition, where the thickness of the lens, $t$, is considered negligible, is the *thin lens*, a concept of great value. Combinations of separated thin lenses may be computed with considerable ease, as will be seen below, and also a lens with actual thickness may be treated as a thin lens if the measurements are made from the *principal planes*, as shown in the following section.

The quantity $1/r$ is defined as the *curvature* of the surface, $c$. Thus, Equation (4.53) may be written

$$\frac{1}{f'} = \frac{1}{f} = \frac{\mu' - \mu}{\mu}(c_1 - c_2) \tag{4.53a}$$

**4.18. Lens Power.** The reciprocal of the focal length ($1/f'$ for a lens, $\mu/f'$ for a refracting surface) is defined as the *power* or *refracting power* of the unit. It is measured in *diopters*, the power being given in diopters when the focal length is given in meters. Thus, a lens with a focal length of 2 meters is a "half-diopter" lens. This terminology is common usage in optometry; in scientific optics, it is not commonly used, although descriptive terms such as "power" and "strong and weak lenses" will often be found.

**4.19. The Thick Lens.** Actual lenses have finite thicknesses. Figure 4.7 shows a typical case, and also shows the *principal planes*, which were defined in the discussion above as the conjugate planes for unit magnification. These planes have an even greater significance, in that, if the distances to object and image are measured from the respective principal planes, the thick lens (paraxially) obeys all the relations which are derived for thin lenses.

It may be shown, by appropriate algebraic manipulation, that in the lens of Figure 4.7, the location of the principal planes with respect to the poles is given by

$$s = -\frac{\mu r_1 t(\mu' - \mu)}{\Delta} \tag{4.54}$$

$$s' = \frac{\mu r_2 t(\mu' - \mu)}{\Delta} \tag{4.55}$$

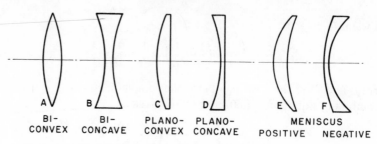

FIGURE 4.8. Basic lens forms. A, B, E and F are the four fundamental forms. C is a special case of A and D of B.

where

$$\Delta = \mu'(\mu' - \mu)(r_1 - r_2) - (\mu' - \mu)^2 t$$

And the focal points are given by

$$f' = -f = \mu'\mu r_1 r_2/\Delta \tag{4.56}$$

For $t = 0$, $s = s' = 0$, and Equation (4.56) reduces to Equation (4.53).

**4.20. Image Equation for a Single Lens.** Equation (4.50) therefore applies to any lens, and may be written

$$\frac{1}{\ell'} - \frac{1}{\ell} = \frac{1}{f'} = (\mu - 1)\left(\frac{1}{r_1} - \frac{1}{r_2}\right) \tag{4.50a}$$

where the quantities refer to the complete lens and are measured, of course, from the principal planes.

This is the general image equation for a single lens immersed in a medium, the ratio of refractive indices of lens and immersion medium being $\mu$. The signs of the surface radii are assigned in accordance with the rule promulgated previously—positive if the center of curvature lies to the right and negative if it lies to the left. The basic types of lenses are the double convex, in which $r_1$ is positive and $r_2$ is negative, the double concave, in which $r_1$ is negative and $r_2$ is positive, and the meniscus, in which both radii have the same sign.

From Equation (4.50a) it can be seen that the double convex lens has a positive focal length, the double concave lens has a negative focal length, and the meniscus lens may be positive or negative depending upon the relative values of $r_1$ and $r_2$. If both $r_1$ and $r_2$ are positive, the lens is positive if $r_2 > r_1$; if both $r_1$ and $r_2$ are negative (lens reversed in position), the lens is positive if $r_1 > r_2$. The four fundamental forms are shown in Figure 4.8.

A more convenient rule of thumb as to the sign of the focal length is that a lens is positive if its center thickness is greater than its edge thickness.

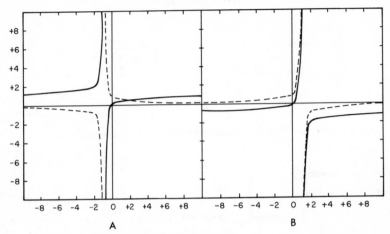

FIGURE 4.9. Object and image relations in positive and negative lenses: (A) positive lens, (B) negative lens. The horizontal axes are the object distance, the vertical axes the image distance, or the linear magnification. Image distances are plotted in solid lines; linear magnification in dotted lines.

**4.21. Object and Image Relations.** The first part of Equation (4.50a) may be used to plot the object and image positions, as shown in Figure 4.9.

For a positive lens, when the object is infinitely distant at the left, the image is at the principal focus (by definition). As the object moves closer to the lens, the image moves away. When the object distance is twice the focal length on the left, the image is at twice the focal length on the right. When the object is at the anterior focal point, the image is at infinity, which is the definition of the anterior focal point.

As the object moves to the right past the anterior focal point, the image appears from infinity at the left and continues to move to the right, toward the lens. When the object is at the lens (second principal plane) the image is also at the lens (first principal plane). For light converging to an object point to the right of the lens, the image is also to the right of the lens, but closer than the object, until, when the object has receded to infinity on the right, the image is at the focal point again.

For a negative lens, the focal point $f'$ is to the left of the lens; for an object point infinitely distant to the left, the image is formed at $f'$. As the object is brought toward the lens, the image also moves toward the lens. When the object is at the focal point $f'$, the image is halfway between this point and the lens. As with the positive lens, for an object at the lens (second principal plane) the image is also at the lens (first principal plane). For object points to the right of the lens, but closer than its anterior focal

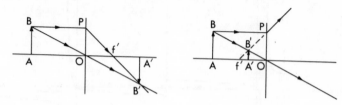

FIGURE 4.10. Image orientation and linear magnification.

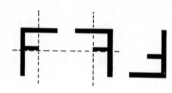

FIGURE 4.11. Image inversions and rotations. At top, the letter is inverted about a vertical axis, then about a horizontal axis. At bottom, the letter has been rotated 180°. The results of the two operations are the same.

point, the image is to the right of the lens, and further away than the object. When the object is at the anterior focal point, the image has receded to infinity. For still further movement of the object to the right, the image appears from infinity at the left, and reaches the posterior focal point when the object has receded to infinity.

**4.22. Image Orientation and Linear Magnification.** The linear magnification is, by definition, $\ell'/\ell$. The sign conventions which have been adopted are such that the sign of the linear magnification indicates the image orientation. If the sign is negative, the image is *inverted* with respect to the object, as shown in Figure 4.10; if the sign is positive, the image is *erect*.

The magnification is also plotted in Figure 4.9.

The diagrams indicate the meridional plane only; in an actual lens, the objects and images are two-dimensional, and an *inverted image* corresponds to one which has been rotated 180° about the optical axis, as shown in Figure 4.11.

**4.23. Real and Virtual Images.** In accordance with the definition of real and virtual images given in Section 4.4, it is seen that, when the image lies to the right of the lens, it is real, and when it lies to the left of the lens, it is virtual. The cases of object point lying to the right of the lens, when

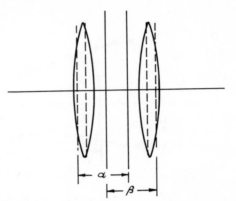

FIGURE 4.12. Location of the principal planes for two positive lenses.

the light is incident from the left, are cases of *virtual objects*. Such situations arise in optical systems where the virtual object for a given lens is the image formed by a preceding lens in the system.

**4.24. Two Thin Lenses.** The case of two thin lenses can be analyzed exactly as was the case of the two surfaces of a thick lens. Derivations for the focal lengths (measured from the principal planes) and the locations of the principal planes shows that if $f'$ and $f$ are the focal lengths of the combination, and $f_i$, $f_i'$ are the focal lengths of the individual lenses,

$$\frac{1}{f'} = -\frac{1}{f} = \frac{1}{f_1'} + \frac{1}{f_2'} - \frac{t}{f_1'f_2'} \tag{4.57}$$

and that the locations of the principal planes are given by

$$\alpha = \frac{f_1't}{f_1' + f_1' - t} \tag{4.58}$$

$$\beta = -\frac{f_2't}{f_1' + f_2' - t} \tag{4.59}$$

Figure 4.12 shows how the quantities are measured.

It is to be noted that, if both the lenses are positive ($f'$ positive and $f$ negative in the sense previously defined), the principal planes are "crossed" —the left principal plane being located to the right of the right principal plane.

**4.25. The Lagrange Invariant.** A theorem of considerable value in optics is the Lagrange theorem. Referring to Section 4.16, which gave the equations for the paraxial case of a single refracting surface, if Equation (4.40) is substituted into Equation (4.41), and the result is substituted in Equation (4.43), the following expression can be obtained

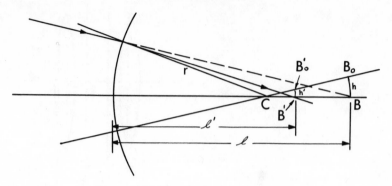

FIGURE 4.13. The theorem of Lagrange.

$$(\ell' - r)\mu'u' = (\ell' - r)\mu u \tag{4.60}$$

Referring to Figure 4.13, which indicates an object point B imaged at B', it is seen that $\ell - r = $ CB and $\ell' - r = $ CB', and the above equation relates these quantities. If an auxiliary optical axis is now drawn through the point C, and arcs of circles centered at C are drawn from B and B' to the new axis, then it is clear that a point $B_0$ at the end of the first arc will be imaged at $B_0'$ at the end of the second arc, since the conditions are exactly the same as for B and B'.

If $h$ and $h'$ are the lengths of these arcs, then they are proportional to the distances CB and CB', so that Equation (4.60) may be written

$$h'\mu'u' = h\mu u \tag{4.61}$$

It is also clear that, for the *paraxial* case, Equation (4.61) is valid for perpendiculars as well as arcs. But $h'/h$ is the linear magnification, so that

$$M = \mu'u'/\mu u \tag{4.62}$$

which gives a simple expression for the magnification of an optical surface in terms of indices and the convergence angle for a *paraxial* image point.

If this were the end of the story, the equation would be of little utility, but it is readily extended to a series of $k$ surfaces, provided only that they are centered on a common optical axis, which is nearly always the case in an optical system. Since the image formed by one surface becomes the object for the next, so that $h_k = h_{k-1}'$, and since $u_k = u_{k-1}'$, Equation (4.61) may be immediately extended into the general form

$$h_k'\mu_k'u_k' = h_1\mu_1u_1 \tag{4.63}$$

and Equation (4.62) can be extended into the general form

$$M = \mu_k'u_k'/\mu_1u_1 \tag{4.64}$$

where $M$ is the linear magnification of the system. The equations are valid for any number of centered surfaces.

Equation (4.63) is the *theorem of Lagrange,* and since the quantity $h\mu u$ becomes a constant for all of the surfaces in a system, it is known as the *Lagrange invariant.* Equation (4.63) is also commonly known as the *Smith-Helmholtz formula,* having been independently derived by these workers.

This relation is a particular case of the more general *Optical Sine Theorem,* discussed below, which expresses the same relation with respect to the case of finite aperture and field.

**4.26. Combination of Optical Systems.** The *cardinal points* of an optical system—the focal points, principal planes and nodal planes—and the three magnifications—linear, longitudinal and angular—are defined only in terms of the paraxial case, as has been shown above. It has also been shown that a thick lens can be treated, for the paraxial case, as a thin lens, by referring distances to the principal planes, and also that, by a similar technique, two thin lenses can be treated as a single thin lens.

It follows, therefore, that a complete (centered) optical system, however complex in terms of numbers of surfaces, can be treated as a single thin lens for the determination of the cardinal points and the magnifications.

It is of interest to consider the possible cases of two separated thin lenses, since this exercise will demonstrate the fundamental arrangement of all of the basic types of optical instruments. There are three classes of combinations: two positive lenses; one positive lens and one negative lens; and two negative lenses.

**4.27. Combination of Two Positive Thin Lenses.** Consider two positive thin lenses, with focal lengths $f_1'$ and $f_2'$, both positive, separated by a distance $d$. The focal length of the combination is, from Equation (4.57)

$$f' = \frac{f_1' f_2'}{f_1' + f_2' - d} \tag{4.65}$$

In Figure 4.14 the value of f' is plotted as a function of the separation, $d$, with the assumption that $f_1' = f_2'$. For $d = 0$ (lenses in contact), $f'$ is a minimum; the combination is equivalent to a single thin lens of half the focal length. As $d$ increases, $f'$ increases also. When $d = f_1'$, the second lens is at the principal focus of the first, and is in the image plane for an infinite object point. It thus contributes nothing to the focal length, and Equation (4.65) reduces to $f' = f_1'$.

When $d = f_1' + f_2'$, the posterior focal point of the first lens coincides with the anterior focal point of the second, and the focal length of the combination is infinite. This is the telescopic system—in this case, the

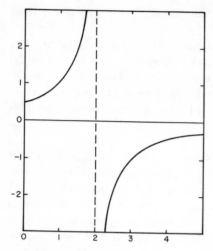

FIGURE 4.14. Focal length of two equal positive thin lenses. The horizontal axis is the separation, the vertical axis the combined focal length, both in units of the focal length of an individual lens.

Keplerian telescope, which has a positive eyepiece. For $d < f'_1 + f'_2$, the system represents an objective, a magnifier, or an ordinary eyepiece.

When $d$ is greater than $f'_1 + f'_2$, $f'$ for the combination is negative, and becomes smaller as $d$ increases. This arrangement represents the optical system of the compound microscope.

**4.28. Combination of Two Negative Thin Lenses.** Consider two negative thin lenses, separated by a distance $d$. The combined focal length is always negative, is a minimum when $d = 0$, and increases as $d$ increases. This combination does not represent any basic optical system.

**4.29. Combination of One Positive and One Negative Thin Lens.** There are two cases to be considered:

(A) Positive lens stronger than negative lens;

(B) Positive lens weaker than negative lens.

*Case (A)*. For $d = 0$, the focal length is positive; it remains positive and decreases as $d$ grows. This case does not represent any basic optical system.

*Case (B)*. For $d = 0$, the focal length is negative, and takes on larger negative values as $d$ increases until, when $d = f'_1 + f'_2$ (the $f$'s being of opposite sign), the focal length of the combination is infinite. Again, this is the case of the telescope—this time the Galilean telescope, which has a negative eyepiece.

For still larger values of $d$, the focal length becomes positive and decreases as $d$ grows. This is the system of the telephoto lens.

**4.30. Extra-axial Points.** The ray-tracing equations which were developed in sections 4.14 and 4.15 are completely general, and apply to rays from any object point, whether or not it is located on the axis. Points

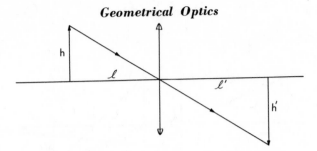

FIGURE 4.15. Extra-axial object and image points.

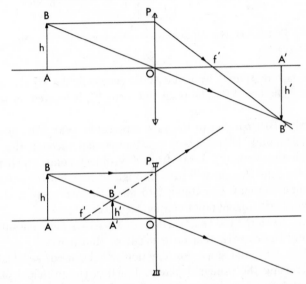

FIGURE 4.16. Graphical image construction for positive and negative thin lenses.

located distant from the optical axis are referred to as *extra-axial points*. By the projective transformation principle, extra-axial object points give rise to extra-axial image points, the ratio of their distances from the axis being the linear magnification. An object is usually considered as a plane perpendicular to the optical axis, and for the paraxial case at least, the image is also a plane perpendicular to the optical axis.

Axial object and image distances for the paraxial case are related by the image equation [Equation (4.44) and (4.50a)] and by the theorem of Lagrange [Equation (4.60)], and the extra-axial image points may readily be constructed as shown in Figure 4.15.

**4.31. Graphical Image Construction.** It is sometimes convenient to construct an image graphically, instead of evaluating the equations. This may be done, for a thin lens, as shown in Figure 4.16.

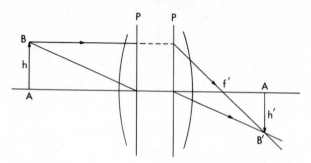

FIGURE 4.17. Graphical image construction for a thick positive lens.

The lens is represented by a line, OP, perpendicular to the axis, AA′. The object is the line AB. The principal focus, $f'$, is located on the axis as shown.

Now, a ray (BP) parallel to the axis, represents a ray from an infinitely distant object point, hence this ray, after passing through the lens, will pass through the focus, $f'$. A ray from any object point which intersects the axis at the lens ($\ell = 0$) will pass through undeviated ($\ell' = 0$, $u' = u$), and hence line BO may be extended to meet the other ray at B′, which, by definition, is the image point conjugate to B.

Figure 4.16(a) shows the construction for a positive thin lens, and Figure 4.16(b) shows the construction for a negative thin lens.

For a thick lens, the same construction can be used, as illustrated in Figure 4.17, using the principal planes. Usually, the principal plane locations are not known, and must be computed from Equations (4.58) and (4.59) so that the graphical method does not avoid computation for this case.

**4.32. Graphical Construction of Principal Planes for Two Thin Lenses.** Figure 4.18 illustrates a method which may be used to find the location of the principal planes for two thin lenses.

The construction shown is for two positive thin lenses. The same principles can be applied for other combinations of two thin lenses.

**4.33. Mirrors.** Except for a brief remark that mirrors may be treated as lenses if the refractive index ratio, $\mu'/\mu$ is taken to be $-1$, mirrors have not been discussed. This substitution is valid for all of the equations discussed above. It must be noted, however, that for a mirror, the image equation [Equation (4.50)] becomes

$$\frac{1}{\ell'} + \frac{1}{\ell} = -\frac{1}{f'}$$

$$(4.66)$$

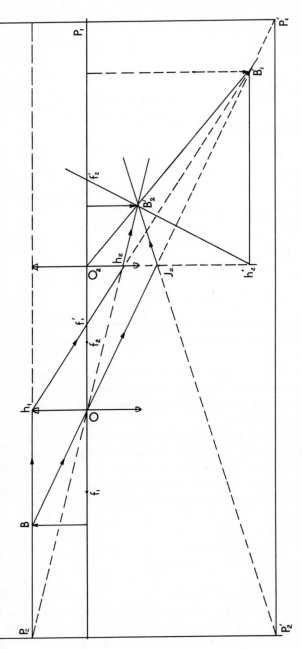

FIGURE 4.18. Graphical construction of principal planes for two positive thin lenses. The construction proceeds as follows: Starting with any object point, $B$, its image in the first lens is constructed by drawing $BO$, extended, and $Bh_1$, then $h_1 f'_1$ extended, to meet at $B'_1$. With $B'_1$ as object point for the second lens, $B'_1 h'_2$ is drawn parallel to the axis, and then $h'_2 f'_2$, through the prime focus of second lens. $B'_1 O_2$ is the ray through the nodal point, and the intersection at $B'_2$ is the final image. The actual rays from the first lens may now be drawn through the final image as $h_2 B'_2$ and $J_2 B'_2$. But $h_2 B'_2$ must have the same height in the second principal plane as $Bh_1$ has in the first principal plane, and it is therefore extended to $P_2$, locating the second principal plane. Similarly, $J_2 B'_2$ has the same height in the second principal plane as $BO$ has in the first principal plane, hence it is extended to $P'_2$, and $P'_2 P'_1$ is drawn parallel to the axis to intersect with $BO$ extended, thus locating the first principal plane.

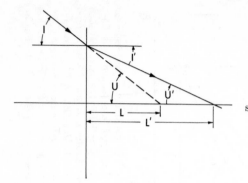

FIGURE 4.19. Refraction at a plane surface.

and that from Equation (4.45)

$$\ell'_\infty = -\frac{2}{r} = \frac{1}{f'} \tag{4.67}$$

Therefore, for a mirror

$$f' = -r/2 \tag{4.68}$$

Thus, when $r$ is *negative* according to the sign conventions above (center of curvature lies to the left of the surface), the focal length (of a mirror) is *positive*, and vice versa.

Also, when a mirror occurs in series with refracting surfaces, the direction of ray travel is reversed at the mirror surface, and thus the signs of $L_{k+1}$ and $U_{k+1}$ (where $k$ is the mirror) must be reversed before proceeding to calculate the $(k + 1)$th surface.

**4.34. Plane Surfaces.** It may be noted that the ray-tracing equations presented in Sections 4.14 and 4.15 break down for plane surfaces, for which $r = \infty$. The case for a plane surface is simpler than for a curved surface, as shown in Figure 4.19, from which is seen that the following equations may be substituted for Equations (4.38) to (4.39)

$$I = -U \tag{4.69}$$

$$\mu' \sin I' = \mu \sin I \tag{4.70}$$

$$U' = -I' \tag{4.71}$$

$$L' = L \tan U/\tan U' \tag{4.72}$$

**4.35. Plane Mirrors.** From the standpoint of image formation, the plane mirror represents a trivial case. Equations (4.69) to (4.72), when applied to a plane mirror $(\mu'/\mu = -1)$ give the simple result

$$L' = -L \tag{4.73}$$

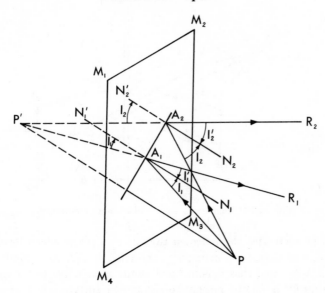

FIGURE 4.20. Image construction in a plane mirror.

and, for the linear magnification, we obtain

$$L'/L = -1 \tag{4.74}$$

By the rule for linear magnification and image orientation (Section 4.20) this would imply an inverted image. Actually, the image in a plane mirror is not inverted; hence it is necessary to amend the orientation rules in the case of a mirror and to state that, for a mirror, the image is inverted when the linear magnification is positive, and vice versa.

Plane mirrors, in the form of totally reflecting prisms, are of frequent occurrence in optical systems, hence the rules for image orientation find frequent application.

**4.36. Image Construction for a Plane Mirror.** As a preliminary to the discussion of image orientations in optical systems, it is useful to construct the image of an object in a plane mirror using the law of reflection as the controlling rule.

In Figure 4.20, let $M_1M_2M_3M_4$ be a plane mirror, and let P be an object point. Construct *any* two rays, $PA_1$ and $PA_2$, from the object point, intersecting the mirror at $A_1$ and $A_2$. The normals to the mirror at the two intersection points are $N_1N_1'$ and $N_2N_2'$. The reflected rays are $A_1R_1$ and $A_2R_2$. By the law of reflection, the angles between the incident and reflected rays and the normals are equal, and the reflected and incident rays lie in a plane which includes the normal.

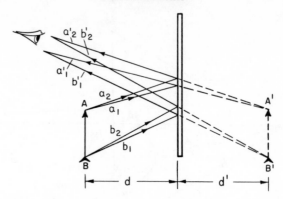

FIGURE 4.21. Image of a finite object in a plane mirror.

It can be seen that the reflected rays lie in a plane which includes the line $A_1A_2$, and that, from symmetry, the triangle $P'A_1A_2$ is similar to the triangle $PA_1A_2$, and that it is inclined at the same angle to the mirror. It follows that $P'$ is on the normal to the mirror surface which contains P, and that they are therefore equidistant from the mirror.

It follows, therefore, that any object will be imaged in a mirror in such a way that lines joining the object and image points are normal to the mirror and that the distances from the mirror to the object and image points are equal. When this rule is applied to a finite object, as shown in Figure 4.21, it is clear that there is no inversion. It is common knowledge, however, that images in plane mirrors *are* inverted, as evidenced by the universal term "mirror image." The reason for this apparent discrepancy will be seen in the following sections.

**4.37. Inversions and Rotations of Images.** Many optical systems contain plane reflecting surfaces which affect the orientation of images; also, image-forming surfaces produce inversions of images in certain cases, as has been discussed above. Descriptions of the effect of various optical components on the orientation of images is one of the most confusing subjects in optics; partly because of the lack of an unambiguous system of definitions. The following system of definitions and descriptions has been found useful as a result of many years of teaching optical principles.

An image (two-dimensional, perpendicular to optical axis) is considered *right-handed* if, by rotation in its own plane, it can be brought into an orientation similar to that of the corresponding object. Thus, the images in Figure 4.22 are all right-handed.

An image is considered *left-handed* if it cannot be brought into agreement with the object by rotation in its own plane. Thus, the images in Figure 4.23 are all left-handed.

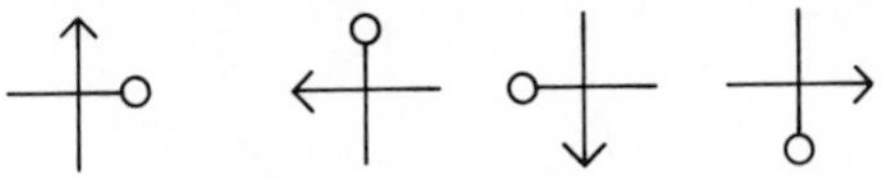

FIGURE 4.22. Right-handed images.

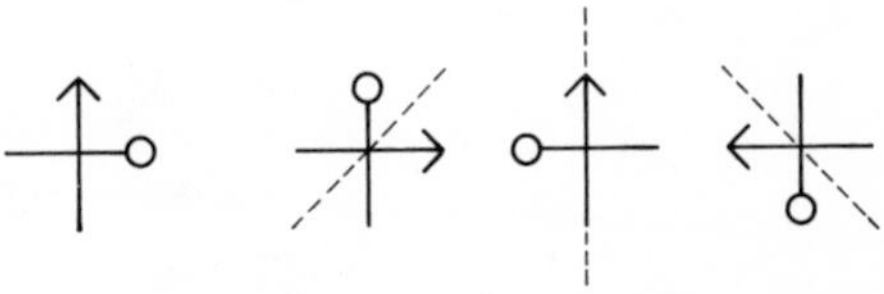

FIGURE 4.23. Left-handed images. The three images on the right are obtained from that on the left by inverting about a single axis. The axes of inversion are indicated by dotted lines.

An image becomes left-handed by an inversion about *one* axis. In Figure 4.23, the axes of inversion which produced left-handedness are indicated.

An image is said to be *rotated* if it is right-handed and a line in the image makes an angle $\theta$ with the corresponding line in the object.

(1) *A single reflection in a plane mirror produces a left-handed image*, because of inversion about an axis which is parallel to the plane of object and image and lies in the plane of the mirror.

(2) A series of inversions produces a left-handed image if the number of reflections (inversions) is odd; a right-handed image if the number is even.

(3) An even number of inversions about any combination of axes, all lying in the plane of the object and image, is equivalent to an image rotation.

The image orientation is judged by observing in a direction opposite to the direction of the light rays.

**4.38. Inversions and Rotations by Mirrors.** The principles set forth above are illustrated in Figures 4.24 and 4.25.

Figure 4.24 shows several cases of an object imaged by a plane mirror at various angles. The axis of inversion is the line in the mirror surface which is parallel to the plane of both object and image. It is seen that the images, viewed in the manner indicated, are left-handed—rotation in their own planes cannot bring them into agreement with the object as viewed from the mirror.

Figure 4.25 shows odd and even series of inversions. It is seen that the resulting images are left-handed for an odd number of reflections, and right-handed for an even number, even though the axes of inversion are not parallel to each other.

It is also seen from Figure 4.25, that all of the even series of reflections produce images which exhibit simple rotation with respect to the object.

**4.39. Axis of Inversion for Object Parallel to Mirror.** When the object, and consequently the image, are parallel to the mirror surface, the rule for the location of the axis of inversion breaks down, since all directions

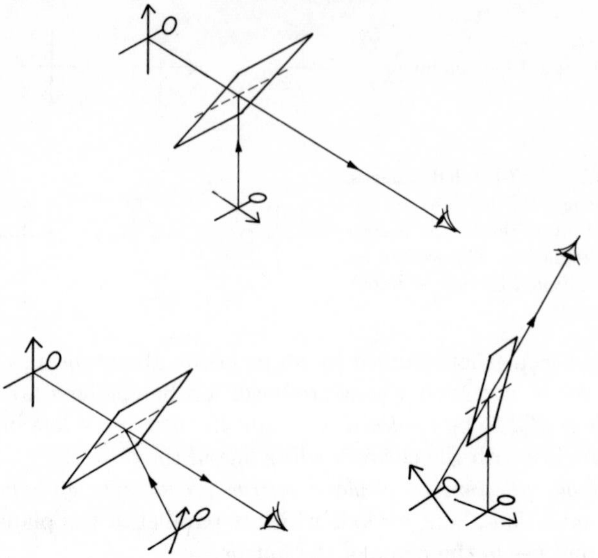

FIGURE 4.24. Inversions in a plane mirror. A single reflection
in a plane mirror produces an inversion. The axes of inversion
are indicated by dotted lines.

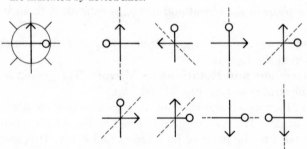

FIGURE 4.25. Series of inversions. In each row, the successive
images are obtained by a series of rotations of the reference
image about the axes shown in dotted lines. The result of an
odd number of inversions is left-handed; that of an even number,
right-handed.

satisfy the condition. What, then, determines the axis of inversion in this
case? This is the oft-asked (and seldom answered) question, "Why is my
image in a mirror inverted from right to left, rather than in some other
direction? " The reader may have seen in the preceding discussion, that
the answer lies in the observer's concept of the orientation of the object.
When the situation is viewed as in Figure 4.21, there is no inversion. But,

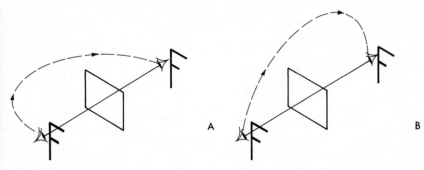

FIGURE 4.26. Axis of inversion in a plane mirror. In each case, the object at the left is imaged in a plane mirror. In A, the result is mentally compared with the original object as seen by an eye rotated about a vertical axis—the result is an apparent inversion from left to right. In B, the comparison is with an eye rotated about a horizontal axis—the result is an apparent inversion from top to bottom.

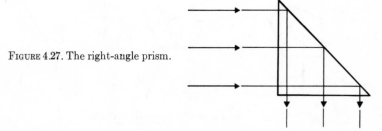

FIGURE 4.27. The right-angle prism.

in viewing Figure 4.21, as drawn, the requirement that both object and image be viewed in a direction opposite to the direction of the light rays has not been fulfilled—the image is seen in this direction, but the object is viewed in the figure from behind, as it were.

When we view our own image in a mirror, we compare it with our face as it would be seen by an observer looking out of the mirror—and in making this comparison, *we imagine ourselves rotated about a vertical axis.* If we imagined ourselves rotated about a horizontal axis, as in Figure 4.26(b), the inversion would be from top to bottom.

**4.40. Total Reflecting Prisms.** It has been shown (Section 2.6) that in the case of the incidence of light on a boundary of a medium with lower refractive index, total internal reflection occurs if the angle of incidence is such as to make the sign of the angle of refraction greater than unity, that is, for angles greater than $I_c$ where $\sin I_c = \mu/\mu'$. If the case is that of glass in air, a ray will not emerge from the glass if the angle of incidence at the surface is greater than $I_c$, where $\sin I_c = 1/\mu$.

Figure 4.27 shows a right-angle prism, which deflects the light through

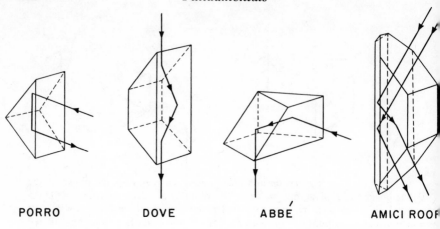

**PORRO**          **DOVE**          **ABBÉ**          **AMICI ROOF**

FIGURE 4.28. Some common forms of totally reflecting prisms.

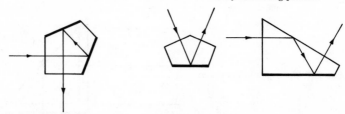

FIGURE 4.29. Some prisms requiring silvered surfaces.

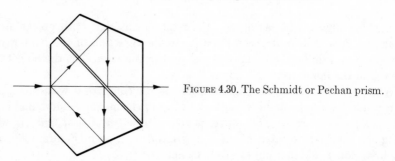

FIGURE 4.30. The Schmidt or Pechan prism.

a right angle. The reflecting face is at an angle of 45° to incident parallel light, and total internal reflection will occur if $\sin 45° > 1/\mu < .707$, or if $\mu > 1.414$. Most glasses have an index of refraction greater than 1.5, so that this prism is a totally reflecting prism for most types of glass.

Many other forms of totally reflecting prisms are used; Figure 4.28 illustrates a few. Other types of prisms, as illustrated in Figure 4.29, are made with silvered surfaces where the incident angles are not sufficiently great to produce total internal reflection.

These and other types of prisms are frequently used in optical instruments to produce changes in direction of the optical axis, or to produce desired image orientations. Mirrors would, in many cases, serve equally well, but prisms are used because their surfaces do not get out of adjustment with each other, and because there is essentially no loss in intensity in a total internal reflection. This gain must be partially balanced by a loss caused by absorption in the glass of the prism.

Sometimes a designer's ingenuity can utilize the same surface of a prism for both total internal reflection and for transmission of the same light beam, depending upon the angle of incidence. Figure 4.30 shows an example of this, the Schmidt prism.

Examples of the use of prisms in optical instruments will be seen in the discussions of specific instruments in Chapter 6.

**4.41. Real Optical Systems.** Most of the discussion above has been in terms of *ideal* optical systems—systems in which every object point has a conjugate image point of zero dimensions. It was shown that this is very nearly true for the *paraxial* case, where the light rays being considered lie entirely within a region very close to the optical axis. This treatment was extremely useful in deriving the basic optical parameters, such as focal length, magnification, etc. In fact, it is so good an approximation that basic optical parameters are defined in these terms.

In practice, one has to deal with real assemblages of optical components, where the rays are not limited to a region closely approaching the optical axis (and furthermore with optical surfaces which are not strictly spherical, but are subject to manufacturing errors), and in such real systems, image points are not zero-dimensional, but are finite in size, even from a geometrical point of view. It has already been pointed out that, although geometrical optics permits zero-dimensional image points, physical optics does not.

The departures of real systems, as computed by the methods of geometrical optics, from the zero-dimensional image points of ideal optical systems, are called optical *aberrations*. In an actual case, a given image point will turn out to be a three-dimensional volume of some finite size, within which all of the rays collected by the system from the corresponding object point will be found; in addition, the centroid of this volume will usually lie at some point other than that corresponding to the image point of an ideal system.

There are many ways of specifying the manner in which the rays in a real system fail to fulfill the conditions of the ideal system; in the course of time, conventions have been established so that there is rather complete agreement among optical designers as to the terminology given to each sort of departure. These are the optical aberrations. The task of the optical designer is so to choose his materials and their dimensions that the real system conforms as closely to the ideal system as the conditions of its intended use require.

The equations for the ideal optical system were derived from the rigorous equations for spherical optical surfaces by the substitution $\sin x = x$; it will be seen, therefore, that the aberrations arise largely because this substitution is not strictly true for angles of finite size. Since

$$\sin x = x - \frac{x^3}{3!} + \frac{x^5}{5!} - \frac{x^7}{7!} + \text{etc.} \qquad (4.75)$$

solutions to the geometrical optics equations may be expressed in a similar form, in which case the first term represents the situation for an ideal system, and the remaining terms represent the aberrations of a real system. We thus have classifications of aberrations as *third-order aberrations*, *fifth-order aberrations*, etc.

Expressing the first term in analytical form is quite simple, as has been shown above. The second term, representing the third order aberrations, may also be set forth in analytic form, and is frequently used in this manner in optical design. A number of investigators have developed analytic expressions for fifth-order aberrations,[3] and these are occasionally used, but they usually require much more mathematical manipulation than is convenient and are therefore not used to any extent in actual optical design. Application of the trigonometric equations shown above (or their equivalents) gives the summation of all the terms directly, and is a straightforward but laborious procedure, since it has to be applied ray by ray and surface by surface. Today, electronic computing machines do the actual mathematical work, and the element of labor involved in making voluminous computations has largely disappeared.

**4.42. Aberrations—Definitions.** There are seven specific aberrations geometrically defined; their definitions are given below. These definitions are useful in design, because each can be related to specific parameters of the optical system; this gives the designer guidance as to his choices of corrections to make to these parameters to improve the system performance. It must be remembered, however, that these definitions merely describe the manner in which light rays fail to pass through the image points predicted for an ideal system. They could have been described in numerous other ways—convention has established those actually in use.

**4.43. Chromatic Aberration.** *Chromatic aberration* is simply the condition which prevails when the light utilized by an optical system covers a finite spectral band. The index of refraction of optical materials is different

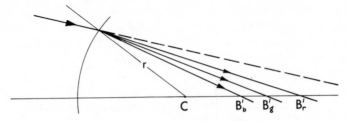

FIGURE 4.31. Chromatic aberration in a positive refracting surface. The suffixes refer to red, green and blue light.

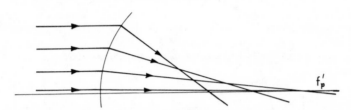

FIGURE 4.32. Spherical aberration in a positive refracting surface.

for different wavelengths of light (dispersion), and consequently the focal length of an optical system becomes a function of the wavelength of the light. The situation for a single refracting surface is illustrated in Figure 4.31. Chromatic aberration is discussed more fully in Section 4.70 *et. seq.* Reflecting surfaces are free of chromatic aberration.

**4.44. Spherical Aberration.** When the rigorous trigonometric equations are applied to a spherical refracting surface, it is found that, for an axial object point, the intersection lengths on the image side of the surface become shorter as the height of the ray on the surface increases. This situation is shown in Figure 4.32.

This condition is known as *spherical aberration*. It is discussed in more detail in Section 4.81 *et. seq.*

**4.45. Coma.** Spherical and chromatic aberration are the only aberrations pertinent to axial points. The remainder of the aberrations are defined in terms of extra-axial points. If the rays from an extra-axial object point are traced through a refracting surface, a situation similar to that shown in Figure 4.33 is found. Rays close to the *principal ray* (ray through the center of the aperture) will intersect the principal ray at a point B'. Rays through the upper and lower edges of the aperture will intersect the principal ray at different points. For the conditions shown in the figure, the upper ray has a shorter intersection length along the principal ray than does the lower ray. This leads to an image patch which has the general

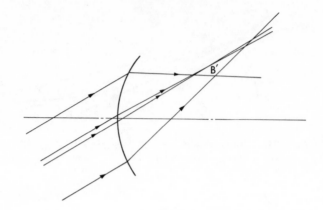

FIGURE 4.33. Coma in a positive refracting surface.

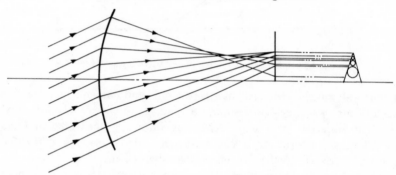

FIGURE 4.34. Development of the coma pattern.

shape of a comet (thus the name *coma*). If rays are traced for concentric circular zones, it is found that they intersect a plane drawn through the image point on the principal ray, as indicated in Figure 4.34, in a series of circles successively further displaced from this ray.

**4.46. Astigmatism.** The ray-tracing equations which were developed in Section 4.14 apply only to the plane of the diagram—the two-dimensional *meridional* case. The actual bundle of rays from an object point, however, is in general a three-dimensional conical bundle. For axial points, all planes containing the optical axis are identical; for extra-axial points, however, the planes are not identical, and to determine the effect of rays which do not lie in the meridional plane, ray-tracing in three dimensions must be undertaken. Such rays are known as *skew* rays. Until the advent of the electronic computing machine, optical designers avoided the tracing of skew rays whenever possible, because of the laborious computations involved. Computations of astigmatism, which results essentially from skew rays, were performed by simplified equations which treated only rays in the meridional (tangential) and the plane perpendicular thereto—the sagittal plane; moreover, they were confined to rays close to the principal ray.

If two fans of rays—one in the meridional and one in the sagittal plane, are traced through a refracting surface, as shown in Figure 4.35, it is found that, for rays very close to the principal ray (so that the effects of coma do not appear), the image point is closer to the lens for the meridional fan than for the sagittal fan. The effect becomes more pronounced as the object and image points depart from the optical axis.

This leads to the over-all effect that lines in the object which lie in the meridional plane are imaged on a different surface than lines which lie in the sagittal plane. This is *astigmatism*. It is also produced by optical surfaces which have different radii of curvature in the two orthogonal planes; such surfaces are toroidal in form, and are occasionally referred to as astigmatic surfaces.

**4.47. Curvature of Field.** It is found that both the tangential and sagittal image points for a plane object normal to the optical axis lie on curved surfaces in general, as shown in Figure 4.36. For a simple positive lens, these surfaces are related as shown, the tangential focal surface show-

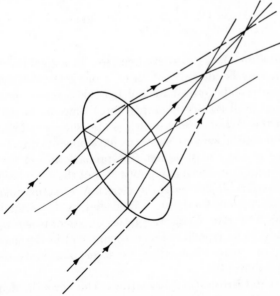

FIGURE 4.35. Astigmatism in a positive refracting surface.

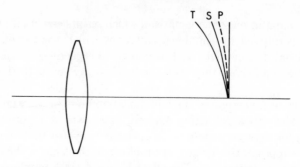

FIGURE 4.36. Focal surfaces in a simple positive lens: (P) Petzval surface, (S) sagittal focal surface, (T) tangential focal surface.

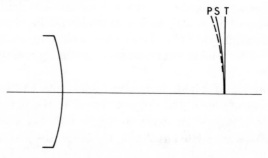

FIGURE 4.37. Focal surfaces for a lens corrected to give a flat tangential field.

ing more curvature than the sagittal surface. In a combination of lenses, this situation may be altered, but there is one relation which invariably holds (for focal points formed by ray fans close to the principal rays): The tangential focal surface is always three times as far as the sagittal surface from the *Petzval surface*, which is also shown in Figure 4.36. The tangential and sagittal surfaces may even have opposite directions of curvature, and one of them may be flat (the primary aim of the designer in photographic lenses) as shown in Figure 4.37, but the 3/1 relation still holds.

**4.48. Distortion.** *Distortion* is the departure of actual image points in a flat focal plane from the location predicted by the Lagrange theorem (Section 4.25). The latter (projective transformation) would require that a square grid object be reproduced as a square grid in the image plane. In actual cases, one encounters either *barrel* or *pincushion* distortion, as illustrated in Figure 4.38.

**4.49. Lateral Chromatic Aberration.** The seventh identified aberration is *lateral chromatic aberration*. Its separate identification is not

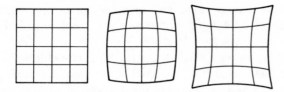

FIGURE 4.38. Barrel (positive) and pincushion (negative) disortion.

always recognized, since there are many types of chromatic aberration of extra-axial points, but its particular importance in ordinary eyepieces makes it deserving of separate consideration. It is simply the variation of distortion with the wavelength of the light, and leads to the reproduction of extra-axial points as little spectra. It is sometimes referred to as *chromatic difference of magnification.*

**4.50. Other Aberrations.** The first six of the above aberrations are the so-called *Seidel,* or *primary,* or *third-order aberrations,* since they may be expressed in analytic form in terms of the third order in the parameters of aperture and field of view. When higher-order terms are included, there are many more possible combinations, and some of these have been identified by names. There are also, of course, variations of all of the geometrical aberrations with the wavelength of the light for refracting systems.

In most cases, these higher-order aberrations are smaller in magnitude than the third-order terms and are much more difficult to compute analytically, so that their discussion in terms of specific nomenclature is not usually found.

## PUPILS AND APERTURES

**4.51. General.** One of the most important aspects of optical instrument design is the location and treatment of pupils and apertures; this subject is all too often treated scantily or not at all in textbooks. Achievement of appropriate pupil conditions is fully as important in the design of a satisfactory optical instrument as the location and quality of images, and the selection of aperture parameters can have a profound effect on instrument performance.

**4.52. Definitions.** The *aperture* of an optical system is defined as the diameter (in object space) of the largest bundle of light which can traverse the system. An optical instrument consists, usually, of a series of components located at various points along a common axis. It may be assumed at this point that these components are circular, and they may differ in size. Also, there may be diaphrams or other non-optical parts which restrict the size of light bundles, for example, the mechanical cells which hold lenses.

Figure 4.39(a) shows a single lens with conjugate object and image, and the light bundles arising from the axial object point and from a point at a distance from the axis. In this case, the diameter of the lens itself furnishes the restriction, and this is thus the *aperture stop* of the "system."

In Figure 4.39(b), a diaphragm has been placed in front of the lens. This diaphragm is now the effective aperture and determines the size of the light bundles admitted. In this figure, the diaphragm has been made equal in size to the lens of (a). In order to admit the bundles which are admitted by the diaphragm, the lens of (b) has to be larger.

Something else has also occurred. In (a), the light bundle from the object point A passed symmetrically through the lens, as did the axial bundle. In (b), the extra-axial bundle is highly unsymmetrical with respect to the axial bundle. It is clear that the task of designing the lens of (b) to give good image quality is different from that presented by the lens of (a). It may be more or less difficult, depending upon circumstances, but it is definitely different.

In Figure 4.39 (c), the diaphragm is located behind the lens. Again, the

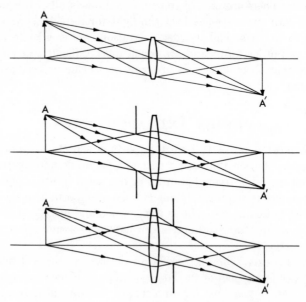

FIGURE 4.39. Effect of a diaphragm on the paths of rays through a lens.

lens required is larger than in (a) and the design task is again different from either of the two previous examples.

Now, in an optical system consisting of a number of separated components, each component acts as an aperture stop with respect to the other components. Figure 4.40 shows the system of an erecting telescope, with the objective acting as aperture stop for the system. It is seen that the oblique light bundles present a different pattern at each lens in the system.

**4.53. Principal Rays.** The ray from an extra-axial object point which passes through the center of the aperture stop is known as the *principal ray* of the oblique pencil. The nominal location of a conjugate image point will be on the principal ray, and deviations of other rays from this point are the aberrations of oblique pencils.

**4.54. Pupils.** In any optical system, consisting of a series of separated components (and possibly diaphragms as well), there will be some component or diaphragm which produces maximum restriction of the light bundles (for a given object point)—this, whether it be an optical component, a diaphragm, or some other mechanical part, is the *aperture stop* of the system.

Consider the simple telescope of Figure 4.41, in which a diaphragm has been inserted, of a size to make it the effective system aperture stop. This does not necessarily represent an actual system, but is presented for illustration only.

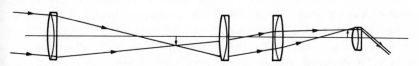

FIGURE 4.40. Path of the ray bundle for an off-axis point in an erecting telescope in which the objective acts as aperture stop.

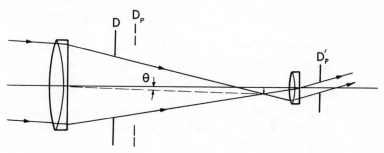

FIGURE 4.41. Entrance and exit pupils in a simple telescope.

Now, the objective will form an image of this diaphragm, D, at $D_p$ in the object space, and the eyepiece will form an image of it at $D_p'$ in image space. These images, $D_p$ and $D_p'$ are called, respectively, the *entrance pupil* and the *exit pupil* of the optical system.

Any system, however complex, will have some effective *aperture stop*, for a specific object point. This aperture stop will have images in object and image space, formed by the components in front of and behind it, and these images are the system *pupils*.

Intermediate images of the aperture stop which may be formed between entrance and exit pupils are also generally referred to as *pupils*.

**4.55. Vignetting.** In general, the effective aperture stop is different for different angles off-axis; this occurs in the optical system of Figure 4.41 when the angle off axis is greater than $\theta$; for these greater angles, the objective itself begins to restrict the light bundle.

This condition of encroachment upon the light bundles defined by the aperture stop, which sets in at a particular field angle, is known as *vignetting*. It is a common occurrence in optical instruments and is not a defect in design. To eliminate it would either increase the required sizes of the components or reduce the available field of view without any significant gain in performance. The effect of vignetting is to reduce the illumination of image points near the edge of the field of view, which is usually not objectionable. There are cases, however, where it is unacceptable, and such instruments must be designed to eliminate it.

**4.56. The Double Nature of an Optical System.** Every optical system is really two. One system forms a series of images of the object; the other system forms a series of images of the aperture stop. Both systems, of course, consist of the same collection of elements, which therefore have to be designed with both functions in mind. Often they are of equal importance to the designer.

Figure 4.42 shows the two optical systems which represent an erecting telescope. Figure 4.42(a) is the system which forms the images of the field of view; Figure 4.42(b) is the system which forms the images of the aperture stop.

In a visual instrument, the exit pupil is the point where the observer places his eye. In a scope for a high-power rifle, for example, it is important that the exit pupil be located sufficiently far behind the instrument to avoid possible injury from recoil, and also that it be large enough so that a person can place his eye within it quickly. In a binocular, it is important that the exit pupil be located so that the brows can be used as a steady rest for the instrument.

In wide-angle camera lenses, good performance is achieved only by

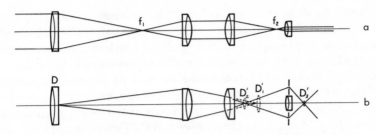

FIGURE 4.42. The two optical systems of an erecting telescope: (a) the imaging system, (b) The pupil-forming system.

locating the aperture stop more or less centrally within the lens. There are innumerable instances where proper location and sizing of pupils is of major concern. Pupils are subject to aberrations, just as images of objects are, and control of pupil aberrations may be just as important as control of image aberrations—usually the aberrations which are important in the case of pupils are different from those which are important in the case of field images.

**4.57. Reciprocal Relations.** There is a sort of reciprocal relation between pupils and images of the field of view. For example, a lens located in a pupil has no first-order effect on pupil imagery, but it has a maximum effect on field imagery. Conversely, a lens located in a field image has no first-order effect on the field imagery, but it has a maximum effect on pupil imagery. Lenses of the latter type, called *field lenses*, are often used to control pupil locations. Their second-order effects are also often used to advantage to shape the focal surfaces.

There is also a reciprocal relation between the aberrations of pupils and those of field images. For example, distortion in the field image shows up as spherical aberration of the pupils. It will be noted that the rays which form the axial image points of the pupils are the principal rays of the oblique pencils of the field images.

## OPTICAL INSTRUMENTS

**4.58. Basic Optical Instrument Parameters.** Optical instruments are described in terms of certain basic parameters, or characteristics, such as focal length, magnification, field of view, pupils, depth of field and relative aperture or speed. Some of these parameters have been discussed above; the definitions and meanings of these and those which have not previously been discussed are developed below.

**4.59. Focal Length.** In an instrument whose function is to form a real (or virtual) image of an object, either distant or close at hand, the fundamental parameter is focal length. This applies to camera objectives, projection lenses, simple magnifiers, and the like. Focal length has been defined above, and it has been shown that a combination of optical elements has a definite focal length, which is the distance from the image of an infinitely distant object to the second principal plane of the system.

This distance is often referred to specifically as the *equivalent focal length*, or *effective focal length*, or simply *efl*, since it is the focal length of the equivalent thin lens which would produce an image of the same size at the same place. Terms such as *back focal length* or *flange focal length* are often found; the first refers to the distance from the last lens surface to the focal plane, and the second to the distance from the mounting flange (usually of a microscope or camera objective) to the image plane.

Even though all optical systems are not utilized to form images of objects at infinity, the term *focal length* correctly refers to the focal length for an infinite object. Sometimes it is specifically identified by the term *principal focal length*.

It is evident that the focal length of an optical system determines the size of the image which is formed. In a camera objective, for example, the focal length establishes the scale of the image which is recorded on the film. A longer focal length gives a larger scale; for this reason, lenses which are intended for the photography of distant objects at an enlarged scale are lenses of long focal length. These are the well-known *telephoto lenses*, for providing close-up pictures of distant objects. The term telephoto refers, not to the focal length itself, but to a particular form of lens whose physical length is short with respect to its focal length; it is described below.

Unless lenses of special form, such as the telephoto form, are used, the space which must be provided for an optical system is, to a first approximation, equal in length to the focal length plus the axial thickness of the system itself from the first element to the second principal plane. This is illustrated in Figure 4.43 for a typical camera objective. Consequently, choice of a long focal length inevitably leads to large (and therefore expensive) lenses.

**4.60. Relative Aperture.** One of the most significant parameters of an optical system is its *relative aperture*, or *speed;* this is of particular consequence in connection with photographic lenses, but it is also significant in other types of instrument.

The relative aperture is defined as the ratio of the focal length to the entrance pupil diameter $(f/D)$ and is usually identified by the symbol $f/(f/D)$. Hence, a lens whose focal length is six inches and whose entrance pupil diameter is 3 inches is referred to as an $f/2$ lens. An $f/1$ lens (whose

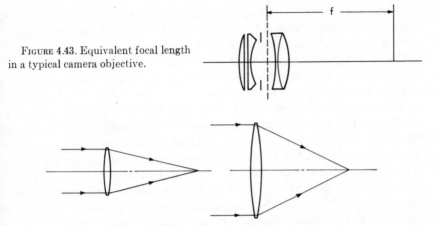

FIGURE 4.43. Equivalent focal length in a typical camera objective.

FIGURE 4.44. Relative aperture. The two lenses shown have the same focal length, but the one on the left has a relative aperture of $f/2$, and that on the right $f/1$. The difference in size is evident.

exit pupil would be 6 inches in diameter for a 6-inch focal length) has a *larger* relative aperture (twice as large) than the $f/2$ lens, and a *higher* speed.

Consider the two cases shown in Figure 4.44—a simple objective lens with a relative aperture of $f/2$, and another of relative aperture $f/1$, both of the same focal length. It is evident that the $f/1$ lens collects four times as much light from a given area of the object as does the $f/2$ lens, since the amount of light collected is proportional to the *area* of the entrance pupil. If both lenses are of the same focal length, then the image of the object area is the same for both, hence the image for the $f/1$ lens has four times the illumination. Thus it is seen that the relative aperture determines the image illumination; in the case of a camera lens, the relative aperture will therefore determine the exposure time required for a given object brightness, and hence the synonym "speed," which is often used in connection with camera lenses.

Camera lenses are customarily designated by focal length and relative aperture; thus, 50 mm, $f/2$; 25 mm, $f/1.5$; 3-inch, $f/4.5$, etc., are common camera lens designations. These designations refer to the largest relative aperture available in the lens; an iris diaphragm to reduce the entrance pupil diameter is ordinarily provided, and the control for this diaphragm is marked with the relative aperture corresponding to a given position. The first lens of the above example, for instance, would probably have diaphragm positions marked $f/2$, $f/2.8$, $f/4$, $f/5.6$, $f/8$, $f/11$, $f/16$, and perhaps $f/22$. Each step produces a decrease in the relative aperture by a factor of

$\sqrt{2}$; therefore, since the required exposure is inversely proportional to the *square* of the relative aperture, each step in the diaphragm position requires a change in the exposure by a factor of 2.

One might ask why, since variable exposure times are also available on most cameras, it is necessary to provide an independent control of the relative aperture. Part of the reason is found in the depth of field provided at different relative apertures, as discussed below (Section 6.20), and part of the reason is the performance of the lens at various settings. Most camera lenses give the best image quality at a relative aperture considerably less than the greatest of which they are capable. Thus, a lens which has an $f/2$ capability may give its best image at a setting of $f/4$, or even $f/8$. It is therefore desirable to use it at its optimum performance aperture whenever possible, using the greater aperture only when light conditions demand it. This is not always the case, however; some forms of lenses actually give their maximum image quality at the maximum relative aperture. Moreover, the provision of both aperture and exposure control gives a much wider range of settings to meet variable light conditions and film sensitivities than would be possible with either alone.

While some lenses give their best performance at maximum aperture, only an extremely poor lens will give its best performance at a very small aperture (such as $f/22$) because for very small apertures, the limit to image quality imposed by diffraction becomes a significant factor.

**4.61. Magnification.** An important factor in many optical instruments is the *magnification*. Two types of magnification have been defined above: *linear magnification*, which is the ratio of size of object and image, and *angular magnification*, which is the ratio of the *apparent* (angular) size of object and image. For distant objects, the concept of linear magnification becomes meaningless, and angular magnification becomes the significant measure.

Linear magnification is of importance in such optical instruments as projectors, enlargers, copying cameras and comparators. The linear magnification is established by the focal length and the object distance, in accordance with the image equation [Equation (4.50)]. Figure 4.45 shows how an optical system (represented by a single lens) of a given focal length may be used to produce various values of linear magnification by changing the object distance.

Most optical instruments of the types referred to above have provision for working over a considerable range of linear magnification by changes in the object distance; thus a slide or motion picture projector may be made to give various magnifications by changing its distance from the projec-

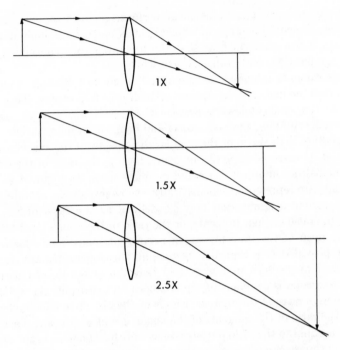

1X

1.5X

2.5X

FIGURE 4.45. Change in linear magnification resulting from a change in object distance.

tion screen and adjusting the distance from slide or film to lens to bring it into sharp focus.

The range of magnification available with a given system is always limited, because the quality of the lens performance cannot be maintained over a very wide range of object distances, and also because, in systems such as projectors, greater magnification requires more illumination (proportional to the square of the magnification). In systems intended to provide reduced-scale images, such as copying cameras, more illumination is required as the ratio of object size to image size becomes smaller. In such instruments, however, the magnification is usually quoted as a fractional number, so that the same rule holds—the greater the magnification, the more illumination is required.

Occasionally, *vari-focus*, or *"zoom"* lenses are provided in such instruments; these lenses, by means of internal movement of the components with respect to each other, can be changed in effective focal length and thus vary the linear magnification without the necessity for a change in the object or image positions. Such lenses are complex and expensive and usually do not give as good an image performance as a conventional lens; moreover, their useful range of adjustment is much more limited, so that it is only in the unusual case that the advantage of maintaining object and image positions makes them worth while.

In instruments intended for visual use, such as telescopes and micro-scopes, it is the *angular* magnification which is of importance. This is illus-trated in the simple telescope system of Figure 4.46. In a telescope, the focal length is infinite, and both object and image lie at infinity. The angular magnification is the ratio of the angular distance from the axis of an image point and its corresponding object point, that is, the ratio of the angles of the principal ray in object space and in image space. In Figure 4.46, object and image are represented schematically—they actually lie at infinity.

The angular magnification may be defined as the ratio of the actual angles, the ratio of their tangents, or the ratio of their sines. In a telescope, it is the ratio of the tangents which is conventionally used—for the field of view provided in a typical telescope, all three measures are essentially equal. It may be seen in Figure 4.46 that the image formed within the simple telescope is common to the triangles formed by it, the optical axis and the rays passing through the center of the objective and the eyepiece. Hence the ratio of the tangents of the angles $\phi$ and $\phi'$ (the angular magnifi-cation) is equal to the ratio of the distances of this image from the objective and the eyepiece. In a telescope, these distances are the focal lengths of the respective elements, so that the angular magnification of a telescope is given very simply by

$$M_A = \tan \phi'/\tan \phi = f_o/f_e \qquad (4.76)$$

where $f_o$ is the focal length of the objective, and $f_e$ the focal length of the eyepiece.

**4.62. Magnification of a Simple Magnifier.** In a simple magnifier, the purpose is to form an enlarged image of an object which is relatively close at hand; the measure of magnification is the angular magnification,

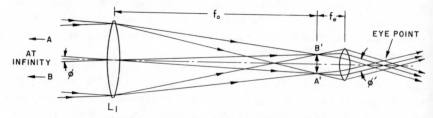

FIGURE 4.46. Angular magnification in a telescope.

because the image is formed at a considerable distance (nominally infinity), but the measure is specified differently than for a telescope, where both object and image are distant.

In a magnifier, the magnification is the ratio of the apparent size of the image to the apparent size of the object viewed from a standard distance. This standard distance is taken to be the near-point of the human eye— the closest object distance at which the eye can be sharply focused. For a young adult, this distance is about 10 inches, so that the standard reference distance for a magnifier is 10 inches, or 250 mm.

Figure 4.47 shows a simple magnifier under two conditions of use. The magnifier may be placed at various distances from the object under examination, and each distance will provide an image whose size depends upon the position of the lens. The magnification provided when the object is placed at the principal focus of the magnifier is shown in Figure 4.47(b).

The angular size of the image is, under this condition, the apparent size as seen from a distance $f$, where $f$ is the focal length of the magnifier. The angular size of the object is the apparent size as seen from the reference distance of 10 inches; hence the angular magnification of the magnifier is simply

$$M_A = 10/f \tag{4.77}$$

when $f$ is expressed in inches.

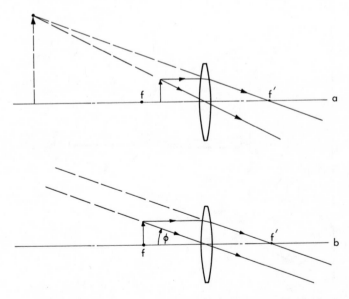

FIGURE 4.47. Angular magnification in the simple magnifier.

**4.63. Magnification of a Compound Microscope.** A compound microscope comprises an objective and an eyepiece, as shown in Figure 4.48. The objective forms a real image of the object in the focal plane of the eyepiece, by means of which an infinitely distant image is viewed by the eye. It is evident from the figure that the angular magnification of a compound microscope is given by

$$M_A = M_o M_e \tag{4.78}$$

where $M_o$ is the linear magnification produced by the objective between object and internal image plane, and $M_e$ is the magnification of the eyepiece considered as a simple magnifier in accordance with Equation (4.77) above.

Compound microscopes are commonly manufactured with a standard distance from objective to internal image plane (160 mm for most American manufacturers), so that the linear magnification provided by the objective is strictly dependent upon the objective focal length.

It is customary to identify microscope objectives and eyepieces by their magnification, so that the magnification of the instrument is simply their product. These are linear magnification at standard tube length for the objectives, and angular magnification for the eyepiece considered as a simple magnifier. Compound microscopes are usually provided with inter-

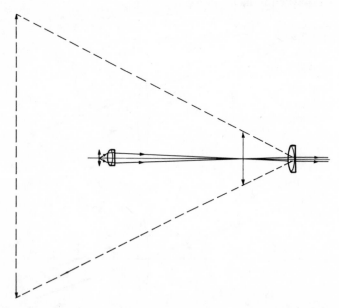

FIGURE 4.48. Angular magnification in the compound microscope.

changeable objectives and eyepieces, so that various combinations may be used to give different magnifications.

**4.64. Relation of Pupils to Magnification in a Telescope.** Consider the simple telescope of Figure 4.49. A light beam parallel to the axis of diameter $D$ will come to a focus on the axis in the internal focal plane, and the bundle will expand until it meets the eyepiece lens, from which it will emerge as a bundle parallel to the axis again (infinite image point) but now of diameter $D'$. It is easy to see that the ratio $D/D'$ is equal to the ratio of the focal lengths of objective and eyepiece, $f_o/f_e$. However, this ratio was established in Equation (4.76) as representing the angular magnification of the telescope.

Now, if the extreme rays of the entrance bundle coincide with the edge of the entrance pupil, as shown in the figure, then these rays will also coincide with the edge of the exit pupil, since the latter is an image of the first, and thus it is shown that the relation

$$M_A = f_o/f_e = \frac{D}{D'} \qquad (4.79)$$

holds, where $D$ and $D'$ are the diameters of the entrance and exit pupils, respectively.

This relation between the pupil diameters and the magnification of a telescope leads to several important conclusions, as will be discussed under the section dealing with telescopes. It can also be shown, although not quite so simply, that this relation holds for the angular magnification of any optical system.

**4.65. Effective Relative Aperture and Linear Magnification.** The relative aperture of an optical system was defined in Section 4.60 as the ratio of focal length to diameter. The *effective relative aperture* of an optical system which produces an image at a distance different from the principal focal length is the ratio of this distance to the diameter. In Figure 4.50, a lens of diameter 2 inches forms an image of an object 3 inches away at an image distance of 6 inches, to produce a linear magnification of 2X. The principal focal length of the lens is 2 inches, and therefore its nominal relative aperture is $f/1$.

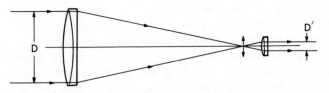

Figure 4.49. Relation of pupils and magnification in a telescope.

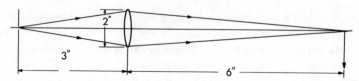

FIGURE 4.50. Effective relative apertures.

The effective relative aperture on the object side is $f/1.5$ $(3/2)$, and the effective relative aperture on the image side is $f/3$ $(6/2)$. It is seen that the ratio of the relative effective apertures is equal to the linear magnification. This relation imposes some important restrictions in practical optical designs.

## FUNDAMENTAL FORMS OF OPTICAL SYSTEMS

**4.66. The Functions of an Optical System.** All optical systems may be placed in two distinct categories—systems whose function it is to produce linear magnification and systems whose function it is to produce angular magnification. Systems in the first category are equivalent in fundamental properties to a single thin lens; those in the second category are equivalent to a combination of two thin lenses. The actual systems are often quite complex.

**4.67. Linear Magnification Systems.** Systems in the first category are those whose function it is to provide an image of a selected object. They are equivalent to a single thin lens, and have two fundamental parameters: *focal length* and *relative aperture*. They may be divided into three classes—*objectives*, *relays* and *magnifiers*. These three classes are illustrated in Figure 4.51, in terms of the equivalent thin lens.

The lens in Figure 4.51(a) is being used as an *objective*—to form a real image of a distant object. The typical application of this use is the camera.

In Figure 4.51(b), the lens is being used as an *optical relay*—to transfer and/or magnify an object by imaging it at a different place and/or a different distance. The typical application is a projector.

In Figure 4.51(c), the lens is used as a *magnifier*—to form a virtual image (nominally at infinity) of a close object. This application is the reverse of the objective; the typical example is the simple magnifier itself.

The three classes are not distinct and separate; rather they represent the end and intermediate points of a continuous series, in which the linear magnification varies from zero (for the objective), through increasing negative values, to infinity (for the magnifier). They may also be considered as a series representing a single lens with the object distance varying

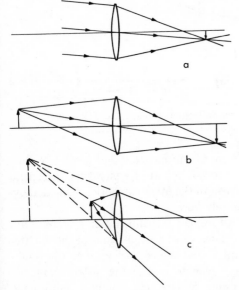

FIGURE 4.51. Linear magnification optical systems: (a) objective, (b) optical relay, (c) magnifier.

from $-\infty$ (for the objective), through decreasing negative values, to $-f$ (for the magnifier). The corresponding image distances vary from $f'$ to $\infty$.

The series represented by object distances from $-f$ to $\infty$ are not found in general application, except as components of systems which conform to the other classifications discussed here, hence they cannot be assigned distinctive names.

**4.68. Angular Magnification Systems.** Systems in the second category are those whose function it is to provide angular magnification of a selected object. They are equivalent to a combination of two thin lenses and have the single fundamental parameter of magnification. They result from the combination of the simple magnifier with either an objective or a relay, and thus are of two classes only—*telescopes* and *compound microscopes*. These are shown in Figure 4.52.

Methods for establishing the angular magnification for both of these systems have been developed above.

These classes, too, form a continuous series rather than being absolutely distinct. A rifle scope, for instance, is classed as a telescope, although often the objects upon which it is used are not infinitely far away. Visual observation instruments are sometimes found where the object distance is of the order of 20 to 40 inches; it would be difficult to decide whether such an instrument should be called a telescope or a microscope, but it quite

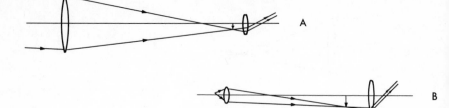

FIGURE 4.52. Angular magnification systems: (A) telescope, (B) compound microscope.

definitely belongs in the series. There are, of course, other possible combinations of two thin lenses; these are not found in general use except as components of systems which conform to the other categories defined above and hence are not classified separately here.

**4.69. Optical Instruments.** All optical instruments or systems have the form of one of the above five classes, or of combinations of them. Often the actual systems are quite complex, and the conformance to the fundamental system form is not always easy to find. Some instruments, like spectrometers, interferometers, range finders, etc., employ non-image-forming components, such as prisms and gratings to accomplish their unique purposes, and the above categorization takes no account of these elements. The instruments, however, also contain image-forming components, and may be classified as systems of conventional type whose light beams are acted upon in specific ways by the non-image-forming components.

## ABERRATIONS

**4.70. Chromatic Aberration—General.** Chromatic aberration is the difference in focal length resulting from the difference in wavelength of light. The refractive index of optical materials varies with the wavelength, the index being greater for the shorter wavelengths. As a result, the focal length is greater the longer the wavelength. As shown in Figure 4.53, *longitudinal chromatic aberration* is defined as the longitudinal difference in intersection lengths for two specific wavelengths—it is positive if the intersection length for the longer wavelength lies to the right of the other, according to the conventions adopted previously. The figure shows how the difference in index affects the path of the rays in a thick lens.

**4.71. Characteristics of Optical Glass.** Catalogs of optical glass list the indices of the various glasses for different wavelengths of light. By

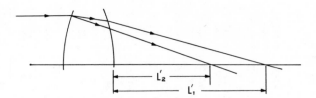

FIGURE 4.53. Longitudinal chromatic aberration.

convention, certain specific spectral lines are selected for catalog listing, the most common being the D-line of sodium, the F and C lines of hydrogen, and the G′ line of hydrogen, the nomenclature being that first adopted by Fraunhofer[4] for the solar spectrum.

The D-line is a bright yellow double line, characteristic of the sodium spectrum; the F-line is a red line and the C-line is a blue line. G′ is a deep blue. Table 4.1 shows a typical listing of optical glasses from a current manufacturer's catalog.

*The V-value.* The differences in the refractive indices for two specific wavelengths is the *dispersion* of the glass. A quantity obtained by the solution of the expression

$$\frac{\mu_D - 1}{\mu_F - \mu_C}$$

is called the V-value, and is of great value in selecting glasses to obtain correction for chromatic aberration. It is an inverse measure of the relative dispersion of the glass in question. The V-values for common optical glasses range from nearly 100 for low-dispersion crown glass to 30 or less for very high dispersion flints.

**4.72. Chromatic Aberration for a Single Surface.** For a single refracting surface of radius $r$ bounding a medium of index $\mu$, the intersection length for incident parallel light is, from Equation (4.45)

$$\ell' = \mu r/(\mu - 1) \tag{4.80}$$

therefore, for two wavelengths, with corresponding indices $\mu_C$ and $\mu_F$, the difference in intersection lengths will be

$$\ell'_C - \ell'_F = \frac{\mu_C r}{\mu_C - 1} - \frac{\mu_F r}{\mu_F - 1} \tag{4.81}$$

which reduces to

$$\ell'_C - \ell'_F = \frac{\mu_F - \mu_C}{(\mu_C - 1)(\mu_F - 1)} \tag{4.82}$$

Since the index for the D-line is nearly midway between $\mu_F$ and $\mu_C$,

TABLE 4.1. Optical Glass Listings*

| Mfr. Des. | Type | 5893 $\mu_D$ | $V_D$ | 5461 $\mu_e$ | $V_e$ | $\mu_F$-$\mu_c$ | 7682 $\mu_{AV}$ / $\frac{\mu_c - \mu_{A'}}{\mu_F - \mu_c}$ | 6563 $\mu_c$ / $\frac{\mu_e - \mu_c}{\mu_F - \mu_c}$ | 5876 $\mu_d$ / $\frac{\mu_e - \mu_d}{\mu_F - \mu_c}$ | 4861 $\mu_F$ / $\frac{\mu_F - \mu_e}{\mu_F - \mu_c}$ | 4358 $\mu_g$ / $\frac{\mu_g - \mu_F}{\mu_F - \mu_c}$ |
|---|---|---|---|---|---|---|---|---|---|---|---|
| FK-1 | 471672 | 1.47062 | 67.24 | 1.47236 | 67.10 | .00700 | 1.46600 / .4077 | 1.46853 / .5471 | 1.47069 / .2372 | 1.47553 / .4529 | 1.47926 / .5329 |
| BK-1 | 510634 | 1.51002 | 63.37 | 1.51201 | 63.13 | .00805 | 1.50477 / .3995 | 1.50762 / .5463 | 1.51009 / .2367 | 1.51567 / .4547 | 1.51999 / .5373 |
| BK-6 | 531620 | 1.53106 | 62.04 | 1.53318 | 61.85 | .00856 | 1.52551 / .3979 | 1.52852 / .5444 | 1.53113 / .2378 | 1.53708 / .4556 | 1.54167 / .5368 |
| K-2 | 516568 | 1.51593 | 56.77 | 1.51817 | 56.57 | .00909 | 1.51013 / .3886 | 1.51325 / .5413 | 1.51602 / .2347 | 1.52234 / .4587 | 1.52731 / .5468 |
| BaK-2 | 540597 | 1.53988 | 59.66 | 1.54211 | 59.44 | .00905 | 1.53407 / .3914 | 1.53720 / .5425 | 1.53996 / .2357 | 1.54625 / .4575 | 1.55119 / .5457 |
| BaLF-1 | 562509 | 1.56239 | 50.90 | 1.56511 | 50.64 | .01105 | 1.55546 / .3790 | 1.55916 / .5385 | 1.56248 / .2357 | 1.57021 / .4615 | 1.57638 / .5584 |
| BaF-7 | 608462 | 1.60790 | 46.20 | 1.61114 | 45.92 | .01316 | 1.59976 / .3719 | 1.60409 / .5357 | 1.60801 / .2352 | 1.61725 / .4643 | 1.62470 / .5661 |
| F-2 | 620363 | 1.61992 | 36.34 | 1.62410 | 36.10 | .01706 | 1.60959 / .3609 | 1.61504 / .5311 | 1.62004 / .2348 | 1.63210 / .4689 | 1.64206 / .5835 |
| LaK-8 | 713539 | 1.71288 | 53.89 | 1.71615 | 53.68 | .01323 | 1.70439 / .3922 | 1.70897 / .5426 | 1.71300 / .2365 | 1.72220 / .4574 | 1.72940 / .5442 |
| SF-6 | 805255 | 1.80489 | 25.46 | 1.81262 | 25.28 | .03163 | 1.78646 / .3438 | 1.79608 / .5229 | 1.80518 / .2315 | 1.82771 / .4771 | 1.84701 / .6102 |
| SFS-1 | 917214 | 1.91726 | 21.37 | 1.92771 | 21.21 | .04293 | 1.89270 / .3347 | 1.90544 / .5187 | 1.91761 / .2310 | 1.94837 / .4812 | 1.97527 / .6266 |

* The above data has been selected from a current optical glass catalog. Most catalogs list refractive index values for a number of other wavelengths, and the list of available glasses is, of course, much more extensive, including a number of items under each of the varieties shown above. The first column is the manufacturer's designation; the second column is a listing by a number made up of the first three digits of the refractive index for the D-line, and the V-value for the D-line (combined with F and C); this type designation is in common use in the industry, and provides an identification which is independent of the particular manufacturer. The numbers listed at the top of the index columns is the wavelength in angstroms.

there is very little error in substituting $(\mu_D - 1)^2$ for the denominator of Equation (4.82), and this yields

$$\ell'_C - \ell'_F = \frac{r}{(\mu_D - 1)V} \tag{4.83}$$

which indicates the usefulness of the $V$-value for estimating chromatic aberration.

**4.73. Chromatic Aberration of a Thin Lens.** Using the equations which have been derived above for the focal length of a thin lens, it may be shown that the chromatic aberration of such a lens, for light incident from infinity, is given by

$$\ell'_C - \ell'_F = f'_D/V \tag{4.84}$$

where $f_D$ is the focal length for the D-line.

**4.74. Achromatism.** Equation (4.84) shows that, even for glasses of the highest practicable $V$-values, the chromatic aberration of even a thin lens amounts to at least 1 per cent of the focal length. For object points nearer than infinity, the aberration becomes even greater. Such a discrepancy would make it impossible to obtain any kind of satisfactory imagery for light over a reasonable spectral range. In the days when there were very few types of optical glass available, and the fact that a considerable range of $V$-values was in fact attainable was not known, it was thought that this was an insuperable obstacle to the manufacture of satisfactory refracting systems, and led (fortunately, perhaps) to the development of mirror systems.

However, if two glasses are selected with different $V$-values, it can be shown (assuming they are two thin lenses in contact) that the chromatic aberration becomes zero when

$$\frac{f_1}{f_2} = -\frac{V_2}{V_1} \tag{4.85}$$

and if the glasses are selected so as to have a considerable difference of $V$-values, the ratio $f_1/f_2$ will be of the order of 3. The lens with the higher $V$-value determines the sign of the focal length of the combination, the other lens being of the opposite curvature. Thus, for a positive combination, the positive lens will have a $V$-value of, say, 90, and it will be combined with a negative lens with a $V$-value of, say, 30, so that $f_2 = -3f_1$, and the focal length of the combination is given by $1/f = 1/f_1 + 1/f_2$, and therefore $f = 3f_1/2$.

Such a lens is called an *achromat*. In an actual lens, the two elements are

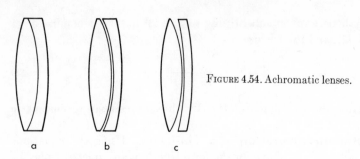

FIGURE 4.54. Achromatic lenses.

a      b      c

usually in contact, or nearly so, and are often cemented together. Figure 4.54 shows several common forms of achromats.

**4.75. Secondary Spectrum.** Equation (4.85) above gives an approximate solution for eliminating the chromatic aberration of two specific wavelengths of light. For an actual lens combination, it is clear that some small adjustments could be made to the focal lengths so that any two specific wavelengths of light could be brought to a common focus, for any selected object distance that the situation might require. When this is done, the combination is said to be *achromatic*.

It is also evident that any wavelengths which are different from the two colors which were selected for achromatization will not come to the achromatic focus, and that for a finite continuous spread of wavelengths in the incident light, there will be a spread along the axis in the neighborhood of the achromatic point where the two selected wavelengths come to a common focus.

This spread is called the *secondary spectrum*. The spread is small with respect to the chromatic aberration of a single lens, and in many instances, it is small enough to be ignored. In more demanding situations, however, it, too, must be corrected, and this can only be accomplished by adding more elements to the system, and usually by using more than two types of glass or other optical material in the system.

**4.76. Chromatic Aberration at Finite Aperture.** The above discussion has been in terms of the *paraxial* region of lenses; when finite apertures are taken into account, there is a further variation of chromatic aberration with the aperture. In general, this is small with respect to the aberration of a single lens on axis. It is a general rule of thumb that the residual chromatic aberration (to be distinguished from secondary spectrum) resulting from a finite aperture is at a minimum when the achromatic condition is established for a circular zone about the axis at a height equal to .7071 of the entrance pupil radius.

**4.77. Minimum Focal Length.** Based upon the known capabilities of the human eye, it is possible to establish tolerances on the amount of chromatic aberration which is acceptable. Using generally accepted assumptions, it is found that the minimum focal length for a single lens is

$$f'_{\text{min.}} = 100 \ D^2 \tag{4.86}$$

where $D$ is the entrance pupil diameter; both $f'$ and $D$ are measured in inches, and a glass of low $V$-value is assumed. For an achromat, only the secondary spectrum limits the focal length, and for an ordinary achromat, it is found that

$$f'_{\text{min.}} = 5 \ D^2 \tag{4.87}$$

It is this limitation which demands that astronomical telescopes, which must have excellent image quality, must have a focal ratio of the order of $f/15$ if the secondary spectrum is to be insignificant. The larger refracting telescopes, like the 36-inch Lick and the 40-inch Yerkes, have only about $\frac{1}{10}$ the minimum focal length demanded by Equation (4.87); this means that they have a considerable secondary spectrum for the full visual range and, therefore, that only a relatively narrow portion of this spectrum is really useful in forming sharp images.

**4.78. Types of Achromatism.** The selection of the F and C spectral lines for establishing achromatism, as was done in the above discussion, creates a particular *type* of achromatism—in this case, *visual type*. If the focal length of an achromatic lens is plotted against the wavelength of the light in the spectrum, a parabolic curve is obtained, as shown in Figure 4.55. It is seen that the various wavelengths come to common foci in pairs.

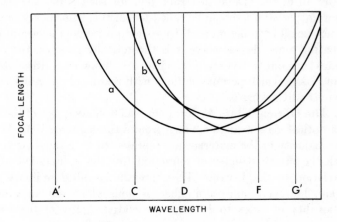

FIGURE 4.55. Typies of achromatism: (a) visual, (b) photo-visual, (c) photographic.

One of these pairs is that selected for the computation. There is a wavelength of minimum focus, midway between the two wavelengths for which achromatism is established. The choice of F and C gives a minimum focus approximately at the sodium D-line, which gives optimum results for visual instruments.

Two other types of achromatism are shown in the Figure—photovisual and photographic. Photovisual achromatism is chosen for those instruments which must be focused visually but which are actually photographic; photographic achromatism is usually established for the blue end of the spectrum, since it is in this region that maximum photographic sensitivity is obtained. There would be no value in using panchromatic emulsions with an *achromatic* lens—the secondary spectrum would not permit taking advantage of the broad spectral sensitivity of the emulsion.

The two wavelengths which are selected for establishing achromatism in a particular system, therefore, are selected to establish the wavelength of minimum focus—in this neighborhood, the secondary spectrum is a minimum.

**4.79. Apochromatism.** By using properly selected optical glasses, or other optical materials, it is, in general, possible to bring three wavelengths together at a common focus. A lens so corrected is termed an *apochromat*. The curve of focal length versus wavelength is a cubic parabola in the first approximation, so that within a fairly broad spectral region, the various wavelengths come to a common focus in groups of three, although at the extremes at both ends of the spectrum, the spread becomes very large. It is possible to design such lenses so that the region of correction covers essentially all of the visible spectrum, and for such lenses the secondary spectrum (or perhaps it should be called tertiary) is vanishingly small.

It is not possible to design such lenses with a random choice of glasses, and even for some glasses where it is theoretically possible, the required curvatures turn out to be excessive. There are, however, a reasonably wide choice of glasses which permit solutions with reasonable physical values of curvatures and thicknesses.

**4.80. The Optical Glass Array.** Figure 4.56 shows a plot of the various types of optical glass available, taken from a catalog *circa* 1963. It is seen that the majority of the materials are represented by a fairly narrow strip in which the principal index of refraction (for the sodium D-line) has a linear relation to the $V$-value. These are the so-called ordinary glasses. There are, however, quite a number of unusual glasses, in which this proportionality of index to $V$-value is violated. Many of these unusual glasses are of recent development, and to their availability can be credited many improvements in optical systems which have been made through

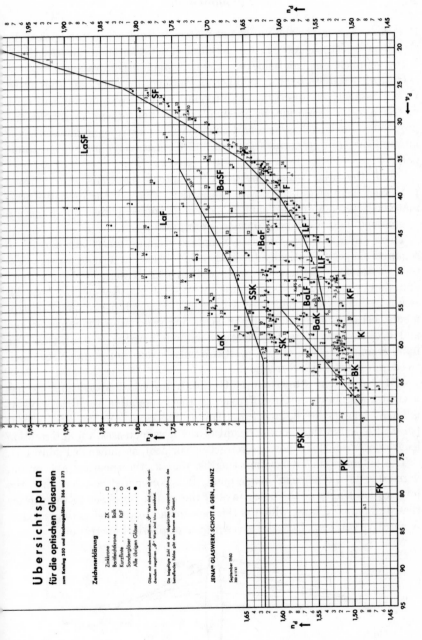

FIGURE 4.56. The optical glass array. The ordinate is the index of refraction for the sodium D-line; the abscissa is the V-value. The glasses are grouped in types; "K" meaning "crown", and "F" meaning "flint".

201

202 *Fundamentals*

the years. The larger the variety of materials from which the optical designer can select, the more he can accomplish in performance, or the greater is the simplicity he can achieve without degrading performance.

Optical designers have also taken advantage of many materials other than glass, such as fused quartz, sapphire, and many minerals and crystals, like sodium chloride, magnesium fluoride and others, to achieve improved results. This has been particularly true in instruments for use in the infrared spectrum, for which most ordinary glasses have little or no transparency.

Often, the price which one pays for optical materials with unusual properties is great difficulty with fabrication. Many of the most desirable materials are soft and difficult to polish to optical perfection; some are hygroscopic and must be protected from moisture.

There are also a few varieties of optical plastics, which are molded to required shapes in optically finished molds. These were used to some extent in wartime instruments, when optical glasses were in short supply, and they are frequently used now in low-cost and low-performance instruments. They are not very satisfactory for high-performance instruments, because of the difficulty of achieving adequate surface perfection, and because they cannot be cleaned without marring the surfaces. The number and variety of optical plastics available does not permit very much freedom in chromatic correction.

**4.81. Spherical Aberration—General.** Spherical aberration, as has been defined above, is the difference in the intersection length of rays at different heights in the aperture. Taking the rays from an axial object point, it is found that, as the height of the rays increases, the intersection length decreases (for a positive refracting surface), as shown in Figure 4.57.

The difference in intersection lengths, that is, the spherical aberration, is referred to the *paraxial* image point. It is considered positive when the intersection length of the outer rays of the bundle lie closer to the surface than the paraxial rays, which is the case for a positive refracting surface. A negative surface, of course, gives negative spherical aberration.

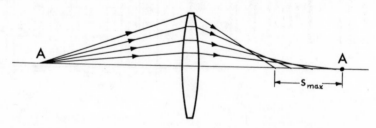

FIGURE 4.57. Longitudinal spherical aberration in a positive lens.

The means for correcting spherical aberration, therefore, is the judicious combination of positive and negative surfaces so distributed that the net effect on the spherical aberration is not cancelled out by the net effect on the system focal length.

**4.82. Exact Equation for Spherical Aberration.** Referring to the fundamental equations [Equations (4.36) to (4.39)], these can be combined to give the expression[5]

$$\frac{\mu'}{L'} = \frac{\mu}{L} + \frac{\mu' - \mu}{r} + 2\frac{\mu(L-r)}{rL} \frac{\sin\left(\dfrac{I'-U}{2}\right)\sin\left(\dfrac{I-I'}{2}\right)}{\cos\left(\dfrac{I'-U'}{2}\right)} \tag{4.88}$$

for a single refracting surface. Discussion of this equation will reveal a number of interesting points.

The left-hand term and the first two terms on the right are exactly the same as Equation (4.44) for the paraxial case of a single surface. In Equation (4.88), however, no approximations were used. It follows, therefore, that the *spherical aberration*, being the difference between the paraxial intersection length and the intersection length for a ray with finite height in the aperture, is represented by the last term in Equation (4.88). There are some special cases for which this term vanishes and for which the spherical aberration is identically zero.

**4.83. The Aplanatic Conditions.** These cases for which there is no spherical aberration, are known as the *aplanatic conditions*, and the object and image points corresponding to them are the *aplanatic points* of a spherical refracting surface.

The first one is a trivial case. When $L = 0$, then $L' = 0$ also. The object point is at the pole of the refracting surface, and the image point is coincident with it.

There are two other cases, however. If $L = r$, then the last term in Equation (4.88) vanishes, and there is no spherical aberration. This corresponds to the case where the incident ray enters along a diameter of the refracting surface. For this case, also, the image point coincides with the object point, since there is no bending of the ray at the surface.

The only other case for which the last term of Equation (4.88) vanishes identically is when $\sin (I' - U) = 0$. It can be shown that this implies

$$L = r\frac{\mu' + \mu}{\mu} \qquad L' = r\frac{\mu' + \mu}{\mu'} \tag{4.89}$$

These are the *aplanatic points*. It will be seen that they both lie on the concave side of the surface. This condition also implies that

$$\frac{\sin U'}{\sin U} = \frac{\mu'}{\mu} \tag{4.90}$$

which is an expression of the optical sine condition, discussed in a following section.

Figure 4.58 shows how the aplanatic points of a spherical refracting surface may be graphically constructed. The existence of these points is utilized in the design of microscope objectives. While the aplanatic condition expressed above holds strictly only for the two specific points on the optical axis, actually the conditions of spherical correction are fairly closely held over reasonable object and image planes intersecting the optical axis at the aplanatic points.

**4.84. Primary Spherical Aberration.** The actual evaluation of spherical aberration by an expression like Equation (4.88) would never be carried out in practice. In order to obtain the quantities $I'$ and $U'$, a trigonometrical ray tracing has to be carried out; the spherical aberration can then be obtained by a simple subtraction from the results of a paraxial ray trace, the latter being easily performed. Optics is replete with situations like this, and therefore much attention has been paid to the simplification of computational effort by the development of approximate relations which may be used for computation to bring a design into a condition where only small further corrections are needed. Then recourse can be had to strict trigonometrical ray tracing, which is a relatively laborious task.

This procedure of doing the preliminary and most extensive computation with approximate relations was much more important in the days when the computations were done by hand with the aid of tables of logarithms and trigonometric functions, and even in the early decades of the present century, when optical computing was done mostly on desk calculators. Today, with electronic digital computers at his command, the optical

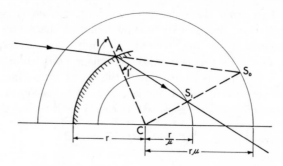

FIGURE 4.58. The aplanatic points of a spherical refracting surface.

designer does many hundreds of times more numerical calculations than before, and the value of approximate expressions has accordingly diminished. However, it has not been eliminated altogether.

If Equation (4.88) is reorganized somewhat, and the paraxial angle approximations are introduced, there results the rather simple expression

$$sph = \tfrac{1}{2} \ell' \, \frac{\ell' - r}{r} \, (i' - u) \, (i - i') \tag{4.91}$$

for whose evaluation only data obtained by a paraxial ray trace is required. This is termed *primary spherical aberration*, and it gives a sufficiently close approximation to the true spherical aberration of a finite surface to permit an optical design to proceed nearly to completion before resorting to strict trigonometrical ray traces.

The primary spherical aberration of a thin lens may be shown to be given by

$$sph = y^2 (a c_1^2 + b c_1 + d) \tag{4.92}$$

in which $y$ is the height of the ray in the aperture; $a$, $b$ and $d$ have definite numerical values which depend only on the focal length of the lens and the location of the object point; and $c_1$ is the curvature $(1/r_1)$ of the first surface of the lens, as previously defined.

**4.85. "Bending" a Lens.** It will be recalled that the focal length of a thin lens is proportional to the *difference* in the curvatures of the two surfaces $(c_1 - c_2)$ (see Section 4.20). It follows that one may alter the shape of a lens by transferring curvature from one surface to the other without altering its focal length. This operation is termed *bending* a lens. Figure 4.59 shows a number of different shapes for a lens of constant focal length.

Equation (4.92) contains only the curvature of the first surface, hence the spherical aberration of all of the lens forms shown in Figure 4.59 have different values for the spherical aberration for a given object point. The form of Equation (4.92) is a parabola, hence there will be a form for which the spherical aberration is a maximum or a minimum, and all other forms correspond to points on the parabola, which extends to plus or minus infinity as the case may be.

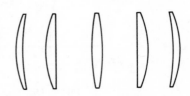

FIGURE 4.59. Bendings of a lens. All of the lenses shown have the same focal length, but different values of the spherical aberration.

This operation of *bending* a lens is the designer's method of introducing correction for spherical aberration. A single positive thin lens, for an object point at infinity, takes the form of a meniscus with the concave surface toward the object for the case of minimum spherical aberration.

**4.86. Higher-order Spherical Aberration.** Equation (4.92) for primary spherical aberration is proportional to the square of the height of the ray in the aperture. The total spherical aberration of a surface or a system may be expressed as an infinite series

$$sph = aY^2 + bY^4 + cY^6 + \text{etc.} \tag{4.93}$$

of which the first term is the primary spherical aberration defined above. Only even-powered terms appear because the equation must be symmetrical in $Y$, as is the assumed centered optical system. The second and higher terms in the equation are referred to as higher-order spherical aberration. Analytical methods for computing the aberration corresponding to the second term have been developed, but they are not commonly in use in optical design. It is customary to compute the primary spherical aberration and then to make a strict ray trace and describe the difference between the two results as "higher-order spherical."

**4.87. Transverse Spherical Aberration.** The *transverse spherical aberration* is the departure of a particular ray from the paraxial image-point, measured in the focal plane of the optical system, as shown in Figure 4.60.

The transverse spherical aberration, which is approximately given by $sph_t = sph \cdot \tan U'$, is the true measure of the seriousness of the aberration in a given situation. When the convergence angle $U'$ is small, the longitudinal aberration may reach considerable numerical values without introducing significant degradation of image points in the focal plane.

**4.88. Circle of Least Confusion.** When the spherical aberration is not zero, each ray at a different height in the aperture will, in general, have a different intersection length, and the image region will be a restricted volume where all of these rays pass relatively close to each other. The situa-

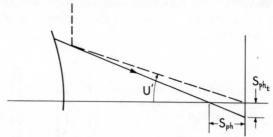

FIGURE 4.60. Transverse spherical aberration.

tion for a positive refracting surface, which exhibits positive spherical aberration, is shown in Figure 4.61. The smallest diameter circle which can be drawn in a plane normal to the optical axis is termed the *circle of least confusion*, or *disc of least confusion*. It is the smallest size which can be achieved in the image of a point object under the particular conditions which prevail, and it is the measure of the defect of spherical aberration as it affects the image quality of the optical system under discussion.

**4.89. Sign Convention for Spherical Aberration.** In a positive refracting surface, the rays at the edge of the aperture come to a focus closer to the surface than do the paraxial rays. This condition is referred to as *positive* spherical aberration. When the focal length for the edge rays is greater than that for the paraxial rays, one has *negative spherical aberration*.

Systems which show a residual of positive spherical aberration are termed *undercorrected* systems, while those with negative residuals are *overcorrected* systems.

**4.90. Achromatic Lenses.** It has been shown, under the discussion of chromatic aberration, how a lens can be made achromatic by the combination of two different types of optical glass of different indices and dispersions into a single lens, usually in the form of a cemented doublet. Correction of the spherical aberration by the bending of a lens has also been discussed. The doublet lens which results from the combination of two glasses to produce achromatism can also be subjected to the bending operation to give it a desired minimum of spherical aberration, and this minimum, when two lens elements (one positive and one negative) are available for manipulation, can in many cases be made zero or nearly so.

Such doublets, compounded of two elements of different kinds of glass, and corrected by bending for a minimum of spherical aberration, are extremely useful building blocks for optical systems. It will be found that nearly all optical systems which are not designed for extremely high performance are made up almost completely of such doublets.

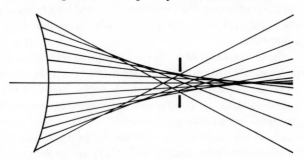

FIGURE 4.61. The circle of least confusion.

In many cases, in a system composed of several achromats in series, the optical designer can achieve an improvement of the over-all system by deliberately introducing over- or under-correction for spherical or chromatic aberration in individual doublets. This is normally an easy matter, since it is as easy to design such a lens to give a specified amount of aberration other than zero, as to design it for a zero result.

In optical systems with high performance or unusual characteristics, such as large apertures or wide fields of view, departure from a simple series of doublets is necessary, but for such instruments as rifle scopes, binoculars, low-power telescopes, and the like, simple achromats are sufficient to give a completely satisfactory result.

**4.91. Extra-axial Aberrations.** Chromatic and spherical aberration are the only aberrations which affect axial image points. When considering extended fields of view, however, other forms of aberration come into account. The manner in which all of the rays from an object point distant from the axis fail to join in an image point which obeys the laws of projective transformation has been divided by convention into aberrations called *coma, astigmatism, curvature of field, and distortion.* In addition to these four, there are spherical aberration of extra-axial image points and transverse chromatic aberration. All of these aberrations have been defined and illustrated in previous sections.

## THE SEIDEL ABERRATIONS

**4.92. Definitions.** Approximate expressions for the extra-axial aberrations identified above, in terms of quantities pertaining to the paraxial case, were developed by Ludwig von Seidel[6] and are consequently generally known by his name. Other workers have also developed similar expressions. The approximations are close for systems which are not severe, and they are used in the same way that the approximations for primary chromatic and spherical aberration for the axial case are used—to bring a new design into a nearly acceptable form by means easier to apply than strict ray-tracing computations.

Actually, there are only five aberrations properly called Seidel aberrations—spherical aberration, coma, astigmatism, curvature of field and distortion. The additional two which have been discussed above—chromatic aberration of the axial bundle and transverse chromatic aberration—have been included because they, also, must be taken into account by the optical designer at the earliest stages of the design task, and because similar approximate methods for dealing with them are in common use.

**4.93. Spherical Aberration of Oblique Pencils.** For any given re-

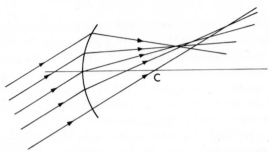

FIGURE 4.62. Spherical aberration in an oblique pencil.

fracting surface, the rays from an extra-axial object point may be referred to an *auxiliary optical axis,* drawn from the object point through the center of curvature of the surface, as shown in Figure 4.62. The image point conjugate to such an object point will be formed on this auxiliary axis (as was shown in a previous section under discussion of the Theorem of Lagrange), and it follows that computations for the spherical aberration of this image point may be performed using the same equations as for an axial image point, but referring the calculations to the auxiliary axis, which, of course, changes with each successive surface through the system.

**4.94. Coma.** Coma is the image defect which causes extra-axial points to be imaged as unsymmetrical flares; its very lack of symmetry makes it one of the most objectionable of the aberrations. Some of its geometrical characteristics have been defined in a previous section.

The Seidel equation shows that coma is proportional to the square of the height of the ray in the aperture and to the first power of the height of the image in the focal plane.

Geometrically, coma may be seen to be a manifestation of spherical aberration which results when the rays from an extra-axial object point do not form a symmetrical complete bundle around the auxiliary optical axis. If all the rays from such a bundle were present, the image patch would be circular and there would be no asymmetry.

This observation leads to the conclusion that the position of the system pupils will have a significant effect upon coma, since it determines the bundle of light which is active in forming an image. This is truly the case, and shifting of the position of the pupil represents one of the most powerful methods for controlling the coma of the system.

**4.95. Astigmatism.** *Astigmatism,* more properly called *astigmatic difference of focus,* is the separation of image points formed by the rays which fall in the meridional plane of the optical system (the plane containing the optical axis and the conjugate object-image point pair) and by those which fall in the orthogonal or sagittal plane. In the case of *pure* astigmatism (all other aberrations being absent) images of object lines in the two orthogonal planes are distinctly separated in the image.

This defect is common in the human eye and is caused by differences in the radius of curvature of the cornea. In optical systems, astigmatism can be caused by undesired differences in radii of curvature of the optical surfaces in two orthogonal planes, but even truly spherical surfaces exhibit astigmatism for extra-axial points.

The Seidel expressions for astigmatism show that it is proportional to the square of the image or object height.

It can be shown that a thin lens always exhibits a rather large amount of astigmatism; the correction of astigmatism in an optical system always requires the use of components with relatively large separations along the optical axis.

**4.96. Curvature of Field.** If there is no astigmatism, the images from an object plane normal to the optical axis are not necessarily formed upon an image plane normal to the optical axis. In general, they are formed upon a parabolic surface known as the *Petzval surface*. The astigmatism is firmly related to the Petzval surface, in that the sagittal and tangential foci both lie on the same side of this surface, with the former at a distance three times that of the latter. The sagittal and tangential focal surfaces are shown in Figure 4.36.

The curvature of the Petzval surface, expressed in terms of its separation from the paraxial image plane, is given by

$$P_C = \tfrac{1}{2} h_k'^2 \sum \frac{(\mu-1)c}{\mu} \tag{4.94}$$

where $h_k'$ is the height of the image for the $k$th (last) lens of a system, and the expression under the summation sign is computed lens by lens for the system. It will be noted that the curve is a parabola and also that it is not dependent upon any axial distances or separations, only upon the total curvatures of the various lenses. The only way it can be minimized is by the combination of positive and negative lenses.

**4.97. Distortion.** Distortion is the departure of image points from the strict locations demanded by a projective transformation. Thus, in the presence of distortion, a square grid object will be imaged as shown in Figure 4.38, which shows the two cases of positive (barrel) distortion, in which the image points are too close to the optical axis, and negative (pincushion) distortion, in which the image points are too far away. Distortion is proportional to the cube of the height of the image point, and is the one aberration which persists for even very restricted apertures.

**4.98. The Characteristic Focal Line.** In the case of an axial image point, all of the rays passing through a circular zone concentric with the

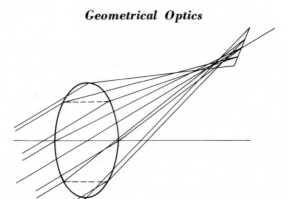

FIGURE 4.63. The characteristic focal line.

optical axis meet, by reasons of symmetry, in a point on the optical axis. In the case of an extra-axial image point, the rays passing through a similar concentric zone meet in pairs along a line which lies in the meridional plane, as shown in Figure 4.63. The projection of this line on the optical axis has a length which is proportional to the coma, and its projection on the image plane has a length proportional to the astigmatism; it can therefore shrink to a point only if both of these aberrations are absent.

**4.99. Interdependence of the Oblique Aberrations.** The oblique aberrations discussed above, as they are expressed in terms of their *primary* or Seidel values, can be shown to have a number of interdependences.[7] These relations are of practical interest only to optical designers, but they reveal quite clearly the kind of atmosphere in which an optical designer must work, and why optical design is not quite the straightforward thing that its mathematical foundation might at first indicate.

One of the most significant relations is that between the Petzval curvature of field and astigmatism, which has been remarked upon several times above, wherein the astigmatic focal surfaces have a definite and fixed relation to the Petzval surface. The Petzval curvature, unresponsive as it is to bendings or axial spacings of components, is a particularly obstinate aberration, and in many systems a considerable amount of it must be accepted. Fortunately, in visual instruments, quite a bit of field curvature can be tolerated because of the accommodating power of the eye. In photographic systems, curvature of field and astigmatism are particularly undesirable, and in such systems extreme measures are often necessary to bring them under control. One of the most effective means for dealing with curvature of field is the introduction of optical elements in or very near to the focal plane; these are known as field lenses, and they have considerable effect upon the field curvature and very little upon the system focal length. Figure 4.64 shows how the variations in thickness of a focal plane lens can alter the field curvature. The actual form of the field surface described by the primary aberration equations is a parabola; higher-order effects can alter this to various forms. Both of these facts often dictate that the field lens must be of nonspherical form.

When astigmatism and Petzval curvature are present, and in any but the most refined systems, some residuals are always present, the best compromise is usually considered to be the case where the tangential astigmatic focal surface is plane, as shown in Figure 4.63c.

The effects of a shift in the position of the system pupils on the values of the primary aberrations are particularly interesting. The spherical aberration, both of axial and extra-axial points, the Petzval curvature and the axial chromatic aberration is unchanged by a pupil shift. Coma is changed *if spherical aberration is present*, so that in a system with spherical aberration, it is theoretically possible to find a pupil position which will eliminate coma (although the required position is not always one which can be achieved). If the spherical aberration is zero, however, shifting the pupil will not correct for coma.

Astigmatism is changed by a shift in the pupil only if there is either coma or spherical aberration present. Distortion is affected only in the presence of astigmatism, coma or spherical aberration. And transverse chromatic aberration is affected by a pupil shift only if there is a finite amount of axial chromatic aberration present.

**4.100. The Optical Sine Condition.** The optical sine condition[8] is a generalization of the theorem of Lagrange (Section 4.25), and is, for an extra-axial point

$$h'_k \mu'_k \sin U'_k = h_1 \mu_1 \sin U_1 \qquad (4.95)$$

where the subscript $k$ refers to the last surface of a system and the subscript unity to the first surface. For an axial point, the sine condition becomes

$$\mu'_k \sin U'_k = \mu_1 \sin U_1 \qquad (4.96$$

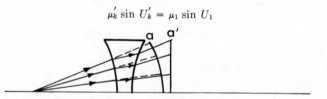

FIGURE 4.64. Change in field curvature by a focal plane lens. The focal surface without the introduction of the field lens is shown at a. The field lens extends the path of the rays to the surface a'.

and for an object point at infinity, it can be expressed in the form

$$\frac{h_0}{\sin U_k'} = f' \tag{4.97}$$

The sine condition expresses the requirement for freedom of a system from coma; at the same time, when the condition is satisfied, all of the geometrical aberrations are small. It will therefore be found that all optical systems which exhibit even moderately high performance adhere very closely to the sine condition.

**4.101. The Limiting Aperture of a Lens.** Equation (4.97) expresses the maximum aperture which a lens corrected for the sine condition can possess. Sin $U_k'$ has a limiting value of unity; for this value, $h_0$, which is the height of an incident ray in the entrance pupil, is equal to $f'$, the focal length of the lens. Thus the relative aperture $(f/2h_0)$ is $\frac{1}{2}$. The limiting relative aperture of a lens is therefore $f/0.5$.

With a lens of this aperture, the ray which enters the entrance pupil at its edge comes to the focal point from a direction perpendicular to the optical axis. Any ray which approaches the optical axis from behind the image plane can hardly contribute to a useful image at that point, so that it is generally accepted that the limiting relative aperture of any optical system is that which yields rays at the image plane which meet it at grazing incidence.

There are, of course, exceptions even to this rule; for example, a search-light reflector can accept rays from its source over a solid angle greater than a hemisphere, and hence has a relative aperture larger than $f/0.5$. Also, when an optical system is not corrected for the sine condition, this

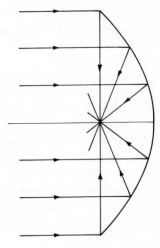

FIGURE 4.65. Parabolic reflector with a relative aperture of $f/0.25$.

limitation on aperture does not exist. For example, a paraboloidal mirror imaging an axial point has a relative aperture of $f/0.25$ for the case of the extreme rays meeting the optical axis at 90°, as shown in Figure 4.65.

Also, when the medium in which the image is formed has a refractive index $\mu$, the effective relative aperture is increased for a larger value of $U'$. The product $\mu' \sin U'$ is referred to as the *numerical aperture*. For air, it has a maximum value of unity, but for a dense medium, its maximum value is $\mu$. Hence the maximum relative aperture becomes $f/(1/2\mu)$. The concept of numerical aperture is usually restricted to the object space of microscopes, and microscope objectives are customarily catalogued according to their numerical aperture. When a liquid with a high refractive index is used between the object and the microscope objective, the numerical aperture may be increased to a value greater than unity, and thereby effect a gain in the illumination. The objectives designed for this use are called immersion objectives, and they work effectively only when the specimen is immersed in the appropriate immersion oil.

**4.102. Third-order Aberrations.** The aberrations which have been discussed above under the terminology of *primary* or *Seidel* aberrations, are often referred to as *third-order aberrations*.

Geometrical imaging may be described in generalized analytical form by means of certain functions known as *characteristic functions* of the medium, which were introduced into optics by W. R. Hamilton.[9] Hamilton's methods form a powerful tool for the systematic analytical investigation of the general properties of optical instruments, and since the advent of the electronic computer, they have become a useful part of the optical designer's technique. Since this book is intended to explain the nature of optics and optical systems to as wide a circle of readers as possible, it has been considered inadvisable to enter into extended discussions of the mathematics involved in the Hamiltonian method, but it is useful to show the results which arise from it in the description of the primary aberrations.[10]

Considering an optical system in the three-dimensional case, the intersection of rays with the image plane can be expressed in the form of a series, of which the first term represents the limiting case of the paraxial region, the term of the second degree is absent, and the primary, or lowest-order aberrations are represented by terms of the third order.

If methods introduced by Schwarzschild are followed, it may be shown that the departures, in the image plane, of ray intersections from the locations given by the paraxial solutions are given by

$$\Delta x = B\phi^3 \sin \theta - 2Fy_0\phi^2 \sin \theta \cos \theta + Dy_0^2\phi \sin \theta$$

$$\Delta y = B\phi^3 \cos \theta - Fy_0\phi^2 (1 + 2 \cos^2 \theta) + (2C + D)y_0^2\phi \cos \theta - Ey_0^3 \qquad (4.98)$$

where the upper-case coefficients are constants of the optical system, and the variables $y_0$, $\phi$, $\theta$ are shown in Figure 4.66. $y_0$ is the height of the ideal image point in the image plane, $\phi$ is the radial angular height of the ray in the exit pupil, and $\theta$ is the position angle of the ray in the pupil.

It is seen that all of the terms are of the third order in the two significant variables ($y_0$ and $\phi$). The terms of these equations express the five Seidel aberrations with complete equivalence to the expressions derived by means of simple trigonometry.

The terms with the coefficient $B$ express the *spherical aberration*. It is seen that the rays from a circular zone in the pupil intersect the image plane in circles concentric about the ideal image point, and of radii $B\phi^3$.

The terms with coefficient $F$ express the coma. It is seen that the intersection in the image plane of the rays from a concentric zone in the pupil is a circle of radius $Fy_0\phi^2$ displaced from the ideal image point by the distance $2Fy_0\phi^2$. The intersection circles from different zones build up the series of displaced circles shown as characteristic of coma in Figure 4.34.

The terms with coefficients $C$ and $D$ express the astigmatism and curvature of the field. It can be shown that $2C + D$ and $D$ are proportional to the reciprocals of the curvature of the tangential and sagittal field surfaces, respectively.

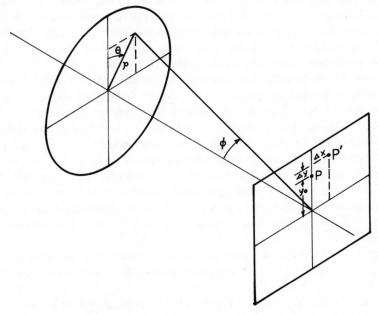

FIGURE 4.66. Geometry of exit pupil and focal plane.

The term with coefficient $E$ represents the distortion. The distance of the ray from the ideal image point is proportional to the cube of the height in the image plane and occurs in the $Y$-direction only.

**4.103. Optical Path Differences.** It has been noted in the discussion of the wave character of light that the phase relations of the light arriving at an image point place a definite limitation on the dimensions of the image point and the distribution of the light therein. It has also been noted that the strict application of geometrical optics takes no account of these phase relations. Thus, it can indicate any degree of precision in the meeting of rays at image points that the computer is willing to cope with in terms of carrying out the results to more decimal places.

When optical systems achieve a degree of correction for aberrations where the residuals, as indicated by geometrical computations, reach values which are no longer large with respect to a wavelength of light, the predictions of geometrical optics with respect to the quality of the image points are no longer valid. For such cases, and there are many of them in modern optical design—particularly in the case of photographic optical systems—different methods must be adopted to determine the system performance.

The most logical method is the computation of *optical path differences*. It will be recalled that the *optical path* was defined as $\mu t$, where $t$ is the geometrical path and $\mu$ is the index of refraction of the medium concerned. The differences in optical paths from an object point through various points in the entrance pupil of an optical system to the image point give the phase relations existing at the image point and hence permit the construction of the diffraction image which is formed at that point.

**4.104. Wave Fronts.** Computations of optical path differences are of common occurrence in modern optical design for optical systems with a high state of correction. It will be seen that such an approach actually determines the shape of the wave fronts which pass through the system. The wave front from an object point is a spherical one, with its center at the object point. When it encounters an optical surface, it is altered in shape. In a perfect optical instrument, the wave front emerging from the exit pupil will be a spherical wave front, concave to the image point, at which it theoretically shrinks to a point. In a real optical instrument, the shape will not be spherical, but will vary as a result of the presence of aberrations.

Figure 4.67 shows the shape of the wave fronts corresponding to the presence of each of the primary aberrations which have been discussed above.

Relations between ray and wave front computations have been discussed by Rayces.[10]

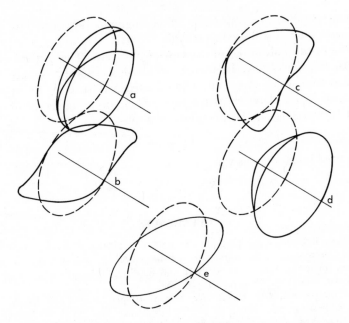

FIGURE 4.67. Wave-front shapes for the Seidel aberrations: (a) spherical aberration, (b) coma, (c) astigmatism, (d) curvature of field, (e) distortion.

**4.105. The Rayleigh Limit.** The amount of aberration which can be tolerated under particular conditions is an important item of information for the optical designer. In the case of systems with a high degree of correction, such a tolerance can be expressed only in terms of the diffraction image.

In a perfect system, the image of a point will consist of a central disc surrounded by concentric dark rings, resulting from diffraction, as described in Section 2.71. The diameter of the central disc is $1.22\lambda/d$. When the system is imperfect, differences in optical path will cause the diffraction pattern to become larger.

As a result of an exhaustive investigation, Lord Rayleigh presented the proposition that there would be no sensible degradation of the image quality in an ideal optical system if the optical path differences for any rays making up an image point did not exceed ¼ wavelength. This is the well-known *Rayleigh limit*[11] which has been used universally as a guide for more than a century. Modern methods of analysis of image quality permit the application of more refined criteria to the problem, with the result that the Rayleigh limit can be shown to be much too coarse for the very highest degree of performance, especially in photographic systems, but the $\frac{1}{4}$ wavelength limit is still used as a guide.

**4.106. Focal Tolerance of an Optical System.** The method of optical path differences may be used to establish the focal tolerance for an optical system which gives diffraction-limited performance. In order that the optical path differences of the rays making up an image point do not exceed $\frac{1}{4}$ wavelength, the tolerance on focus is

$$\delta = \pm \lambda / 2\mu' \sin U' \tag{4.99}$$

The focal range is twice this, or

$$R = \lambda / \mu' \sin U' \tag{4.100}$$

## REFERENCES

1. J. Maxwell, *Quart. J. Pure & Appl. Math.*, **2**, 233 (1858).
2. This presentation of the projective transformation as applied to an optical system follows that given by M. Born and E. Wolf, "Principles of Optics," p. 150 *et seq.*, New York, Pergamon Press, 1959.
3. K. Schwarzschild, *Abh. Kohgl. Ges. Wis., Gottingen, Math-Phys. Kl.*, **4**, Nos. 1, 2, 3 (1905–6).
   M. Herzberger, *J. Opt. Soc. Am.*, **29**, 395 (1939).
   F. Wachendorf, *Optik*, **5**, 80 (1949).
   J. Focke, Dissertation, Liepzig, 1951.
4. J. Fraunhofer, *Gilbert's Ann.*, **56**, 1264 (1817).
5. See A. Conrady, "Applied Optics and Optical Design," p. 72 *et seq.*, Dover, 1957.
6. L. Seidel, *Astr. Nachr.*, **43**, No. 1027, 289; No. 1028, 305; No. 1029, 321 (1856).
7. See reference 5, p. 333 *et seq.* for a more complete discussion.
8. R. Clausius, *Pogg. Ann.*, **121**, 1 (1864).
   H. Helmholtz, *Pogg. Ann. Judelband*, 557 (1874).
   E. Abbe, *Jenaisch Ges. Med. Nature*, **129**, (1879); *Carl Report Phys.*, **16**, 303 (1880).
9. W. Hamilton, *Trans. Roy. Irish Acad.*, **15**, 69 (1828); **16**, 1 (1830); **16**, 93 (1831); **17**, 1 (1837).
10. See reference 2, p. 210 *et seq.* for the development.
11. Lord Rayleigh, *Phil. Mag.*, **8**(5), 403 (1879).

# CHAPTER 5

# Radiometry and Photometry

**5.1. Definitions.** *Radiometry* is the measurement of radiant energy; *photometry* is the measurement of light, where light is defined as that portion of radiant energy which produces the sensation of vision. Thus, radiometry is concerned with total radiant energy over the entire electromagnetic spectrum, whereas photometry is concerned only with that region of the spectrum to which the eye is sensitive and, moreover, is restricted to the relative capability of energy within this spectrum to produce sensation.

As has been seen, atoms and molecules, when in excited states and in a relatively free condition, as in a low-temperature gas, radiate nearly monochromatically at frequencies determined by the differences in their energy levels. Substances with high density, such as liquids and solids, radiate according to the laws of black body radiation as given by the *Planck equation* and the *Stefan-Boltzmann equation* (see Section 1.26 *et seq.*). Planck's equation shows that the spectrum of radiation extends theoretically from zero to infinity and that the location of the peak in terms of either frequency or wavelength is governed by the temperature of the body. The Stefan-Boltzmann equation gives the radiant energy output, and shows that it is proportional to the fourth power of the absolute temperature.

**5.2. Radiometric and Photometric Units.** It is only very recently that there has been available a standardization of units and nomenclature for photometry. Actually, the situation is not even yet completely standardized, although the activities of the American Standards Association, the Committee on Colorimetry of the Optical Society of America, and other groups have resulted in the adoption of certain standards of nomenclature and definitions which are finding their way into the literature. The nomenclature and definitions used in this book are those recommended by the Committee on Colorimetry; the symbols have been adopted by the American Standards Association. Much of the existing literature, especially that published prior to the current decade, will use nomenclature and symbols, and frequently definitions, according to different conventions. This situation has made the subject of photometry extremely confusing to the occasional reader.

**5.3. Units, Symbols and Nomenclature.** Table 5.1 lists the nomenclature, units, symbols, dimensions and defining equations for the various quantities involved in both radiometry and photometry on a comparative basis. The concepts are identical for both—all of the units have the constant relation:

$$\frac{\text{Photometric Unit}}{\text{Radiometric Unit}} = K \text{ (relative luminosity)}$$

All of the units are, in general, spectrally dependent; when used without subscript, they are understood to represent the integrated value over the spectrum; when used in a spectrally dependent sense, the subscript $\lambda$ is appended. Thus, the radiance, $N$, of a body is its radiance for the entire spectrum; the radiance, $N_\lambda$, is its radiance as a function of wavelength; the luminance, $B$, is its luminance (radiance $\times K$) for the entire spectrum, and the luminance, $B_\lambda$, is its luminance as a function of wavelength.

The primary unit is *power*, or energy per unit time; in radiometric terms, it is the *watt;* in photometric terms, it is the *lumen*. Other terms are defined with reference to the power.

**5.4. Luminosity Curve.** Figure 5.1 is the *luminosity curve*—in the older literature, it is called the visibility curve. It is the relative response of the human eye to a constant power input as a function of wavelength. It is universally given in a normalized form, with the peak at unity. The curve represents a plot of the ratio lumens/watt; at the peak response of the human eye (555 m$\mu$), this ratio has the value 682 lumens/watt.

If a source of radiant energy has the radiance given by a curve $N = f(x)$, then its luminance is represented by a curve which is the product of $f(x)$ and the luminosity curve. The same is true for other pairs of radiometric-photometric units. Table 5.2 gives the values of the luminosity curve points.

**5.5. Fundamental Relations.** The fundamental relations of radiometry and photometry are identical. In the following, these relations are derived in terms of the radiometric units. The equations are numbered with suffix R to indicate this. Following the derivations, the corresponding equations for photometry are listed, using the same numbers with suffix P.

There are two fundamental equations.

Let a differential area $dS$ (Figure 5.2) emit radiation at the rate of $N$

TABLE 5-1. RADIOMETRIC AND PHOTOMETRIC UNITS

| Definition | Radiometric | | | | Photometric | | | | Dimensions* |
|---|---|---|---|---|---|---|---|---|---|
| | Name | Symbol | Unit (mks) | Defining Equation | Name | Symbol | Unit (mks) | Defining Equation | |
| Energy | Radiant energy | $U$ | joule | $U = \int P \, dt$ | Luminous energy | $Q$ | talbot | $Q = \int F \, dt$ | $ML^2T^{-2}$ |
| Energy per unit area | Radiant density | $u$ | joule/meter² | $u = \dfrac{dU}{dA}$ | Luminous density | $q$ | talbot/meter² | $q = \dfrac{dQ}{dA}$ | $MT^{-2}$ |
| Energy per unit time—power | Radiant flux | $P$ | watt | — | Luminous flux | $F$ | lumen | — | $ML^2T^{-3}$ |
| Flux per unit area | Radiant emittance | $W$ | watt/meter² | $W = \dfrac{dP}{dS}$ | Luminous emittance | $L$ | lumen/meter² lambert foot-lambert | $L = \dfrac{dF}{dS}$ | $MT^{-3}$ |
| Flux per unit solid angle | Radiant intensity | $J$ | watt/steradian | $J = \dfrac{dP}{d\Omega}$ | Luminous intensity | $I$ | lumen/steradian candle candela | $I = \dfrac{dF}{d\Omega}$ | $ML^2T^{-3}$ |
| Flux per unit solid angle per unit projected area | Radiance | $N$ | watt/steradian-meter² | $N = \dfrac{1}{f(\theta)} \dfrac{d}{d\Omega}\left(\dfrac{dP}{dS}\right)$ | Luminance | $B$ | lumen/steradian-meter² candle/meter² lumen/meter² | $B = \dfrac{1}{f(\theta)} \dfrac{d}{d\Omega}\left(\dfrac{dF}{dS}\right)$ | $MT^{-3}$ |
| Flux input per unit area | Irradiance | $H$ | watt/meter² | $H = \dfrac{dP}{dS'}$ | Illuminance | $E$ | meter-candle foot-candle | $E = \dfrac{dF}{dS'}$ | $MT^{-3}$ |
| Ratio of reflected to incident flux | Radiant reflectance | $\rho$ | — | $\rho = P_r/P_i$ | Luminous reflectance | $r$ | — | $r = F_r/F_i$ | — |
| Ratio of transmitted to incident flux | Radiant transmittance | $\tau$ | — | $\tau = P_t/P_i$ | Luminous transmittance | $t$ | — | $t = F_t/F_i$ | — |
| Ratio of absorbed to incident flux | Radiant absorbance | $A$ | — | $A = P_A/P_i$ | Luminous absorptance | $a$ | — | $a = F_A/F_i$ | — |

* Mass, Length, and Time.

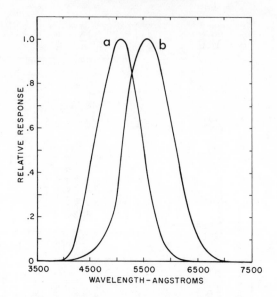

FIGURE 5.1. The luminosity curve. The ordinate is the relative response of the human eye to radiation of a given wavelength. (a) Scotopic. (b) photopic.

watts per unit solid angle per unit projected area in the direction $\theta$ from its normal. Then the total *radiant power*, or *flux*, will be

$$dP = N \, dS \, d\Omega \tag{5.1R}$$

where $\Omega$ is a differential element of solid angle and $N$ is the *radiance* (watts/steradian-meter²)

Now, in general, $N$ will be a function of $\theta$, so that

$$dP = N_0 f(\theta) \, dS \, d\Omega \tag{5.2R}$$

If this radiation falls upon an area $dS'$, at distance $r$, whose normal is at angle $\phi$ to the line joining it and $dS$, then the differential solid angle involved is

$$d\Omega = \frac{dS' \cos \phi}{r^2} \tag{5.3R}$$

The *irradiance*, or radiant power per unit area falling upon $dS'$ is defined as

$$H = \frac{dP}{dS'} \tag{5.4R}$$

TABLE 5.2. RELATIVE EYE RESPONSE

| Wavelength (Å) | Photopic | Scotopic |
|---|---|---|
| 3800 | 0.0000 | 0.0006 |
| 3900 | 0.0001 | 0.0022 |
| 4000 | 0.0004 | 0.0093 |
| 4100 | 0.0012 | 0.0348 |
| 4200 | 0.0040 | 0.0966 |
| 4300 | 0.0116 | 0.1998 |
| 4400 | 0.0230 | 0.3281 |
| 4500 | 0.0380 | 0.4550 |
| 4600 | 0.0600 | 0.5672 |
| 4700 | 0.0910 | 0.6756 |
| 4800 | 0.1390 | 0.7930 |
| 4900 | 0.2080 | 0.9043 |
| 5000 | 0.3230 | 0.9817 |
| 5100 | 0.5030 | 0.9966 |
| 5200 | 0.7100 | 0.9352 |
| 5300 | 0.8620 | 0.8110 |
| 5400 | 0.9540 | 0.6497 |
| 5500 | 0.9950 | 0.4808 |
| 5600 | 0.9950 | 0.3288 |
| 5700 | 0.9520 | 0.2076 |
| 5800 | 0.8700 | 0.1212 |
| 5900 | 0.7570 | 0.0655 |
| 6000 | 0.6310 | 0.0333 |
| 6100 | 0.5030 | 0.0159 |
| 6200 | 0.3810 | 0.0074 |
| 6300 | 0.2650 | 0.0033 |
| 6400 | 0.1750 | 0.0015 |
| 6500 | 0.1070 | 0.0007 |
| 6600 | 0.0610 | 0.0003 |
| 6700 | 0.0320 | 0.0001 |
| 6800 | 0.0170 | 0.0001 |
| 6900 | 0.0082 | 0.0000 |
| 7000 | 0.0041 | 0.0000 |
| 7100 | 0.0021 | 0.0000 |
| 7200 | 0.0010 | 0.0000 |
| 7300 | 0.0005 | 0.0000 |
| 7400 | 0.0003 | 0.0000 |
| 7500 | 0.0001 | 0.0000 |
| 7600 | 0.0001 | 0.0000 |

## The Luminosity Curve

Photopic vision is obtained with the cones of the retina, which yield color vision; the peak occurs at 5556Å. Scotopic vision is obtained with the rods of the retina, which are not color sensitive; the peak occurs at 5110Å.

Data from "American Institute of Physics Handbook" New York, McGraw-Hill, 1957.

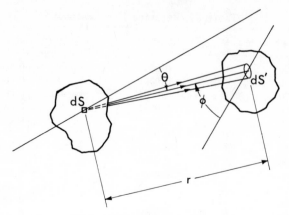

FIGURE 5.2. Geometry for illumination analysis.

Substituting from Equation (5.3R) gives

$$H = \frac{dP \cos \phi}{d\Omega \, r^2}$$  (5.5R)

and substituting from Equation (5.2R) gives

$$H = \frac{N_0 f(\theta) \, dS \cos \phi}{r^2}$$  (5.6R)

Equation (5.2R), which may be written

$$N_0 = \frac{1}{f(\theta)} \frac{d}{d\Omega} \left( \frac{dP}{dS} \right)$$

and Equation (5.6R) may be considered to be the two fundamental equations of radiometry. Nearly all radiometric and photometric problems involve finding $dP$ from Equation (5.2R), establishing a relation between the illuminated area $dS'$ and the radiating area $dS$, $dS' = f(dS)$, and then finding the illuminance, $H$, from Equation (5.6R).

The *intensity*, $J$, is defined as the power per unit solid angle, or

$$J = \frac{dP}{d\Omega}$$  (5.7R)

Hence, using Equation (5.2R)

$$J = N_0 f(\theta) \, dS$$  (5.8R)

The total power radiated from unit area is the *radiant emittance*, defined as

$$W = \frac{dP}{dS} \qquad (5.9\text{R})$$

Thus, using Equation (5.2R)

$$W = N_0 f(\theta) \, d\Omega \qquad (5.10\text{R})$$

A plane surface radiates into a solid angle $2\pi$, therefore, the *radiant emittance* will be

$$W = 2\pi N_0 \int_0^\theta f(\theta) \, d\theta \qquad (5.11\text{R})$$

but $\theta_{max} = \pi/2$, so that

$$W = 2\pi N_0 \int_0^{\pi/2} f(\theta) \, d\theta \qquad (5.12\text{R})$$

The radiant emittance, $W$, is the quantity given by the Stefan-Boltzmann law (see Section 1.27)

$$W = \epsilon\sigma T^4 \qquad (5.13\text{R})$$

where $\epsilon$ is the emissivity, $\sigma$ is the Stefan-Boltzmann constant, and $T$ is the temperature in °K.

**5.6. Lambert's Law.** The ease with which radiometric and photometric problems may be solved depends largely on the nature of the function $f(\theta)$. Often it is of such a form as to make the necessary integrations extremely complex. Where the radiating surface may be considered to be a *uniform diffuser*, however, the problems can be made simple. A uniform diffuser is defined as a surface which appears to be of the same brightness* in all directions. This implies that $N = f(\theta)$, which is defined as the power per unit *projected area* per unit solid angle, is constant. The projected area is $dS \cos\theta$; hence, for a uniform diffuser

$$f(\theta) = \cos\theta \qquad (5.14\text{R})$$

This is Lambert's Cosine Law, and this kind of distribution is frequently referred to as a Lambertian distribution.

Applying this relation to Equation (5.12R) gives

$$W = 2\pi N_0 \left[ \int_0^{\pi/2} \sin\theta = 2\pi N_0 \right. \qquad (5.15\text{R})$$

* The term *brightness*, which was used frequently in the past to describe several different phenomena, is no longer used as a definitive term. It is used here in a subjective sense only.

**5.7. Corresponding Photometric Equations.** The total *luminous flux* is

$$dF = B \, dS \, d\Omega \tag{5.1P}$$

where $B$ is the *luminance* (lumens-unit area$^{-2}$-steradian$^{-1}$). A number of different terms are in common usage to denote luminance. The unit of *luminous intensity* (lumens per steradian), given in Equation (5.7P), is the *candle*, or *candela*, and luminance is luminous intensity per unit area. Thus, luminance may be expressed as candelas per square meter which is called *nits*, or as candelas per square centimeter which is called *stilbs*. The terms stilb and nit are used in illuminating engineering, but are not in common usage in optics. Luminance may also be expressed as candelas per square foot. Use of the term foot-candle for luminance is incorrect—this term should be reserved for *illuminance* (see below).

Recognizing that $B = f(\theta)$ gives

$$dF = B_0 f(\theta) \, dS \, d\Omega \tag{5.2P}$$

The *illuminance*, or luminous power per unit area falling upon an area $dS'$, is defined as

$$E = \frac{dF}{dS'} \tag{5.4P}$$

and making the same substitutions as in the case of radiometry gives

$$E = \frac{B_0 f(\theta) \, dS \cos \phi}{r^2} \tag{5.6P}$$

Equations (5.2P) and (5.6P) are the fundamental equations of photometry.

The *intensity*, $I$, is defined as

$$I = \frac{dF}{d\Omega} \tag{5.7P}$$

and, from Equation (5.2P)

$$I = B_0 f(\theta) \, dS \tag{5.8P}$$

The unit of luminous intensity is the *candle*, or *candela*, which is an intensity of 1 lumen/steradian. Until recently, the standard was a sperm candle of specified size and composition. The current standard is a 1 cm$^2$ area of a blackbody at the freezing point of platinum, which has an assigned intensity of 60 candelas. The rounding off to the value 60 introduces a slight (less than 1 per cent) variation from the prior standard, so that the term *candela* officially replaces the term *candle* to denote this variation. The adoption of a blackbody standard places the relation between radiometry and photometry on a much firmer basis, since the radiant intensity of this standard source is exactly definable.

The *illuminance* is expressed in a number of different ways. An illuminance of 1 lumen/cm² is a *phot;* 1 lumen/m² is a *lux.* These terms are used in illuminating engineering but not generally in optics. An illuminance of 1 lumen/m² is generally known in optics (and photography) as a *meter-candle.* It is the illumination on a spherical surface which has at its center a point source with an intensity of one candle. An illuminance of 1 lumen/ft² is referred to as a *foot-candle.*

The total power radiated from unit area is the *luminous emittance, L,* defined as

$$L = \frac{dF}{dS} \tag{5.9P}$$

hence, using Equation (5.2P)

$$L = B_0 f(\theta) \, d\Omega \tag{5.10P}$$

A plane surface radiates into a solid angle $2\pi$, therefore, the *luminous emittance* will be, by analogy with Equation (5.12R)

$$L = 2\pi B_0 \int_0^\theta f(\theta) \, d\theta \tag{5.12P}$$

For a Lambertian source, by analogy with Equation (5.15R), the luminous emittance is

$$L = 2\pi B_0 \tag{5.15P}$$

so that a Lambertian source with a luminance of one lumen/steradian (a luminous intensity of one candela) has a total luminous emittance of $2\pi$ lumens.

The luminous emittance is known under a number of names. An emittance of 1 lumen/cm² is a *lambert;* 1 lumen/ft² is a *foot-lambert;* 1 lumen/m² is an *apostilb* (not used in optics).

The useful relations:

$$1 \text{ lambert} = \frac{1}{\pi} \text{ candelas/cm}^2$$

$$1 \text{ foot-lambert} = \frac{1}{\pi} \text{ candelas/ft}^2$$

may be noted.

**5.8. The Illumination of an Image.** Consider an entrance pupil of radius $U$ and a ring of width $d\theta$ and radius $\theta$ (Figure 5.3). The area of the ring is $r\, d\theta \cdot 2\pi r \sin\theta = 2\pi r^2 \sin\theta\, d\theta = da'$.

From Equation (5.4P)

$$dF = E\, dS' \tag{5.16}$$

But, from Equation (5.6P)

$$E = \frac{B_0 f(\theta)\, dS \cos\phi}{r^2} \tag{5.17}$$

For this case, $\phi = 0$, and, for a Lambertian source, $f(\theta) = \cos\theta$, hence

$$dF = \frac{B_0 \cos\theta\, dS}{r^2}\, 2\,\pi r^2 \sin\theta\, d\theta = 2\,\pi B_0 \sin\theta \cos\theta\, d\theta\, dS \tag{5.18}$$

Integrating over $\theta = 0$ to $U$

$$F = 2\,\pi B_0\, dS \int_0^U \sin\theta \cos\theta\, d\theta = \pi B_0\, dS \sin^2 U \tag{5.19}$$

Now, the image of $dS$ formed by the optical system is $dS'$, and if this image were a source illuminating the exit pupil, we would have

$$F' = \pi B_0'\, dS' \sin^2 U' \tag{5.20}$$

where $U'$ is the exit pupil angular aperture.

But, if no losses are assumed for the optical system, the flux from the exit pupil is equal to that received at the entrance pupil, so that $F' = F$,

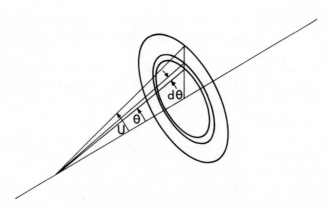

FIGURE 5.3. Entrance pupil geometry.

and therefore

$$B_0' \, dS' \sin^2 U' = B_0 \, dS \sin^2 U \qquad (5.21)$$

If the system is corrected for the sine condition (and this will always be the case, at least to a very close approximation), then

$$\mu' Y' \sin U' = \mu Y \sin U \qquad (5.22)$$

where $Y$ and $Y'$ are object and image heights, respectively. Therefore, $dS'/dS = (Y'/Y)^2$, and Equation (5.22) becomes

$$B_0' = B_0 \frac{\mu'}{\mu^2} \qquad (5.23)$$

In a visual instrument, the light forming the image passes on into the observer's eye, so that $B_0'$ is the luminance of the image. It is seen that the image luminance is proportional to the square of the ratio of the indices of refraction of image and object spaces.

When these indices are equal, as in the case of an instrument in air,

$$B_0' = B_0 \qquad (5.24)$$

and it is seen that the image illumination is equal to the object illumination for the case of a lossless optical system. Since no real system is completely lossless, it follows that the image is always fainter than the object. This is the proof of a very important rule: no optical instrument can ever make an object appear brighter than it appears to the unaided eye. Equation (5.24) is completely independent of the instrument parameters, except for the assumption that the transmission is 100 per cent and that the sine condition is satisfied. Neither magnification nor size of pupil is a factor.

As was pointed out in the previous chapter (Section 4.64), the magnification, in an instrument such as a telescope or microscope, is equal to the ratio of diameters of entrance and exit pupils. An instrument with a large entrance pupil can collect more light from an object than the unaided eye, by the ratio $(D/D')^2$, where $D$ is the entrance pupil diameter and $D'$ is the diameter of the eye pupil. All of this light can be brought into the observer's eye by introducing magnification of at least $D/D'$, thereby making the exit pupil no larger than the pupil of the eye. More light enters the eye than in the case of unaided vision. However, the area of the image on the retina is increased in the same proportion $(D/D')^2$ as the quantity of light, so that the illumination per unit area on the retina is unchanged.

This rule does not hold for point sources, since the size of a point source is unchanged by magnification; therefore, the collection of more light which is focused into the same size of image results in an increase of apparent brightness. This is the case for stars, and it is well known that stars which are too faint to be seen with the unaided eye can be made visible in a telescope. The phenomenon is valid only for optical systems sufficiently well corrected that the apparent size of the star image is limited by the optical quality of the instrument and not by the magnification. Astronomical telescopes closely approach diffraction limited imagery for points on the optical axis, and in increase in aperture may therefore actually cause the star images to be smaller than would be the case for a smaller telescope. In any event, the star image will fall upon a single receptor in the retina, regardless of the magnification, and will therefore appear brighter.

**5.9. Illumination in a Photographic Image.** The illumination in the image plane is, from Equation (5.4P)

$$E = \frac{F}{dS'} \tag{5.25}$$

therefore, using Equation (5.20P)

$$E = \pi B' \sin^2 U' \tag{5.26}$$

but $\pi \sin^2 U' = \Omega'$ is the solid angle of the exit pupil for an axial image point, as shown in Figure 5.4. Hence

$$E = B'\Omega \tag{5.27}$$

The area of the exit pupil is $\pi r^2$. At a field angle $\phi$, the projected area is $A = \Omega r^2 \cos \phi$, and the solid angle as viewed from an off-axis image point at field angle $\phi$ is

$$\Omega' = \frac{A}{r^2 \sec^2 \phi} = \Omega \cos^3 \phi \tag{5.28}$$

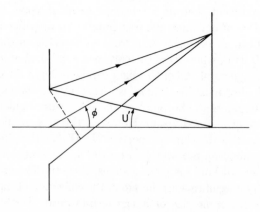

FIGURE 5.4. Image illumination.

and the illumination for the off-axis image is, therefore

$$E' = B'\Omega' \cos \phi = B'\Omega \cos^4 \phi \qquad (5.29)*$$

This is the well-known $\cos^4$ law of photographic illumination, which is a serious restriction in wide angle photographic systems. In aerial cartographic cameras, for example, the field of view may be $90°$ or more, and the illumination at the edge of the field, from the $\cos^4$ law is thus $\cos^4 45° = \frac{1}{4}$ with respect to the illumination on axis. It is possible, by introducing strong coma into the exit pupil, to so distort it for off-axis points that a considerable correction for the $\cos^4$ condition may be introduced. This is done in a inverse number of existing lenses.

**5.10. Photographic Exposure.** Equation (5.29) gives the image illuminance for a photographic system. It will be noted that the illuminance is independent of the object distance, but depends only on the object luminance and the solid angle of the exit pupil. The exit pupil solid angle is the inverse square of the relative aperture of the system.

This explains why the exposure setting for a camera does not depend upon the distance of the object, but only upon the object luminance and the relative aperture of the lens. It should be noted that when the object distance is not large with respect to the focal length, the effective relative aperture is a function of object distance.

**5.11. Image Illumination in the Microscope and Telescope.** For an image in a telescope or microscope of radiance $B'_0$, the illuminance on the retina of the observer's eye is, by analogy with Equations (5.26) and (5.23)

$$E = \pi B'_0 \sin^2 V \mu' \qquad (5.30)$$

where $\pi \sin^2 V$ is the solid angle of acceptance of the eye, and $\mu'$ is the index of refraction of the vitreous humor of the eye. It should be noted that this expression depends only on $B'_0$ and $V$—not upon the object distance $r$.

If the exit pupil of the instrument is larger than the pupil of the eye, then the illuminance on the retina is restricted to the value given by Equation (5.30) and is independent of the instrument pupils. If the exit pupil is smaller than the pupil of the eye, then Equation (5.26) determines the illuminance. Applying the sine condition to Equation (5.26) to make the substitution

$$\sin U' = \frac{\mu}{\mu'} \frac{1}{M} \sin U \qquad (5.31)$$

results in

$$E = B'_0 \left[ \frac{\mu}{\mu'} \right]^2 \frac{1}{M^2} \sin^2 U \qquad (5.32)$$

* For regions close to the axis and in the principal focal plane this equation takes the useful approximate form $E' = \pi B'/4F^2$, where $F$ is the relative aperture.

and, when $\mu' = 1.0$, for air

$$E = \frac{B_0'\,\mu^2 \sin^2 U}{M^2} \tag{5.33}$$

This is the case for the compound microscope, for which the exit pupil is always much smaller than the pupil of the eye, and $\mu'$, the index of the image space, is that for air. Now $\mu \sin U$ is the *numerical aperture* of the microscope, so that the illuminance of the image at a given magnification is proportional to the square of the numerical aperture. This explains why numerical aperture is an important parameter of the compound microscope, which is always starved for light at high magnifications. By using an immersion material surrounding the object, $\mu$ can be made greater than unity, so that the numerical aperture can be greater than unity.

**5.12. Illuminance from an Infinite Source.** Let an aperture of area $A$ be irradiated by a Lambertian source of infinite extent at distance $r$ (see Figure 5.5). If the radiance of the source is $N$, then the flux at the aperture is $dP = N\,dS\,d\Omega$. But the solid angle of the aperture, from a direction $\theta$ is $A \cos \theta / r^2$. And the differential source area, $dS$ is $r^2\,d\theta\,d\phi$, where $\phi$ is the angle in the plane perpendicular to the diagram.

Therefore

$$P = NA \iint_s \cos \theta\,d\theta\,d\phi \tag{5.34}$$

where $\phi$ varies from 0 to $2\pi$ and $\theta$ from 0 to $\pi/2$. Hence

$$P = NA \int_0^{2\pi} d\phi \int^{\pi/2} \cos \theta\,d\theta = 2\,\pi NA \tag{5.35}$$

From Equation (5.3R), the irradiance is $H = P/A$, hence

$$H = 2\pi N \tag{5.36}$$

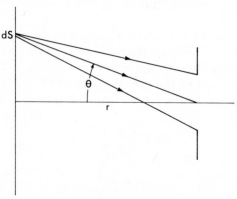

FIGURE 5.5. Illumination from an infinite plane.

But, from Equation (5.12R), $2\pi N$ is the emittance of a Lambertian source of radiance $N$. Therefore, *the irradiance* (or illuminance) *from an infinite Lambertian source is numerically equal to the radiant* (or luminous) *emittance of the source.*

It is customary to describe the "brightness" of the sky in terms of an emittance (watts/cm², foot-lamberts, etc.). Obviously, the unit of area is meaningless for the sky, but the above relation shows the usefulness of such a description. If the emittance of the sky is, say, 5000 foot-lamberts, then the illuminance on the earth, or on the aperture of an instrument, is 5000 foot-candles.

**5.13. Illumination by a Collimated Beam.** Searchlights, or projection collimators, are often used to illuminate objects at a distance. The relations shown above for images formed by optical instruments apply. Equation (5.24) shows that the *luminance* of the image formed in air by an optical instrument is equal to the luminance of the original object (when there are no transmission losses in the instrument). Figure 5.6 shows the optical arrangement of a searchlight.

The object is a small light source, such as a carbon arc; the image is at infinity, and has the same angular size as the object, as seen from the system pupil. Now, an observer at a distance which is large with respect to the focal length of the searchlight will see the image as of this same angular size, and, if the distance is sufficiently great, the image will be larger than the aperture of the searchlight, so that only that portion of it which is covered by the searchlight aperture will be visible.

Now the *luminance* of the image [Equation (5.24)] is equal to the luminance of the object. But the size of the image is equal to the size of the aperture. Hence its *intensity*, and therefore the *illuminance*, is increased by the factor $A/a$, where $A$ is the area of the searchlight aperture and $a$ is the area of the source.

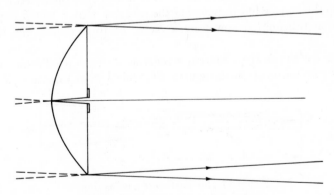

Figure 5.6. Paraboloidal searchlight mirror.

Therefore, the illuminance produced by a searchlight is the same as would be produced by a source of the same luminance as the actual source, but of a size equal to the aperture of the searchlight. The intensity of a searchlight beam is sometimes referred to as the *beam candlepower*, which is the intensity of a source equal in size to the searchlight aperture.

**5.14. Active and Passive Signalling Systems.** The illumination of a distant object by a searchlight beam is often used as a means for obtaining a signal. The signal may be the visible effect of the illumination, as in an ordinary searchlight, or the returned signal from the object in the case of a radar beam or an infrared searchlight. The magnitude of the returned signal is quite different for the case of a passively reflecting object and of an object which consists of an optical reflector.

Figure 5.7 shows the case of a passively reflecting object. If $S$ is the area of the source (the searchlight), and $S'$ the area of the illuminated object, then the flux intercepted by the object is

$$P_1 = J_0 S/r^2 \tag{5.37}$$

where $J_0$ is the intensity of the searchlight beam and $r$ is the object range. The object will reradiate with an intensity

$$J_1 = kP_1 \tag{5.38}$$

where $k$ is a factor which involves the reflectance of the object and its radiance function. For a Lambertian reflector with no losses, $k = 1/\pi$.

The flux returned to the receiver will be

$$P_2 = J_1 S/r^2 = kJ_0 S'/r^4 \tag{5.39}$$

where it is assumed that the receiver has the same aperture as the searchlight, which is often the case, since in many systems the same aperture serves as both transmitter and receiver. It is seen that the signal is proportional to the inverse fourth power of the range, so that it would require an increase in transmitted power by a factor of 16 to double the effective range.

Figure 5.8 shows the situation when the object is a reflector. This reflector forms an image of the source, $S''$, which, from Equation (5.24) has

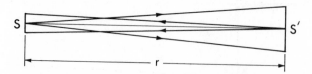

FIGURE 5.7. Illumination of a diffuse target.

the same radiance as the source, and whose area is equal to the area of the reflector (if the reflector is small with respect to the searchlight).

Therefore, for this case, the intensity of the returned signal is

$$J_1 = J_0 \frac{S'}{S} \tag{5.40}$$

and therefore

$$P_2 = J_0 S'/r^2 \tag{5.41}$$

again assuming no losses in the system. This is seen to be proportional to the inverse square of the range, rather than to the fourth power. Systems

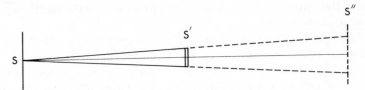

FIGURE 5.8. Illumination of a spectrally reflecting target.

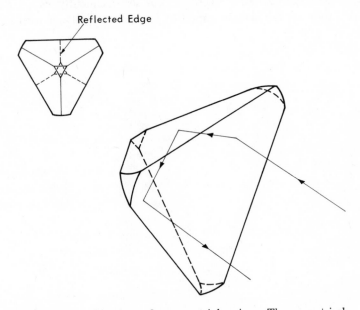

FIGURE 5.9. The retroreflector, or triple mirror. The geometrical form is the corner of a cube. The example drawn is a solid glass prism; the device may also be made as a reflector, in which case it consists of three mirrors.

which have an optical reflector at the target are usually referred to as "cooperative" systems. They are often found in situations where the "targets" are friendly—for example, systems for tracking guided missiles and friendly satellites—and also in range measuring systems used for surveying. Both radar and optical spectral regions are used.

The terms "active" and "passive" usually distinguish between systems where an illuminating beam is used (active systems) and those where an object is detected by virtue of its own radiation (passive systems). On this basis, all radar systems are active systems. The difference in performance between a system where a cooperative reflector can be used on the target and those used for the observation of unfriendly targets is significant, varying with the square of the range in the first case and as the fourth power of the range in the second.

A flat mirror will serve adequately as the cooperative reflector, but it must be so oriented as to return the beam exactly to the receiver. It is more usual to have "retroreflectors," or "corner mirrors," which have the property of returning a beam directly to its source. The geometry of the retroreflector is shown in Figure 5.9. It is a constant-deviation device, whose angle of deviation is 180°. These devices are frequently called "triple mirrors"; they are familiar, in imperfect form, as the buttons used in road signs.

# PART II

# OPTICAL SYSTEMS
# and
# DEVICES

# CHAPTER 6

# Optical Imaging Systems

**6.1. Introduction.** Part I has dealt with the nature of light, its characteristics and the ways in which it interacts with matter. Its wave character, demonstrated in diffraction and interference, and also in geometrical optics, whose rays are interpretable as normals to the wave fronts, has been described. Its particle character, revealing itself in phenomena such as the photoelectric effect, has also been discussed.

In this second part, the application of the properties of light to the creation of optical systems and devices is discussed. This chapter deals with systems whose function it is to form images. The distinction between imaging and non-imaging forms of optical systems is an arbitrary one, and somewhat nebulous, and is adopted merely for the purpose of presenting topics in some kind of formal order. The imaging systems discussed in this chapter comprise visual instruments, such as telescopes and microscopes, and systems for producing images on various surfaces, such as photographic film or motion picture screens. Television cameras are also optical imaging systems, but discussion of these and similar apparatus is covered under the title of electro-optical systems in Chapter 10.

## OPTICAL SYSTEM COMPONENTS

**6.2. Components.** Optical imaging systems are made up of components, which may be classified as *objectives, eyepieces,* and *optical relays*. These three types of components will be recognized as the three members of the first category of optical systems described in Section 4.67. While they are distinct components of complete optical instruments, they are in themselves *systems*, in that they usually consist of a number of separate elements.

The *objective* in an optical instrument forms the first image of the object; this is usually a real image, but in some systems it may be virtual. In a camera, the photographic surface is placed in the plane of this image, and no further optical components are involved. In other instruments, however, this first image may be transferred by one or more *relays*, for the purpose of magnifying it, changing its orientation, or merely moving it to a more convenient location. In visual instruments, an *eyepiece* is added to permit viewing by the observer.

**6.3. Telescope Objectives.** Lenses used as objectives in telescopes are usually of relatively simple form. The human eye has an angular resolution of about 1 minute of arc, is restricted to a very small field of really good definition, and possesses a considerable range of accommodation. Therefore a moderate tolerance in aberrations can be allowed in visual instruments, except when they are of such high magnification that small imperfections become visible to the eye. This situation occurs only in astronomical instruments, and at high magnifications, the field of view becomes so small that even simple optical components give very high performance.

The most common type of objective found in visual instruments, such as low-power telescopes and binoculars, is the simple achromatic lens, illustrated in Figure 4.54. As shown in that Figure, the two-element *achromat* may be either a cemented doublet or a "broken-contact" form. In small diameters, the cemented doublet is almost always found. In larger diameters, it is very difficult to cement lenses without imperfections in the cement layer and without strain in the lenses, and the broken-contact form is often found. Optically there is no essential difference if the two inner surfaces are of the same shape; mechanically, it is more difficult to mount the separate elements of the broken-contact form so that they are correctly and permanently centered and uniformly spaced apart. The tolerances on centering and spacing, in highly corrected astronomical objectives, are of the order of a few tens of microns.

There are two other reasons for the occurrence of broken-contact achromats. One is that there are bound to be minute variations in the actual manufactured article from the specifications of the designer, and especially in elements of large diameter, these variations may be sufficient that the two surfaces do not fit closely enough to permit the cement layer to compensate for the differences without creating bubbles and other irregularities. The second reason is that the existence of four surfaces instead of three gives the optical designer an additional degree of freedom to achieve better performance in designs where precise aberrational correction is required.

A form sometimes found in very old astronomical telescopes, in which the negative flint element is spaced at a considerable distance from the positive crown element, is called the *dialyte* objective. It was adopted at a time when large blanks of flint glass were difficult to procure, and the reduction in diameter made possible by spacing the flint far from the crown was economically and logistically attractive.

The *telephoto* form of objective, however, illustrated in Figure 6.1, has a different purpose. In this form, the positive element is usually an achromat, and it is followed by a negative lens (not necessarily of flint glass) at a considerable distance. The advantage of this form is that its principal planes are at a considerable distance in front of the first element, so that the physical length of the system is less than its effective focal length. In applications where over-all system length must be kept as small as possible, the telephoto lens finds application. As might be expected, it is not amenable to as high a degree of aberrational correction as a conventional objective.

**6.4. Eyepieces.** The *eyepiece* in a visual optical instrument has the function of forming a final virtual image at a considerable distance (nominally at infinity) for convenience in viewing, and of forming the exit pupil of the instrument in a location convenient to the observer and the purpose of the instrument.

As has been shown under geometrical optics, the focal length of the eyepiece is a factor in determining the magnification of the instrument—the shorter the eyepiece focal length, the greater is the magnification. It would appear desirable to make the eyepiece focal length as short as possible in order to make the over-all instrument of minimum size, but there are other factors to consider. If the apparent luminance of the image is to be maintained anywhere near the luminance of the object, then the pupil of the observer's eye must be filled, or nearly filled, with light—that is, the exit pupil diameter must be near the diameter of the eye pupil (about 5 mm). This requirement usually determines the required eyepiece focal length as a function of the instrument magnification and the entrance pupil

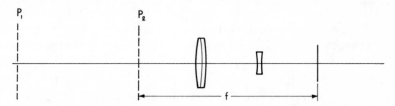

FIGURE 6.1. The telephoto lens. The focal length, f, is considerably greater than the physical length from the first glass surface to the focal plane. Because of the greater focal length, the scale of the photography is larger than it would be for a conventional lens of equal physical length.

diameter. It will be remembered that the ratio of diameters of entrance and exit pupils is equal to the magnification. Sometimes, as in gun sights, it is desirable to make the exit pupil even larger than the eye pupil in order to make the eye position less critical. This makes the required focal length even greater. Again, a long eye relief is sometimes needed, as in a rifle scope, this also increases the required focal length.

Consequently, very short focal length eyepieces are not often found, focal lengths of from 0.5 to 2 inches are the normal range. In most instruments, the entire optical system, including the eyepiece, is designed as a complete system, and there will be a balancing of aberrational residuals among the components. Consequently, an eyepiece designed for one instrument will not usually give its best performance when used with another. An exception to this is in astronomical telescopes and microscopes, for which "standard" eyepieces are used interchangeably. Eyepieces of a variety of focal lengths permit changing the magnification in a convenient manner. In microscopes, magnification changes are also accomplished by interchangeable objectives, in astronomical telescopes, changing of objectives is not feasible.

**6.5. Types of Eyepieces.** There are a number of conventional types of eyepieces which are widely used, the Huygens and Ramsden being the most common. Both the Huygens and Ramsden eyepieces consist of two separated single plano-convex lenses; in the Huygens form (A in Figure 6.2), the two lenses are of different focal length, the field lens having a longer focal length than the eye lens. The convex surfaces face in the same direction. The principal image in the Huygens eyepiece is formed between the two lenses, which makes it inconvenient for use with a reticle whose image is affected by the aberrations of the eye lens alone; these are rather large without the compensating effect of the field lens.

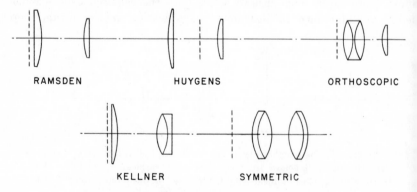

FIGURE 6.2. Some common types of eyepieces.

In the Ramsden form, the two lenses have the same, or very nearly the same, focal length, the convex sides are turned toward each other, and the separation is nearly equal to the focal length of one of the lenses. This provides a primary focal plane outside the field lens, and this form is therefore more convenient for use with a reticle.

Both forms represent optimum solutions for a balance of oblique aberrations for the case of two simple lenses. Some residual aberrations are present, but they are relatively small, and the eyepieces are quite satisfactory for not too demanding applications. Even when these forms are used in a design, however, they are often altered slightly with respect to the individual lens focal lengths and their separation in order to provide optimum performance for a particular application.

The principal planes of these eyepieces are "crossed," as shown in Figure 6.2. This is characteristic of an optical system consisting of two separated thin lenses. As a result, the eye relief is less than the eyepiece focal length.

**6.6. The Kellner Eyepiece.** The principal residual defect in the Ramsden type of eyepiece is lateral chromatic aberration, (corrected in the Huygens type) which appears largely because the separation is usually made less than the optimum condition calls for in order to make the focal plane fall a little away from the surface of the field lens, so that imperfections and dust on this lens do not become quite as disturbing. This residual aberration can be minimized by achromatizing the eye lens. When this is done, the eyepiece is known as a *Kellner*, or achromatized Ramsden type (Figure 6.2C).

**6.7. The Simple Magnifier.** An optical device used for viewing ordinary objects under low magnification, by simply holding the device between the eye and the object, is called a simple magnifier. These are often used as reading aids for people with poor vision, by stamp collectors for close examination of their treasures, by watchmakers and other fine artisans for close work, and in many other applications.

Often the simple magnifier is a single positive lens, which, of course, has large aberrational residuals and therefore does not provide a very satisfactory image, except over an extremely narrow field of view. Ordinary eyepieces are often used as magnifiers, in which case the Huygens arrangement is not useful.

Arrangements which are often used in simple magnifiers are shown in Figure 6.4. The single positive lens is used as a reading glass, and the aberrations are not too severe for magnifications of the order of 2× to 3× over a limited field; its only advantage is that it is simple and inexpensive. The Coddington and triplet forms are used for higher magnifications—of the order of 5× to 10×. The conventional "loupe" of the watch-

FIGURE 6.3. A set of interchangeable eyepieces as supplied with an astronomical telescope. (*Courtesy Unitron Instrument Co.*)

maker is usually a simple positive lens, giving a magnification of 2× to 3×.

All of these magnifiers are useful only for monocular (one-eyed) vision. The simple reading glass is often made large enough to encompass both eyes, but the result is far from satisfactory, for the eyes cannot fuse the resulting images. A type of magnifier is represented schematically in Figure 6.4D, in which aspheric surfaces are provided to facilitate binocular viewing.

Either eyepieces or simple magnifiers are often referred to as *oculars.* The term *eyepiece* is usually reserved for magnifiers which are a part of an optical instrument.

**6.8. Magnification of a Simple Magnifier.** As was discussed in Section 4.62, when the object is placed at the principal focus of a simple magnifier, the magnification (angular) can be expressed as $10/f$, where $f$ is the focal length. Ten inches is the standard reference distance for the determination of this magnification.

It is possible, however, to place the magnifier so that the virtual image is formed at a finite distance, and this is frequently done, especially by young people and by those not accustomed to the use of optical instruments for long periods of time. This condition requires the active use of accommodation by the eye and is therefore more likely to lead to fatigue than were the eye "relaxed" to view an object at infinity. In this case, the magnification depends upon the location of the magnifier and also upon the location of the eye with respect to it. Since the apparent size of the image *as seen from the lens* is the same as the apparent size of the object, it is evident that the closer the object is to the lens, the greater is the magnification for an eye held at the lens. It is also evident that the distance of the final image cannot be made less than the near point of distinct vision, or the eye cannot focus upon it. This, as has been stated above, is about 10 inches for a young adult and is greater for older people.

For any given position of the magnifier with respect to the object, the magnification decreases as the eye is moved away from the magnifier. Therefore, the maximum magnification for a simple magnifier is obtained when the virtual image is formed at the near point of the eye and the eye is held directly against the magnifier.

**6.9. Optical Relays.** Optical relays have been previously defined as optical systems for transferring an image from one point to another. The purpose for this transfer may be merely a geometric one—to locate the image in a different place; more usually, it is for the purpose of changing its orientation or to introduce magnification.

Optical relays used in visual instruments for changing the orientation of the image so that the observer sees it in its proper attitude (right-handed and erect) are called *erecting systems* or *erectors*. These systems may, in many instruments, also combine the functions of magnification and image transfer.

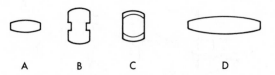

A       B       C       D

FIGURE 6.4. Some common types of simple magnifiers: (A) single lens, (B) Coddington, (C) triplet, (D) aspheric reading glass.

For the purposes of this discussion, reflecting components—mirrors and prisms—are included in the discussion of optical relays, although they do not form new images, but merely displace and/or reorient them. They are frequently used as erecting systems.

Figure 6.5 shows a common form of lens erecting system, which is here called a *collimating erector*, although this name is not in general use. It consists of a pair of lenses—usually achromatic—with a relatively wide separation. They are so located that the first image plane is at the principal focus of the first lens, and the second image plane is at the principal focus of the second lens. Thus, the rays between the two lenses are *collimated*, i.e., they proceed from infinite object and/or image points. This arrangement has the small advantage that the separation of the lenses is not critical; an instrument of this form may be disassembled by separating it between the two erecting lenses and reassembled without undue concern about alignment.

If the focal length of the two lenses is the same, the image transfer is accomplished at unit magnification, and the image is *inverted* (rotated 180°). The two lenses may be made of different focal length to provide magnification.

Figure 6.6 shows a form of erecting system often used in moderate power telescopes. It is usually composed of single lenses, and is frequently incorporated mechanically with the eyepiece, thus forming a unit known as a *terrestrial eyepiece*. Astronomical telescopes, which consist of merely an objective and an eyepiece, give inverted images; this makes no difference to astronomers, but it would be inconvenient to use this form of telescope for viewing objects in a landscape—thus the term *terrestrial* for an erecting eyepiece system.

The purpose of incorporating the erector with the eyepiece is to permit

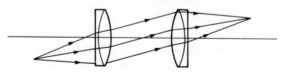

FIGURE 6.5. Lens erecting system—collimating type.

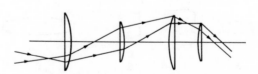

FIGURE 6.6. Terrestrial eyepiece. An erecting system combined with an eyepiece.

a telescope to be used for either astronomical or terrestrial purposes by the interchange of eyepieces.

**6.10. Varifocal Erecting Systems.** Some telescopes are provided with a means for changing the magnification by changing the position of lenses in an erecting system. Figure 6.7 shows the functional arrangement for accomplishing this. At A, the lenses of the erecting system are shown in the position of maximum magnification. For the purposes of this diagram, the lenses are assumed to be of the same focal length, although this may not be the case in an actual instrument. If the focal lengths are the same, then merely interchanging their relative distances from object to image provides the reciprocal of the original magnification, which is the minimum magnification. The distance between object and image planes remains the same, so that no further adjustment in the instrument is necessary.

In some instruments, only these two alternate positions are provided, giving two values for the over-all magnification. In other instruments, it is possible to change the magnification continuously and still maintain the object and image planes in the same location. Over a limited range, whose extremes are represented by reciprocal arrangements such as those shown in Figure 6.7, for any position of one of the lenses, there is a position for the other so that the image will be formed at the same point. These various

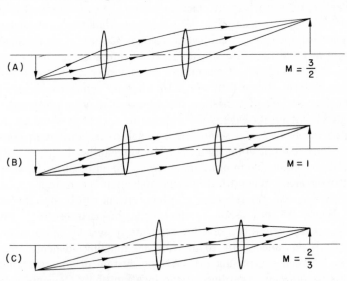

FIGURE 6.7. Varifocal erecting system. The positions of the lenses are shown for three values of linear magnification—maximum, minimum and unit power.

relative positions of the lenses form a continuous variation of magnification.

Such arrangements are now known under the name of "zoom" systems, although they were in common use before this term, which was invented for application to certain types of photographic objectives, was proposed. The required motions of the lenses is nonlinear, and for a simple two-lens solution, one of the lenses moves in opposite directions in different parts of the range.

These arrangements have a certain convenience, but are not too frequently found. A price in terms of image quality has to be paid for the flexibility—more in the case of the continuously variable arrangement than for the two-step configuration. It is not usually possible to keep the image in focus with satisfactory precision in the continuous arrangement, and there is a considerable variation in image quality with magnification.

**6.11. Prism Erecting Systems.** The most common application of prism erecting systems is in binoculars, but they are used in a wide variety of instruments. Prisms are also commonly used to change the direction of the optical axis of an instrument in order to give it a configuration which suits its particular purpose. A periscope for use in a submarine or a tank is an example.

Flat mirrors would serve equally as well, from an optical standpoint, as the reflecting prisms which are usually found. Unless a large aperture is required, however, prisms have the advantage that the relation between their reflecting faces is not subject to change because of mechanical misalignment or movement; in addition, their surfaces are more easily maintained—dust does not affect reflectivity to the same extent as it does on the surface of a front-surfaced mirror, and when, as sometimes is necessary, the reflecting surface of a prism is metallized, it may be protected with a coating of paint on its back. Mirrors used in optical systems are always coated on the front surface—not on the back as is familiar in household mirrors; the extra reflection from the front, unmetallized surface, although faint and not noticeable in ordinary mirrors, would be objectionable in an optical instrument. When total internal reflection occurs in a prism, as is frequently the case, the reflectivity is higher than can be obtained with a mirror. Figure 6.8 shows some common types of prism erecting systems.

In those cases where two or more separate prisms make up an erecting system, it is not uncommon to find optical imaging elements (lenses or mirrors) between the prisms. An erecting system of the reflecting type performs its function regardless of the location of its elements along the optical axis. In the optical system shown in Figure 6.9, the erecting system consists of the Penta prism in the head and the roof prism in the lower

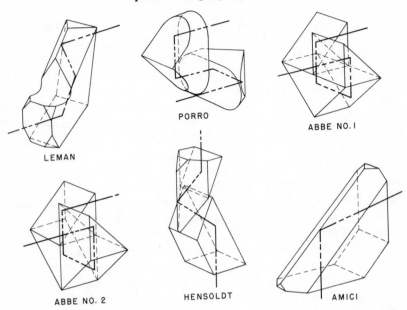

PORRO

ABBE NO. I

LEMAN

ABBE NO. 2

HENSOLDT

AMICI

FIGURE 6.8. Some common types of prism erecting systems. None of these prisms require silvered surfaces. It will be noted that the Porro and both of the Abbe systems are optically identical—they differ only in the construction.

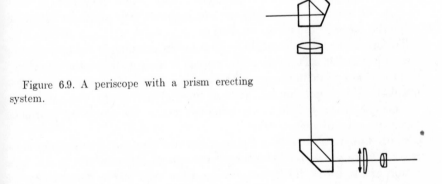

Figure 6.9. A periscope with a prism erecting system.

bend. The objective lens is located between. This form of optical system is used in some military gunsights.

**6.12. Requirements for an Erect Image.** In Chapter 4, it was shown that a right-handed image can always be brought into the same orientation as the object (erected) by rotation about the optical axis. It was also shown that a left-handed image cannot be erected by rotation.

If there are an even number of reflecting surfaces in an optical system (excluding image-forming mirrors) then the image is right-handed, although it may not be erect. If the system has an odd number of reflecting surfaces, the image is left-handed, and cannot be erected without the addition or deletion of one of the reflecting surfaces.

When the image is right-handed, but not erect, it can be rotated into the erect position only by changing the reflecting surface arrangement in the instrument, or by adding more reflecting surfaces, *in pairs*, in an appropriate orientation.

The general rule, therefore, follows: *For an erect image, there must be an even number of reflections in the system.*

**6.13. Derotating Prisms.** In many optical systems, bends are necessary to accomplish some specific purpose, and the reflecting surfaces which are introduced to produce these bends may result in a left-handed or a right-handed, non-erect image. This occurs, for example, in the system of Figure 6.9 if the prism in the upper head is rotated about a vertical axis to scan along the horizon. In the position shown in the Figure, the system has an erect image; if the upper prism is rotated 90°, the image is rotated through a similar angle.

In cases of this sort, *derotating prisms* are used. Derotating prisms have the property that they rotate an image when the prism is rotated about the optical axis. Figure 6.10 shows a few common varieties.

Derotating prisms have the common property that they always contain an odd number of reflecting surfaces, and that they rotate the image at twice the speed of the prism rotation.

To correct the image rotation resulting from scanning in the optical system of Figure 6.9, a Dove derotating prism is inserted below the objective, and the Penta prism in the head is changed to a right-angle prism (see Figure 6.11). The derotator is driven at one-half the angular speed of the right-angle prism, and the image remains erect for the observer, regardless of the direction of view.

**6.14. Constant-deviation Prisms.** Certain types of prisms have *constant deviation;* i.e., the deviation of the optical axis is unchanged by rotation of the prism. These prisms are often used where insensitivity to prism alignment about a particular axis is desired. Figure 6.12 shows some types of constant-deviation prisms.

The prisms shown at A and B are constant-deviation with respect to one axis of rotation of the prism, which is shown. The Penta prism is almost universally used in optical rangefinders because of its constant-deviation property. The prism shown in D is the retroreflector, or triple mirror, whose reflecting surfaces form the corner of a cube. This arrangement is constant deviation about all axes of rotation, so that a ray of light incident

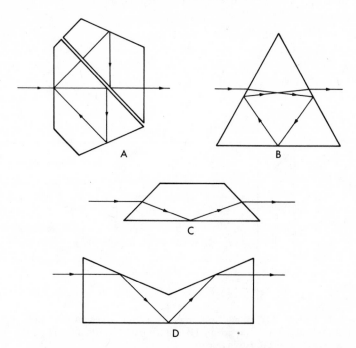

FIGURE 6.10. Some common types of derotating prisms. These prisms have the common properties that the exit direction is parallel to the entrance direction and they have an odd number of reflections: (A) Schmidt or Pechan prism, (B) Delta prism, (C) Dove prism, (D) K prism.

FIGURE 6.11. A periscope with a derotating prism.

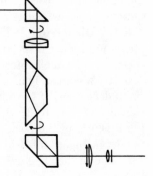

upon it is returned in the direction from which it came, regardless of the orientation of the prism.

In the optical spectrum, the retroreflector is frequently used in signalling systems; it is the element which is used in retroreflective road signs for re-

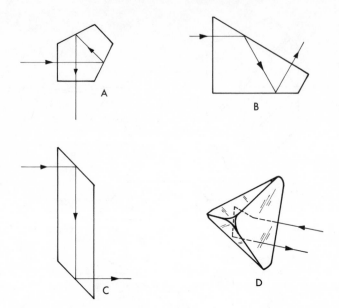

FIGURE 6.12. Some common types of constant-deviation prisms: (A) penta prism, (B) unnamed, (C) rhomboid, (D) retroreflector or triple mirror.

turning the beams of headlights to the driver. In this application, the retroreflectors are deliberately made imperfect—if they were perfect, the light would return to the headlights and would never be seen by the driver.

In the radar spectrum, retroreflectors are made of three reflectors mounted as the corner of a cube; they are used for alignment of radar antennas and as signal return devices on cooperative targets.

**6.15. Dispersing Prisms.** Prisms are used in spectrographic instruments to produce a spectrum by dispersion. These will be discussed under spectrographs in Chapter 8.

**6.16. Wedges.** Thin prisms, called *wedges*, are often used to produce small deflections of the optical axis. When a triangular prism is oriented as shown in Figure 6.13, with the ray within the prism parallel to its base, the prism is in the position of *minimum* deviation. The deviation of the ray ($\Delta$ in Figure 6.13) is a minimum for this position.

It can be shown that,[1] for small angles $u$ and $i$, the deviation is given by

$$\delta = (\mu - 1)\theta \tag{6.1}$$

where $\theta$ is the apex angle of the prism. When this angle is small, the actual

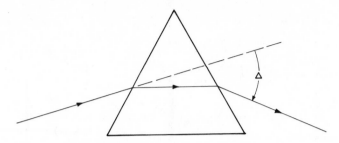

FIGURE 6.13. Minimum deviation in a prism.

deviation does not vary significantly from this value even when the position of minimum deviation is not maintained.

*Counter-rotating Wedges.* Variable deviation may be provided by counter-rotating wedges, as shown in Figure 6.14.

Let the deviation of each of the two wedges be $\Delta$. If they are mounted with their bases parallel, but opposite, the deviation of the first wedge is $\Delta$, and that of the second is $-\Delta$, so that they cancel.

If the first wedge is rotated through $\theta$, and the second through $-\theta$, as shown in the figure, then the horizontal components, $\Delta \sin \theta$ and $-\Delta \sin (-\theta)$, cancel and therefore

$$\Delta_h = 0 \tag{6.2}$$

while the vertical components, $\Delta \cos \theta$ and $-\Delta \cos (-\theta)$, add, and

$$\Delta_v = 2\Delta \cos \theta \tag{6.3}$$

Counter-rotating wedges are used in rangefinders to measure the paral-

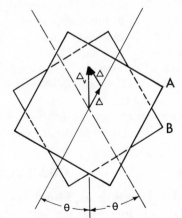

FIGURE 6.14. Counter-rotating wedges.

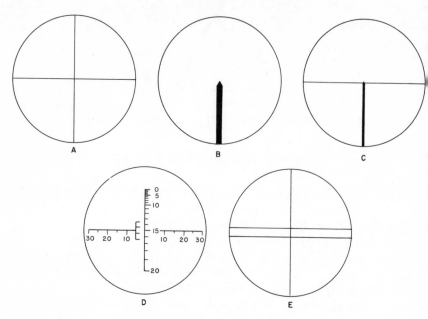

FIGURE 6.15. Some common reticle patterns.

lax of the target, which determines range, and sometimes in systems for scanning a spot across a straight line.

**6.17. Reticles.** *Reticles* are patterns placed in the focal plane of an optical instrument for the purpose of providing a reference. Sometimes, the reticle is a simple cross-hair, as shown in A of Figure 6.15. Figures 6.15 B and C show two other varieties used in rifle scopes. More complicated patterns are often used, especially in military instruments. Grid reticles are provided in microscopes for some types of work, such as blood cell counting. Measurement scales are frequently found.

Reticles are usually engraved on glass, and filled with a suitable material. Occasionally, reticles will consist of fine wires strung across the field of view. They are placed in a focal plane, so that they will be in focus with the image.

When an instrument contains a lens erecting system, and a focusing eyepiece, the reticle is usually placed in the first focal plane.

## CHARACTERISTICS

**6.18. Focusing of Visual Instruments**—*the Diopter*. Most optical instruments for visual use have provisions for focusing to accommodate the eye of the observer. The normal human eye has the capacity to focus for objects from infinity (far point) to a minimum distance (near point) which varies with the age of the individual, being about 10 inches for a young adult. Many individuals are affected with *ammetropia*, which describes a displacement of the near and far points from their normal positions. In *myopia*, the far point is at a finite distance, and the near point is usually closer than normal. Such individuals wear eyeglasses with negative power to permit them to focus on distant objects. In *hyperopia*, the far point is beyond infinity (actually corresponding to a virtual object behind the observer), and the near point is farther away than normal. Age is always accompanied by a progressive hyperopia, referred to as *presbyopia*.

Normally, a visual optical instrument should be focused so that the final image lies at infinity; this permits an observer with normal vision to observe the image at his far point, hence with an eye which is relaxed to a maximum.

However, individuals not accustomed to using optical instruments continuously find great difficulty in relaxing the eye sufficiently to observe at the far point and, if left to their own choice, will focus an instrument so that the final image lies not far beyond their near point of vision. In doing this, they introduce *refracting power* into the instrument, making it equivalent to eyeglasses.

This power is conventionally described in the same terms as the refracting power of eyeglasses, that is, in *diopters*. Refracting power is the reciprocal of the focal length. Thus, if $P$ is the refracting power, and $f$ the focal length, then

$$P = 1/f \tag{6.4}$$

when $f$ is expressed in *meters*, then $P$ is expressed in *diopters*. Thus, if a visual instrument is focused so that the final image lies 2 meters in front of the observer, the instrument is said to be set at $-\frac{1}{2}$ diopter. If the instrument is set (by an observer with hyperopia) so that it forms an image 4 meters behind the observer, it is said to be set at $+\frac{1}{4}$ diopter.

**6.19. Parallax.** *Parallax* is a term used to describe the apparent shift of a near object with respect to a distant object as the observer moves from side to side. Hold the index finger vertically at arm's length and observe its projection against a distant scene as it is observed first with one eye and then with the other. It appears to shift from side to side; this is parallax.

Parallax causes errors in the reading of clocks and gages when they are observed from the side and the hands are not in contact with the face. Parallax is used to measure the distances of the nearer stars by observing their apparent shift against the background of more distant stars when seen from opposite sides of the earth's orbit. Parallax is used in range finders, which observe a target from two ends of the instrument and detect its apparent shift of direction.

Parallax also occurs in optical instruments which contain reticles when the image of the field of view is not in exact coincidence with the plane of the reticle pattern. When this condition occurs, a shift of the observer's eye from one side of the exit pupil to the other causes the reticle to shift with respect to the image.

Parallax can cause errors in a sighting instrument such as a rifle scope, so that it is important that such instruments be adjusted so that the image of the field of view falls exactly on the reticle. Parallax also provides a sensitive method for focusing an optical instrument.

**6.20. Depth of Focus and Depth of Field.** The *depth of focus* of an optical instrument is the difference in focal position which can be tolerated without sensible degradation of the image quality. Obviously, its value depends upon what is considered to be "sensible degradation," and will vary with circumstances.

Let $x$ be the permissible image spread due to defocusing, this value having been established by some suitable criterion. Then, as can be seen in Figure 6.16, the depth of focus, $s$, or range over which the focused image may vary, is

$$s = 2xF \tag{6.5}$$

where $F$ is the relative aperture of the system in the image space.

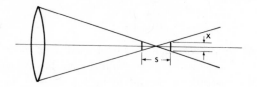

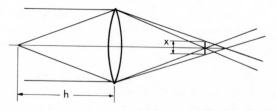

FIGURE 6.16. Depth of focus and hyperfocal distance.

The *depth of field* is the corresponding range of distances in the object space which will displace the final image over a range $s$. From the Newtonian form of the lens equation, $xx' = f^2$, it is seen that the depth of field is

$$s' = f^2/s = f^2/2xF = fD/2x \qquad (6.6)$$

where $D$ is the aperture of the optical system.

**6.21. Hyperfocal Distance.** In photographic systems, a distance called the *hyperfocal distance* is sometimes specified. This is the distance of an object whose image is displaced from the principal focal plane by an amount which will degrade the image quality by an acceptable tolerance. Using the relation of Equation (6.5), the hyperfocal distance can be shown to be

$$h = \frac{D + x}{x} \qquad (6.7)$$

In small cameras, it is customary to use an image degradation criterion of one angular mil ($x = f/1000$), and tables are frequently provided giving the corresponding hyperfocal distance. This criterion is quite arbitrary and may not always be appropriate. Substituting in Equation (6.7) gives, for this assumption

$$h \approx 1000F \qquad (6.7a)$$

where $F$ is the relative aperture.

**6.22. Resolving Power and Resolution.** The *resolution* of an optical system is its capacity for imaging fine detail. It may be expressed in either linear or angular terms. In the case of an astronomical telescope, the *resolving power* is the capacity of the instrument for "separating" the images of close point objects. Since astronomical telescopes, for objects on the optical axis, are corrected to the highest possible degree, the resolving power is determined essentially by the diffraction pattern of the circular aperture for point sources of light (stars).

In Section 2.71, the diffraction pattern of a circular aperture for a point source was seen to consist of a bright central disc of diameter $1.22\lambda/D$ where $D$ is the aperture diameter, surrounded by a series of circular rings. An intensity plot of this diffraction pattern was shown in Figure 2.43. When two close point objects are imaged by an optical system, the diffraction patterns overlap, and the result is the sum of their separate intensity plots. Figure 6.17 shows the results for two patterns which are separated by a distance $\lambda/D$, $1.22\lambda/D$ and $2\lambda/D$. It is seen that the separation of the central pair represents the case for which a slight dip in the intensity pattern halfway between the centers of the two images just be-

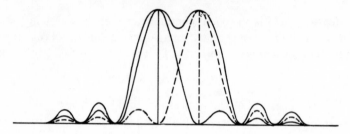

FIGURE 6.17. Diffraction pattern for two close points.

gins to appear. By convention, this condition represents the limit of resolution of the optical system in question.

The *diffraction-limited resolving power* of a circular aperture, therefore,
expressed in *angular* terms, is

$$\theta = 1.22\lambda/D \qquad (6.8)$$

where $D$ is the *diameter* of the exit pupil of the system.

Rigorously, the dimension involved is not the diameter, but the quantity
$2\mu'L' \sin U'$. For the usual case, $\mu'$ is unity, $L' =$ the focal length, and
therefore, when $U'$ is small, the quantity $2\mu'L' \sin U'$ is equal to the
diameter. For the object space, the quantity becomes $2\mu L \sin U$, which is
the real reason for the adoption of the name *numerical aperture* for the
quantity $\mu \sin U$. This term is used in connection with microscopes, but it
is applicable to any form of instrument.

The linear separation of the images in the focal plane for the case of
diffraction-limited resolution is the focal length times the angular separation given by Equation (6.8), or

$$s = 1.22\lambda f/D \qquad (6.9)$$

but $f/D = F$, the relative aperture, so that

$$s = 1.22\lambda F \qquad (6.10)$$

For light of wavelength 5500Å, $1.22\lambda = .00055$ mm $= .000022$ inch.
Equation (6.8) may be expressed in the form usually used in astronomy,
by substituting the inch measure above, and expressing $\theta$ in seconds of arc
instead of in radians (1 radian $= 206,265$ seconds) to give

$$\theta(\text{seconds}) = 4.5/D \qquad (6.11)$$

where $D$ is the telescope aperture in inches.

In instruments used for imaging pictorial fields of view, it is customary
to express the *resolution* in terms of the number of resolvable elements per
millimeter. The number of elements per unit length is the reciprocal of the

element size, so substituting the value of 1.22λ (in millimeters) into Equation (6.10), and taking the reciprocal, gives the resolution:

$$\tilde{s} = 1500/F \text{ (lines/mm)} \tag{6.12}$$

It should be noted that the angular resolving power of an instrument is determined by the diameter of its aperture, and is independent of focal length. On the other hand, the resolution in lines per millimeter is dependent upon the relative aperture and is independent of the physical size of the instrument. Resolution in lines per millimeter is a useful measure of the relative amount of detail in a given image—it tells nothing regarding the ability of the instrument to resolve detail in the objects it views. The measure of capacity for resolving detail in an object is the angular resolution, which is given for the diffraction-limited case by Equation (6.8); this is dependent upon the instrument *aperture* only.

The expression "lines per millimeter" comes from the field of photography, where the word *lines* refers to the conventional forms of targets used for testing lenses, which are illustrated in the chapter on optical measurements. These targets consist of blocks of parallel lines, and thus permit the measurement of resolution in different directions.

In an actual instrument, the resolution is not often that set by the diffraction limit of the aperture concerned. In most instruments, residual aberrations establish the resolution limit at a somewhat degraded level from the diffraction criterion. Lines per millimeter is the customary method of expression; if this is $\tilde{s}$ for a given instrument, then its angular resolution, in radians is $1/\tilde{s}f$.

More meaningful measures of the performance of optical systems have been developed in recent years, based upon the concepts of communications theory; these are discussed in Chapter 9.

The term "diffraction-limited" optical system is often heard—this refers to a system whose state of correction is such that its performance is reasonably close to the limit set by diffraction. This has always been the case for astronomical instruments working close to the optical axis; recently, however, it has been possible to produce systems of considerable complexity and with extended fields of view whose performance is sufficiently good to justify the term diffraction-limited.

**6.23. Dependence of Resolving Power on Wavelength.** The resolving power as set by the diffraction limit is proportional to the wavelength of the radiation involved, as evident in Equations (6.8), (6.9) and (6.10). In the infrared region of the spectrum, where the wavelengths involved may be of the order of 10 to 20 times that of the visible spectrum, the resolving power of a given aperture is degraded by this factor.

In radar and microwave systems, the wavelengths are in the millimeter and centimeter region, and are tens of thousands of times as large as for the visible spectrum. A microwave system working at 1-cm wavelength, for example, would require an antenna aperture of more than a thousand feet to equal the diffraction limit of a one inch aperture working in visible light. This explains the immense antennas which are erected for work in radio astronomy and in high-precision radar tracking equipment. In radar systems, the use of coherent illumination makes it possible to work well below the actual diffraction limit for some applications; in radio astronomy, the instruments are dependent upon the incoherent radiation received from celestial bodies, and hence their resolving power is limited by diffraction.

**6.24. Field of View.** The term "field of view" has been used in previous chapters as if it were self-explanatory. It is the angular extent of the scene which is formed in the final image by the instrument.

A single lens will form images of everything within a hemisphere, but of course the image quality is reasonably good only within a limited region about the optical axis. When a number of lenses are put in series to form an instrument, the field of view of the combination is limited by the sizes of the lenses and their distribution—that is to say, by the pupil conditions of the instrument.

The actual field of view of an instrument is usually limited by a physical diaphragm placed in a focal plane. The size of the field of view admitted by this diaphragm is determined by decision of the designer with respect to image quality and to vignetting. Vignetting has been explained in Section 4.55 as the blocking of light to off-axis image points by the pupil system.

In visual instruments, a considerable amount of vignetting at the edge of the field of view is commonly permitted; the eye is not highly sensitive to moderate changes in illumination, and a decrease of as much as 50 per cent in the image illumination at the edge of the field is not usually objectionable. Allowance of vignetting makes it possible to provide a wider field of view without increasing the size of the elements in the system.

**6.25. Other System Characteristics.** Additional characteristics of optical systems, which are important in their description and definition, have been dealt with at length in previous sections. These include *magnification, eye relief, relative aperture, pupil diameters, focal length,* and others.

## TELESCOPES

**6.26. The Simple Telescope.** The definition of a *telescope*, as discussed in Section 4.12, is an optical system whose focal length is infinite. Both

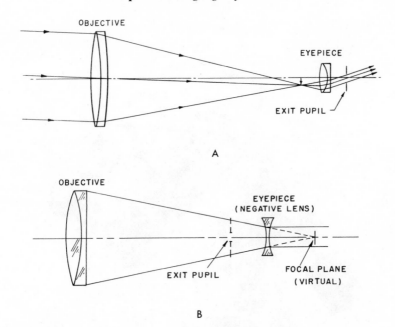

FIGURE 6.18. Two forms of the simple telescope: A-Keplerian; B-Galilean.

object and image lie at infinity. The *simple telescope* consists simply of an objective and an eyepiece, so arranged that their separation is equal to the sum of their focal lengths. Figure 6.18 illustrates the two forms of simple telescope: the Keplerian, A, which has a positive eyepiece, and the Galilean, B, which has a negative eyepiece.

The Keplerian is the most commonly used form and is the form of all refracting visual astronomical telescopes. The image is inverted, but in astronomical work this is of no consequence.

The Galilean telescope has an erect image—it can therefore be used for terrestrial applications without the need for an erecting system. It is used in inexpensive binoculars. The fact that its exit pupil is inside the instrument, and therefore inaccessible to the eye, is a serious defect which severely limits the field of view.

**6.27. Reflecting Telescopes.** Reference has been made to the fact that curved mirrors have the same optical properties as the curved surfaces of lenses, the effective index of refraction for the case of reflecting surfaces being $-1.0$. The use of mirrors in place of lenses in optical systems have two advantages: (1) they can be fabricated in much larger sizes than are possible with lenses because they need not be transparent, and therefore

FIGURE 6.18A. A typical astronomical refracting telescope. This model is a 4-inch diameter instrument, equipped with a number of accessories. The main optical system is furnished with six eyepieces, interchangeable by means of a turreted mount. There is a low-power finder telescope at the left of the main tube, and a high-power finder at the right, the latter also equipped with a six-eyepiece turret. Focusing knobs for the main telescope and for the high-power finder can be seen. Both polar and declination axes have graduated circles, and a mechanical clock drive is mounted on the pedestal. (*Courtesy Unitron Instrument Co.*)

not completely homogeneous, and (2) they have no chromatic aberration since the effective index of refraction does not vary with wavelength. Their disadvantage in an optical system is that there is only one surface available for the optical designer to manipulate.

There are several conventional forms of reflecting telescopes which have been known and in use for a long time as astronomical instruments.[3] These are based upon surfaces which, *by definition*, produce aberration-free images of infinitely distant points. It is easy to show that the reflecting surface required to focus a beam of rays parallel to the axis to a point is a paraboloid of revolution. The cross section of such a surface, which is a parabola, is shown in Figure 6.19. The geometrical definition of a parabola is the locus of points whose distances from a point and a line are equal. Let the line be a wave front, as shown in the figure, and the point be the focus. Then the parabola satisfies Fermat's principle (Section 2.43).

It is also possible to define a reflecting surface which will maintain perfect imagery between two conjugate axial points at finite distances; there are two solutions: the ellipsoid and the hyperboloid, illustrated in Figure 6.20 as their cross sections—the ellipse and the hyperbola.

It may be shown, for both of these surfaces, that their geometrical definitions satisfy Fermat's principle, as was the case for the parabola and an infinite object point.

The paraboloid alone, and the combination of the paraboloid with an optical relay consisting of either an ellipsoid or an hyperboloid, form the three conventional forms of reflecting telescope—the *Newtonian*, the *Cassegrainian* and the *Gregorian*, described below.

These forms give diffraction-limited imagery on the optical axis by

FIGURE 6.19. The parabola.

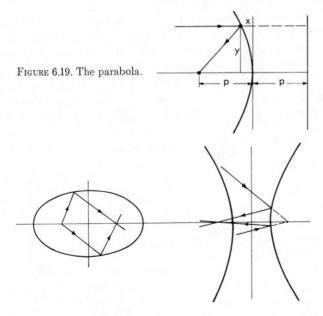

FIGURE 6.20. The ellipse and the hyperbola.

geometrical definition (provided they are fabricated to the correct curvature to a fraction of a wavelength of light). They do not permit any control of off-axis aberrations because the surface forms are already defined by the axial requirement. As a result, they are useful in their basic form only for very limited fields of view; in most astronomical applications, this is not a particularly severe restriction.

**6.28. The Newtonian Telescope.** The Newtonian telescope utilizes a single paraboloidal mirror, with a diagonal flat mirror for projecting the image outside the entrance beam to make it available to the observer. It is illustrated in Figure 6.21.

Coma is the predominant aberration in the paraboloidal mirror; this aberration, which it will be remembered affects only off-axis points, sets in so rapidly that the paraboloidal mirror has a useful field of view of less than a degree in most cases. It is possible to introduce refracting elements near the focal plane to make a partial correction for this condition, thus extending the useful field of view to some extent. Ross has designed such corrective systems.[4]

In the Hale 200-inch telescope on Mt. Palomar, which, being the largest telescope currently in existence, is logically the most famous, the aperture is sufficiently large that the observer can ride in a cage at the prime focus of the paraboloidal mirror, making a diagonal mirror unnecessary. The telescope is illustrated in Figure 6.22.

**6.29. Compound Reflecting Telescopes.** The combination of a paraboloidal primary mirror with either an ellipsoidal or an hyperboloidal secondary mirror comprises a *compound reflecting telescope.* The geometrical relation of the three forms are shown in Figure 6.23.

In the Cassegrainian form, an hyperboloidal convex secondary mirror is interposed in front of the primary focus, and a secondary focus is formed, usually behind the primary, where it is readily accessible to photographic

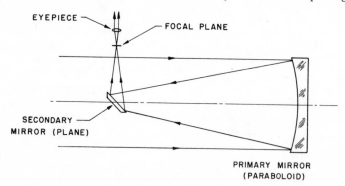

FIGURE 6.21. Conventional form of the Newtonian telescope.

FIGURE 6.22. The 200-inch Hale Telescope at Mt. Palomar. This is the largest telescope so far constructed, having a primary mirror diameter of 200 inches. Its primary focal length is 660 inches, and secondary mirrors provide for a variety of arrangements with longer focal lengths. It has a paraboloidal primary mirror—when used with secondary mirrors, it becomes Cassegrainian in form. This illustration shows an observer at the instrument's prime focus; this is the only telescope large enough to permit this sort of arrangement. Although there is no diagonal mirror, the prime focus is often referred to as the Newtonian focus. (*Photo by Mt. Wilson Observatory*)

plate or eyepiece. In the Gregorian form, a concave ellipsoidal secondary mirror is located beyond the primary focus, also forming a secondary image, which may be located behind the primary mirror. The Gregorian form is not often found in use, its optical performance being somewhat inferior to the Cassegrainian. Even the Cassegrainian form, however, has most of the comatic defect of its paraboloidal primary, and is useful only over a very limited field.

The presence of the secondary mirror changes the system focal length

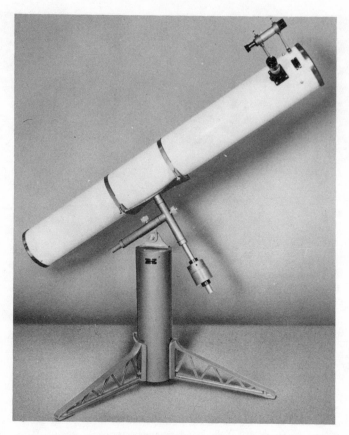

FIGURE 6.22A. A typical Newtonian telescope. This telescope, of a size commonly used by amateur observers, has a 6-inch diameter paraboloidal primary mirror. It is shown on an adjustable equatorial mount and has a small finder telescope at the eyepiece end. (*Courtesy Cave Optical Co.*)

from that of the primary mirror. Equation 4.57 for the focal length of two thin lenses may be written

$$f = \frac{f_1 f_2}{f_1 + f_2 - t} \tag{6.13}$$

where $f$ is the combined focal length, $f_1$ and $f_2$ the focal lengths of the two components, and $t$ their separation. Incidentally, this equation also shows that the condition for a telescope ($f = \infty$) applies when $t = f_1 + f_2$.

FIGURE 6.22B. Balloon-borne telescope Stratoscope I. The cylindrical tube in the center of the framework is the telescope—a 12-inch diameter Cassegrainian reflector with a resolving power of better than ½ second of arc. The framework is the structure which carries it below a plastic balloon. This instrument, carried to 80,000 feet, obtained photographs of the sun which showed details of its surface structure never before clearly observed. Its successor, Stratoscope II, a 36-inch diameter telescope, has also flown. (*Courtesy Perkin-Elmer Corp.*)

Figure 6.24 shows the geometry of the Cassegrainian.

The *amplification* of the instrument is the ratio of the effective focal length of the combination, $f$, to the focal length of the primary, $f_1$. The $f$/No. of the instrument is the $f$/No. of the primary times the amplification. Amplifications of the order of 4 or 5 are common, occasionally reaching as high as 10. It is evident that to produce an instrument with a relative aperture of, say, $f/6$, with an amplification of 3, the relative aperture of the primary must be $f/2$. Since it is generally impracticable to produce a paraboloidal mirror with a relative aperture of greater than $f/1$ to a

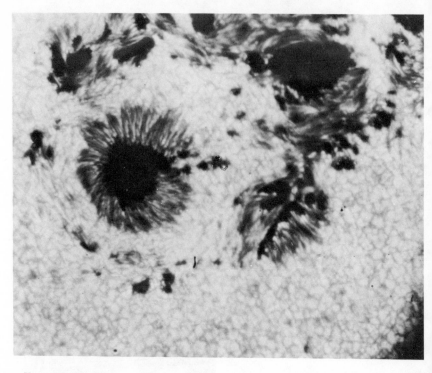

FIGURE 6.22C. Fine structure of the solar surface. This photograph, in the region of a small group of sunsports, was obtained with the instrument shown in Figure 6.22B. The sun's surface is seen to be dotted with more or less independent clouds of incandescent gas. (*Courtesy Perkin-Elmer Corp.*)

high degree of optical perfection, the Cassegrainian form of telescope is not readily made with large relative apertures, especially when the amplification is made moderately high in order to provide a long focal length within a limited length of instrument. $f/8$ to $f/10$ are common values for this type of instrument.

The following equations give the relations between the variables shown in Figure 6.24.

$$s_6 = \frac{f}{f_1} (f_1 - t) = G(f_1 - t) \tag{6.14}$$

$$f_2 = \frac{G}{1 - G_1} (f_1 - t) \tag{6.15}$$

$$G = \frac{f}{f_1} \tag{6.16}$$

FIGURE 6.22D. The Baker-Nunn Satellite Tracking Telescope. Its 30-inch diameter primary mirror works in conjunction with a correction plate containing three elements. At the edge of its 15° field of view, 80 per cent of the light from a star is imaged within a spot only 50μ in diameter. A three-axis mounting drives the instrument to follow the motion of satellites, thus obtaining a maximum exposure on the photographic film for these faint objects. The optical design is a modification of the classical Schmidt camera, developed by Dr. J. G. Baker; optical elements were manufactured by Perkin-Elmer. (*Courtesy Perkin-Elmer Corp.*)

It should be noted that $f_1$ is positive for a concave mirror, and $f_2$ is negative. The distance $t$ is counted positive. The diameter of the secondary mirror is larger as the amplification is reduced, so that very low amplifications are not practicable because they lead to a large obstruction of the aperture, and consequent loss of illumination and degradation of image.

It is quite feasible to provide more than one Cassegrainian secondary with a given primary mirror, and this is customarily done in large astronomical instruments. Figure 6.25 shows how three different secondaries may be used with a single primary to provide three different focal lengths

FIGURE 6.22E. Super-Schmidt Meteor camera. This is a Schmidt-type optical system, as modified by Baker. It has a relative aperture of about $f/0.6$. A number of these instruments are in use, for the purpose of surveying the sky to record meteors. (*Courtesy Perkin-Elmer Corp.*)

(and relative apertures). An extreme focal length, such as shown in the Coudé focus in Figure 6.25 is useful in astronomical work for spectrographic purposes; in the Hale telescope, for example, a focal length of 6000 inches is provided for a spectrograph. The light beam is piped through the axes of the instrument mount to an observation chamber below the observatory floor.

The Gregorian form of compound reflecting telescope is, as has been mentioned, not often found in use. It gives an erect image, which is perhaps one of the reasons for its lack of popularity, since it is different in this respect than other astronomical instruments.

Observations with large astronomical telescopes are carried on almost exclusively by photography, therefore it is not rigorously correct to call them telescopes—they should be called cameras. However, they are capable of visual use and are on rare occasions thus employed. For certain types of work, such as planetary observation, the human eye has an advantage over the photographic plate, in that it can take advantage

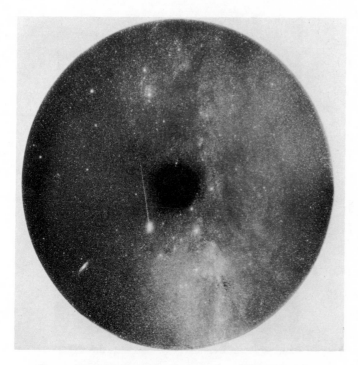

FIGURE 6.22F. Photograph from the Super-Schmidt. Because of the very high relative aperture of this instrument, illustrated in Figure 6.22E, there is vignetting at the center of the field, due to the focal plane assembly. A meteor trail appears near the middle of the photograph. The breaks in the trail are caused by a shutter in the camera; they permit measurements of the meteor's velocity (*Courtesy Perkin-Elmer Corp.*)

of the variations in atmospheric "seeing" and obtain unusually clear definition in those transient instants when the seeing becomes excellent. The photographic plate must integrate the variations in image quality due to seeing over the duration of the exposure.

The larger telescopes are used for the most part to collect observations of the fainter and more distant objects in the universe, and thus require the integrating power of the photographic plate, exposed for a long period of time (sometimes hours) to record these dim objects. Brighter objects can be left for the smaller instruments.

**6.30. Diffraction Images with Obstructed Apertures.** Any obstruction to the aperture of an optical system has its effect on the size and shape of the diffraction image it forms. If the obstruction is symmetrical and small, the degradation is not particularly serious, but large obstruc-

FIGURE 6.22G. The ADH telescope. This telescope, named for the three observatories sharing in
its construction, installation and use (Armagh,
Dunsink and Harvard), was designed by Baker,
and is a 32-inch diameter, $f/3.75$ system, of an
aspheric Cassegrainian form. (*Courtesy Perkin-
Elmer Corp.*)

tions or unsymmetrical ones may deteriorate the image quality due to
undesirable diffraction patterns to an unacceptable extent. Figure 6.26
shows the patterns produced by several types of apertures.

Any centered reflecting optical system cannot avoid aperture obstruction; even with a single mirror, one must place something in the focal plane
or the instrument is useless. It is possible, however, to avoid aperture obstruction with a so-called off-axis system. Such systems represent a section
cut from a larger, centered system, and therefore would more correctly
be called "off-center" systems; but the term "off-axis" is in common use.
Figure 6.27 shows an example of such a system, using the conventional
Cassegrainian form as an example.

When the mirrors forming such a system are not spherical, as would be

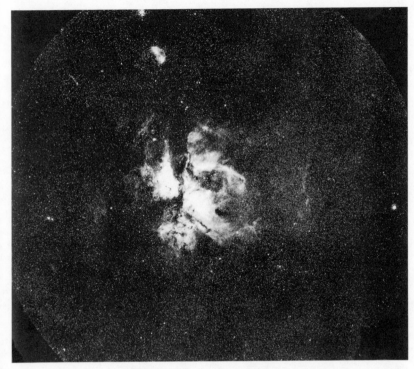

FIGURE 6.22H. Photograph from the ADH telescope. This photograph, of the nebulosity in the Eta Carinae region of the Southern sky, shows the excellent image quality of this instrument, illustrated in Figure 6.22G. (*Courtesy Perkin-Elmer Corp.*)

the case for the Cassegrainian shown, or for any of the systems discussed above, fabrication of the necessary off-center sections is extremely difficult if they are made from blanks of the size of the final mirrors. Except for the very largest sizes, it is customary either to fabricate the elements in full size, and then cut out the section required, or to embed the required blank, together with other pieces of glass, in a mold which simulates the full-sized element and then grind and polish it as if it were full size. Some of the systems described below consist of spherical surfaces, and in these cases, the manufacture of off-axis systems is greatly facilitated.

**6.31. Catadioptric Systems.** A *catadioptric* system is a system which combines refracting and reflecting surfaces. Many modern optical systems utilize the catadioptric form to obtain very high performance, especially in large-scale instruments. The fundamental philosophy of most of these systems is the correction of the aberrations of a spherical reflecting system

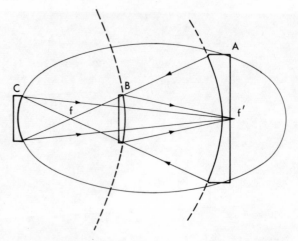

FIGURE 6.23. Geometrical relations of the Newtonian, Cassegrainian and Gregorian telescopes. The Newtonian focus is at $f$; the Cassegrainian and Gregorian foci are at $f'$. $f$ and $f'$ are the two foci of an hyperbola (Cassegrainian) or ellipse (Gregorian).

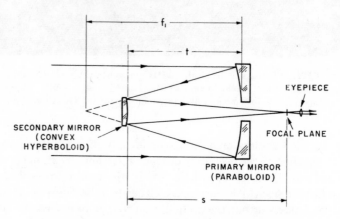

FIGURE 6.24. Geometry of the Cassegrainian telescope.

by the addition of refracting elements which have very little optical power, but a considerable effect on aberrations—primarily spherical aberration.

The defect of spherical aberration is appropriately named, because it arises from the spherical form of standard optical surfaces. It can be traced essentially to the simple mathematical fact that $\sin x \neq x$. Now, it would be quite feasible to use, instead of spherical surfaces, surfaces which

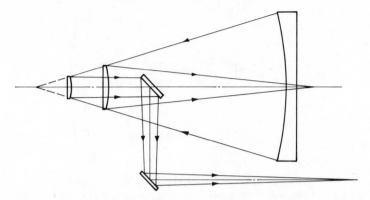

FIGURE 6.25. Telescope with three alternate focal planes. By appropriate substitution of secondary mirror and diagonal, the Newtonian focus, shown at the extreme left, may be replaced by a Cassegrainian focus behind the mirror, or a Coude focus at a point off the telescope mount.

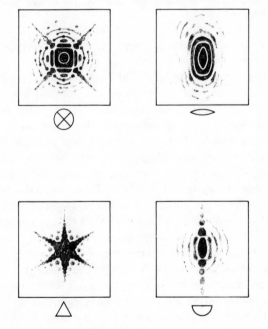

FIGURE 6.26. Diffraction patterns for a number of aperture shapes.

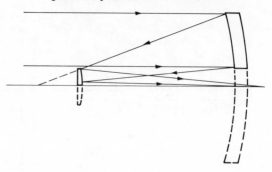

FIGURE 6.27. The unobstructed reflector. In this form, an assymetrical section of a conventional Cassegrainian telescope is used; the result is an unobstructed entrance beam. The relative aperture of the actual system is less than half that of the centered system of which it is a part; thus the latter usually corresponds to a relatively "fast" system in most instances.

are so shaped that the emergent wave front is perfectly spherical; this would do away with spherical aberration completely.

Surfaces which depart from spherical form are called *aspheric surfaces,* and are becoming more and more common in optical systems. Two important factors affecting their use must be considered. The first is that although optical designers have recognized the advantages to be gained through the use of such surfaces for a great many years, it is only in very recent times that fabrication techniques have become adequate to produce aspheric surfaces of almost any specified shape to the degree of precision which is possible for spherical surfaces. Even now, the labor involved in fabrication and testing is many times that required for spherical surfaces, so that economic factors have to be taken into account.

The second factor is that although one could design a very simple objective lens, using aspheric surfaces, which is completely free of spherical aberration for an axial point, it does not necessarily follow that it is corrected for an off-axis point. In fact, the usual result is that such a surface will give poorer off-axis imagery than a conventional spherical lens form. So that aspheric surfaces, while of very great utility, are not the panacea for achieving perfect optical systems with little design effort. The paraboloid is a prime example of an aspheric surface which gives perfect axial imagery.

Another factor which has led to more frequent use of aspheric surfaces in modern optical system design is the use of high-speed digital computers for optical design work. Aspheric surfaces are not easy to compute, but the electronic computer is not concerned with computational labor—it merely takes a little longer.

**6.32. The Schmidt Camera.** The forerunner of a large variety of catadioptric systems was the Schmidt camera, built and described by Bernhardt Schmidt in 1915.[5] Its fundamental concept is a monument to simplicity. If a spherical mirror is provided with an aperture stop at its center of curvature, it will form images over an extended field (limited only by the size of the mirror and the projective distortion of the aperture stop) which, although afflicted with heavy spherical aberration, are completely free of coma and astigmatism.

If, now, a thin plate with zero optical power is placed at the aperture stop and provided with an aspheric surface so shaped as to correct for the spherical aberration of the mirror, theoretically perfect imagery over a very wide field of view can be achieved. Each image point lies on an auxiliary optical axis drawn through the center of the aperture stop,

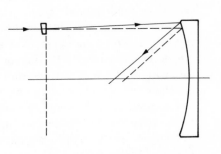

FIGURE 6.28. Principle of the Schmidt camera. The ray which would normally be reflected from the spherical primary (shown in dotted line) is bent by the correction plate so that it intersects the axis coincident with the rays from a zone of smaller diameter. The correction plate is made of aspheric form so that rays at all heights intersect the axis, after reflection, in a geometrically precise image point.

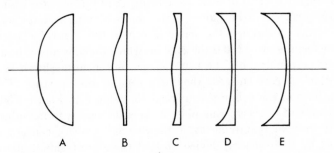

A       B       C       D       E

FIGURE 6.29. Forms of the correcting plate for a Schmidt camera. The shape of the correcting plate depends upon the designer's selection of the zone for which the plate introduces zero deviation. The form at "C", giving zero deviation for a zone at 0.7 the aperture height is the usual form chosen.

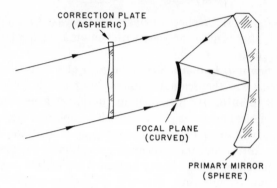

FIGURE 6.30. Arrangement of the Schmidt camera.

which is the center of curvature of the mirror, so that the final image is formed on a spherical focal surface whose center is the center of curvature of the primary mirror and whose radius is equal to the focal length, since the focal length of a mirror is one-half its radius of curvature. Figure 6.28 shows the fundamental design principle of the Schmidt camera.

As in any optical surface with undercorrected spherical aberration, the rays from concentric zones of a spherical mirror meet at points which are closer and closer to the mirror as the zones become larger, as is indicated in Figure 6.28. In determining the shape of the aspheric surface for the corrector plate at the aperture stop, the designer has the choice of bringing all of the zonal foci together at any selected zone. The shape of the required surface depends upon this choice. If the designer chooses to bring all of the rays to the paraxial focus, then the required surface is like A of Figure 6.29; if he chooses to bring all of the rays to the marginal focus, the surface will be like F. For choices of intermediate zones, the surface forms go through the series shown in the Figure. The zone for which the focus is corrected is the zone for which the tangent to the aspheric surface is perpendicular. The usual choice is the form shown in Figure 6.29C, which is corrected for the .7071 zone of the aperture. Thus, the common form of the Schmidt camera is that shown in Figure 6.30.

This choice of the correcting plate form is the easiest to manufacture.

The theoretical requirements of the Schmidt camera concept are not quite met by the practical device, so that there are residual aberrations. The form of the correcting plate is not the same for all field angles, so that the correction is complete only for the axial point. The plate, although thin, and conventionally made of low dispersion glass, still has a small amount of chromatic aberration. The magnitude of these aberrations is, however, quite small over a rather large field of view (10 to 20°), and the system is, because of its symmetrical form, completely free of coma and astigmatism, except for small residuals introduced by the tilted position of the correcting plate for off-axis rays. The Schmidt camera, therefore, represents a highly corrected optical system with a wide field of view, significantly superior to the paraboloid in its optical performance.

It has some practical disadvantages which limit its utility except for special purposes. Because the correction plate is located at the center of curvature, the system is twice as long as a Newtonian of equal focal length. And its focal surface is not flat, but spherical, which presents considerable mechanical difficulties in the necessary shaping of films and plates. Due to the first difficulty, the Schmidt camera is usually seen only with large relative apertures ($f/1.0$ to $f/3.0$) and with wide fields of view, both of which cannot be readily attained by paraboloids. Due to the second difficulty, the practicable field of view is often smaller than would otherwise be possible.

**6.33. Schmidt Camera Variants.** Many variants of the Schmidt camera have been designed for the purpose of reducing the already small aberrational residuals of the conventional form to still smaller defects. Refracting elements near the focal plane have been introduced to flatten the field, resulting in a number of varieties of "flat-field Schmidts." [6] Achromatic correction plates have been introduced to minimize the chromatic residuals of the standard form. The principle of the correction plate at the center of curvature has been applied to two-mirror systems to produce Schmidt-Cassegrainian forms of a number of types.

These variants are too numerous to describe individually.[7] Figures 6.31 through 6.33 illustrate three specific types.

**6.34. Concentric Meniscus Systems.** Another family of catadioptric optical systems, in which the correction of spherical aberration of a

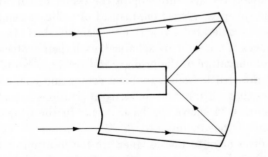

FIGURE 6.31. The "solid" Schmidt. Schmidt camera constructed from a single block of glass. A well permits access to the focal plane.

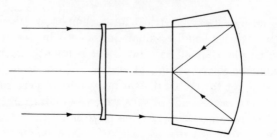

FIGURE 6.32. "Thick-mirror" Schmidt. A slightly different version of the arrangement shown in Figure 6.31, which permits ready access to the focal plane.

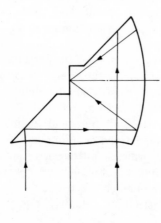

FIGURE 6.33. Folded "solid" Schmidt.

primary spherical mirror is achieved in a different way, was pioneered by Maksutov[8] and Bouwers.[9]

In these systems, the aperture stop at the center of curvature is maintained, but the spherical correction, instead of being accomplished by an aspheric plate, is generated by a thick meniscus shell. In the Bouwers form, the surfaces of the shell are spherical, with their centers of curvature at the center of curvature of the primary mirror. Thus, all of the surfaces in the system are struck from a common center and complete symmetry is achieved, so that all uniquely off axis aberrations are eliminated by definition. Figure 6.34 shows the basic form. In the Maksutov system, the concentricity is not maintained.

The two choices open to the designer are the location of the shell and its thickness; with these two degrees of freedom, he can correct for spherical aberration and achieve a very small chromatic residual—this is sufficient to give a somewhat better performance over an extended field than is given by the Schmidt camera. The centered system has the additional practical advantages that it contains only spherical surfaces, which are easier to fabricate and to hold to specified levels of precision, and when made in the form illustrated in solid lines in Figure 6.34a, it is shorter in length than the Schmidt—although still longer than a paraboloid.

There is also an inverse form in which the meniscus shell is oriented with its convex side to the object and is placed beyond the center of curvature; it is shown in dotted lines in Figure 6.34a. Since there is no optical advantage to this form, and it merely makes the instrument longer, it is not generally used.

Like the Schmidt camera, the concentric meniscus system has had innumerable variants, including some proposed by the initiators themselves. Departures from strict concentricity have been made in the interests of improved performance over limited fields of view; the system has been adapted to Cassegrainian forms, of which one interesting example is shown in Figure 6.34b, the secondary being formed on the rear surface of the

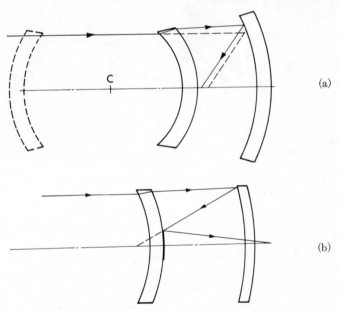

(a)

(b)

FIGURE 6.34. Catadioptric meniscus systems. The upper drawing shows the Bouwers concentric system; two alternate positions for the meniscus corrector are shown. The position shown in dotted line is not often used. The lower drawing shows a two-reflector form of the meniscus system of Maksutov.

FIGURE 6.34A. A compact astronomical telescope made in the concentric meniscus form. (*Courtesy Questar Corp.*)

meniscus shell. This form is used in a popular commercial astronomical telescope.

**6.35. The Dall-Kirkham Telescope.** Many variants on the conventional Cassegrainian telescope have been devised and constructed, by Schwarzschild,[10] by Ritchey and Chretien,[11] and by Baker *et al.*[12, 13] Their descriptions may be found in the literature. One type, however, is worthy of mention because it is rather frequently used in moderate-sized optical systems; this is the Dall-Kirkham variant of the Cassegrainian.

In the Dall-Kirkham system, the secondary mirror, which is nominally a hyperboloid, is made spherical, and an aspheric figure is placed on the primary mirror to provide complete spherical correction of an axial image point. It is, of course, possible with a two-mirror system to achieve spherical correction of an axial point by shaping one of the mirrors to compensate for any given shape of surface on the other, subject only to the condition that they not obstruct each other.

Various combinations yield varying degrees of image quality in off-axis images. The Cassegrainian form, combining a paraboloid and an hyperboloid, is a favorable choice. The Dall-Kirkham variant is adopted merely for the convenience of fabrication of a spherical secondary mirror, convex mirrors being particularly difficult to figure to aspheric forms, mostly because they are difficult to test. It happens that this form, with spherical secondary and a primary which departs just enough from a paraboloid to correct for the spherical aberration of the secondary, is also a fortunate choice for off-axis imagery, its performance being only very slightly inferior to the basic Cassegrainian. The required form on the primary mirror is ellipsoidal.

Oddly enough, a two-mirror system in which the primary is a concave sphere and the convex secondary is figured to give perfect axial imagery, turns out to have extremely heavy coma, making it inferior even to the paraboloid.

**6.36. Fabrication of Aspheric Surfaces.** Although the designer of an optical system containing aspheric surfaces, such as a Schmidt camera, or a Dall-Kirkham Cassegrainian, or even the conventional paraboloidal mirror and the hyperboloidal mirror of the basic Cassegrainian, can specify the shape of these surfaces to any desired degree of precision, in the actual process of forming the surfaces, the optician never measures them to the designer's specifications in the final finishing process.

The surface will be ground as closely as possible to the designer's specifications and measured to a template or by a micrometer. When the polishing stage is reached, however, the surfaces are always measured by optical means. A test pinhole (artificial star) or perhaps a grid pattern is set up, and the surface in question is placed together with the other surfaces in the system, and the quality of the imagery is examined. Certain tests, such as the Foucault test, which is described in Chapter 8, permit the examination of spherical aberration, zone by zone, and the surface is returned to the polishing lap and worked to remove the defects shown by the test. The result is that in the final system, say a conventional Cassegrainian, the two mirrors are shaped more or less empirically to give a perfect axial image. In the process, small deviations in one mirror may be corrected by compensating deviations in the other, so that in the end, one never really knows the exact shape of the surfaces. The departure from the mathematical specifications is, of course, small, and does not invalidate the designer's basic solution.

In high-performance optical instruments, this technique is universally followed; were it not, systems would never give the performance the designer has called for, since it is not possible to make optical surfaces to the required accuracy (fractions of a wavelength of light) by testing with such crude devices as micrometers and templates. Surfaces are given their final form through the guidance of actual optical tests, either by the examination of artificial star images or of zonal deviations of the surfaces, as with the Foucault test, or frequently by interferometric examination of the forms of the wave fronts.

For this reason, elements in high-quality optical systems are not interchangeable, a fact which always seems to surprise the uninitiated.

## BINOCULARS

**6.37. Definition.** An optical instrument is *binocular* when it is adapted for the use of two eyes; a one-eyed instrument is called *monocular*. Thus there are binocular microscopes and binocular telescopes. By custom, handheld telescopes arranged for binocular vision are referred to simply as *binoculars*. They are perhaps, with the exception of cameras, the most widely known optical instruments.

There are several reasons for preferring binocular to monocular instruments. It is much more comfortable to view with both eyes—it is the normal mode of observation, and leads to much less fatigue, especially for long periods of observation. There is also a small but definite improvement in perception when two eyes are used. But the greatest advantage in binocular instruments is the capability for *stereoscopic* vision which they provide.

Sometimes it is desirable to distinguish between instruments which merely provide two identical views of a single object, so that two eyes can be used, and those which provide slightly different views of the object, so that stereoscopic vision is achieved. The writer has favored the term *biocular* for those two-eyed instruments, such as the "binocular" microscope, which do not provide stereo vision.

**6.38. Stereoscopic Vision.** Although properly a subject for the optics of vision, with which this book is not directly concerned, it is necessary to understand something of *stereoscopic vision* to recognize the functions of binocular instruments.

Stereoscopic vision, or more commonly, stereo vision, is the process of fusing the images from the two eyes which permits us to perceive depth. Figure 6.35 shows how the separation of the two eyes (about 2½ inches) results in images of a solid object which are slightly different from each

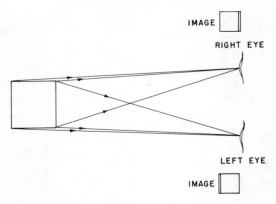

FIGURE 6.35. Image disparity in binocular vision.

# FLN          FLN

FIGURE 6.36. Stereoscopic effect resulting from image disparity. The letter (L) in the above is displaced slightly to the left in the right-hand picture. If the picture is viewed stereoscopically, the letter appears to be located closer to the eye than the background letters. This is the principle of the anaglyph.

other. Their difference is the result of *parallax* (see Section 6.19). These slightly different images are "fused" in the brain to give the perception of depth or solidity.

The difference in the images results from the finite separation of the two eyes, and thus the degree of stereo vision is proportional to this separation, or "base line." Instruments or techniques which provide views as seen from the ends of a longer base line will enhance the stereo effect. This occurs in most types of binoculars, in which the separation of the objectives is greater than the separation of the eyes.

The stereo effect is utilized in the stereoscope, in which pictures taken from two separated points are presented separately to the two eyes with the aid of parallel optical systems. There are stereo cameras, in which two separate photographs are taken simultaneously with dual lenses, and the finished photographs are presented in a stereoscope. Overlapping aerial photographs taken from separated points provide "stereo pairs" from which ground elevations may be determined.

When a stereo pair is presented at a separation equal to that of the eyes (2½ inches) it is possible to observe them and obtain the stereo effect without optical aid. Figure 6.36 shows such a pair, in which the letter L is

FIGURE 6.37. A stereoscopic pair of aerial photographs. This illustration may be viewed stereoscopically, with or without the aid of a stereoscope such as is shown in Figure 6.86. (*Courtesy Perkin-Elmer Corp.*)

displaced slightly to the left in the right-hand picture. Hold the page 12 to 15 inches from the eyes and try to "fuse" the two pictures. Attempting to project them to infinity will help. Failure is no cause for alarm—this is a very difficult task for the untrained observer.

Figure 6.37 is a stereo pair of aerial photographs, which may be viewed in the same way.

Figure 6.36 is an example of how a stereo effect may be achieved artificially by preparing pictures which differ from each other in the same way as the images of real objects in the two eyes would differ when they are located at varying distances from the observer. "3-D" cartoons are prepared in this way; the separate pictures are drawn one in red and one in green. When viewed with special glasses with red and green filters, the pictures are separated between the two eyes, and the displacement results in a stereo effect. Such pictures are referred to as *anaglyphs*.

In stereo motion pictures, dual optical systems are used in both camera and projector, as shown in Figure 6.38. These dual images are projected simultaneously on the screen, and the viewer wears special glasses which

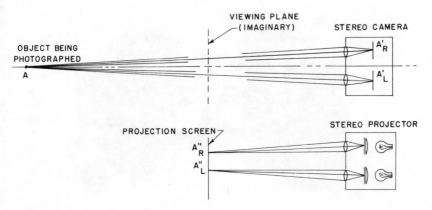

FIGURE 6.38. Projection of stereoscopic pictures.

serve to separate the images between the two eyes, so that the left eye sees only the image intended for it, and the right eye sees only its image. The two most commonly used methods for separating the images are separation by color and separation by polarization. In color separation, one image is usually red and the other green; in polarization separation, the light which forms the two images is polarized in mutually perpendicular planes. Special viewing devices are necessary with either method.

Numerous schemes for providing stereo effects without special glasses have been devised and are seen from time to time in advertising displays. None of them have proved very satisfactory for widespread use. Recently, a popular magazine published a sample of a stereo picture which purports to be the first example of a process which can produce stereo effects on a printed photograph without the need for optical aids. The photograph is divided into very narrow strips (finer than the limit of vision) and viewed through prismatic strips in a plastic overlay.

If a stereo pair is reversed, that is, if the right eye sees the picture intended for the left eye, and vice versa, an inverse stereo effect is produced, in which objects appear "inside-out." This may not be readily perceived, however. In stereo vision, as in many other optical effects, familiarity and experience play significant roles. When the eye-brain combination is presented with a picture which is outside the realm of experience, it often responds by making it into something which is familiar. Thus many optical illusions are born. Recent experiments with computer-generated patterns indicate, however, that in stereo vision, the actual disparity of images is the primary factor in the perception of depth.[14]

**6.39. Binocular Terminology.** It has become customary to refer to binoculars (binocular telescopes) as "6 × 30," "7 × 50," etc. The first

FIGURE 6.39. 6 × 30 binoculars. (*Courtesy Carl Zeiss, Inc.*)

number indicates the magnification, and the second the diameter of the entrance pupil in millimeters. The exit pupil diameter is, of course, the entrance pupil divided by the magnification. For a 6 × 30 binocular, the exit pupil is 5 mm in diameter; for a 7 × 50, it is 7 mm in diameter. This is why the 7 × 50 binocular is often referred to as a "night glass"—it has a large exit pupil, which can fill the pupil of the eye even when it is dark adapted.

The most popular sizes of binoculars are 6 × 30, 7 × 50, and 7 × 35, in that order. One finds many other sizes, however.

**6.40. Binocular Erecting Systems.** Most binoculars use prism erecting systems. The reason for this is that a telescope with a prism erecting system is much shorter in length than one with a lens erector, and furthermore, the use of prisms permits placing the objectives at a greater separation than the eyes. In the smaller instruments, this enhances the stereo effect; in an instrument with an entrance pupil diameter greater than about 2 inches, there would be mechanical interference if the center-to-center distance of the objectives were equal to the separation of the eyes.

Figure 6.42 is a cut-away view of a binocular with Porro prism erecting systems; this is the type most frequently found. Some binoculars are found with the Hensoldt prism erecting system, which was illustrated in a previous section. This system gives only a very small interobjective offset. Figure 6.43 shows how the Leman prism makes for a very small, compact instrument. This arrangement is usually found only in small binoculars, around 3 × 15 in size. Figure 6.44 illustrates a typical instrument of this type.

**6.41. Focusing Arrangements.** Two general types of focusing ar-

FIGURE 6.40. 7 × 35 binoculars. This is a "lightweight" form. (*Courtesy Bausch & Lomb*)

rangements are provided with binoculars—central focusing and individual eyepiece focusing. In the central focusing type, which is more common, both eyepieces are mounted to a central post, which is racked in and out to focus both eyepieces simultaneously. In addition, one of the eyepieces (usually the right) is furnished with an individual focus, so that compensation for a difference between the two eyes—which is the rule rather than the exception—can be made. Figures 6.39 and 6.40 show the central focusing type; Figure 6.45 shows a model with individual focusing. There is little advantage of one type over the other.

**6.42. Interpupillary Adjustment.** Binoculars have provision for setting the eyepieces at the appropriate distance for the separation of the individual observer's eyes (interpupillary distance). Because of the relatively high magnification and small exit pupil of binoculars, it is necessary that the exit pupils be aligned with the pupils of the eyes. Interpupillary distances range in the population from 58 to 72 mm—a variation of more than half an inch—so that adjustment is necessary. Interpupillary adjustment of binoculars is almost universally achieved by rotating the two

FIGURE 6.41. 15 × 60 binoculars. Note provision for clamping to a tripod. At this magnification, hand holding is generally impracticable. (*Courtesy Carl Zeiss, Inc.*)

FIGURE 6.42. Binocular construction. This cutaway view is typical of most binocular construction. Note the Porro prism erecting system, the air-spaced objective lens, and the complex wide-field eyepiece. (*Courtesy Carl Zeiss, Inc.*)

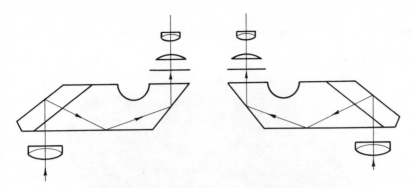

FIGURE 6.43. Binocular arrangement using Leman prisms.

FIGURE 6.44. Leman prism binoculars. In this model, the objective separation is less than the interpupillary distance, so that the stereo effect is not pronounced. The arrangement gives maximum compactness. (*Courtesy Ercona Corp.*)

FIGURE 6.45. Binocular view showing interpupillary scale. This is a 6 × 30 military model. Note the individual focusing eyepieces. Note also the British spelling for reticle. (*Courtesy Charles Frank, Inc.*)

barrels on a central hinge; Figure 6.45 shows a view in which the interpupillary scale, at the forward end of the central hinge, is visible. It is customarily marked in millimeters.

**6.43. Binocular Adjustments.** There are a number of adjustments necessary in binoculars to achieve a satisfactory instrument which are unique to this form of optical system.

The diopter scale on the eyepieces should be adjusted so that it reads zero when the instrument is focused for infinity. The interpupillary scale should be adjusted to read the correct pupil separation. If the binocular contains a reticle, the instrument should be adjusted for parallax. The most important adjustment, however, is *collimation*.

This term refers to the alignment of the optical axes of the twin telescopes exactly parallel to each other. The muscles of the human eye which move the eyeball from side to side and up and down ordinarily work together, so that both eyes turn in the same direction and by the same amount. If we concentrate upon an object, however, the eyes will adjust themselves automatically to converge on that object.

When binoculars are properly collimated, the muscular effort required of the eyes to converge on a particular object in the field of view is similar to that required in normal vision. If they are not properly collimated, this concentration on an object may require the eyes to converge too strongly, to diverge, or even for one eye to point up and the other down.

If the error of collimation is large, the eyes cannot compensate for it, and the result is *double vision*, which is immediately apparent. If the error is small, however, it is insidious, because the eyes will compensate for it without the observer being aware, and it will lead rapidly to fatigue.

**6.44. Rifle Scopes.** There are, of course, many other standard instruments of the telescopic form. Most familiar, perhaps, is the rifle scope,[15] of which there are a number of types. They all contain an objective, a reticle, an erecting system (almost always of the lens type) and an eyepiece. Figure 6.46 shows a typical optical arrangement, and a few typical instruments.

These instruments are designed to achieve the characteristics important in a rifle scope, which are a given magnification, a large exit pupil, a

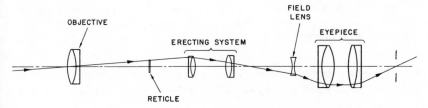

FIGURE 6.46. Typical optical arrangement of a rifle scope.

FIGURE 6.46A. A 4 X rifle scope. This size of instrument is usually called a big game scope. The mounting, to a Winchester 70, illustrates the fixed type of mount used with scopes which have a reticle adjustment for elevation and windage. (*Courtesy W. R. Weaver & Co.*)

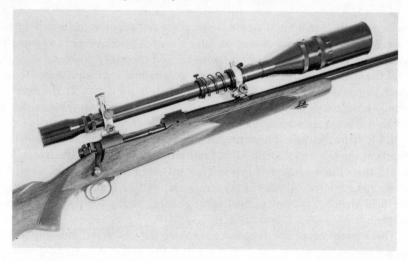

FIGURE 6.46B. A high-power target scope. Such scopes are used on small caliber rifles for target range shooting. This illustrates a micrometer rear mount, used for elevation and windage adjustments. (*Courtesy John Unertl Optical Co.*)

long eye relief, and an extremely rugged mechanical construction to withstand the shocks of fire. Typical rifle scope reticles have been shown in a previous figure.

Rifle scopes range in magnification from $20\times$, for a scope used with high-powered .22 caliber rifles on a target range to the much smaller 2 to $5\times$ scopes used for big game hunting.

In rifle scopes, perhaps more than with any other optical instrument, the penalties paid for too much magnification are most severely felt. Higher magnification reduces the field of view, so that it is more difficult to pick up a target; it may reduce the illumination, so that it is more difficult to see in unfavorable light; and it magnifies the unsteadiness of the hunter.

The reticles of most rifle scopes are adjustable vertically and laterally to permit the hunter to set range and windage corrections. These, of course, must be particularly sturdy and reliable.

**6.45. Spotting Scopes.** Another form of telescope frequently seen is the spotting scope—used for observation of targets on the rifle range, for spotting small or large game, or merely for general viewing. Figure 6.47 shows two familiar types.

Spotting scopes are usually made with magnifications of 15 to $20\times$. Of the two types shown in the figure, one has a lens erecting system, the other a prism erecting system.

(A)

(B)

FIGURE 6.47. Two types of spotting scope. (A) shows a straight telescope with terrestrial eyepiece. (B) is a telescope with a prism erecting system. (*A-courtesy O. F. Mossberg & Sons, B-Courtesy D. P. Bushnell & Co.*)

## MICROSCOPES

**6.46. Definitions.** The compound microscope[16] was defined in Section 4.68 as the second type of optical instrument designed to produce angular magnification—the first type being the telescope. Telescopes are for the purpose of viewing distant objects, microscopes are for the purpose of viewing close objects. There is no rigorous dividing line—many instruments which are made for the viewing of objects at moderate distances might be classed as either microscopes or telescopes—but in a general sense, the distinction is quite clear.

The basic optical system of the compound microscope is shown in Figure 6.48. It consists of an objective and an eyepiece; the function of the objective is that of a relay with a large difference in conjugate distances; the function of the eyepiece is the same as for a telescope—to form a distant image for visual viewing by the observer.

There is a single image plane, directly beneath or within the eyepiece; therefore the image in the microscope is *inverted*. It is customary to provide a number of different interchangeable objectives with microscopes; sometimes these are mounted in a revolving nosepiece, as shown in Figure 6.50.

Several other features will be noted in Figure 6.49. Directly beneath the objective is the *stage*, where the specimen is mounted; beneath the stage is the *condenser*, and beneath the condenser is an adjustable mirror. Specimens for examination under a microscope are customarily mounted on glass slides, which are placed upon the stage. The adjustable mirror provides a means for reflecting light through the specimen, and the condenser permits a high concentration of light in those cases where it is necessary. It is not always necessary to use a condenser. Figure 6.50 shows the complete optical arrangement of a microscope, including the mirror, condenser and slide.

**6.47. Magnification.** The magnification of the compound microscope has been discussed previously. It is the product of the magnification of the eyepiece, considered as a simple magnifier, and the lateral magnification of the objective, considered as a relay, or

$$M = M_e M_o \tag{6.17}$$

The magnification of the eyepiece is dependent upon its focal length, as shown in Section 4.62. The magnification of the objective depends upon its *working distance* and the *tube length*, the working distance being the distance from the object to the first principal plane of the objective, and the tube length being the distance from the second principal plane to the image. The tube length is a standard with microscope manufacturers, and is usually 160 mm, although for one manufacturer it is 170 mm.

**6.48. The Numerical Aperture.** The *numerical aperture* of an optical system is the quantity $\mu \sin U$, where $\mu$ is the index of refraction of the medium in which the object or image lies and $U$ is the convergence angle

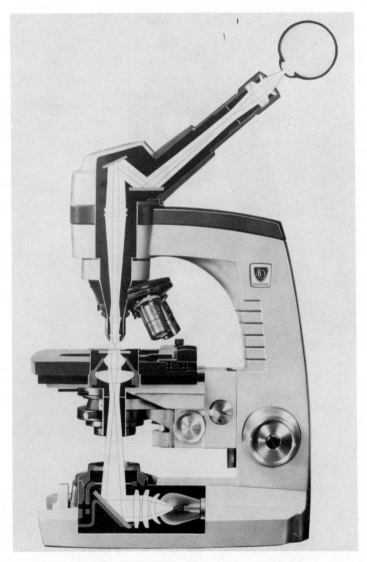

FIGURE 6.48. Optical arrangement of the compound microscope. The instrument illustrated includes a pair of mirrors to
provide an inclined eyepiece, and a set of weak lenses in the
vertical tube, neither of which are essential to basic optical
form. (*Courtesy American Optical Co.*)

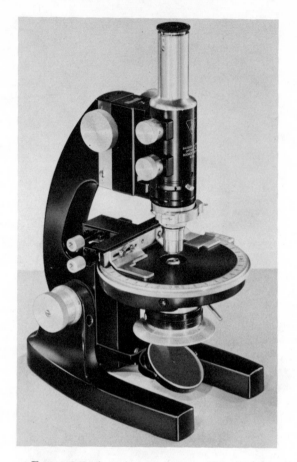

FIGURE 6.49. A typical microscope. This model features a micrometer slide holder and a rotating stage with an angular scale. *(Courtesy Bausch & Lomb)*

of the ray from an axial point which just enters the aperture at its extreme edge. This quantity has been previously discussed; it is equivalent to one-half the $f/\text{No.}$ of a lens. In fact, the numerical aperture is a more rigorous definition of the relative aperture.

The numerical aperture is important in determining the illumination of the image in an optical instrument; it also has a significance in determining its diffraction-limited resolving power.

In telescopes, the value of $\mu$ is nearly always unity, which limits the relative aperture to a value not greater than unity. In a microscope, an optically dense liquid may be placed between the object and the lens, thus providing a value of $\mu$ greater than unity (in practice, about 1.6) and permitting a larger numerical aperture than would be possible with a *dry* system and, consequently, greater illumination and higher resolving power. The objectives used in this fashion must be specially designed for this purpose and are known as *immersion* objectives.

**6.49. Microscope Objectives.** Good microscope objectives are designed with great care, because their magnification is so high that aberrational defects will show up readily. There are three general types—achromatic, semi-apochromatic, and apochromatic. These are illustrated in Figure 6.51.

Achromatic objectives are used for low magnifications. They are achromatically corrected to bring two colors to a common focus—usually the F- and C-lines—and are spherically corrected for one color—usually the D-line. They are provided in focal lengths from a minimum of 8 mm to about 64 mm. Semi-apochromats, or fluorite objectives, take advantage of the special qualities of fluorite to achieve nearly apochromatic correction with a relatively simple lens form. They are provided in the mid-range of focal lengths, from 4 to 16 mm. Apochromatic objectives are provided in the shorter focal lengths, from 1.5 to 4 mm. Objectives with focal lengths of 3 mm or less are nearly always immersion objectives.

A fairly recent development is the so-called plano objectives, which are designed to minimize Petzval curvature and thus provide a much wider field of good definition; the principle utilized in the optical design was proposed by Boegehold.[17] Also of recent origin are variable magnification "zoom" objectives for microscopes.

It is customary for manufacturers to mark objectives with both their focal lengths and their magnifications. Eyepieces are also marked with magnifications, so that the over-all magnification of the instrument with a particular combination of objective and eyepiece can be readily determined. These markings are based upon a specific standard tube length. The range of objective focal lengths from 1.5 to 64 mm provides a range of objective magnification from 2.5 to 100×.

A few types of reflecting microscope objectives have been designed,[18] and one variety is shown in Figure 6.52.

A few points about microscope objectives should be noted. They are designed for a specific tube length and, therefore, will not work at their best performance in a different tube length, although the variation in tube lengths of standard microscopes is not sufficient to be significant. Most

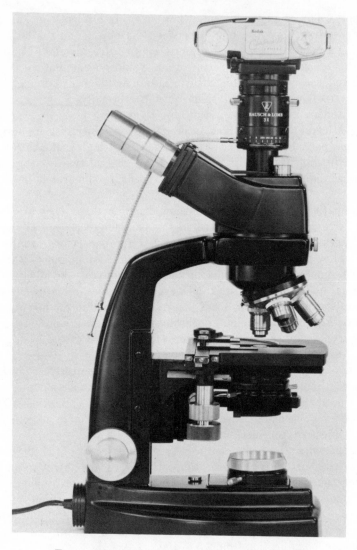

FIGURE 6.50. Microscope with arrangement for photography. This model features a turreted nosepiece, with four objectives, and a built-in lamp, as well as a variable power "zoom" lens, which provides a continuous range of magnification. The tilted eyepiece avoids the need for tilting the entire microscope, as is done with instruments such as that shown in Figure 6.49. (*Photo courtesy Bausch & Lomb*)

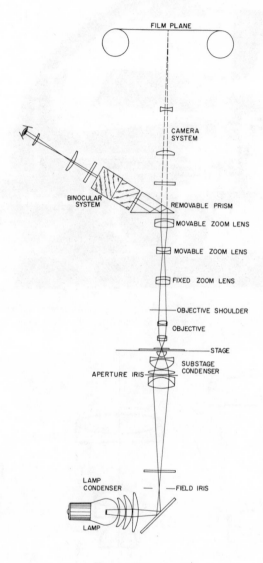

FIGURE 6.50—*Cont'd*

microscope specimens are mounted with *cover glasses*, thin glass plates which are cemented to the slides over the specimens to protect them. This cover glass, although very thin (0.17 to 0.18 mm), has a significant optical effect at the higher magnifications; objectives of short focal length are

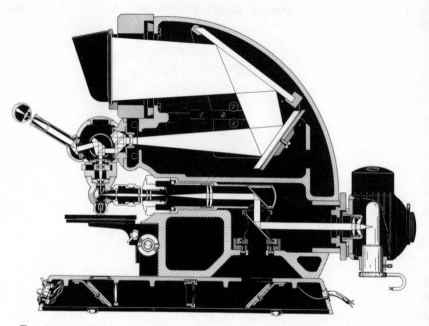

FIGURE 6.50A. Microscope with projection screen. In this microscope, a view is provided on a projection screen as well as through the eyepiece. (*Courtesy Carl Zeiss, Inc.*)

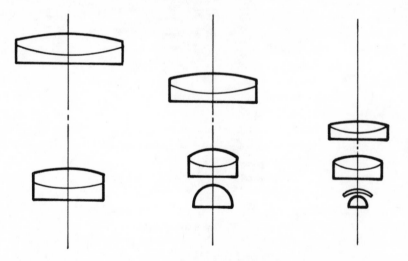

FIGURE 6.51. Three conventional forms of microscope objective. The different forms correspond to the progressive increase in complexity required as the focal length becomes shorter. The lens at the left is a standard "achromatic" form, used for low magnifications; the lens at the right is a short focal length, oil immersion type.

FIGURE 6.52. Reflecting microscope objective of Burch. Reflecting objectives are useful in dealing with ultraviolet light, to which ordinary glasses are opaque.

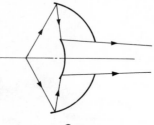

Microscope                          Camera

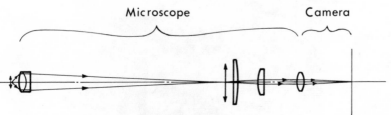

FIGURE 6.53. Optical arrangement for using a camera with a microscope which does not have a special attachment for this purpose. The eyepiece is used and is adjusted to give collimated light. The camera lens is placed (if possible) at the microscope exit pupil.

corrected for the effect of this cover glass and should be used only with a cover glass of the proper thickness. Immersion objectives will not work effectively dry, and vice versa.

**6.50. Microscope Eyepieces.** Microscope eyepieces are also provided in a variety of focal lengths, of which 25 and 10 mm are the most popular. Microscope eyepieces are usually of the Huygenian type, because of its slightly better transverse chromatic aberration correction; but when reticles are used in a microscope, as is sometimes the case, a Ramsden or Kellner eyepiece must be used.

When the microscope is used with a camera, in the arrangement shown in Figure 6.53, special photomicrographic eyepieces will give better results than standard eyepieces.

The exit pupil of a microscope is very small—a fraction of a millimeter for the higher magnifications, and the eye relief is only a few millimeters. For those individuals who, because of eye defects other than ammetropia, must wear eyeglasses, special *high eye-point* eyepieces are available.

**6.51. Microscope Illumination.** Illumination is always a problem in a microscope. It is impossible to fill the pupil of the observer's eye with light (it will be remembered that this would require an objective aperture equal to $M$ times the diameter of the eye pupil), so that the apparent illumination is $1/M^2$ times the actual illumination on the object, without any allowance for losses in the instrument. At the higher magnifications, it is often quite difficult to illuminate the specimen sufficiently.

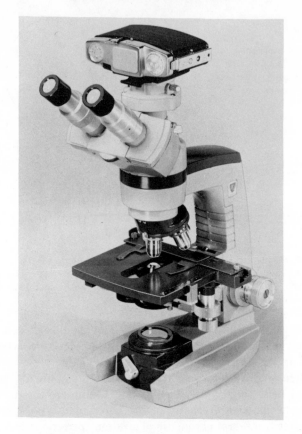

FIGURE 6.53A. Microscope with camera attachment. This is a common arrangement in modern instruments. (*Courtesy American Optical Co.*)

For low magnifications and specimens with good transmission qualities, it is sometimes sufficient to use light from a window reflected from the adjustable mirror below the stage; for higher magnifications, the condenser is necessary. A microscope lamp is a standard accessory. In modern microscope equipment, built-in light sources are commonly found.

It is important that the specimen be illuminated over the area being viewed and also that the entrance pupil of the objective be filled with light.

**6.52. Microscope Condensers.** Figure 6.54 shows one form of microscope condenser. These are optical relays of large relative aperture, whose function it is to concentrate light on the specimen. For critical applications, microscope condensers can become quite complex.

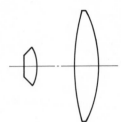

FIGURE 6.54. The Abbe microscope condenser.

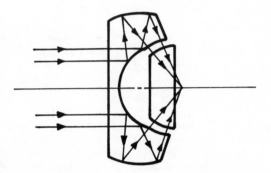

FIGURE 6.55. The cardioid condenser. This form is used for "dark-field" illumination.

Figure 6.55 shows a *cardioid* type of condenser, for the purpose of providing *dark-field illumination*. The light which passes through the specimen is directed so that it does not enter the objective lens. The objects in the field of view are detected by the light which they scatter into the objective. This type of system is used for observing small particles—particles as small as $.004\mu$ in diameter can be detected by this technique, although this dimension is about five times smaller than the effective limit of microscope resolution.

**6.53. Types of Illumination.** The standard condenser may be arranged to give two different types of illumination—*critical* illumination and *Kohler* illumination.

With critical illumination, which is not really critical but was once thought to be, a diffuse source is imaged directly on the specimen, as shown in Figure 6.56A. The only requirement which is really important is that the numerical aperture of the condenser be equal to that of the objective, so that the entrance pupil of the latter will be filled with light. It is also important that the source be sufficiently diffuse that its image, which is in the same plane as the specimen, does not provide any image detail which can be confused with that of the specimen.

In Kohler illumination, an image of the source is placed at the principal focus of the condenser, so that the light from the condenser onto the specimen is *collimated*. The usual arrangement is shown in Figure 6.56B, an auxiliary lens L being used to form the source image in the condenser focal

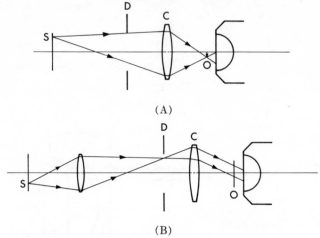

(A)

(B)

FIGURE 6.56. "Critical" and "Kohler" illumination in the microscope. (A) shows critical illumination; the source is imaged on the specimen. (B) shows Kohler illumination; the source is imaged at a diaphragm which is located at the focal plane of the condenser. The light at the specimen is collimated. Since each point in the specimen receives light from all parts of a finite source, it is not coherent illumination, as is sometimes stated.

plane. The condenser, in turn, images the iris diaphragm D on the specimen; this image becomes the exit pupil of the condenser, and the image of the source is at infinity. The iris diaphragm is adjusted to illuminate that portion of the specimen which is under examination. The specimen is illuminated by beams of collimated light reaching it from different angles. Each beam has emerged from a specific object point, and it is thus apparent that the light in any one of these beams is spatially coherent.

**6.54. Diffraction Imagery in the Microscope.** The imagery in a microscope may be analyzed with reference to the theory of diffraction by a method due to Abbe.[19]

Consider a small grating placed in the specimen plane of a microscope and illuminated by collimated light from a single axial point source, as shown in Figure 6.57. The light is coherent, the grating will act as a diffraction grating, and the parallel bundle of light will be diffracted in various directions, as shown in the figure, where the angles $\theta_1$ and $\theta_2$ correspond to the first and second maxima, respectively.

There will be a Fraunhofer diffraction pattern in the focal plane of the objective, since the source is imaged at this point. The light passes on to illuminate the image plane.

Now, the nature of the diffraction pattern in the zero-order maximum

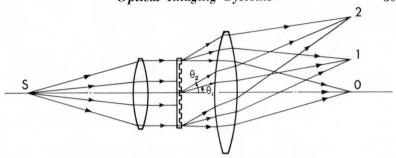

FIGURE 6.57. Diffraction image in the focal plane of a lens.

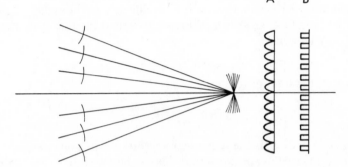

FIGURE 6.58. Interference in the image plane.

(the central beam) is the same as would be obtained from a clear circular aperture at the grating location, thus the illumination on the final image plane is the same as for a clear aperture, i.e., uniform illumination across the image plane. Consequently, the light from the zero-order maximum alone cannot provide any detail in the image.

Light passing through the secondary maxima reach the image plane by different optical paths and therefore interfere in the image plane. The interference is that of spherical waves from displaced centers, as shown in Figure 6.58. If the first maxima only are present, the interference distribution across the image plane is the $\cos^2$ pattern shown at A in Figure 6.58, and it can be shown that the size of the pattern coincides with the magnified grating image. If additional maxima are included, the pattern sharpens, until, for a large number of maxima, the pattern approaches the square-wave pattern of B, which is an exact image of the grating.

Now, the number of maxima which appear in the focal plane of the objective is governed by the objective aperture. The angle corresponding to the $m$th maximum is given by

$$\mu d \sin \theta_m = \lambda \qquad (6.18)$$

where $d$ is the line spacing of the grating.

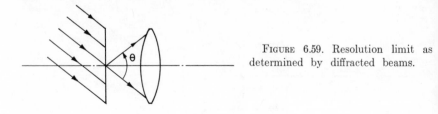

FIGURE 6.59. Resolution limit as determined by diffracted beams.

Since the pattern on the image plane first begins to appear when the objective admits the first maximum, this may be accepted as the limit of resolution for a grating of spacing $d$, and this occurs when the zero-order and the first-order maxima just enter the objective at the opposite extremities of the aperture, as shown in Figure 6.59, and for this case, Equation (6.18) may be written

$$2\mu d \sin \theta = \lambda \qquad (6.19)$$

from which the limit of resolution becomes

$$d = \frac{\lambda}{2\mu \sin \theta} = \frac{\frac{1}{2}\lambda}{(\text{N.A.})} \qquad (6.20)$$

since $\mu \sin \theta = $ N.A. is the numerical aperture of the objective.

When converted to angular terms, this can be shown to be exactly equivalent to the diffraction limit $(\lambda/D)$ for a circular aperture (see Chapter 9) with the assumption that $\mu = 1.0$.

**6.55. Limit of Magnification.** For light of wavelength $0.5\mu$, and a microscope objective with a numerical aperture of 1.3 (a common value for oil-immersion objectives), the value of $d$ as given by Equation (6.20) comes out to about $0.2\mu$. The resolution of the eye is, under the best conditions, about $\frac{1}{3}$ milliradian. If we take the ratio of $\frac{1}{3}$ milliradian to the angular subtense of $0.2\mu$ at the standard viewing distance of 250 mm, we obtain a value for the magnification required to enlarge this smallest resolvable object to the resolving power limit of the eye as about 400×. In practice, a final apparent size of about 1 milliradian is considered a comfortable value, and this gives a magnification of 1200×.

Any magnification greater than this will make objects appear larger to the eye, but will not result in any improvement in detail. Thus, a value of about 1000× may be taken as the limiting magnification of a microscope working in visible light. With ultraviolet light, an increase in magnification may be achieved, because $\lambda$ is shorter, but the eye cannot view directly in ultraviolet; recourse must be had to photography or fluorescent screens.

**6.56. Phase Contrast.** Some interesting and startling effects may be obtained by controlling the light which passes through the Fraunhofer diffraction pattern at the focus. A real object may be considered to be made up of a collection of gratings of different spacings. If masks are placed in the Fraunhofer pattern at points corresponding to the maxima for a particular line spacing, the resolution for this particular spacing may be destroyed, without affecting the resolution for other spacings, both finer and coarser (see Chapter 9).

When the objects being examined are nearly transparent, very little contrast is available in the image under ordinary conditions. The objects actually create differences in phase but not in amplitude, and since the eye is insensitive to phase, the image plane appears uniformly illuminated. If, however, obstructions are placed in the Fraunhofer pattern, these phase differences may be made to produce interference in the image plane, and the objects become visible.

In the *dark ground* technique, the zero-order maximum is blocked; in the Schlieren technique, the diffraction maxima on one side are blocked. Both of these techniques are effective.

The most effective technique, however, is the *phase-contrast* method of Zernicke.[20] In this technique, the zero-order maxima are not blocked, but they are retarded in phase by the introduction of a glass plate of the proper thickness. This does not reduce the illumination, but generates interference patterns in the image plane which show up the transparent objects in excellent contrast. The phase contrast may be either *positive* or *negative;* in the former, thicker objects appear darker, in the latter, they appear lighter than the background. A more complete explanation of the phase contrast technique is given in Section 9.35.

In practice, illumination is not produced by a point source, so that the diffraction maxima in the objective focal plane are not points, but are images of the source. In phase contrast microscopy, the usual technique is to provide an annular ring illumination source and a *phase plate* in the objective focal plane in the form of a ring. Figure 6.60 shows the optical system of the phase-contrast microscope.

**6.57. Interference Microscopy.** Several microscope arrangements exist for producing interference between light which has passed through the

(A)                              (B)

FIGURE 6.60. Arrangement for phase contrast. (A) Schematic arrangement, with phase plate in focal plane of a lens. (B) Typical actual location of phase plate in a compound microscope objective.

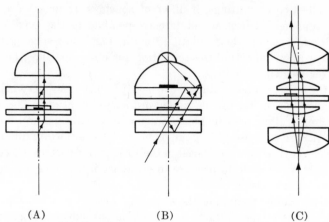

(A)                        (B)                        (C)

FIGURE 6.61. Interference microscope objectives: (A) Lebedev,
(B) Dyson, (C) Smith.

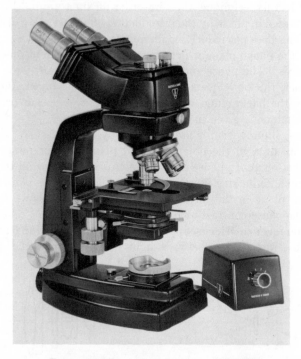

FIGURE 6.62. Binocular microscope. Since both
eyes view through a single objective, the binocular microscope does not give stereo vision.
(*Courtesy Bausch & Lomb*)

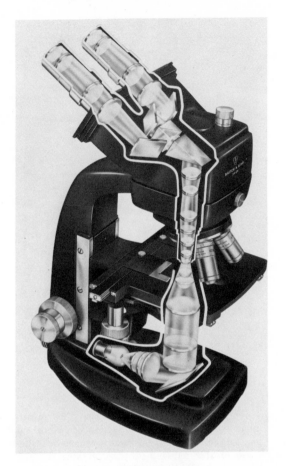

FIGURE 6.62—*Cont'd*

specimen and light which has not;[21] three of these are shown in Figure 6.61, one by Dyson and one by Smith.

**6.58. Special Forms of Microscope.** There are a number of special forms of microscope for special purposes. A fairly common instrument is the *binocular microscope*, illustrated in Figure 6.62. This instrument does not, as might at first be supposed, provide stereoscopic vision. It has only one objective, the light being divided by a beam splitter between two eyepieces. The binocular microscope is convenient for cases where it must be used continuously for a long period of time, since it eliminates the inconvenience and fatigue associated with the use of a monocular instrument.

Stereoscopic vision is provided by the *stereoscopic microscope*, illustrated in Figure 6.63. Two complete microscopes are provided, mounted at

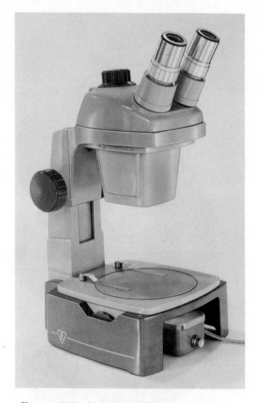

FIGURE 6.63. A stereo microscope. This instrument contains two optical systems, inclined at an angle so as to view the same specimen field. Because of this requirement, the working distance cannot be made small, and therefore the magnification is limited. This instrument contains variable power objectives of the "zoom" type. (*Courtesy Bausch & Lomb*)

a converging angle which equals the normal convergence angle of the eyes when viewing objects at the near point.

The stereoscopic microscope cannot be made with very high magnification because of physical interference in the objective area for the very short working distances which would be required.

In order to provide logical stereo vision, the stereoscopic microscope should have erect images; hence, it is provided with erectors, usually of the prism type.

*Polarizing microscopes* are used for examining small specimens with

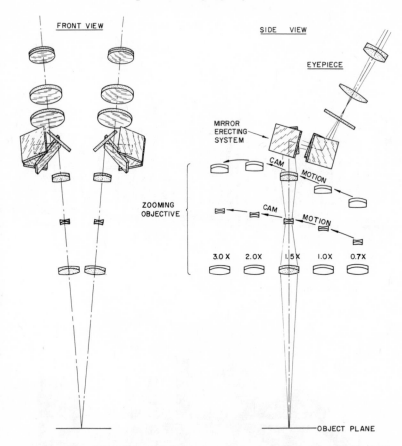

FIGURE 6.63A. Optical system of the microscope shown in Figure 6.63. The cam motions provided in the variable power objectives is shown at the right. (*Courtesy Bausch & Lomb*)

polarized light. The optical system is shown in Figure 6.64. A polarizer behind the specimen and an analyzer in the microscope are the essential additional components. The Amici-Bertrand lens is used to focus on the rear focal plane of the objective, where, as has been discussed above, the diffraction patterns are formed. This mode of operation is used to examine crystals for polarization effects.

**6.59. Microscope Accessories.** Various accessories are available for use with microscopes. For the examination of opaque specimens, vertical illuminators (Figure 6.65) are used. The microscope lamp, for controlled illumination, has been mentioned above. Reticles are provided for special

Standard Polarizing Microscope
Sectional Drawing

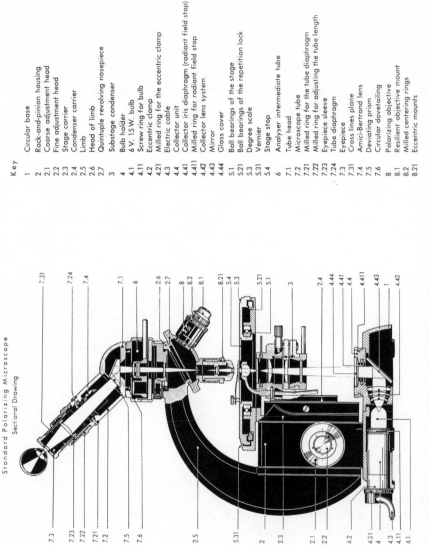

Key

1 Circular base
2 Rack-and-pinion housing
2.1 Coarse adjustment head
2.2 Fine adjustment head
2.3 Stage carrier
2.4 Condenser carrier
2.5 Limb
2.6 Head of limb
2.7 Quintuple revolving nosepiece
3 Substage condenser
4 Bulb holder
4.1 6 V. 15 W. bulb
4.11 Screw ring for bulb
4.2 Eccentric clamp
4.21 Milled ring for the eccentric clamp
4.3 Electric cable
4.4 Collector unit
4.41 Collector iris diaphragm (radiant field stop)
4.411 Milled ring for radiant field stop
4.42 Collector lens system
4.43 Mirror
4.44 Glass cover
5.1 Ball bearings of the stage
5.21 Ball bearings of the repetition lock
5.3 Degree scale
5.31 Vernier
5.4 Stage stop
6 Analyser intermediate tube
7.1 Tube head
7.2 Microscope tube
7.21 Milled ring for the tube diaphragm
7.22 Milled ring for adjusting the tube length
7.23 Eyepiece sleeve
7.24 Tube diaphragm
7.3 Eyepiece
7.31 Cross lines plane
7.4 Amici-Bertrand lens
7.5 Deviating prism
7.6 Circular dovetailing
8 Polarizing objective
8.1 Resilient objective mount
8.2 Milled centering rings
8.21 Eccentric mounts

FIGURE 6.64. A polarizing microscope (*Courtesy Carl Zeiss, Inc.*)

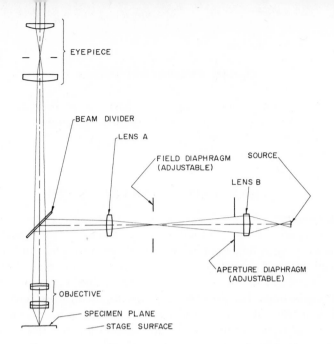

FIGURE 6.65. Arrangement of a typical vertical illuminator. (*Courtesy Bausch & Lomb*)

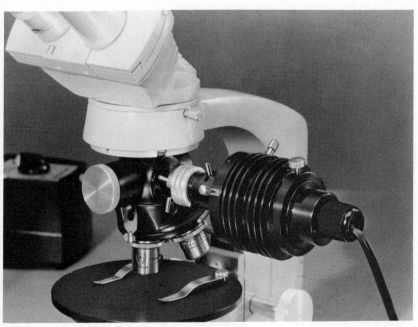

FIGURE 6.65A. Another form of vertical illuminator. (*Courtesy American Optical Co.*)

work, such as blood counts. Arrangements for micro-positioning the speciment slide on the stage are common. Attachments for projecting an image onto a photographic plate through the eyepiece are available; special eyepieces are usually used.

## OTHER VISUAL INSTRUMENTS

**6.60. General.** There are innumerable other optical instruments for visual use; space does not permit describing them all. A few varieties, however, are in common use, and justify at least brief mention. While each has its special name, derived from its particular use, all can be classified as representing one of the five basic instruments defined above.

**6.61. Periscopes.** The word periscope means, literally, to "look around." In optical instruments, the term periscope is applied to instruments for observing out of or into otherwise visually inaccessible locations. Their applications are legion. The best known, perhaps, is the submarine periscope, by means of which the submarine's occupants can maintain visual contact with the outside world while submerged. There are also periscopes for viewing from aircraft, for bombing or gunsighting; these instruments often provide for scanning over a large area of the outside world.

There are also periscopes for viewing the interiors of chambers where nuclear experiments are performed and for viewing the interiors of compartments; of course, there is also the familiar rhomboidal form of periscope for looking over walls or out of trenches.

Figure 6.66 shows, schematically, the arrangement of a submarine periscope. These instruments are all designed specifically for a particular application, and the illustration does not represent any particular design.

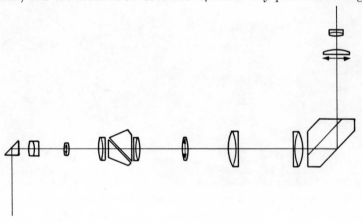

FIGURE 6.66. Schematic arrangement of a submarine periscope.

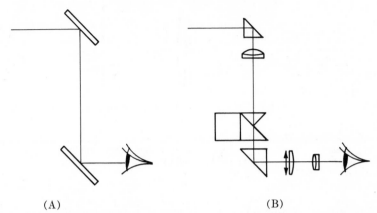

(A)            (B)

FIGURE 6.67. Two types of periscope. (A) simple two-mirror periscope, (B) periscope containing a telescope.

The problem in a submarine periscope, and in many other periscopes, where the tube must be relatively long and of small diameter, is to transfer the light down the long tube without losing too much of it. This is accomplished by a series of optical relays, as shown in the Figure. The periscope shown is provided with a scanning prism at the top, so that the observer may direct the line of sight throughout a complete circle, and a derotating prism to correct the image rotation which occurs as a result of the scan. An alternative method, used in many periscopes, is to rotate the entire instrument and "walk around" it when scanning.

Figure 6.67 shows the simple "over-wall" periscope, consisting of two plane mirrors, and a more elaborate form including a telescopic system. In modern tank periscopes, which are furnished for the crew members for general observation and also for gunsighting, both types of system are often included in a single instrument—the simple mirror arrangement is used for general viewing, and the telescopic system is provided with a moderate magnification. There are also systems in which the telescope is of unit magnification and is used solely for the purpose of projecting a reticle pattern against the target for gunsighting purposes.

**6.62. Viewfinders.** There is a class of optical instruments, generally known under the name of *viewfinders*, by analogy with the viewfinders found on cameras, which are arranged in a slightly different manner from other visual optical instruments and are deserving of special comment. They are becoming more numerous for several types of application.

These instruments are essentially telescopes, but they differ in not having a conventional eyepiece; the image of the external field of view is presented on a *viewing screen*. This viewing screen may be either a translucent screen or a clear lens. When a translucent screen is used, the instrument is simply

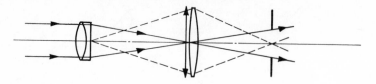

FIGURE 6.68. Optical arrangement of the viewfinder.

FIGURE 6.69. Two types of simple camera viewfinders.

a projector (see Section 6.71). The type with a clear lens in the projected image plane is somewhat unique. It is illustrated in Figure 6.68.

The focal plane lens in this instrument is a *field lens*, and its purpose is to form a pupil for the observer's eye. In these instruments, however, the purpose is to permit the observer to view with only a moderate restriction of his head position, hence the exit pupil formed by the field lens must be large and at a considerable distance (1 to 2 feet) from the instrument.

These instruments are subject to the general rule relating angular magnification and pupil diameters, and therefore if the exit pupil diameter is to be large, either the magnification must be small or the objective extremely large.

The most common use of this type of instrument is in aircraft, where they are used, among other things, for photographic viewfinding. The purpose is to include a wide field of view; as a result, the magnification is less than unity (½ to ⅕).

The same type of arrangement has been used in ordinary cameras for a long time, and both translucent screen and clear field lens types are found. Figure 6.69 shows the usual arrangement for both types.

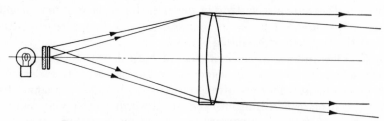

FIGURE 6.70. Optical system of the projector collimator.

**6.63. Collimators.** *Collimators* are used for the sole purpose of providing an image at infinity. They are often called projector collimators.

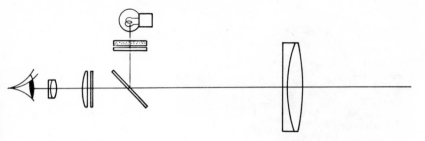

FIGURE 6.71. Optical arrangement of the autocollimator.

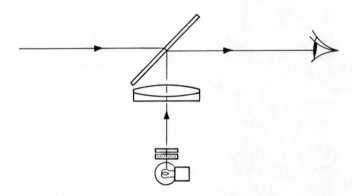

FIGURE 6.72. Optical arrangement of the collimating gunsight.

Figure 6.70 shows the general arrangement, the components being an il-luminated reticle and a collimating lens, which takes the general form of a telescope objective.

Figure 6.71 shows a modified arrangement, which is an *auto-collimator*. The instrument is also provided with a comparison reticle and an eyepiece. When the collimated beam is reflected from a surface whose normal is parallel to the collimator optical axis, the returned image of the reticle falls exactly upon the comparison reticle under the eyepiece. The instrument then serves to determine when the reflecting surface is exactly perpendicu-lar to the collimator axis.

Collimators are extensively used to provide an image at infinity for optical testing purposes, to determine alignment and also to provide a laboratory means for focusing of cameras and telescopes. The auto-colli-mator provides a means of alignment and is frequently used in tooling ap-plications and in the alignment of such devices as inertial platforms in guided missiles just prior to launch. These inertial platforms are controlled by gyros and accelerometers which can automatically align the platform

FIGURE 6.73. A typical surveyor's transit. This cutaway view shows the optical system, including an internal focusing lens, reticle and terrestrial eyepiece. An optical arrangement for leveling the instrument is also shown. (*Courtesy W. & L. E. Gurley*)

to the direction of gravity. A horizontal, or azimuth reference is also needed, however, and this is frequently provided by an optical instrument of the auto-collimating type.

Another application of the collimator is the provision of a reticle pattern at infinity for aiming purposes; application of the principle to tank periscopes was mentioned above. Figure 6.72 shows an arrangement which is frequently used in fighter aircraft. The collimated light from the projection lens is reflected by a *combining glass* to the eye of the pilot, who then sees the reticle image at infinity. The combining glass is unsilvered and has a reflectivity of the order of 10 per cent; the target is seen directly through the glass.

FIGURE 6.74. A typical cystoscope.

**6.64. Theodolites.** Theodolites and transits are instruments used for surveying. Their optical components consist of a small telescope with a reticle. The optical axis of this telescope is the reference which establishes a direction. Mechanical scales on the instrument measure the angles through which this optical axis must be turned to point at specific objects, and thus their angular direction is measured.

The theodolite is based upon the fundamental principle, often used in applications of optics to measurement, that a light ray is infinitely rigid and is, by definition, a straight line. From a precise point of view, it is subject to bending when directed through non-isotropic media such as atmospheres, and this must often be taken into account in accurate work.

**6.65. The Cystoscope.** The cystoscope, illustrated in Figure 6.74, is representative of several instruments of similar type for the purpose of viewing the interiors of human organs.

They are essentially periscopes, but of very small diameter and considerable length, and are constructed in a similar manner to periscopes, with a succession of relays to transfer the image down the long, narrow tube. Some are furnished with one or more optical hinges, as shown in the figure; others are straight and rigid. Small electric lamps are provided at the head for illuminating the interior of the cavity to be examined. Many of these instruments have been given names describing their specific use, for example, the *bronschoscope*, the *resectorscope*, etc.

**6.66. Range Finders.** The optical range finder uses the phenomenon of

parallax to determine the distance of objects. When an object is viewed
from two separated points, its angular direction with respect to the line
joining these two points (the *base line*) is displaced by an amount which
is proportional to its distance. Figure 6.75 shows the so-called range triangle. If the range is $R$ and the length of the base line is $B$, then the parallactic angle is

$$\tan \phi = B/R \qquad (6.21)$$

For the very small angles involved, $\phi$ may be expressed in radian value;
therefore

$$R = B/\phi \qquad (6.22)$$

Optical range finders consist fundamentally of two telescopic systems,
separated by the base line, whose images are superimposed in the focal
plane. If the magnification of the instrument is $M$, then the apparent separation of the two images is $M\phi$.

Figure 6.76 shows, schematically, the arrangement used in military
range finders. The two telescopes are mounted rigidly in an optical tube,

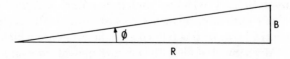

FIGURE 6.75. The range triangle.

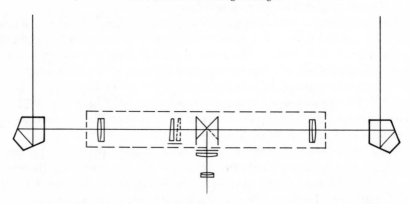

FIGURE 6.76. Arrangement of the optical range finder. The region enclosed in
dotted lines is the optical bar; the structure of this is made very rigid. Since
penta prisms are constant-deviation devices (in the plane of the range triangle),
the optical bar may be mounted more or less softly within the outer case, which
carries the prisms.

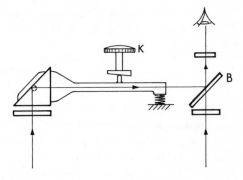

FIGURE 6.77. A typical camera range finder. Rotation of the knob, which focuses the lens, introduces a small rotation in the prism. The eye views simultaneously through the direct window and off the beam splitter B through the prism.

and they view the target through Penta mirrors or prisms at the ends of the base line. Penta prisms or mirrors are constant-deviation systems (in the plane in which the parallax occurs), hence the required rigidity of the system is confined to the optical tube, which is kept relatively short and is "floated" inside the external housing.

Figure 6.77 shows an optical range finder which is often found on cameras.

The parallactic angle may be measured in various ways. The most direct method is to change the direction of the line of sight of one of the telescopes. Since the angles to be measured are of the order of seconds of arc, this is usually accomplished by means of a moving optical wedge. The instrument is adjusted until the two images coincide, and the range is read on a dial.

The images may be combined in various ways. The field may be split in a direction parallel to the base line, and the instrument is adjusted until a vertical line in the target object is aligned in the two halves of the field (coincidence type). The images may be presented completely but in different colors, as is common in camera range finders, or the range finder may be *stereoscopic*, having two eyepieces and a pair of reticles which, when shifted transversely in the focal plane, appear to the observer to move in and out along the line of sight.

**6.67. Accuracy of Range Finders.** Differentiating Equation (6.22) gives

$$dR = \frac{R^2}{B} \, d\phi \tag{6.23}$$

Now, the ability of the human eye to detect parallactic displacement is commonly considered to be about 12 seconds of arc (about ⅕ the resolution limit).[22] The same order of precision applies to the detection of parallax by stereoscopic means. Thus, the minimum detectable difference, $d\phi_m$ is $12/M$ seconds of arc, or $.00006/M$ radians. Substituting in Equation (6.23) gives

$$dR_m = \frac{.00006R^2}{BM} \qquad (6.24)$$

The accuracy is thus inversely proportional to the square of the range and proportional to the base length and the magnification.

It is usually considered that the maximum useful range of a range finder is that value for which the error is 10 per cent. Using this criterion in Equation (6.24) gives, for the maximum range,

$$R_{\max.} = 1500BM \qquad (6.25)$$

For a 1-meter base military range finder, with a magnification of 15×, the maximum range according to the above equation is about 20,000 meters. For the small camera range finders, whose base length is not more than 3 inches and whose magnification is about unity, the maximum range is of the order of a few hundred feet, which is quite adequate for the focusing of a camera.

## PHOTOGRAPHIC INSTRUMENTS

**6.68. The Camera.** The camera is the fundamental photographic instrument, and it is perhaps the simplest of all optical instruments in that it consists simply of an objective lens, which forms an image on the focal plane where the photographic emulsion is placed. Descriptions of even the common types of cameras and their operating principles and complexities would require a volume in itself, but this book is concerned only with the optical aspects of the instrument.

**6.69. Photographic Objectives.** While a camera consists of only one optical component—the objective—this single component can become more complex than many optical systems containing a variety of components. The fundamental purpose of a photographic objective is to provide an image of adequate size and quality on the focal plane where the film is placed. This is not a simple requirement. In the first place, the field must be relatively large; most cameras have fields of view of from 30 to 60°, and some lenses are required to cover fields as large as 120°. The field must also be flat, to a fraction of the depth of focus of the system over its entire area; this requirement alone is a very severe one. In addition, the distortion must be kept sufficiently low that it does not become evident in the photograph; in cartographic cameras, the distortion is kept to microns. The chromatic correction must be very high—apochromatic in any good camera lens, and moreover, the lens is usually asked to work at a relatively high $f$/No. so that the exposure will not be unreasonably long.

All of these requirements make photographic objectives one of the most difficult tasks for the optical designer. Before the advent of the electronic computer, the designing of a photographic objective might take an expert optical designer and his staff a year or more to complete.

Photographic objectives have the essential characteristics of focal length and relative aperture. Focal lengths are expressed in either millimeters or inches, and the usual values of relative aperture are $f/1.5$, $f/2.0$, $f/2.8$, $f/4.0$, $f/5.6$, $f/8.0$, $f/11$. These are the *maximum* relative apertures for the particular lens; iris diaphragms are provided to reduce the relative aperture as conditions dictate.

It will be noted that the above range of values constitutes a geometric series for which $r = \sqrt{2}$. Since the illumination on the image plane is proportional to the square of the relative aperture, a change in relative aperture by one step in the above series increases the required exposure time by a factor of two, which is the reason for the adoption of $\sqrt{2}$ as the geometric ratio. Objectives with relative apertures not in accordance with the above series are found, $f/3.5$ and $f/4.5$ being fairly common.

Photographic objectives are difficult to classify into particular types. Each designer of popular lenses has used his own ingenuity to balance the aberrations in an acceptable manner. There are, however, some basic forms which actual designs resemble to a greater or less degree.

Inexpensive cameras are often provided with lenses of the single meniscus type, illustrated in Figure 6.78. This form, with the aperture stop located at the point which gives zero coma, is shaped to give a flat tangential field, which is usually a standard compromise in camera lenses. Because of its considerable spherical aberration, it can be given a relative aperture no greater than about $f/11$.

The lens may be placed either in front of or behind the stop, the latter arrangement being more common. The next step in increasing complexity is that of an achromatic meniscus. Two meniscus lenses are sometimes pro-

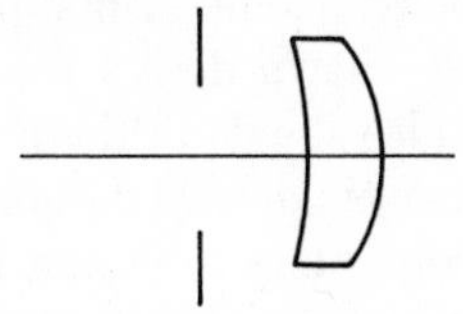

FIGURE 6.78. The single meniscus lens.

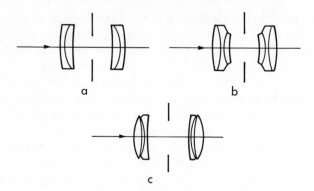

FIGURE 6.79. Some typical photographic objectives:
(a) rapid rectilinear, (b) dagor, (c) cine anastigmat.

vided, one on each side of the aperture stop in the double meniscus form.
When these are each made achromatic, the combination is known as the
rapid rectilinear lens, also common on inexpensive cameras.

The rapid rectilinear is a simple embodiment of the *symmetrical objective*, which consists of groups of similar components symmetrically disposed about a central stop. In a completely symmetrical system, coma, distortion and lateral color are absent by definition, provided the object and
image planes are also symmetrical. In a photographic lens, the object
is at infinity and the image is at the principal focal plane, so that symmetry
is not completely maintained. Nevertheless, the symmetrical form provides
a starting point for the designer, who may then introduce asymmetries to
correct for the aberrations created by the object-image asymmetry. The
symmetrical arrangement is characteristic of a number of photographic
objectives, some of which are illustrated in Figure 6.79. Wide-angle objectives, particularly, are frequently of the symmetrical form.

Other photographic objectives take asymmetrical forms; there are three
particular varieties which are often found to be closely simulated—the
triplet, the Petzval lens and the telephoto.

Figure 6.80 illustrates the so-called Cooke triplet, designed by H. D.
Taylor in 1895; many modern lenses have been derived from this basic arrangement of two positive components spaced apart from a central negative
component. The best known derivatives of the Cooke triplet, the Tessar
and the Pentac, are also shown in the Figure.

A recent development in optical design procedures has been the program-
ming of electronic computers to design lenses automatically. A few years
ago, a computer designed all of the possible forms of the Cooke triplet for

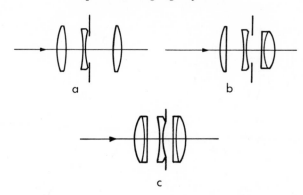

FIGURE 6.80. The Cooke triplet and derivatives: (a) Cooke triplet, (b) Tessar, (c) Pentac.

FIGURE 6.81. The Petzval lens.

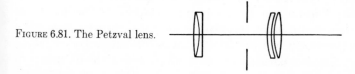

a selected choice of glasses as an exercise in automatic design programs. It required a few hours of computer time.

The Petzval type of objective consists of two widely separated positive lens groups with an internal stop. It provides very high quality imagery over a small field at a moderately wide aperture. The original Petzval portrait lens form and some derivatives are illustrated in Figure 6.81.

The telephoto lens consists of a positive lens group followed by a negative group at a considerable separation. It has the feature of being shorter in length (from front surface to image plane) than its focal length, and it is often used for long focal length lenses interchangeable with "standard" lenses in hand cameras. As has been previously pointed out, it is the counterpart of the Cassegrainian telescope.

When used as a long focal length lens, the "amplification" may be fairly large, in order to take advantage of the short length feature of the lens. Used with low amplifications, it is the basis for several photographic lenses. The basic form and a derivative are shown in Figure 6.82.

A few photographic lenses of catadioptric form, following the arrangements of Bouwers and Maksutov, are commercially available; this type of lens is used even more frequently in special applications involving large apertures.

Lenses with continuously variable focal length, achieved by the axial

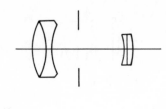

FIGURE 6.82. Some typical telephoto lens arrangements.

movement of internal components, are among recent developments in photographic objectives. These are known as "zoom" lenses and are frequently used in motion picture and television applications.

**6.70. Quality Parameters.** In commercial applications, the quality of photographic lenses is usually assessed by subjective means. Most good camera lenses give image quality that cannot be quantitatively compared except by careful measurement; since the usual purpose of these lenses is to give pictorial photographs which appeal to the eye, this kind of value assessment is reasonable.

Among the lenses intended for pictorial work, the degree of complexity is often more or less proportional to the maximum relative aperture which is provided. An $f/1.5$ lens will in general be much more complex and expensive than a lens whose maximum opening is $f/4$. The faster lens gives the owner much more flexibility in adaptation to varying light conditions and in photographing moving objects.

The objective measure of image quality is resolution, usually expressed in lines/mm. At the near point of the eye (250 mm), a resolution of 10 lines/mm is at the limit of detection, and a resolution of 5 lines/mm will be judged as excellent by most observers. Therefore, a photographic objective which has a resolution of 5 lines/mm is quite satisfactory if its product is always viewed as a contact print. If enlarged photographs are to be made, however, then the resolution of the original lens should be better by the enlargement ratio, which may be of the order of 5×. Most good lenses for amateur use provide resolutions of the order of 25 to 30 lines/mm.

For motion picture cameras, and for photographs which are to be projected on a screen at high magnification, the standards become higher; most amateur motion picture lenses are designed to provide a resolution at a level of about 40 lines/mm.

In professional and scientific work, where the photographic product is used for precision measurement, even higher resolutions are demanded.

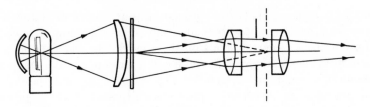

FIGURE 6.83. Optical arrangement of the projector.

**6.71. Projectors.** A projector is essentially a large-scale microscope without an eyepiece. Its purpose is to project an image onto a viewing screen at a relatively high magnification. The general arrangement of a projector is shown in Figure 6.83.

The system consists of a light source, a condenser, the plate or film holder, and the projection lens. The subject matter may be a motion picture or a still picture in the form of a slide. The recent advent of the 35-mm camera and color transparencies has made the slide projector a common device in the home.

The illumination system in the projector is usually arranged so that the image of the source, which is generally a tungsten filament, is formed in the entrance pupil of the projection lens, and the film or plate is placed close to the exit pupil of the condenser; this assures uniform illumination over the subject and maximum flux through the projection lens.

The focal length of a projection lens determines the maximum size of image on the screen which may be provided in a given distance from projector to screen (throw distance). If $D$ is the throw distance, and $f$ the focal length of the projection lens, then the maximum available magnification, using the image equation, is

$$M = \frac{D}{f} - 1 \qquad (6.26)$$

It must be remembered that the illumination on the screen will be proportional to the intensity of the light source and inversely proportional to the square of the magnification. For large projection magnifications, the light source must be quite powerful to give good illumination; projection lamps of 500 watts are common, and for large-screen projection, powers up to several thousand watts are not uncommon.

**6.72. Cartographic and Photogrammetric Instruments.** Cartography is the making of maps; photogrammetry is the measurement of geometric space from photography. Both depend heavily upon photography, and in both areas a number of specialized optical instruments have been developed for dealing with the photographic data.

Ancient maps were made from ground measurements and astronomical observations; modern maps are made from aerial photography, aided by carefully measured control points on the ground. The conventional technique of aerial photography is the taking of a series of overlapping photographs down a "flight line" as shown in Figure 6.84. In general, these photographs are taken from successive positions which are not known precisely and with the camera oriented at angles which are subject to considerable error.

It is mathematically possible, without knowing the exact camera stations or orientations, to determine the coordinates of any ground point appearing in the photography, in three dimensions, provided the following conditions are met:

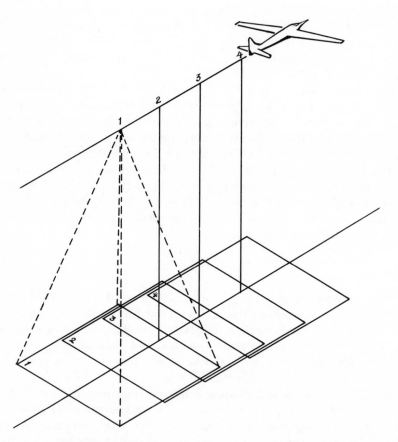

FIGURE 6.84. Conventional technique for vertical aerial photography.

(1) There must be at least four points in one of the photographs whose ground coordinates are precisely known (control points).

(2) The successive photographs must overlap sufficiently that there are always two photographs upon which any ground point is imaged, so that measurements made from a control point to a set of subsidiary control points (pass points) may be transferred to a succeeding photograph.

(3) The geometry of the camera (focal length and distortion) must be precisely known.

This computational process is known as aerial triangulation;[23] it is involved and tedious, but straightforward, and is done on electronic computers. This technique, and the machines and methods which have been developed for carrying it out, can produce maps of large areas of the earth's surface to accuracies of the order of a few feet on the ground. When Rommel brought his troops to North Africa in World War II, the absence of adequate maps was one of his first concerns. Before committing his troops to battle, he insisted on aerial mapping of the entire North African shore, from Tunis to Alexandria. The job was accomplished with one aircraft, one flight, and one roll of film, to cover an area four miles wide and 1500 miles long.

**6.73. Stereoplotting.** The overlapping aerial photographs provide stereo pairs, which may be viewed with a stereoscope to give the effect of relief. Figure 6.85 contains a pair of aerial photographs which may be viewed in stereo. The trained observer will not need optical aid, but most individuals will require a stereo viewer, such as that shown in Figure 6.86.

For larger photographs, which may not be placed 2½ inches apart, larger stereo viewers, such as that shown in Figure 6.87 are available; they may be provided with magnification.

For the preparation of contour maps, the *stereoplotter* (Figure 6.88) is used. This instrument comprises two projectors, one for each of the aerial photographic pair. These are projected to form aerial images just above the horizontal table. When the projectors are properly adjusted to simulate the actual position and orientation of the camera when the photographs were taken, the projected images form a *stereo model* in space. The projections are in two complementary colors, so that where the two projected images of an object meet in space, a black and white image is seen.

The operator uses a small adjustable table with a white matte surface. He adjusts the height of this table to represent a given ground elevation, and then moves it about the table, following the images of the ground points which coincide at that elevation; a marker at the bottom of the table traces out a contour line. Recently, instruments have been developed for accomplishing this task automatically.

FIGURE 6.85. Aerial stereophotographs. (*Courtesy Perkin-Elmer Corp.*)

FIGURE 6.86. A folding pocket stereoscope. Interpupillary adjustment is provided by a slide coupling between the two bodies. This sort of instrument is required by most individuals to view stereoscopically pairs such as are presented in Figures 6.37 and 6.85. (*Courtesy Air Photo Supply Corp.*)

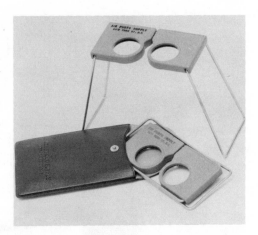

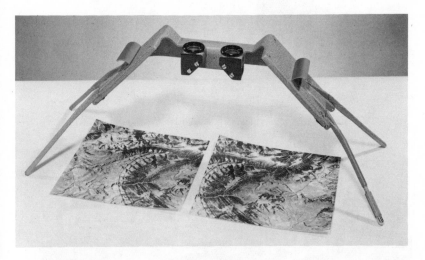

FIGURE 6.87. A mirror stereoscope. This form of instrument is used for stereoscopically viewing large photographs, which cannot be placed at the normal interpupillary distance. (*Courtesy Fairchild Space & Defense Systems*)

Figure 6.89 illustrates a *stereocomparator*. Its principle is similar to that of a stereoplotter, in that it images the two photographs of a stereo pair. In the stereocomparator, however, the operator views the images through eyepieces, in which are reticles which can be adjusted to match the apparent height of an object seen in the stereo model. The precise measurement of this adjustment then gives the elevation of the ground point in question. Stereocomparators are instruments of high precision, and are

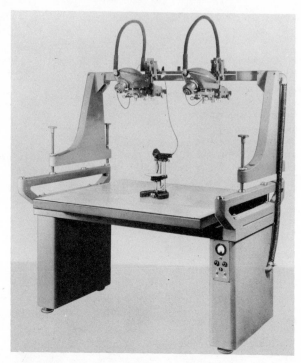

FIGURE 6.88. A typical stereo plotter. The projectors in this instrument have the ellipsoidal condensers illustrated in Figure 6.94. (*Courtesy Bausch & Lomb*)

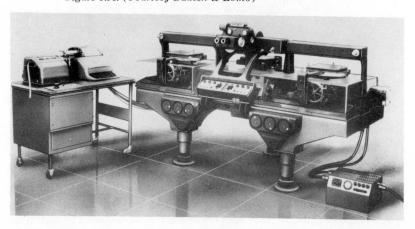

FIGURE 6.89. A precision stereocomparator. This form of instrument is used for making precision height measurement from photographic stereo pairs. Provision is shown for obtaining printout on an electric typewriter and/or transfer of coordinate data to a digital computer. (*Courtesy OMI Corp. of America*)

used to make accurate measurements of control and pass points for aerial triangulation, and for the control of charts and maps.

Photographic maps in the form of photomosaics are often prepared. Since the dozens of photographs which form the mosaic are taken from cameras pointed in various directions and from varying altitudes, the photographs must be corrected for *scale* and for *tilt*. The *scale* of an aerial photograph is the ratio of distance on the photograph to distance on the ground, which is equal to the ratio of the camera focal length to the altitude. The scale of a photograph is changed merely by magnifying or demagnifying it.

*Tilt* is caused by the camera optical axis not being vertical when the photograph is taken. Sometimes tilt is deliberately introduced in order to cover a wider area, and the result is an *oblique* photograph. Even in vertical photography, however, there is usually a small amount of tilt, which

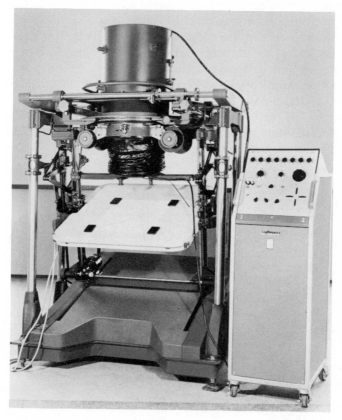

FIGURE 6.90. An autofocus rectifier. (*Courtesy Bausch & Lomb*)

varies from photograph to photograph because of aircraft instability. Tilt causes a difference in scale in different parts of the photograph; the photograph is not *orthographic*. It must be *rectified* before it can be used in a map.

Rectification is accomplished by projecting the photograph onto a tilted image plane in such a way as to correct for the tilt introduced by the camera. The conventional instrument for this purpose is the *autofocus rectifier*, illustrated in Figure 6.90.

This instrument makes use of an optical condition known as the Sheimpflug condition, shown in Figure 6.91. If a lens is presented with an object located on a plane tilted to the optical axis, then, if O′ is the image of the axial object point O, the entire image will be in focus on a plane through O′ tilted so that the object and image planes meet in the plane of the lens.

This is a first-order condition and arises from the paraxial image equation. In order for the image to be sharp over a reasonable field of view, the relative aperture of the lens must be quite small. Rectifier lenses customarily work at relative apertures of $f/16$ to $f/22$. A typical lens used for this application is the Hypergon (Figure 6.92), which is seen to be a rather extreme form of the symmetrical objective.

**6.74. Other Applications of Photogrammetry.** Photogrammetry and aerial triangulation have been discussed above in connection with aerial photography and map making, which is their most active role. The principles involved, however, are not limited to this application, and photogrammetry has many other fields of service.

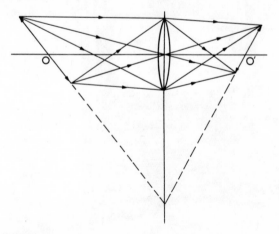

FIGURE 6.91. Optical principle of the autofocus rectifier.

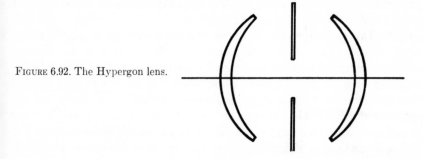

FIGURE 6.92. The Hypergon lens.

Whenever two photographs of a set of points in three dimensions are available, each taken from a different viewpoint, the principles of aerial triangulation can be applied and the actual location in space of these points can be determined by photographic measurements and computation, provided there are enough reference points in the situation to permit a solution. The technique is used to measure the trajectories of missiles and satellites, as well as of projectiles and atomic particles, and of many other objects and phenomena. Indeed, even the measurement of the parallax of the stars to determine their distances is an application of the principles of photogrammetry.

## SYSTEMS WITHOUT CIRCULAR SYMMETRY

**6.75. General.** In all of the prior discussion, it has been more or less tacitly assumed that the systems being discussed were symmetric about the optical axis and that the conditions in the plane of the diagrams were common to all planes containing the axis. This is usually a reasonable assumption, and nearly all systems, even systems with aspheric surfaces, are of this form. In special cases, however, systems and surfaces which are asymmetric about the optical axis are required.

The most common case of asymmetric optical systems is found in ordinary eyeglasses for the correction of astigmatism. In the astigmatic eye, the cornea of the eye (or the lens, rarely) has an asymmetric curvature, so that its focal length in one meridional plane is different from that in another. This is corrected by providing the patient with eyeglasses which have an opposite ratio of focal lengths. Examples of cylindrical lenses are also found in optical instruments where it is required to provide convergence or divergence in one plane but not in the orthogonal one.

Another much publicized use of nonsymmetrical optical systems is in one form of wide-screen motion picture recording and projection. An external field of view much wider than it is high is recorded on a film frame of normal width-height ratio (about $\frac{2}{3}$).

**6.76. The Cylinder.** The cylinder has an infinite focal length in one meridian and a finite focal length in the meridian perpendicular thereto, the latter being given by the conventional lens formula [Equation (4.50a)]. A point object will be imaged as a line parallel to the axis of the cylinder. This form of element is sometimes found in optical instruments, for example in the Rayleigh refractometer (see Section 8.41), where it takes the extreme form of a solid glass rod. It is also useful in many instances in shaping the image of a symmetrical aperture to fit a detector, for example.

**6.77. The Toroid.** The general form of asymmetric optical surface is the toroid. This is the surface generated by a circle which is rotated about an axis in its own plane but displaced from the center of the circle, as shown in Figure 6.93. When the axis of rotation is outside of the circle, the result is the doughnut. The analysis of an optical system containing toroids requires simply the analysis of two separate systems, representing the meridional planes through the sections having maximum and minimum curvature, which are orthogonal to each other.

Occasionally, optical surfaces representing generations by the rotation of curves other than circles, e.g., hyperbolas and ellipses, are found. In one type of photogrammetric projector, for example, the condenser is formed of an unsymmetrical section of an ellipsoid, as shown in Figure 6.94. The paraboloidal mirror of a reflecting telescope is a prime example.

Techniques for the direct fabrication of toric surfaces are in common

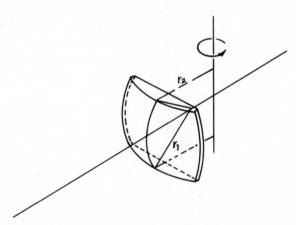

FIGURE 6.93. The toroid.

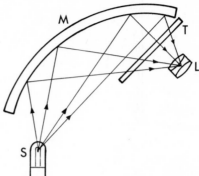

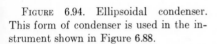

FIGURE 6.94. Ellipsoidal condenser. This form of condenser is used in the instrument shown in Figure 6.88.

use. In the case of other asymmetric surfaces, it is common practice to use the cut-out section of a symmetrical surface, whenever this is possible.

**6.78. Anamorphic Systems.** Systems which form images in which the magnification is different in the different meridians are known under the name of *anamorphic systems*. The best known examples are the "Cinemascope" camera and projection lenses. The focal length in the horizontal meridian is roughly one-half of the focal length in the vertical meridian, so that each frame has a normal vertical field of view but a horizontal field of view approximately twice as great as normal. Similarly formed projection lenses project the normal-sized frame onto to a screen which is of normal height but of twice the normal width.

The effect, in motion picture systems, is striking. The problems of designing and producing such lenses are considerable. Not only must a lens giving a wide angle of view be created, but the resolution in the wide angle direction must be particularly good if it is not to be noticeably poorer than in the vertical direction; in addition, while the focal lengths are different in the two meridians, the *back focal length* must be the same.

Other wide-screen motion picture systems use multiple cameras and projectors of conventional form, with special provisions for blending the images in the overlap region.

**6.79. The Fresnel Lens.** The imaging effects of lenses depend primarily on the surface curvatures—the thickness having at most a second-order effect. The actual thicknesses of optical components result from requirements imposed by the curvatures chosen and the fact that the thickness cannot be negative.

Essentially the same focusing effects can be obtained in an optical element if the surfaces are divided into small elements and these elements are brought together in a common plane normal to the optical axis, as shown in Figure 6.95. Lenses of this type are in common use for non-critical

FIGURE 6.95. The Fresnel lens with curved segments.

FIGURE 6.96. The Fresnel lens with flat segments.

applications, and are known as *Fresnel* lenses. The resultant breaking up of the aperture into small zones destroys the continuity of the wave front, and therefore such lenses do not provide high performance, but are very useful in many applications where good image quality is not essential.

It is only a step from the slightly curved zones shown in Figure 6.95 to a saw-tooth form, as shown in Figure 6.96, the slope of the teeth varying continuously from center to edge. This form of lens, fabricated in thin plastic sheet, is commonly available, and is very useful for many applications such as pupil-forming projection screens, condensers, etc. The saw tooth is cut as an expanding helix on a lathe, the cutting tool being changed in angle from center to edge. A master so formed may be used as a die for the economical forming of the actual lenses. Lenses of this type which are several feet in diameter and $\frac{1}{8}$ to $\frac{1}{4}$ inch thick are common. Relative apertures of the order of $f/0.5$ are customary.

This type of lens form is standard in automotive headlights. Here the segments are unsymmetrically arranged and are designed to direct the light of the headlamp so as to form a shaped beam. Most of the light from the lamp itself is collimated by a paraboloidal reflector. The arrangement is shown in Figure 6.97.

FIGURE 6.97. Cross-section of a typical automobile headlight lens of the "sealed-beam" type. (*Courtesy General Electric Co.*)

This type of lens is also frequently used in small searchlights and is a standard arrangement in the projectors used in lighthouses.

## REFERENCES

1. J. Strong, "Concepts in Classical Optics," New York, W. H. Freeman, p. 303, 1958.
2. See reference 1, p. 343.
3. A comprehensive bibliography on reflecting telescopes of all types is given in "Bibliography on Reflection Optics," Armed Forces-NRC Vision Committee, University of Michigan, 1947.
4. F. Ross, *Astrophys. J.*, **81**, 156 (1935).
5. B. Schmidt, *Central-Zeitung Optik Mechanik*, **52**, (1931) Heft 2; M. H. Hamburg, *Sternw. Bergedorf*, **7**, No. 36, p. 15 (1932).
6. Flatfield forms of the Schmidt camera and associated topics are discussed extensively in the following series of papers:
    E. Linfoot or E. Linfoot and F. Wynne, *Monthly Notices Roy. Astron. Soc.*, **103**, 210 (1943); **104**, 48 (1944); **105**, 193 (1945); **105**, 334 (1945); **108**, 81 (1948); **109**, 279 (1948); **109**, 535 (1949); **111**, 75 (1951); *Proc. Phys. Soc. London*, **57**, 199 (1945); **55**, 481 (1943).
7. D. Hendrix and W. Christie, *Sci. Am.*, **161**, (August, 1939); also in "Amateur Telescope Making—Book 3," New York, Scientific American, 1953.
8. D. Maksutov, *J. Opt. Soc. Am.*, **34**, No. 270 (1944).
9. A. Bouwers, "Achievements in Optics," Amsterdam, Elsevier, 1946.
10. Schwarzschild investigated the general case of a two-mirror objective with rotationally symmetric mirrors that satisfied the sine condition. K. Schwarzschild, *Ges. Wiss. Gottingen Math. Phys.*, **IV**, Pt. II (1905).
    None of these forms are suitable for telescopes, but are currently of interest for radar antennas. Roberts has recently developed parametric solutions for these forms: G. Roberts, *J. Opt. Soc. Am.*, **54**, 1111. (1964).
11. G. Ritchey, *L'Astronomie* (December, 1927); *J. Roy. Astron. Soc. Canada* (May–June, 1928).
12. J. Baker, *Proc. Am. Phil. Soc.*, **82**, 339 (1940); **82**, 323 (1940); *Publ. Am. Astron. Soc.*, **10**, 218 (1942); in (A. Ingalls, Ed.) "Amateur Telescope Making—Book 3, p. 1, New York, Scientific American, 1953.

13. G. Dimitroff and J. Baker, "Telescopes and Accessories," Blakiston, 1945.
14. K. Ogle, *J. Opt. Soc. Am.*, **46**, 269 (1956).
    I. Ishak, I. Hefzalla and Y. Badawy, *J. Opt. Soc. Am.*, **46**, 303 (1956).
    R. Weabe, *J. Opt. Soc. Am.*, **46**, 907 (1956).
    B. Julesz, *Science*, **145**, 356 (1964).
15. A practical discussion of the rifle scope and its use is given in T. Whelen, "Telescopic Rifle Sights," Harrisburg, Pa., Telegraph Press, 1944.
    See also E. Brown, "Basic Optics," New York, Stoeger Arms Corp., 1949.
16. A practical discussion of the microscope and its use is given in F. Munoz, "The Microscope and its Use," *Chem. Publ.* (1943).
    A comprehensive discussion of new developments in microscopy is given by P. Slater, *Indus. Res.*, 82 (May, 1964).
    For a number of recent papers on microscope developments, see *Appl. Opt.*, **3** (September, 1964).
17. H. Boegehold, *Wiss. Mikroskopie*, **55**, 17 (1938).
18. C. Burch, *Proc. Phys. Soc.*, **59**, 41, 47 (1947).
    D. Grey, "Proceedings of London Conference on Optical Instruments, 1950," New York, John Wiley & Sons, p. 65, 1952.
19. E. Abbe, *Arch. Mikroskopische Anat.*, **9**, 413 (1873).
20. F. Zernicke, *Z. Tech. Phys.*, **16**, 454 (1935); *Phys. Z.*, **36**, 848 (1935); *Physica*, **1**, 689 (1934); **9**, 686, 974 (1942).
    M. Françon, "Le Contraste de Phase en Optique et en Microscopie," *Rev. d'Optique* (1950); *Appl. Opt.*, **3**, 1033 (1964).
    A. Bennett, H. Osterberg and O. Richards, "Phase Microscopy," New York, John Wiley & Sons, 1952.
21. J. Dyson, *Proc. Roy. Soc. London Ser. A*, **204**, 170 (1950); *Nature*, **171**, 743 (1953); also in reference 1, p. 377.
    A. Lebedev, *Rev. d'Optique*, **9**, 385 (1930).
    J. St. L. Philpot, "Contraste de Phase et Contraste par Interferences," p. 42, 1952.
    F. Smith, Brit. Patent No. 639014, 1950.
22. Concepts of the resolution limit of the human eye may require revision as a result of the accomplishments of Glenn, Cooper, and other astronauts in viewing the earth from space, as reported by W. Clark, F. Morris and J. Culver, *Space-Aeronautics*, **41**, 99 (March, 1964).
23. Cf "Manual of Photogrammetry," 2nd ed., p. 309, American Society of Photogrammetry, 1952.

# CHAPTER 7

# Optical Detection

**7.1. General.** Radiation throughout the optical region of the spectrum is detected and measured by its interaction with matter in various types of *radiation detectors*. In the visible region of the spectrum, radiation is detected for the purposes of measurement and for the purpose of the recording of images. For the recording function, photographic film is the most common and best known detector, but in applications such as television, the necessity for turning the detected radiation into an electrical signal makes it much more convenient to utilize detectors which perform this function directly.

The infrared region of the spectrum is not accessible to visual techniques, and photographic emulsions are useful only in a very limited region close to the visible band. Direct radiation detectors therefore find wide use in the infrared. Infrared analytical equipment[1] has found a useful field in a number of industrial processes, and infrared signaling and detection systems have several commercial applications;[2] but the primary development in infrared technology has been in the area of military equipment, where its unique characteristics are the ability to detect strong infrared sources, such as rocket and jet engine exhausts, to penetrate camouflage and to make possible covert reconnaissance and observation. Most of the development effort in infrared detectors has been the result of military interest.

The ultraviolet region of the spectrum has not been an active field, due primarily to the opacity of the atmosphere for this radiation, making it necessary to operate in vacuum when wavelengths shorter than 2900Å are involved. With the exploitation of space, it may be expected that ultraviolet technology will show increased activity.

343

## PHOTOGRAPHIC DETECTION

**7.2. The Photographic Process.** The photographic process is based upon the capacity of certain chemical compounds to absorb photons and thereby change their molecular state. The fundamental class of compounds with this characteristic are the silver halides. Upon the absorption of photons, the substances become "sensitized" so that when subjected later to the action of a *developer*, the molecules dissociate and precipitate free silver, whereas those molecules which have not become sensitized are unaffected.

In recent years, many new developments in photosensitive materials have been underway, and materials have become available which undergo chemical change upon the action of radiation—many of them without the need for a developer. Some of these actions are reversible, some are not. Materials which develop by the action of heat, and thermoplastic materials which undergo physical deformation, are among the recent developments. And materials other than the silver halides, such as the diazo-type materials, which are used extensively for reproduction purposes, have been known and in use for a long time. Many of these processes have advantages over conventional photographic materials, in resolution, in convenience of processing, and in other areas, but none of them, at the present writing, even approach the sensitivity of silver halide emulsions, and therefore have not yet found wide application in the direct detection of radiation.

Space does not permit discussion of these numerous techniques, or even a very thorough discussion of the conventional photographic materials; the literature on photography is voluminous,[3] and it is therefore unnecessary to discuss it except in those areas directly associated with the optical aspects of photographic detection.

**7.3. Photographic Emulsions.** In photographic emulsions of the silver halide type, the photosensitive material is deposited in *grains*. After sensitization by the absorption of photons, each grain *develops* or fails to develop as a unit and leaves a dark or a clear area on the developed negative. The emulsion, after exposure to an optical image and the resulting absorption of photons, is said to have a *latent image*, which is turned into a permanent image by the precipitation of silver under the action of the developer.

It requires the absorption of a certain number of photons to sensitize a grain; the number required is somewhat independent of the size of the grain, so that increasing the grain size is a means of improving the sensitivity of the emulsion, since large grains will require a shorter exposure to absorb the required number of photons. Grain size, of course, affects the *resolution limit* of the emulsion, so that there is an important trade-off between sensitivity and resolution. Modern photographic emulsions come in an almost endless variety, and the chemical details are complex and varied, so that this reciprocity rule between sensitivity and resolution is no more than a rule of thumb, but it is quite real, and represents a fundamental limitation on photographic detection.

The number of photons required to produce a latent image varies from 10 to 100 per grain. The shorter the wavelength of the radiation, the higher is the energy of the photon, and therefore, fewer photons are required to produce the latent image, although the relation is not linear. The sensitivity of the emulsion as a function of wavelength is also affected by the characteristics of the gelatin which acts as a carrier for the silver compounds; emulsions for use in the infrared and the ultraviolet require special chemical treatment.

One of the most important characteristics of the photographic emulsion as a radiation detector is that it is totally integrating—its response, measured as the number of developable grains per unit of illuminance, is a linear function of time over a wide range of exposure.

**7.4 The Developed Image.** If a developed photographic emulsion is measured (with a microdensitometer) and its *density* is plotted against the logarithm of the *exposure*, a curve such as shown in Figure 7.1 is obtained. The density is defined by the relation

$$D = \log \frac{1}{T} \tag{7.1}$$

where $T$ is the transmission, and the exposure is defined as the illuminance times the exposure time—usually expressed in meter-candle-seconds.

This is called an H & D curve (from Hurter and Driffield).[4] The variations in brightness over the optical image which was exposed on the film are represented by variations in density in the developed emulsion. The shape and position of the H & D curve is determined by the characteristics of the emulsion and the nature of the developer and the time and conditions of development. If the development time is increased, the curve becomes steeper and moves to the left; if the negative is left in the developer long enough, it will become completely black.

The slope of the H & D curve is the *gamma* for the particular developer and cycle involved. In the linear part of the curve, the relation

$$D = \gamma \log E \tag{7.2}$$

holds. At its top, the curve is asymptotic to the saturation density for the particular emulsion involved; at the bottom, the curve is prevented from going to zero density by *fog*. Fog level is a function of the type of emulsion

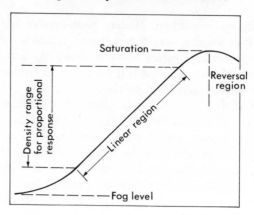

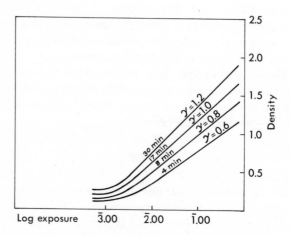

FIGURE 7.1. The $D \log E$ curve for a photographic emulsion. This curve is often called the H & D curve, from Hurter and Driffield, who developed it. The upper figure shows the geometrical characteristics of the curve; the lower figure shows the curves as published for a typical emulsion, the value of $\gamma$ being determined by the duration of development.

and its history; it represents the limit of the emulsion as a detector of energy. Fog represents silver grains developed at random.

The aim in photography, at least in pictorial photography, is to include in the linear slope of the curve the full range of light variation in the scene. When the exposure is determined by a measurement of the average scene illuminance, as is the case when an exposure meter is used in a normal fashion, it is usually most desirable to expose the film and develop it so that for an exposure corresponding to the measured average illuminance, the density of the developed film is unity, and the gamma is just sufficiently high to spread the linear portion of the curve over the full range of illuminance that is present in the scene. For innumerable special purposes, other criteria with respect to exposure and gamma will prevail.

*Contrast* (see Chapter 9), or comparative density of a dark portion of the image to a light portion, is given by $\gamma$; increase in contrast is accomplished only at the cost of dynamic range—the range of illuminance over which effective response is maintained. In development, gamma is usually controlled by a *gray scale*—a scale of steps of equal density difference. For pictorial photography, a dynamic range of eight steps is sufficient for normal scenes, the conventional step being a density difference of 0.15. A typical photographic negative emulsion will have a dynamic range of 12 or more steps.

Definition of density as the logarithm of the opacity corresponds to the well-known psychophysical law that the response is proportional to the olgarithm of the stimulus. Equal steps in density appear to the eye to be equal *increments* of brightness—actually, they correspond to equal *ratios* of intensity. The same phenomenon is recognized in establishing the magnitudes of the stars.

**7.5. Exposure Index.** Photographic materials are rated for sensitivity by a number called the *exposure index*. There are a number of standards, the best known being that adopted by the American Standards Association in 1960, and called the ASA Speed. By definition

$$\text{ASA Speed} = 0.8/e \qquad (7.3)$$

where $e$ is the exposure, in meter-candle-seconds, required to give a density of 0.1 above fog. The exposure is

$$e = E't \qquad (7.4)$$

where $t$ is the exposure time in seconds, and, from Equation (5.29), $E' = B'\Omega$, $\phi$ being considered zero (on axis). But, from Equation (5.24), $B' = B$, and since the solid angle of the aperture is $\Omega = \pi D^2/4f^2 = \pi/4F^2$, we have

$$e = \frac{\pi B}{4F^2}\, t \qquad (7.5)$$

where $B$ is the luminance of the object and $F$ is the relative aperture of the optical system. In a practical case, the value of $e$ in Equation (7.5) must be multiplied by the transmission of the optical system—or the $f/\text{No.}$ of the lens substituted by the "T-Stop." The T-Stop is the $f/\text{No.}$ of a lens multiplied by the square root of its transmission.

To obtain an answer in meter-candle-seconds from Equation (7.5), the object luminance must be expressed in candles/meter$^2$, the standard unit. Scene luminances are more commonly given in foot-lamberts, in which case, the value must be multiplied by $10.76/\pi$, since foot-lamberts is the luminous emittance rather than the luminance and 10.76 is the number of square feet in a square meter (see Section 5.7).

The ASA Speed is customarily given by film manufacturers on the film package; the ASA Speed of a typical photographic film (Eastman Plus-X) is 125; therefore, it requires an exposure of .0064 meter-candle-seconds.

**7.6. Granularity and Graininess.** The resolution of a photographic emulsion is limited by its microscopic structure, which consists of individual grains of metallic silver, distributed in a random pattern. The *average* number of grains per unit area is proportional to the exposure, but the actual number of grains in different areas of equal size and with equal exposure will vary from this average. These statistical fluctuations follow a Gaussian distribution (see Section 2.40), and if a trace is made across a developed photograph with a microdensitometer and the microscopic fluctuations in density are plotted with the number of fluctuations of a given amplitude as ordinate and the amplitude as abscissa, the curve will resemble the Gaussian error curve.

The phenomenon is called *granularity*, and its measure is the *standard deviation* of the error curve, $\sigma$. It will, of course, depend upon the particular photographic emulsion being considered, and it will also depend upon the size of the scanning aperture in the microdensitometer. $\sigma$ is a standard measure of emulsions, and the customary scanning aperture size used in developing the $\sigma$ reported in film manufacturers' literature is $24\mu$.

The term *graininess* refers to the visual sensation produced when the magnification is sufficiently high that the discontinuities in density caused by grains and grain clumps become detectable to the eye. This measure determines, for a given material and set of conditions, the maximum magnification which may be utilized. Space does not permit a thorough discussion of granularity and graininess here; exhaustive discussions are to be found in the literature.[5]

## CHARACTERISTICS OF RADIATION

**7.7. Blackbody Radiation.** All radiation in the optical region has its origin in radiating atoms and molecules, which give rise to specific spectral line emission, modified by local environment, or in blackbody radiation. The detection and measurement of spectral emission is the domain of spectroscopy, which is discussed somewhat briefly in Chapter 8. The subject matter of this chapter is the detection and measurement of general radiation, where the purpose is to detect an object or to measure the total quantity of radiation, in some specified spectral band, which may be wide or narrow depending upon the situation.

The basic laws of blackbody radiation were discussed in Chapter 1, the significant relations for the purpose of the present discussion being the Stefan-Boltzmann law [Equation (1.38)] for the total radiation from a blackbody and Planck's law [Equation (1.32)] giving the spectral distribution of energy for a blackbody.

Figure 7.2 presents curves drawn by means of Planck's equation for

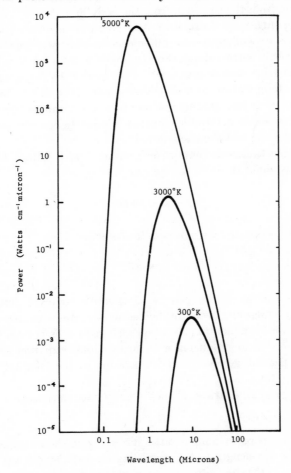

FIGURE 7.2. Blackbody radiation for different temperatures.

blackbodies at several temperatures. Some important facts about these curves are to be noted. The total radiation, or area under the curve, is in accordance with the Stefan-Boltzmann law, and increases as the fourth power of the temperature. The peak wavelength of radiation moves toward the short-wavelength end of the spectrum as the temperature increases. Despite this fact, every curve completely envelops any curve corresponding to a lower temperature, so that at *any given wavelength*, there is always more radiation from a hotter body. For example, although the wavelength of peak radiation from the sun is twenty times shorter than that for a body at the earth's surface temperature, there is more radiation at that body's peak emission from the sun than from the body in question.

**7.8. Differentials of Radiation.** Many optical detection and measurement systems depend upon the differences in radiation between specific bodies and their surroundings. For example, a jet engine exhaust seen against a radiating background, such as the sky or the earth, appears as a difference in temperature to a detecting system. The distinction between the object and its background is made in some optimum spectral band, and the difference is determined by the relative temperatures and emissivities of the body and the background.

If the Stefan-Boltzmann law is differentiated with respect to the temperature, it is found that

$$\frac{dF}{dT} = 4\alpha\sigma T^3 \tag{7.6}$$

and if it is differentiated with respect to the emissivity, $\alpha$,

$$\frac{dF}{d\alpha} = \sigma T^4 \tag{7.7}$$

so it is seen that emissivity can be an effective factor in determining a difference in radiation, even for bodies at the same temperature. The effect of a given incremental percentage change in emissivity is about one-fourth as effective in producing a change in total radiation as the same incremental percentage change in temperature at the "normal" temperature of 20°C (300°K).

**7.9. Energy of Radiation.** Planck's relation for the energy of a photon,

$$E = h\nu \tag{7.8}$$

shows that the energy available varies directly with the frequency, so that a photon at a wavelength in the visible region (say 5500Å) has twice the energy (when converted into ergs) of a photon at a wavelength of $1.1\mu$, in the near infrared, and 10 times the energy of a photon at a wavelength of $5.5\mu$, in the intermediate infrared. This is an important factor in comparing the sensitivities of detectors which operate in different spectral regions. Detectors at the three wavelengths mentioned above will have the same sensitivity on an energy basis if they respond, respectively, to one, two, or 10 photons. In Figure 7.3, the photon energy is plotted as a function of wavelength.

**7.10. Atmospheric Transmission.** The transmission of the atmosphere for radiation of various wavelengths is of importance in many detection problems. The atmospheric transmission is highly selective when the entire optical spectrum is being considered.

There are three principal factors at work. In the short-wavelength region —the visible spectrum and the ultraviolet—the principal factor is the Rayleigh fourth-power scattering (see Section 3.5) for which the scattering varies as the fourth power of the wavelength. This is the case for wavelengths which are shorter than the scattering particles, which for Rayleigh scattering are the molecules of the atmospheric gases.

At the longer wavelengths, Mie scattering (see Section 3.6) occurs;

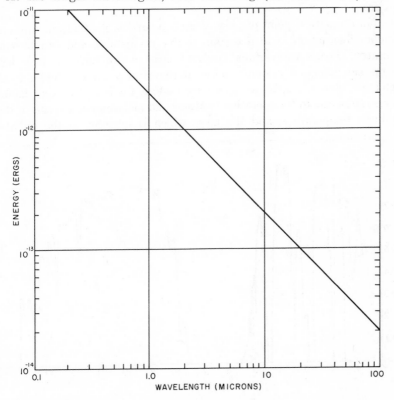

FIGURE 7.3. The energy of a photon as a function of wavelength.

this is the case for wavelengths which are of the same order of size as the scattering particles. This scattering region involves particles in the atmosphere other than the atmospheric gases—dust, water droplets, aerosol suspensions, etc., which occur in most real atmospheres. For a pure atmosphere, Mie scattering is quite small.

The third factor is the selective absorption of the atmospheric gases and of the atmospheric water vapor, which is nearly always present in significant quantitites. Water vapor, carbon dioxide and oxygen all have strong absorption bands in the infrared spectral region. Figure 7.4 charts the spectral transmission of a clear atmosphere, identifying the prominent features.[6]

**7.11. Noise.**[7] The term "noise," long familiar to electrical engineers, has only recently made its way into optics. Noise, in the broadest sense, is any fluctuation in a measured quantity which is due to some cause other than a fluctuation in the actual thing being measured. It is always noise of one kind or another which eventually limits the capability of measuring devices.

From a practical point of view, noise is a *random* fluctuation. Any non-random fluctuation is to a certain degree predictable and can be compensated. There are various kinds of noise which. must be considered in optical detection systems: noise in electrical amplifiers, noise in the detectors themselves, noise caused by various kinds of external disturbances, noise due to the vibration of atoms and molecules as a result of their ambient temperature, and the noise which is inherent in the radiation

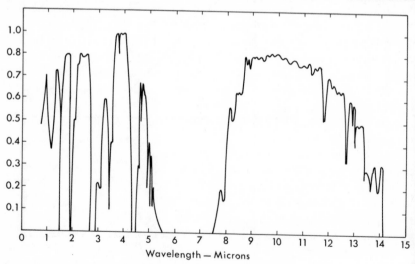

FIGURE 7.4. The relative transmission of the atmosphere.

being detected. This latter type of noise—radiation or photon noise—is discussed in the following section. Other types of noise are discussed in connection with those areas where they are of greatest concern.

**7.12. Radiation Noise.**[8] The origin of radiation is changes in state in atoms and molecules by the emission of photons. Now, photons are emitted by a semi-random process. When an atom absorbs a photon and changes to an excited state, it will, after some interval of time, spontaneously emit a photon and drop to a lower energy level. The *average* lifetime of the excited state is determinable and has been discussed in Section 3.50. The actual time of emission of a specific photon is predictable only on a statistical basis, so that when photons are received by a detector, they do not come in a regular sequence, but fluctuate in time. The statistics governing the emission of photons are the *Bose-Einstein* statistics, and they give the mean square radiation noise power in a bandwidth $\Delta f$ as

$$\bar{P}_N{}^2 = 8S\sigma k T^5 \Delta f \tag{7.9}$$

where $S$ is the source area, $\sigma$ is the Stefan-Boltzmann constant, $k$ is Boltzmann's constant, $T$ is the absolute temperature, and $\Delta f$ is the bandwidth, in cycles per second of the measuring device. This is so-called *white* noise, for which the power per unit bandwidth is independent of the measuring frequency.

Nearly all detection systems operate with an alternating signal at some convenient frequency. This is done partly because it is convenient to amplify alternating current, as compared with direct current, and also because detection systems operating on a direct current basis are subject to drifts and changes in sensitivity to which ac systems are not subject. Also, there is a definite bandwidth of observation determined by the time of observation, equal to $2\pi/t$, where $t$ is the time of observation. For example, systems which scan a field of view have a "dwell time" on a particular target, determined by the target angular size and the angular speed of scan; this in turn, determines a frequency by the above relation, and if the system is intended to detect all targets of this size or larger, the bandwidth extends from 0 to $2\pi/t$.

Systems which "look" at a target for a relatively long period of time are actually systems which have a very narrow observation bandwidth, and thus have a reduced radiation noise, in accordance with Equation (7.9). Another way of looking at the situation is to say that the noise can be averaged out by integration over a period of time, because the noise is as often positive as negative with respect to the signal, and thus would theoretically integrate to zero over a sufficiently long time. This is exactly equivalent to reducing the bandwidth by a longer observation time.

Radiation noise represents the ultimate limit of sensitivity of a radiation

detecting system. This radiation noise may come from a background at a
steady level, such as the sky, it may come from a background which
fluctuates in a spatial sense, such as a landscape, or it may even come from
the radiation level of the target itself. The performance of detection systems
is usually expressed in terms of a "signal-to-noise" ratio, which is the ratio
of the signal power to the mean square noise power. A system is often said
to have a performance limit at the level where the signal-to-noise ratio
is unity. This is an arbitrary criterion; there are many factors in a particular situation which determine the signal-to-noise level which represents
limiting performance. In many systems, a signal-to-noise of the order of 3
to 10 is necessary; in others, for example, where exhaustive processing of
the data is undertaken, the operating level may be considerably below the
noise.

## DETECTION SYSTEMS

**7.13. General Characteristics.** The discussions of this chapter are
confined to radiation detectors, their mechanisms and characteristics. There
are no "standard" forms of optical detection and measurement systems—
each specific application calls for its own arrangement. In general, there
will be an optical system, usually in the form of a camera, whose function
it is to form an image of the target field on the detector. The target field
may be large or small, depending upon the purpose of the equipment, and
the detectors may be single or multiple. The device may be designed to
"scan" a field of view in some kind of a suitable pattern, and this scan may
be accomplished by optical means or by scanning a detector array either
mechanically or electronically.

Figure 7.5 shows a typical arrangement for an instrument generally
known as a *radiometer*. The image of a small target is focused by an optical
system on a detector element, and the output signal of this detector is
presented to an indicating device. In the arrangement shown, the instrument is a total energy radiometer; the output of the detector represents the
energy received over the spectral range to which the optical system is
transparent and to which the detector is sensitive.

If a means is provided in the instrument for passing only a small portion
of the spectrum at a time, and the energy on the detector is "scanned"
by moving this small section of the spectrum throughout the spectral range
to which the instrument is sensitive, it becomes a *spectro-radiometer*, and
will measure the spectral radiation curve of the target in question.

Figure 7.6 shows an instrument in which a linear array of detectors is
provided. Each detector has a separate electronic channel, and their out-

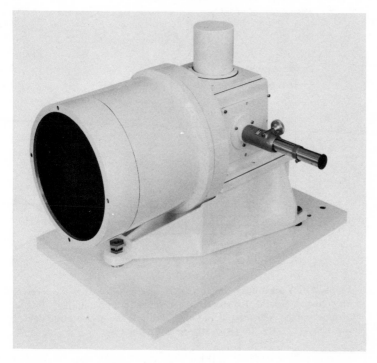

FIGURE 7.5. A typical radiometer. This model has an aperture diameter of 15 inches. The microscope is used for aiming. (*Courtesy Perkin-Elmer Corp.*)

puts can be presented on a suitable display device, such as a cathode ray oscilloscope. Each detector "sees" a small target area, and if the instrument is "scanned" in a direction normal to the line of the detector array, and the display is swept in the corresponding direction in synchronization with the scan, a picture is obtained, which displays the target scene in the spectral band to which the instrument is sensitive.

Figure 7.7 shows, schematically, the arrangement of a television camera. Here the detector is a television camera tube, which is actually a two-dimensional detector array, which is scanned electronically and the output presented on a *kinescope*, which is essentially a cathode ray oscilloscope of special design. The operation of this kind of system is described in the following Chapter.

These are simplified examples of a large class of optical detection systems. With suitable choices of detectors, these systems can be designed for operation in the ultraviolet, the visible, or the infrared regions of the spectrum.

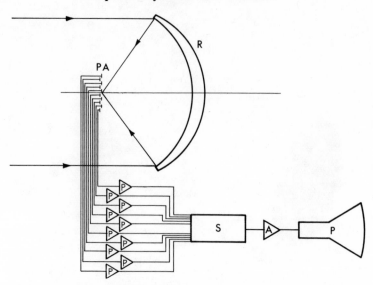

FIGURE 7.6. A scanning radiometer or target detector. R is the receiver or objective; PA is the detector array; P refers to a preamplifier; S is an electronic switch; A is a signal amplifier, and P is the presentation device, shown here schematically as a cathode ray tube.

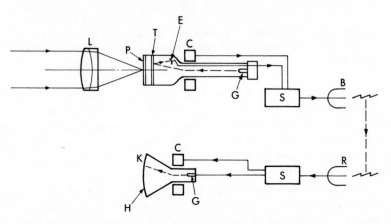

FIGURE 7.7. Schematic arrangement of a television system: (L) Objective lens; (P) Photocathode; (T) Electron target; (E) Electron multiplier; (C) Deflection coils; (G) Electron gun; (S) Signal processing; (B) Broadcast antenna; (R) Receiving antenna; (K) Picture tube; (H) Phosphor.

FIGURE 7.7A. A typical television camera. This model provides a number of lenses of different focal length mounted on a turret. (*Courtesy Radio Corp. of America*)

The variety of devices in the infrared spectrum is perhaps larger than in other regions, because it is only by means of this kind of instrumentation that this spectral region is available for use. In the visible spectrum, instruments for use with the human eye and with photographic film are possible.

**7.14. Optical Materials.** In spectral regions outside of the visible, ordinary optical glasses cannot normally be used, since they are not transparent. There are a wide variety of optical materials which have been exploited for the infrared and ultraviolet spectral regions.[9] Some of these are minerals, which have been "grown" in the form of large single crystals; others are synthetic crystals.[10] Table 7.1 lists the properties of a selected group of these materials.

TABLE 7.1. PROPERTIES OF SOME COMMON INFRARED TRANSMITTING MATERIALS

| Material | Symbol | Transmission | | Refractive Index (Approx.) | Melting or Softening Temperature (°C) | Coefficient Expansion per °C × 10⁶ | Water Resistant |
|---|---|---|---|---|---|---|---|
| | | Short-wave length Cutoff ($\mu$) | Long-wave length Cutoff ($\mu$) | | | | |
| Fused silica (quartz) | SiO | — | 4.5 | 1.42 | 1710 | 0.5 | Yes |
| Titanium dioxide | TiO | — | 5.5 | 2.5 | 1825 | 8 | Yes |
| Sapphire | Al₂O₃ | — | 6.3 | 1.72 | 2030 | 6 | Yes |
| Lithium fluoride | LiF | — | 7.5 | 1.35 | 870 | 37 | No |
| Calcium fluoride | CaF₂ | — | 11 | 1.38 | 1360 | 24 | No |
| Sodium fluoride | NaF | — | 15 | 1.3 | 980 | 36 | No |
| Magnesium fluoride | MgF₂ | — | 7.5 | 1.38 | 1255 | 18 | Yes |
| Sodium chloride | NaCl | — | 23 | 1.45 | 801 | 44 | No |
| Silver chloride | AgCl | 2* | 25 | 1.95 | 458 | 30 | Yes |
| Arsenic trisulfide | As₂S₃ | — | 12 | 2.4 | 210 | 25 | No |
| Potassium bromide | KBr | — | 40 | 1.49 | 730 | 43 | No |
| Thallium-bromide-iodide | KRS-5 | — | 40 | 2.29 | 415 | 58 | No |
| Germanium | Ge | 2 | 55 | 4.00 | 936 | 6 | Yes |
| Silicon | Si | 1.5 | 15 | 3.42 | 1420 | 4.2 | Yes |
| Selenium | Se | 1.5 | 30 | 3 | 35 | — | — |
| Calcite | CaCO₃ | — | 5 | 1.5 | 894 | 25 | No |
| Potassium iodide | KI | — | 50 | 1.57 | 723 | 43 | No |

* Must be protected from visible light.

Reflecting optical systems find considerable favor in detection systems outside the visible spectrum, since they are not subject to the problems of transparency in a selected spectral region. It is not usually possible, however, to obtain satisfactory systems by using mirrors alone, so that these special optical materials in the form of correcting plates and elements for catadioptric systems, and often for simple windows, find wide application. Even with the large list of materials, the limitations on the designer are much more severe than in the very extensive list of ordinary optical glasses for the visible spectrum, so that the achievement of a high optical performance level is usually much less probable than in the case of visual systems.

**7.15. Types of Detectors.** The methods of classifying radiation detectors are many; for the purposes of this discussion, they may first be divided into two general types: photon detectors and thermal detectors. Further subdivisions will become evident in the ensuing discussion.

Photon detectors are those detectors which respond to individual quanta of radiation. Their region of spectral sensitivity is selective, for reasons which will be seen below. The absorption of photons from incident radiation gives rise to internal changes in the detector, which are converted into an electrical signal and taken from the output.

Thermal detectors, on the other hand, are nonselective in the spectral sense; they absorb all of the radiation, which is converted into heat in the detector and raises its temperature. This rise in temperature, in turn, is converted into an electrical signal and taken from the output.

Photon detectors may be subdivided into photoemissive detectors and photoconductive detectors. The first class operate by means of the photoelectric effect, discussed in Section 3.24. Photoconductive detectors are those in which the absorption of photons leads to a change in the conductivity or resistivity of the detector. Some slightly different effects, which occur in the same type of materials as does photoconduction, are discussed together with photoconduction.

Thermal detectors are of several classes, of which the best known are thermocouples, in which the temperature change generates a voltage, and bolometers, in which the temperature change results in a change in resistivity. There are also the Golay cell, which is discussed below, and a few unusual types, such as the evaporagraph and the interference edgegraph, which are not discussed here, but are referenced to existing literature. A complete coverage of the field of detection and its application has not been attempted; the purpose has been to show the basic mechanisms of radiation detection and their general characteristics.[11]

## PHOTOEMISSIVE DETECTORS

**7.16. The Photoelectric Effect.** The photoelectric effect,[12] in which the absorption of a photon leads to the ejection of an electron, has been discussed in Section 3.24. This effect is sometimes called the *external* photoelectric effect, to distinguish it from the effects which take place in photoconductors, which are really photoelectric in character. In the external photoelectric effect, atoms are ionized by the absorption of a photon. It has been pointed out in the prior discussion that the ejected electrons are characterized by the fact that their rate of generation is linearly proportional to the rate of energy absorption, but that their individual kinetic energy depends entirely on the wavelength of the incident radiation.

This phenomenon is easy to understand.[13] In order for an atom to become ionized, the forces binding the electron to the nucleus must be overcome. If $e$ is the electron charge, then the energy required to produce ionization may be expressed as $e\phi$, where $\phi$ is defined as the *work function* for the material in question. At some radiation frequency, $\nu_0$, there is the equality

$$h\nu_0 = e\phi \tag{7.10}$$

and it is seen that $\nu_0$ is the minimum frequency which will produce ionization—that is, give rise to the photoelectric effect.

If photons of frequency $\nu$ are absorbed, they will have the energy $h\nu$, and therefore the kinetic energy of the ejected electron will be

$$hc\left[\frac{1}{\lambda} - \frac{1}{\lambda_0}\right] = E = \tfrac{1}{2}mv^2 = h\nu - h\nu_0 = h\nu - e\phi \qquad (7.11)$$

The kinetic energy of the ejected electron is, therefore, proportional to the frequency of the absorbed radiation, a conclusion which is completely confirmed by experiment.

Among the natural elements, the lowest work function is that for cesium, which is $\phi = 1.9$ eV; this corresponds to a wavelength of $0.65\mu$, which is in the visible spectrum. Thus, no *elemental* photoemitter has a response which extends beyond the visible spectrum. Some alloys, however, exhibit a work function sufficiently low to extend their photoemissive response somewhat into the infrared.[14] For example, an alloy of silver-oxygen-cesium (Ag-O-Cs), known as an S-1 photo surface, has a work function $\phi = 1$ eV, which extends its response to a wavelength of $1.2\mu$.

**7.17. Quantum Efficiency.** A prominent characteristic of photon detectors is their *quantum efficiency*—the ratio of the number of events in the detector to the number of photons received; this number is always less than unity. In photoelectric detectors, the quantum efficiency is the number of ejected electrons per photon received. For a photographic emulsion, the quantum efficiency is the number of developable grains produced per photon absorbed; this was seen to be in the range .01 to .001.

For photoemissive detectors so far developed, the quantum efficiencies range from $10^{-5}$ to $10^{-1}$; for the S-1 surface, for example, it is $3 \times 10^{-3}$ at the peak response wavelength. The quantum efficiency, of course, is a function of frequency or wavelength, going rapidly to zero at the limiting frequency $\nu_0$.

**7.18. Response of Photoemissive Surfaces.** Figure 7.8 plots the relative spectral response of several typical photoemissive surfaces currently available. As is customary, these curves are drawn on a relative, rather than an absolute basis, since their purpose is only to show relative spectral response. Response on an absolute basis is best shown for a complete detector, which includes not only the photosurface itself, but the means for detection of the ejected electrons.

It will be noted that there is a very steep drop-off at the limiting frequency $\nu_0$. Theoretically, the photoelectric effect will occur for any frequency higher than the limiting frequency; the drop-off in response as the higher frequencies are approached is caused by conditions which have

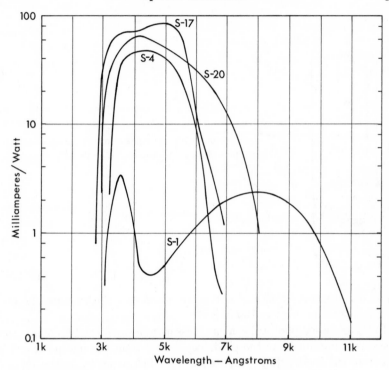

FIGURE 7.8. Relative response of typical photoemissive surfaces. Any of these surfaces are generally available in photomultiplier and other types of phototubes.

nothing to do directly with the photoelectric effect; in the curves shown, the most effective factor limiting response at higher frequencies is the transmission of the envelope which encloses the photo surface, which always operates in a vacuum or in a low-pressure gas. For surfaces intended for use in the visible spectrum, glass envelopes are used; these, of course, are opaque to ultraviolet. When detectors are used in the ultraviolet, it is necessary to provide them with ultraviolet transmitting envelopes—usually quartz.

**7.19. The Phototube.** The standard photoemissive detector is the *phototube*.[15] This, as illustrated in Figure 7.9, consists of the photo surface, S, and an anode $a$ which collects the ejected electrons. The anode carries a positive charge with respect to the cathode, which is the photo surface, so that the ejected electrons are drawn to it by electrostatic forces. The first phototubes were made by Elster and Geitel, in 1889.[16]

Phototubes are made in two general types—vacuum and gas-filled. The response time of the vacuum photocell is its outstanding feature; it is

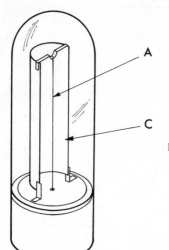

FIGURE 7.9. Schematic arrangement of a typical phototube: (A) anode; (C) cathode.

about $10^{-8}$ second, so that it is possible to operate the vacuum phototube at frequencies as high as 100 Mc.

In the gas-filled phototube, a gas pressure of a small fraction of an atmosphere is maintained. As the electrons ejected from the photo-cathode are drawn to the anode, they generate additional electrons by ionization of the gas, and thus more electrons are collected at the anode. The improvement in sensitivity can be as high as 10X. Thus, the gas-filled photocell provides a higher signal output for a given incident intensity. It does this at the cost of response time. The time constant for a gas-filled phototube is of the order of $10^{-4}$ second, so that the response begins to drop for operating frequencies of 1 kc.

**7.20. The Photomultiplier.** The *photomultiplier*, or *electron-multiplier phototube*,[17] is probably the most widely used photoemissive detector for high performance applications. From the standpoint of the detection mechanism, it is no different from the vacuum phototube, but the anode is coated with a secondary emission material, and is followed by a series of secondary anodes, as shown in Figure 7.10.

A secondary emission material is a material which, when impacted by an electron, produces a number of secondary electrons; these secondaries are collected by the second anode, which in turn produces additional secondaries.[18] The electrodes are shaped to favor the passage of the secondary electrons to the succeeding electrode rather than to their point of origin. The effect of the arrangement is to produce a cascading of electron emission from electrode to electrode down t. e tube. Each electrode, of course,

FIGURE 7.10. The photomultiplier tube.
C. Collector
G. Grid
S. Shield

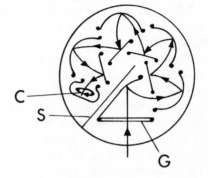

is positively charged to a potential higher than that of the preceding electrode.

The secondary emission factor, $R$, may be as high as 10. With 10 or 12 secondary electrodes—called *dynodes*—in series, the multiplication of the tube is $10^{10}$ or $10^{12}$. The dynode stages represent a built-in, multi-stage *amplifier;* the same general effect and an equivalent gain could be achieved with a standard phototube and a multi-stage electronic amplifier. The advantage of the photomultiplier is that the internal noise of the electron multiplier amplifier can be kept quite low; it would be possible to provide external amplifiers with an equivalent noise level, but they would be very expensive and would represent very difficult design and maintenance problems. In addition, the electron multiplier is very small and compact and has a very high reliability.

The time constant of the photomultiplier is not quite as high as that of the simple vacuum photocell, but it is sufficiently high to permit operation nearly to the 100 Mc level.

**7.21. Phototube Response Ratings.** The response of phototubes is conventionally rated in terms of photometric units rather than radiometric units, although the latter units would be more meaningful and more convenient for many applications. The flow of electrons from the photo surface to the cathode constitutes an electric current, and the input radiation is best described in terms of its power (lumens or watts). Thus, the response of phototubes is usually expressed as *amperes per lumen.* In applications to spectral distributions other than that of the visibility curve, the characteristics of this curve must be taken into account.

Typical responses of photo cathodes are from 20 to 200 $\mu$A per lumen of incident radiation. At the wavelength of peak visibility, 1 watt = 682 lumens, so that these responses become, *for this wavelength,* $1.4 \times 10^{-2}$ to $1.4 \times 10^{-3}$ amperes/watt.

**7.22. The Square-law Detector.** The power developed in an output circuit of resistance $R$ is $P = I^2R$; thus the power is proportional to the square of the input power. A detector which exhibits this relationship is customarily known as a *square-law detector*.

**7.23. Thermal Emission.** In most applications, the limiting performance of phototubes is set by thermal emission from the photo cathode. Even if no radiation is received on the cathode, there will be random emission of electrons because of thermal agitation in the material as a result of its ambient temperature, and these electrons will be drawn to the cathode and will give rise to a small output current, known as the *dark current*, since it is the current which appears when the tube is placed in complete darkness. For typical phototubes, this dark current corresponds to an input radiation as low as $10^{-15}$ to $10^{-16}$ watts. This is equivalent to a rate of incident photons of 200 to 300/sec. By contrast, the threshold of the human eye is stated to be about 40–90 photons/sec.[19]

The dark current can be reduced by cooling the cathode, since the thermal noise is proportional to the temperature. By this means, it is possible to use photocells to "count" photons.

## PHOTOCONDUCTIVE DETECTORS

**7.24. Photoconductive Materials.** Materials may be divided into three definite classes: conductors, insulators, and semiconductors.[20] The conductors are the metals. They are characterized by values of resistivity less than about $10^{-3}$ ohms/cm. The insulators are the dielectrics—they are characterized by values of resistivity greater than about $10^{12}$ ohms/cm. Between these two extremes lie the *semiconductors*.

Conduction implies the flow of electrons through the material; in metals, electrons are relatively free to flow; in dielectrics, electrons are not free to flow; semiconductors represent a range in which more or less restricted electron flow is possible. Now, when an electric current is carried through a material, the electrons flow into it from the external circuit at one end and out of it into the external circuit at the other. If all that were involved were a passage of individual electrons through the material, the material would have a large negative charge while it was conducting, representing the electrons which are in transit from one end to the other. This phenomenon does not occur; actually there are copious quantities of "free" electrons in the material, and when an additional electron is added from the external circuit, one of these free electrons flows out into the circuit to maintain the electrical neutrality of the material itself.

The metal, even when not conducting an electric current, has these free electrons; however, since it is not negatively charged, these electrons must be normal inhabitants of some energy level of atoms in a stationary state. This means that in a metal, some electrons, at least, must be very loosely bound to their respective atoms, so that they can rather freely move about from atom to atom. Metals are normally crystalline in structure, and the atoms dispose themselves in a lattice network such that there is no real one-to-one association of some of the electrons with individual atoms— the electrons are shared between atoms.

In the dielectrics, electrons are firmly bound in the lattice, and are not free to move about, so that the effect of the introduction of electrons from an external circuit is merely to create an electrostatic charge on the material.

Semiconductors also have a lattice and are crystalline in form; in many cases, a block of semiconductor material is itself a single crystal. Two types of bonding in the lattice structure exist—covalent bonding and ionic bonding. In covalent bonding, an element which has less than half of the electrons needed to complete an electron shell (see Section 3.44), enters into a crystalline combination with an element which has more than half of the electrons needed to complete an electron shell. The first element "shares" its electrons with the second, so that in the lattice structure, both elements may be said to have complete shells.

In considering the electrical properties of semiconductors, one is concerned only with the outer shells of the atoms; there may be inner complete shells which are unaffected by the electrical processes involved and hence are ignored for this purpose. Electrons which exist outside of closed shells are referred to simply as *electrons;* electrons which would be needed to complete a closed shell are referred to as *holes.* Thus, lithium, which has a closed shell of two electrons (helium) and one "valence" electron, provides this one electron to a covalent bonding with, say, fluorine, which has seven of the necessary eight electrons in its outer shell, and thus provides a "hole."

In ionic bonding, an atom of lithium, with one valence electron, may combine in a lattice with another element with one valence electron, perhaps with another atom of lithium, in such a way that a single electron is shared by the two atoms. This leaves an extra electron which is in a more or less free state; it is needed to maintain the electrical neutrality of the material, but it has no specific atom to associate with.

**7.25. Valence and Conduction Bands.** Each electron in an atom has a discrete number of possible energy levels, which are revealed by its spectral absorption and emission behavior. In the lattice of a solid material, however, these discrete energy levels, because of the proximity of other atoms and electrons, are modified, so that they become an energy *band*. A typical difference in energy levels in a free atom would be 0.1 eV (1 eV = 1.6 × $10^{-19}$ joules); in a lattice, however, the difference in energy levels within a band may become of the order of $10^{-14}$ eV. In solid materials, the outer shell electrons distribute themselves into two distinct bands, known as the *valence band* and the *conduction band*. This situation is illustrated by diagrams of the type shown in Figure 7.11.

Electrons in the conduction band are "free" electrons—they can move about in the material and take part in electrical conduction. Electrons in the valence band are relatively tightly bound to their position in the lattice. The separation between the valence and conduction bands is the *forbidden band*, characterized by the condition that, while electrons in energy levels corresponding to points in this band are not entirely absent, the probability of an electron being in this forbidden band is relatively low. The level at which the probability for the presence of an electron is ½ is called the *Fermi level*. Under certain special conditions, it lies midway of the forbidden band, which has an energy width of the order of one to a few electron volts in semiconductors.

The distinction between the three aspects of the solid state—metals, insulators and semiconductors—is easy to define in terms of the forbidden band. In metals, there is no forbidden band; all of the outer shell electrons are in the conduction band and are relatively free to move about. In insulators, the forbidden band is very wide, and in semiconductors, the forbidden band has a width of from one to a few electron volts.

**7.26. Electrons and Holes—Carriers.** The absence of an electron in a spot where one might be located is called a *hole*. In comparison with an electron, which carries a negative charge, a hole carries a positive charge. Although a hole is the absence of something, it is as real in terms of its electrical characteristics in the phenomenon of conductivity as is an electron—it has associated energy levels which may be located in either the conduction band or the valence band, and it is as mobile as an electron.

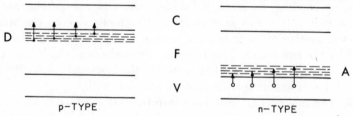

FIGURE 7.11. Energy levels in a semiconductor. V is the valence band; F is the forbidden band; C is the conduction band; D represents donor levels; A represents acceptor levels.

Both electrons and holes, when they lie in the conduction band, are called *carriers*. The one which exists, in a given material, in the highest concentration, is called the majority carrier; the other is the minority carrier.

**7.27. Excitation.** The action of a photoconductor is now readily understood. Absorption of the energy of a photon raises the energy levels of carriers from the valence to the conduction band and thus provides more carriers which are reflected in a change in the conductivity of the material.

There are two types of excitation: intrinsic and extrinsic. In intrinsic excitation, the incident photon frees an electron-hole pair by raising both electron and hole into the conduction band. In extrinsic excitation, the incident photon raises either an electron or a hole into the conduction band.

The raising of an electron or a hole from the valence into the conduction band is a phenomenon exactly like the phenomenon of photoemission, which is the reason for frequently referring to it as the internal photoelectric effect. The minimum energy required for the process is given by an expression exactly like Equation 7.10:

$$\Delta E = h\nu_0 = \frac{hc}{\lambda_0} \tag{7.12}$$

Also, exactly as in the photoemissive phenomenon, any excess energy in the incident quantum appears as kinetic energy of the released carrier. If $\Delta E$ is put in electron volts and $\lambda_0$ in microns, Equation 7.12 becomes

$$\lambda_0 = \frac{1.2406}{\Delta E} \tag{7.13}$$

**7.28. Impurities.** Homogeneous compounds provide *intrinsic* semiconductors. In these, the action of incident photons is to create electron-hole pairs. When impurities are added to a semiconductor, they may provide either extra electrons or extra holes. When the impurity contributes electrons it is known as a *donor* impurity, and the "doped" material becomes an *n-type* semiconductor (for negative). When the impurity contributes holes it is known as an *acceptor* impurity, and the doped material becomes a *p-type* semiconductor. The reader may recognize the similarity between photoconductors and transistors—the materials involved are very much the same, and sometimes identical.[21]

The impurities may be introduced in two ways—as *substitutional* impurities, in which case the impurity atoms take the place of the normal inhabitants of the lattice, or as *interstitial* impurities, in which case the atoms of the impurity occupy locations between the normal inhabitants.

Either type of impurity may be either a donor or an acceptor, as the case may be. Impurity semiconductors are *extrinsic* semiconductors.

**7.29. Action in a Photoconductor.** In a photoconductor at an ambient temperature, $T$, there will be an equilibrium concentration of carriers. These carriers are characterized by a charge $e$, equal to the electronic charge, an average lifetime, $\tau$, and a mobility, $\mu$. At the prevailing temperature, carriers will be generated by thermal excitation at a generation rate, $g$. The number of carriers existing in the equilibrium state will be[22]

$$n = g_e \tau_e \tag{7.14}$$

for electrons, and

$$p = g_h \tau_h \tag{7.15}$$

for holes, where $n$ is the number of carrier electrons and $p$ the number of carrier holes, $g_e$ and $g_h$ being the generation rate for electrons and holes, respectively. Thus, the total number of carriers will be

$$N = g_e \tau_e + g_h \tau_h \tag{7.16}$$

The carriers are continuously generated by thermal excitation and are subject to exponential decay by internal mechanisms of recombination, discussed below.

The conductivity of the semiconductor will be

$$\sigma = (n\mu_e + p\mu_h)e \tag{7.17}$$

If, now, the semiconductor is irradiated by photons of sufficient energy, *excess carriers* will be generated at rates $g_e'$ and $g_h'$, and the conductivity under the irradiated condition will be

$$\sigma_p = (n + \Delta n)e\mu_e + (p + \Delta p)e\mu_h = e\mu_h[bn + p + (b + 1)] \tag{7.18}$$

where $\Delta n$ and $\Delta p$ are the excess carriers ($\Delta n = g_e' \tau_e$, $\Delta p = g_h' \tau_h$), and $b$ is the mobility ratio, $\mu_h/\mu_e$. More importantly, the relative change in the conductivity is

$$\frac{\Delta \sigma}{\sigma} = \frac{\sigma_p - \sigma}{\sigma} = \frac{\Delta n(b + 1)}{bn + p} \tag{7.19}$$

The denominator of Equation (7.19) expresses the number of carriers in the material in the absence of irradiation; consequently if the conductivity change is to be made high, the carrier concentration due to thermal excitation must be low; cooling of the detector offers a method of reduction of thermal excitation, and in many situations, thermal excitation sets the limit on performance.

**7.30. Diffusion and Recombination.** When carriers are generated, they diffuse through the material, and eventually disappear through one of various types of recombination.[23] This process is characterized by the lifetime, $\tau$, and by a quantity known as the *diffusion length*, which is usually of the order of a few atomic diameters. Under the action of the potential difference which exists during connection to a circuit, a drift is superimposed on the normal diffusion process.

Recombination may take place in a direct radiative transfer, resulting in the emission of a photon; in photoconductors this is not a major contributor, but it is important in lasers. A carrier may transfer its energy to another carrier, raising the latter to a higher energy level, which may not place it in the conduction band. The energy of the carrier may also be transferred into a quantized vibrational energy of the lattice—these quantized vibrational energies are referred to as *phonons*.

A major source of recombination energy loss is in trapping at recombination and trapping centers in the lattice, from which the energy is eventually lost through other recombination actions.

**7.31. p-n Junctions.** When a $p$-type and an $n$-type semiconductor are fused to give what is known as a $p$-$n$ junction, the $p$-type material, having an excess of holes, becomes positively charged with respect to the $n$-type material, which has an excess of electrons, and this charge across the barrier causes the conduction band in the $n$-type material to become depressed, and the valence band in the $p$-type material to be raised, to the point where the Fermi levels of the two materials are aligned. There now exists a *potential barrier* at the junction. Carriers can flow in a preferred direction across the barrier—electrons in one direction and holes in the other, and the junction has become a *rectifier*.[24]

A well known example of the optical application of $p$-$n$ junctions is the *solar cell*. This device, invented in 1954 by Chapin, Fuller and Pearson,[52] has received considerable attention because of its use in satellites for the direct conversion of sunlight into electrical power.

It is a very simple device, consisting merely of a silicon plate with a $p$-$n$ junction about $2\mu$ below the illuminated surface. The incident light produces electron-hole pairs, the hole diffusing to the junction, thereby producing a current.

Cells are typically about $1 \times 2$ cm in size, and show an output as high as 100 watts/m$^2$, which represents a 14 per cent conversion efficiency for sunlight. The theoretical maximum efficiency for this device is about 22 per cent, since a considerable amount of light is lost by reflection at the incident surface, and photon energy above the threshold requirement for the production of a carrier pair is lost. This threshold corresponds to a wavelength of about $1\mu$.

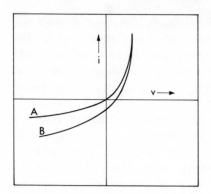

FIGURE 7.12. Photovoltaic effect: (A) Current-voltage characteristic for "dark" condition; (B) Characteristic when irradiated.

**7.32. The Photovoltaic Effect.** If a *p-n* junction is irradiated with photons of sufficient energy, excess carriers are created, which cause a change in the height of the potential barrier across the junction—this results from the *photovoltaic* effect.[25] If the junction is connected in an open circuit, a voltage is generated; if it is connected in a closed circuit, a current is generated. If an external electric field is applied, the device is the *photodiode.*[53]

Figure 7.12 shows the electrical characteristics of a photovoltaic detector. In the "dark" condition, the application of a voltage across the junction causes a current to flow, as shown by the upper line in the diagram. When irradiated, a voltage or a current appears, depending upon whether the external circuit is open or closed.

**7.33. The PEM Effect.** If an external magnetic field is applied to a photoconductor, there will be a separation of electrons and holes which causes a difference in potential between the two sides of the flake of material. This effect is the *photoelectromagnetic* effect,[26] and it is a mechanism used for detection.

There are also phototransistors,[27] consisting of *n-p-n* or *p-n-p* junctions, in which the effects of the generation of carriers by the absorption of photons are somewhat more complex than the actions described above.

## NOISE IN SEMICONDUCTORS[6]

**7.34. Types of Noise.** Semiconductors are afflicted with three types of noise, each arising from a different mechanism. These are identified as *Johnson* noise, *generation-recombination* (*gr*) noise, and *current* noise. In addition to these noise sources, which are characteristic of the semiconductor itself, there are various other contributing noises in a practical situation, including radiation noise from the incident radiation, and the noise sources in the electronic circuits which must be associated with the detection system to obtain a useful result.

The noise in a complete system which sets the performance limit is the combination of all of the noise elements. Usually they can be combined on a root-mean-square basis.

**7.35. Johnson Noise.** *Johnson noise,*[28, 29] or *thermal noise*, is characteristic of the flow of current through an electrical resistance; it arises from the thermal agitation of the material and is therefore a function of temperature. It is "white" noise, being independent of frequency, and its value can be derived from basic thermodynamic considerations.

The mean square noise *voltage* in an electrical resistance is

$$\overline{v_n}^2 = 4kTR\,\Delta f \qquad (7.20)$$

and the mean square noise *current* is

$$\overline{i_n}^2 = 4kT\,\Delta f/R \qquad (7.21)$$

where $k$ is Boltzmann's constant, $T$ the absolute temperature, $\Delta f$ the bandwidth and $R$ the resistance. Combining these two gives the noise *power*, which is actually the more fundamental concept

$$P_n = v_n i_n = 4kT\,\Delta f \qquad (7.22)$$

and is seen to be independent of the resistance and a function of the system bandwidth and temperature only. Since most noise sources are independent of frequency over the operating frequency range, it is often customary to call the value of $T$, which would be required in Equation (7.22) to give the actual observed noise power, the "noise temperature" of the system. It is usually considerably higher than the actual ambient temperature.

Cooling of detectors is an effective means of reducing the Johnson noise.

**7.36. Generation-recombination Noise.** Generation-recombination noise arises from the statistical fluctuation of the number of carriers in a semiconductor.[30] The carriers are subjected to the generation-recombination process, and this, of course, is statistical and has time variations which produces the gr-noise. Its value is therefore a function of the number of carriers and their lifetime. The mean square noise current from gr-noise is given by

$$\overline{i_n}^2 = \frac{kI_0^2\tau}{\bar{N}(1 + \omega^2\tau^2)}\,\Delta f \qquad (7.23)$$

where $I_0$ is the average current, $\bar{N}$ is the average number of carriers, $\tau$ is the carrier lifetime, and $\omega = 2\pi f$, where $f$ is the operating frequency, and $\Delta f$ is the bandwidth.

**7.37. Current Noise.** Semiconductors are afflicted with a noise commonly called *current noise* because of its proportionality to the current, but also frequently called "$1/f$ *noise*" because of its inverse proportionality to the operating frequency. Its true source is not precisely known,[31] but it appears to be associated with the actual structure of the material, its granularity, lattice dislocations, surface texture, and similar characteristics. Its value may be expressed in the form

$$\overline{i_n}^2 = \frac{k_1 I^{\alpha} \Delta f}{f^{\beta}} \tag{7.24}$$

where $k_1$ is a constant describing the size and shape of the sample, and $\alpha$ and $\beta$ are constants which vary with the material involved. $\alpha$ is usually approximately 2.0, and $\beta$ is very close to unity—this is the $1/f$ dependence.

**7.38. General Noise Expression for Semiconductors.** From Equations (7.21), (7.23) and (7.24), a general noise expression for a semiconductor takes the form

$$\overline{i_{\mathrm{N}}}^2 = \left[ \frac{k_1 I^{\alpha}}{f^{\beta}} + \frac{k_2 I^2}{1 + (f/f_1)^2} + \frac{4kT}{R} \right] \Delta f \tag{7.25}$$

where $k_1$, $k_2$, $f_1$, $\alpha$ and $\beta$ are constants pertaining to the particular material and sample involved.

If the values of the noise are plotted against operating frequency for a particular detection arrangement, the curve looks like that shown in Figure 7.13. The thermal noise, which is independent of frequency, dominates

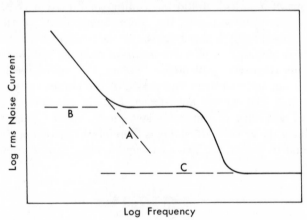

FIGURE 7.13. General behavior of noise in a semiconductor: (A) Current ($1/f$) noise curve; (B) generation-recombination noise; (C) thermal noise.

at the high frequency end of the plot. At the low-frequency end, the $1/f$ dependence of current noise causes it to become the dominating factor. In the intermediate frequency region, it is usually gr-noise which dominates. This noise source is constant at low frequencies, but drops off at frequencies higher than the inverse of the carrier lifetime.

## METHODS OF RATING PHOTON DETECTORS

**7.39. Performance Measures.** The usefulness of specific detectors for a particular application depends upon a number of factors. The "sensitivity" as measured by the minimum input signal which will produce a useful output signal is, of course, of very great importance, but such factors as the spectral range over which the detector is operative, its time constant, its performance as a function of the operating frequency and others, must also be taken into account. A number of specific characteristics have been defined, and are in general use, to permit evaluation of a detector with respect to these various factors. The most significant measures are the *noise equivalent power*, the *noise equivalent input*, the *detectivity*, a measure known as $D^*$, and the *responsivity*. The *quantum efficiency*, which has been defined in the course of the discussion of photoemissive detectors, is also a general measure of performance. Jones[32] has been instrumental in bringing a high degree of order and rigor to the specification of radiation detector characteristics.

**7.40. NEP and NEI.** The *noise equivalent power*, *NEP*, of a detector, is defined as that input power which will produce an output signal equal to the mean square noise. It is thus the signal level which will produce a signal-to-noise ratio of unity. It is defined by the equation

$$\text{NEP} = HA_\text{d} \left( \frac{v_\text{n}}{v_\text{s}} \right) \frac{1}{\Delta f^{1/2}} \tag{7.26}$$

which applies to a measurement made under specified conditions, where $H$ is the irradiance, $A_\text{d}$ the detector area, $v_\text{n}$ and $v_\text{s}$ are the noise voltage and the signal voltage, respectively, and $\Delta f$ is the bandwidth. The usual dimensions are watts and centimeters, so that NEP has the dimensions watt (cycles/sec)$^{-1/2}$.

The NEP is a function of the wavelength. For the measure to be meaningful, the conditions of the measurement must be known, as must the dependence of the detector performance on the various parameters. The standard measuring conditions for infrared detectors are irradiance by a blackbody source at a temperature of 500°K, an operating frequency of

90, 400 or 800 cycles/sec, a bandwidth of 1 to 5 cycles/sec, a detector area of 1 cm² and a detector temperature of 22°C (295°K).

The NEP of a detector, in accordance with the above equation, will depend upon the detector area, so that the measure applies to a specific *detector*, rather than to a detector material. When the NEP is divided by the detector area, it is known as the *noise equivalent input*, or *NEI*. The NEI has the dimensions watt-cm⁻² (cycles/sec)⁻¹/².

The reciprocal of the NEP is often called the *detectivity*, D. This then has the dimensions (cycles/sec)$^{1/2}$-watt⁻¹. This measure has the advantage that the numerical value becomes larger as the measure becomes more favorable. Measures of sensitivity always suffer from the fact that it is difficult to assign adjectives such as "higher" or "lower" to numbers which become more favorable as they become numerically smaller.

**7.41. D\* and D\*\*.** Noise has the fairly general property of being proportional to the square root of its fundamental parameters, and thus detector noise is proportional to the square root of the detector area for most cases. To take account of this dependence, Jones has proposed a measure,[33] which is termed $D^*$ (pronounced "D-star") because it is the same type of concept as the detectivity, $D;$ this value has come into quite general use. $D^*$ is defined as follows:

$$D^* = \frac{1}{\text{NEI } A_d^{1/2}} = \frac{A_d^{1/2}}{\text{NEP}} \tag{7.27}$$

and therefore has the dimensions cm-(cycles/sec)$^{1/2}$-watt⁻¹.

Figure 7.14 shows the plots of $D^*$ as a function of wavelength for a variety of detectors.

In cases where a detector application is performance limited by radiation noise from the field of view, a situation which represents the ultimate performance that can be achieved in that particular application, the performance is dependent upon the solid angle from which the detector receives the noise-bearing radiation. A performance measure which takes this situation into account is known as $D^{**}$ (D-doublestar), which is defined[34] as

$$D^{**} = \left(\frac{\Omega}{\pi}\right)^{1/2} D^* \tag{7.28}$$

where $\Omega$ is the solid angle of irradiation. A detector used in a situation where its performance is limited by background radiation noise has been called a "BLIP" detector (background-limited-in-performance).[35]

**7.42. The Responsivity.** The *responsivity* of a detector is defined as the output signal per unit input signal and can thus be written, using the

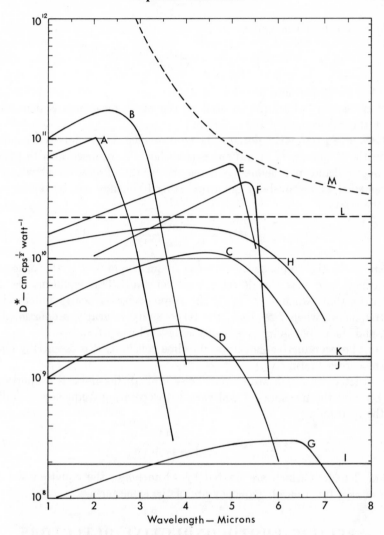

FIGURE 7.14. Spectral $D^*$ of representative infrared detectors: (A) Lead sulfide—room temperature; (B) Lead sulfide—195°K; (C) Lead selenide—77°K; (D) Lead telluride—77°K; (E) Indium antimonide (photoconductive mode)—77°K; (F) Indium antimonide (photovoltaic mode)—77°K; (G) Indium antimonide (photo-electro-magnetic mode)—room temperature; (H) Gold-doped germanium—77°K (intrinsic response at 1.8μ omitted); (I) Thermistor bolometer; (J) Thermocouple; (K) Golay cell; (L) Photon noise limit for thermal detectors at room temperature; (M) Photon noise limit for photoconductive detectors at room temperature.

definition of terms as above,

$$\mathcal{R} = \frac{v_s}{P} = \frac{v_s}{HA_d} = \frac{v_n}{P_N(\Delta f)^{1/2}} = \frac{D^* v_n}{(A_d \Delta f)^{1/2}} \qquad (7.29)$$

and has the dimensions of volts per watt.

Responsivity, of course, as well as the other measures, is dependent upon the wavelength of the radiation.

**7.43. Frequency Response.** The performance of detectors is dependent upon the frequency of operation, as was shown in connection with photoconductive and photoemissive detectors in the discussion above. The dependence of responsivity upon operating frequency can be represented by the relation

$$\mathcal{R}(f) = \frac{\mathcal{R}_0}{(1 + 4\pi^2 f^2 \tau^2)^{1/2}} \qquad (7.30)$$

where $\mathcal{R}_0$ is the responsivity for zero frequency (dc), $f$ is the operating frequency, and $\tau$ is the detector time constant. This equation has the property that, when $f \ll \frac{1}{2}\pi\tau$, the responsivity is nearly independent of frequency; when $f \gg \frac{1}{2}\pi\tau$, the responsivity is nearly proportional to $1/f$, and the responsivity is 0.71 of the dc level when $f = \frac{1}{2}\pi\tau$.

For photoconductive detectors, the time constant, $\tau$, is essentially equal to the carrier lifetime.

For detectors which are current noise limited, the noise is proportional to $1/f$, and the measure $D^*$ will vary with operating frequency according to the relation

$$D^*(f) = \frac{k f^{1/2}}{(1 + 4\pi^2 f^2 \tau^2)^{1/2}} \qquad (7.31)$$

For detectors which are limited by white noise, the equations for $D^*$ and $\mathcal{R}$ as a function of frequency are of the same form.

## SPECIFIC PHOTOCONDUCTIVE DETECTORS

**7.44. Intrinsic Photoconductors.** In the visible region of the spectrum, there has been no great need to develop photoconductive materials with a high performance level, due to the existence of photoemissive devices for these wavelengths. When there is no overriding problem of ambient light level, however, photoconductive devices are quite convenient, and such materials are used in items such as exposure meters and photosensitive automatic equipment of various types. Thallium sulfide (thalofide) was one of the earliest materials to be developed;[36] silicon[37] and selenium[38] are photoconductors of moderate sensitivity, and more sensitive detectors are available in cadmium sulfide,[39] cadmium selenide and selenium-selenium oxide, the latter being the well-known barrier layer photocell. It operates as a photovoltaic device.

In the infrared, where the photon energy is insufficient to produce photoemission, photoconductive detectors are the most sensitive means available for detection, and there has been an extensive development of materials in a never-ending quest for higher and higher sensitivities, longer and longer wavelength response, and shorter and shorter time constants.[40]

The most common intrinsic photoconductors with response extending into the infrared spectrum are lead sulfide, lead telluride, lead selenide, indium antimonide and germanium.

*Lead sulfide* (PbS)[41] is the best and longest known infrared photoconductor. It has the highest sensitivity of any detector within its operating spectral band, which extends to about $2.5\mu$ at room temperature and beyond $3\mu$ when the detector is cooled. Its time constant is 200 to 500 $\mu$sec.

*Lead telluride* (PbTe) has a spectral response extending to about $4\mu$, and a time constant of about 25 $\mu$sec; it can be operated satisfactorily only when cooled. *Lead selenide* (PbSe) has a spectral response extending to $6\mu$ when cooled and a similar time constant; this material can be operated at room temperature with a spectral response cutoff at about $4\mu$.

All of the lead compounds above are limited by current noise.

*Indium antimonide* (InSb) is grown as an artificial crystal. Its spectral response extends to about $7\mu$, and it can be operated as a photoconductive, photovoltaic, or photoelectromagnetic detector. Its time constant, about 1 $\mu$sec, is better than that of the lead compounds. Indium antimonide appears to be limited only by Johnson noise;[42] it has the disadvantage, however, of a fairly low responsivity.

*Germanium* (Ge) is also an intrinsic photoconductor, with a fairly narrow spectral response at about $1.8\mu$. Because this is a relatively narrow-band response, germanium is not often used as an intrinsic photoconductor, although germanium photodiodes are commonly available.

**7.45. Extrinsic Photoconductors.** The primary application of germanium has been as the base material for the insertion of impurities to produce a wide variety of extrinsic photoconductors with a wide range of response. Best known of these varieties are germanium doped with gold (Ge:Au), with gold and antimony (Ge:Au,Sb), with zinc (Ge:Zn), with copper (Ge:Cu), with cadmium (Ge:Cd), and germanium-silicon alloys doped with gold (Ge-Si:Au) and with zinc and antimony (Ge-Si:Zn,Sb). Some of these materials have spectral response extending beyond $30\mu$, and

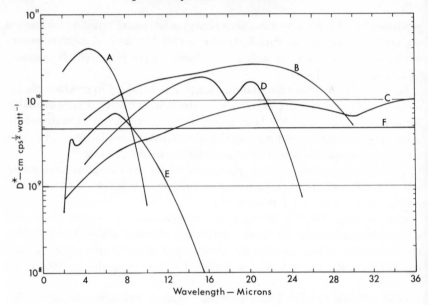

FIGURE 7.15. Spectral $D^*$ of representative long-wavelength detectors: (A) Ge: Au (65°K); (B) Ge: Cu (4.2°K); (C) Ge: Zn (4.2°K); (D) Ge: Cd (4.2°K); (E) Ge-Si: Au (50°K); (F) Superconducting bolometer.

some of them have time constants of less than .01 $\mu$sec. Some of these detectors are plotted in Figure 7.15.

## THERMAL DETECTORS

**7.46. Fundamentals.** The basic operation of thermal detectors is the absorption of radiant power on a nonselective basis; this power is turned into heat in the detector, thus raising its temperature. On an energy basis, the sensitivity of thermal detectors is independent of the wavelength of the radiation and thus plots as a horizontal line on charts such as Figure 7.15. This nonselectivity is modified somewhat in particular cases by the absorptivity characteristics of the material.

The two basic types of thermal detectors are the bolometer and the radiation thermocouple: in the former, the rise in temperature results in a change in conductivity; in the latter, the rise in temperature of a dissimilar metal junction with respect to a reference junction generates a voltage difference.

**7.47. Bolometers.** There are three basic types of bolometers—metal resistance, semiconductor, and superconducting. The metal resistance bolometer has the characteristic variation of conductivity with temperature which is true for all metals:

$$R = R_0[1 + \gamma(T - T_0)] \tag{7.32}$$

where $R_0$ and $T_0$ are reference resistance and temperature, and $\gamma$ is the *temperature coefficient of resistivity*. Materials with a $\gamma$ as high as 0.5 per cent/°C are available.[43]

In the semiconductor bolometer, the material is a semiconductor, and the change in conductivity as a result of temperature rise is determined by the change in the carrier generation rate; this is exponential with temperature. Semiconductor bolometers are commonly called *thermistors*.[44]

Many metals exhibit *superconductivity* at very low temperatures. When the temperature drops below a certain critical value, the resistivity essentially disappears. This characteristic is used in the superconducting bolometer,[45] which is maintained at the critical temperature point; incident radiation raises the temperature beyond the critical point, and the resistivity rises suddenly. The critical temperature point is in the region of 1 to 100°K; at this critical temperature, whose exact value depends upon the material, the resistivity changes from zero to a finite value in a range of 0.1 to 0.01 degree. To obtain an output which varies with the input over a useful range, it is necessary to maintain the ambient temperature of the superconducting bolometer to a tolerance of about ±.0001°K. This is not easy to do, so that, while the superconducting bolometer is a highly sensitive detector, it has not found wide application.

**7.48. Thermocouples and Thermopiles.**[46] The thermoelectric effect is well known and is the basis for many thermometric instruments. When two metals of dissimilar electrochemical characteristics are fused in a junction and connected in an electrical circuit, a temperature difference between the junction and the external circuit generates an emf in the circuit. In the radiation thermocouple, two of these junctions are provided; one is maintained at a constant reference temperature and the other is irradiated with the input signal.

A *thermopile* is a series of thermal detectors connected together. Either bolometers or thermocouples may be used. In the case of thermocouples, the generated emf's are linearly additive; in the case of bolometers, the resistance change can be shown to be equal to the sum of the resistance changes in the individual elements.

**7.49. The Golay Cell.** The Golay cell[47] is a different type of thermal detector which is in sufficiently wide use to deserve special comment. This detector consists of a gas-filled cell closed by an optically reflective membrane. Changes in the gas temperature cause changes in its volume and hence changes in the curvature of the membrane. These changes in curvature are detected by the reflection of a light beam from the membrane. These cells can be made of quite small dimensions, and the performance of this type of detector compares well with that of the more conventional types discussed above.

**7.50. Other Thermal Detectors.** Some other types of thermal detectors have been devised, which depend upon the action of temperature in distorting sensitive surfaces, such as oil films and thermoplastic materials, and changes in the spectral absorption of materials as a function of temperature. Examples of the first technique are the *evaporagraph*[48] and thermoplastic recording tape. Examples of the second are the *photo-thermionic* image converter[49] and the *absorption edgegraph*.[50] These techniques are experimental at the present time and are not described in detail; they are described in the reference literature. Havens has computed the theoretical limit of sensitivity of an ideal thermal detector.[51]

**7.51. Comparative Performance of Detectors.** Figure 7.16 shows the relative performance of a number of different radiation detectors as a function of wavelength.

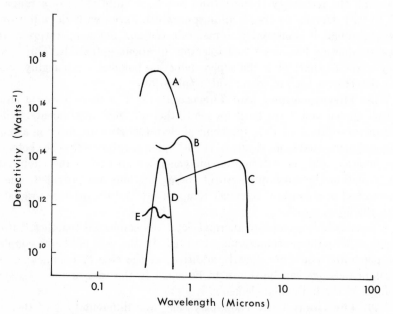

FIGURE 7.16. Relative performance of radiation detectors: (A) S-4 photo surface; (B) S-1 photo surface; (C) lead sulfide; (D) human eye; (E) super XX film.[32]

TABLE 7.2. CHARACTERISTICS OF TYPICAL INFRARED DETECTORS

| Detector | Mode | Operating Temperature (°K) | Wave-length of Peak Response ($\mu$) | Cutoff Wave-length ($\mu$) | Time Constant ($\mu$sec) | Dominant Noise |
|---|---|---|---|---|---|---|
| PbS | PC | Ambient | 2.1 | 2.5 | 250 | $1/f$ |
| | PC | 195 | 2.5 | 3.0 | 500 | $1/f$ |
| | PC | 77 | 2.5 | 3.3 | 500 | $1/f$ |
| PbSe | PC | Ambient | 3.4 | 4.2 | 4 | $1/f$ |
| | PC | 195 | 4.6 | 5.4 | 125 | $1/f$ |
| | PC | 77 | 4.5 | 5.8 | 50 | $1/f$ |
| PbTe | PC | 77 | 4.0 | 5.1 | 25 | $1/f$ |
| Ge:Au | PC | 77 | 5.0 | 7.1 | 0.1 | $1/f$-gr |
| | PC | 65 | 4.7 | 6.9 | 0.1 | $1/f$-gr |
| Ge:Zn | PC | 4.2 | 36 | 40 | .01 | $1/f$ |
| Ge:Cu | PC | 20 | 20 | 30 | 0.1 | $1/f$-gr |
| Ge-Si:Au | PC | 50 | 10 | 13 | 0.1 | gr |
| InSb | PC | Ambient | 6.5 | 7.3 | 0.2 | $1/f$ |
| | PC | 77 | 5.0 | 5.5 | 2 | $1/f$ |
| | PV | 77 | 5.3 | 5.6 | 1 | $1/f$-gr |
| | PEM | Ambient | 6.2 | 7.0 | 0.2 | $1/f$-thermal |
| Balometer | | Ambient | | | 1500 | Thermal |
| Thermocouple | | Ambient | | | 30,000 | Thermal |
| Golay cell | | Ambient | | | 20,000 | Thermal |
| Superconducting bolometer | | Ambient | | | 500 | Thermal |

Code: PC—photoconductive; PV—photovoltaic; PEM—photo-electromagnetic; gr—generation-recombination; $1/f$—current noise.

Table 7.2 lists a number of detectors and some of their characteristics which are not brought out on the chart.

## REFERENCES

1. R. Barnes, R. Gore, V. Liddell and V. Williams, "Infrared Spectroscopy—Industrial Applications and Bibliography," New York, Reinhold Publishing Corp., 1944.
2. Cf. H. Hackforth, "Infrared Radiation," Part II, New York, McGraw-Hill Book Co., 1960.
3. Suggested texts are:
   C. Neblette *et al;* "Photography," 6th ed., Princeton, N.J., D. Van Nostrand, 1962.
   C. Mees, "The Theory of the Photographic Process," Revised ed., New York, Macmillan, 1954.
4. Hurter and Driffield, *Phot. J.*, **22,** 145 (1898).
5. Selwyn, *Phot. J.*, **75,** 571 (1935); **82,** 208 (1942).
   L. Jones and G. Higgins, *J. Opt. Soc. Am.*, **47,** 312 (1957); also cf. reference 3.

6. Data plotted in the figure are from the reports of T. Elder and J. Strong, *J. Franklin Inst.*, **225**, 159 (1953).
   See also:
   H. Gebbie *et al., Proc. Roy. Soc. London Ser. A.*, **206**, 81 (1951).
   J. Taylor and H. Yates, *J. Opt. Soc. Am.*, **47**, 223 (1957).
   W. Middleton, "Vision Through the Atmosphere," University of Toronto Press, 1952.
7. For general discussions of noise, see:
   A. van der Ziel, "Noise," Englewood Cliffs, N.J., Prentice-Hall, 1954.
   R. Jones, *Advan. Electron.*, No. 5 (1953).
   J. Freeman, "Principles of Noise," New York, John Wiley & Sons, 1958.
   D. Bell, "Electrical Noise," London, D. Van Nostrand, 1947.
   A. van der Ziel, "Fluctuation Phenomena in Semiconductors," New York, Academic Press, 1959.
   W. Schottky, *Ann. Physik*, **57**, 541 (1918); *Phys. Rev.*, **28**, 74 (1926).
   Cf. also references 8, 20, 28–32, 42 and 51.
8. J. Carson, *Bell System Tech. J.*, **10**, 374 (1931).
   R. Jones, *J. Opt. Soc. Am.*, **37**, 879 (1947).
   R. Fellgett, *J. Opt. Soc. Am.*, **39**, 970 (1949).
   Cf. Kruse *et al.*, reference 11.
9. S. Ballard, K. McCarthy and W. Wolfe, "Optical Materials for Infrared Instrumentation," University of Michigan, Rep. 2389-11S, January, 1959.
10. H. Buckley, "Crystal Growth," New York, John Wiley & Sons, 1951.
11. Infrared technology is discussed thoroughly in a number of recent books:
    R. Smith, F. Jones and R. Chasmar, "The Detection and Measurement of Infrared Radiation," London, Oxford University Press, 1957.
    H. Hackforth, "Infrared Radiation," New York, McGraw-Hill Book Co., 1960.
    P. Kruse, L. McGlauchlin and R. McQuistan, "Elements of Infrared Technology," New York, John Wiley & Sons, 1962.
    M. Holter, S. Nudelman, G. Suits, W. Wolfe and G. Zissis, "Fundamentals of Infrared Technology," New York, Macmillan, 1962.
    J. Jamieson, R. McFee, G. Plass, R. Gruble and R. Richards, "Infrared Physics and Engineering," New York, McGraw-Hill Book Co., 1963.
    Photoelectric technology is discussed in V. Zworykin and E. Ramberg, "Photoelectricity," New York, John Wiley & Sons, 1949.
12. H. Hertz, *Ann. Physik*, **31**, 421 (1887).
13. After it was explained by A. Einstein, *Ann. Physik*, **17**, 132 (1905).
14. For discussion of various photoelectric materials, cf. Zworykin and Ramberg, reference 11, Ch. 3.
15. Cf. Zworykin and Ramberg, reference 11, Chs. 6 and 7.
16. J. Elster and H. Geitel, *Ann. Physik*, **38**, 497 .(1889); **41**, 161 (1890); *Physik. Z.*, **14**, 741 (1913).
17. Cf. Zworykin and Ramberg, reference 11, Ch. 9.
18. R. Kollath, *Physik. Z.*, **38**, 224 (1937); *Ann. Physik*, **39**, 59 (1941); **1**, 357 (1947).
    H. Bruining and J. deBoer, *Physica*, **5**, 17 (1938); **6**, 823, 834 (1939).
    H. Bruining, *Physica*, **5**, 901 (1938).
    A. Reimann, "Thermionic Emission," New York, John Wiley & Sons, 1934.
    Cf. also Zworykin and Ramberg, reference 11, Ch. 8.
19. R. Barnes and M. Czerny, *Z. Physik.*, **79**, 436 (1932).

20. For more comprehensive discussions of the physics of semiconductors, see:

C. Kittel, "Introduction to Solid State Physics," New York, John Wiley & Sons, 1953.

A. Dekker, "Solid State Physics," Englewood Cliffs, N. J., Prentice-Hall, 1957.

A. van der Ziel, "Solid State Physical Electronics," Englewood Cliffs, N. J., Prentice-Hall, 1957.

T. Moss, "Optical Properties of Semiconductors," London, Butterworth, 1959.

J. Blakemore, "Semiconductor Statistics," New York, Pergamon Press, 1961.

J. Shive, "The Properties, Physics and Design of Semiconductor Devices," Princeton, N. J., Van Nostrand, 1959.

R. Smith, "Semiconductors," Cambridge, University Press, 1959.

R. Bube, "Photoconductivity of Solids," New York, John Wiley & Sons, 1960.

N. Hannay, *Inter. Sci. & Tech.*, 65 (October 4, 1963).

Also cf. Kruse *et al.*, reference 11, Ch. 6.

21. W. Shockley, "Electrons and Holes in Semiconductors," Princeton, N.J., D. Van Nostrand, 1960.

22. A. Rose, *Proc. IRE*, **43**, 1950 (1955).

23. Cf. Blakemore, reference 20, Ch. 6; Bube, reference 20, p. 303.

24. L. Grondahl, *Rev. Mod. Phys.*, **5**, 141 (1933).

W. Schottky, *Physik. Z.*, **31**, 913 (1930).

B. Lange, *Physik. Z.*, **31**, 139, 964 (1930); "Photoelements," New York, Reinhold Publishing Corp., 1938.

25. E. Bequerel, *Compt. Rend.*, **9**, 145 (1839).

26. P. Kruse, *J. Appl. Phys.*, **30**, 770 (1959).

27. J. Shive, *J. Opt. Soc. Am.*, **43**, 239 (1953).

28. J. Johnson, *Phys. Rev.*, **32**, 97 (1928).

29. H. Nyquist, *Phys. Rev.*, **32**, 110 (1928).

30. Cf. Kruse *et al.*, reference 11, p. 41.

31. Cf. Kruse *et al.*, reference 11, pp. 24, 263.

32. R. Jones, *Advan. Electron.*, No. 5 (1953); No. 11 (1959); *J. Opt. Soc. Am.*, **37**, 879 (1947); **43**, 1 (1953).

33. R. Jones, *Proc. Infrared Information Symposium (IRIS)*, **2**, No. 1, 9 (1957).

34. R. Jones, *Proc. IRIS*, **5**, No. 4, 35 (1959); *J. Opt. Soc. Am.*, **50**, 1058 (1960).

35. E. Burstein and G. Picas, *IRIS Meeting* (Feb. 3, 1958).

36. R. Cashman, *J. Opt. Soc. Am.*, **36**, 356 (1946).

T. Case, *Phys. Rev.*, **15**, 289 (1920).

A. von Hippel *et al.*, *J. Chem. Phys.*, **14**, 355, 370 (1946).

37. G. Teal, J. Fisher and A. Treptow, *J. Appl. Phys.*, **17**, 879 (1946).

38. W. Adams and R. Day, *Proc. Roy. Soc. London Ser. A*, **25**, 113 (1877).

C. Fritts, *Am. J. Sci.*, **26**, 465 (1883).

B. Lange and W. Eitel, *Mineral. Petrog. Mitt.*, **41**, 435 (1931).

L. Bergmann, *Physik. Z.*, **32**, 286 (1931).

39. R. Frierichs, *Phys. Rev.*, **72**, 594 (1947).

40. For a comprehensive list of detector materials characteristics, see Kruse *et al.*, reference 11, Ch. 10.

41. T. Odarenko, "German Wartime Developments in Infrared," Dept. of Commerce, OTS Report PB-95308, March, 1948.

J. Bose, U. S. Patent 755,840 (1901).

A. Cashman, OSRD Report 5998, October, 1945.

42. Suits, Schmitz, and Terhune, *J. Appl. Phys.*, **27**, 1385 (1956).
43. J. Shive, *J. Appl. Phys.*, **18**, 398 (1947).
    R. Jones, *J. Opt. Soc. Am.*, **43**, 1 (1953).
    R. Chasmar, W. Mitchell and A. Rennie, *J. Opt. Soc. Am.*, **46**, 469 (1956).
    D. Lovell, in NAVORD 5495 (see reference 44).
44. W. Brittain and J. Becker, *J. Opt. Soc. Am.*, **36**, 354 (1946).
    R. deWaard and E. Wormser, in NAVORD Rep. 5495, Pt. 1, April 30, 1958, ASTIA
        Document AD 160106; Proc. IRE, **47**, 1508 (1959).
45. D. Andrews, *Phys. Soc. London, Report 1-2*, 56 (1946).
    Andrews, Milton and deSorbo, *J. Opt. Soc. Am.*, **36**, 518 (1946).
    R. Milton, *Chem. Rev.*, **39**, 419 (1946).
    N. Fuson, *J. Opt. Soc. Am.*, **38**, 845 (1948).
46. J. Daunt, "Thermocouple Design," Oxford University Press, 1946.
    D. Hornig and B. O'Keefe, *Rev. Sci. Instr.*, **18**, 7, 474 (1947).
47. M. Golay, *Rev. Sci. Instr.*, **18**, 346, 357 (1947); **20**, 816 (1949).
48. M. Czerny, *Z. Physik*, **1**, 53 (1929).
    M. Czerny and P. Mollet, *Z. Physik*, **85**, 108 (1938).
49. M. Garbuny *et al.*, Westinghouse Res. Labs. Final Report, Contract AF33(616)-
        2282, 1956.
50. Harding, Hilsum and Northrop, *Nature*, **181**, 691 (1958).
    Hilsum and Harding, *S.E.R.L. Tech. J.*, **10**, No. 1, 26 (1960).
51. R. Havens, *J. Opt. Soc. Am.*, **36**, 355 (1946); *Proc. IRIS*, **2**, No. 1, 5 (1957).
52. D. Chapin, C. Fuller and G. Pearson, *J. Appl. Phys.*, **25**, 676 (1954).
53. D. Kleinman, *Bell System Tech. J.*, **40**, 85 (1961).
54. I. Spiro, R. Jones and D. Wark, *Infrared Physics*, **5**, 11 (1965).

# CHAPTER 8

# Optical Measurement

**8.1. General.** Optics is one of the primary tools of measurement. The three fundamental dimensions of the physical world are mass, length and time; it is difficult to conceive a measurement which concerns the dimension of length in which some principles of optics are not intimately involved—if only in the operation of visual comparison of a scale.

Much of the optical measurement of length—and its associated quantity, direction—involves the fundamental principle that a ray of light is, by definition, a straight line,* and has the useful property of infinite rigidity.

The subject of optical measurement separates itself conveniently into two parts—measurements associated with the wave properties of light, comprising measurements involving dispersion, diffraction and interference, and measurements involving alignment, which might be said to utilize the particle properties of light, in that they make use of the straight-line propagation qualities of light rays.

Certain optical tests which are in widespread use and are therefore of general interest, are included in the discussions of alignment techniques.

The Schlieren technique for the examination of transparent media, such as the air in a wind tunnel, is included in this Chapter; although it is not strictly an optical measurement technique.

## DISPERSION

**8.2. The Dispersing Prism.** The dispersing action of a prism was mentioned in Section 6.15, where it was shown that, because of the dependence of the index of refraction on the wavelength of the light, the angle of refraction for an obliquely incident ray increases with decreasing

---

* In an homogeneous and isotropic medium.

wavelength. A prism therefore separates a beam of light into its component wavelengths when the light falls obliquely on one or more of the prism surfaces.

This property was shown to be taken into account in total reflecting prisms, which are almost always so constructed that the light enters and leaves at normal incidence; otherwise chromatic aberration is produced which cannot be corrected by lens elements, since it is asymmetric. The property, however, is used in prism instruments for spectral analysis.

Before the development of the diffraction grating, prisms were the primary constituents of all spectroscopic or spectrographic instruments; the grating is a much more powerful tool and in modern instruments is usually used in preference to prisms wherever conditions permit. The grating, however, is wasteful of light—even when special "blazes" are used to concentrate the light in a single order; when the situation is such that illumination levels are poor and every precaution must be taken to preserve light, prisms are still used.

**8.3. Deviation of a Prism.** Figure 8.1 shows a cross section of a conventional dispersing prism. A ray of light entering the prism at an angle of incidence $I_1$ is refracted at the first surface, meets the second surface at an angle of incidence $I_2$ and is refracted into the external medium. The angle $\Delta$ is the *deviation* of the prism, and is obviously equal to

$$\Delta = I_1 + I_2' - \theta \tag{8.1}$$

where $\theta$ is the apex, or *refracting angle*, of the prism.

It would be possible to introduce the law of refraction and write a general expression for the deviation; this would be a function of the angle of incidence, $I_1$, the index of refraction, $\mu$, and the refracting angle, $\theta$. It would be rather complex and not of much practical use.

**8.4. Minimum Deviation.** If the prism is rotated with respect to the

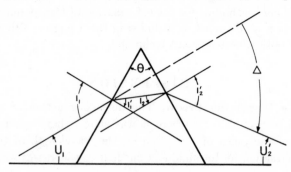

FIGURE 8.1. Deviation of a prism.

incident ray, i.e., about an axis normal to the diagram in Figure 8.1, it is found that there is a position where the deviation $\Delta$ is a minimum, and this case is of considerable interest.

Minimum deviation occurs for the condition shown in Figure 8.2, where the ray inside the prism is parallel to the base, and the incident and refracted rays are symmetrical with the prism apex angle. This may be shown by differentiating Equation (8.1) with respect to $I_1$, setting the result equal to zero, and substituting the necessary values from the law of refraction.

For this case, Equation 8.1 reduces to

$$\Delta = 2I_1 - \theta \tag{8.2}$$

and it is found that

$$\sin I_1 = \mu \sin \frac{\theta}{2} \tag{8.3}$$

Equations (8.2) and (8.3) provide a basis for measuring the index of refraction of the prism, for they may be combined and written in the form

$$\mu = \frac{\sin \left[ \dfrac{\theta + \Delta}{2} \right]}{\sin \dfrac{\theta}{2}} \tag{8.4}$$

where the angle $\theta$ can be measured and the prism can be set up and rotated so that the condition of minimum deviation is achieved and the angle $\Delta$ can be measured. This is a standard method of measurement of index of refraction in cases where it is convenient to cut the material into a prism of known angle. The measurement must be made in monochromatic light, of course, since the angle of minimum deviation depends upon the wavelength.

**8.5. Dispersion of a Prism.** The change in the deviation as a function

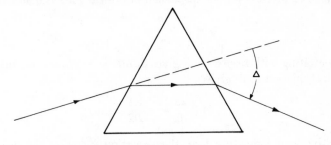

FIGURE 8.2. Minimum deviation.

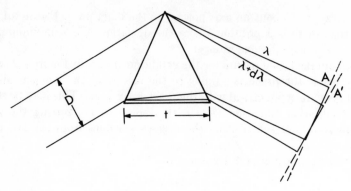

FIGURE 8.3. Dispersion of a prism.

of wavelength is the *dispersion* of the prism. The dispersion is defined as the rate of change of deviation with wavelength:

$$\frac{d\Delta}{d\lambda} = \frac{d\Delta}{d\mu} \cdot \frac{d\mu}{d\lambda} \tag{8.5}$$

This can be derived, for the case of minimum deviation, from the geometry of Figure 8.3. The dispersion is the angle $d\theta$ in the figure, or the angle of tilt between two plane wave fronts for two wavelengths differeing by $d\lambda$. This angle is $AA'/D$, where $D$ is the diameter of the beam, and $AA'$ is the optical path difference for the two different wavelengths. But this optical path difference is $\delta\mu(t_1 - t_2)$, where $\delta\mu$ is the difference in the index of refraction for the two wavelengths. If the beam fills the prism, $t_1 = 0$, and $t_2$ is the base length, $t$. Hence $d\Delta/d\mu = t/D$, and Equation (8.5) therefore becomes

$$\mathfrak{D} = \frac{d\Delta}{d\lambda} = \frac{t}{D}\frac{d\mu}{d\lambda} \tag{8.6}$$

By Cauchy's formula for the dispersion of optical glass [Equation (3.5)],

$$\mu = A + \frac{B}{\lambda^2} + \cdots \tag{8.7}$$

Differentiating with respect to $\lambda$ gives $d\mu/d\lambda = -2B/\lambda^3$, and substituting this in Equation (8.6) gives

$$\mathfrak{D} = \frac{d\Delta}{d\lambda} = -\frac{2tB}{D\lambda^3} \tag{8.8}$$

the negative sign indicating that the deviation increases for decreasing wavelength.

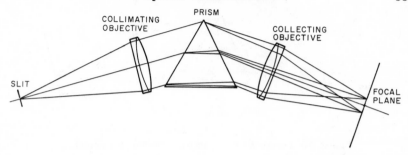

FIGURE 8.4. Schematic arrangement of a prism spectrograph.

The above derivation assumed the condition of minimum deviation; since this condition is met for only one wavelength, there is a variation of dispersion with wavelength. There is also a variation of dispersion with angle of incidence. In general, there is an angle of incidence (for a particular wavelength) for which the dispersion is a minimum; this angle is in general not the angle of incidence corresponding to minimum deviation.

**8.6. Formation of a Spectrum.** Figure 8.4 shows schematically the conventional arrangement of a prism spectrograph. The source is an illuminated slit, which is normal to the diagram. An objective collimates the light from the slit, which then enters the prism as a parallel bundle and is deviated. Another objective collects this light and forms images of the slit in its focal plane; the position of these images will be determined by the deviation, and hence by the wavelength of the light.

There is thus produced, at the focal plane of the collector lens, a series of images of the slit, whose position indicates the wavelength of the light forming them. This is a *spectrum*, and the term "spectral line" is derived from this series of slit images. If the source consists of a few widely separated monochromatic wavelengths—for example, for an incandescent low-pressure gas—the spectrum is a pattern of isolated slit images, or lines, and is a "line spectrum." If the source is a blackbody, the spectrum will be a continuous one, the individual slit images being merged into an unbroken continuum. In the case of the sun, the spectrum is a continuous one, produced by the light from the *photosphere*, upon which are superimposed many "dark" lines (first observed by Fraunhofer[1]), representing the absorption of the gases in the low-pressure *chromosphere* of the sun. The lines are dark by contrast only—actually there is considerable emitted energy within the lines themselves.

Figure 8.4 shows the prism mounted at minimum deviation; this is the customary arrangement in a spectroscope or spectrograph, but is not an essential one. It would be possible to form a spectrum with a prism by using only a single lens, as shown in Figure 8.5, but the slit images would not be

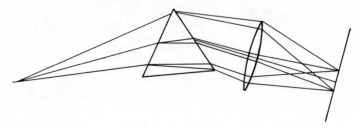

FIGURE 8.5. Formation of a spectrum without a collimator.

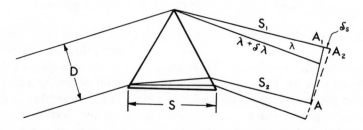

FIGURE 8.6. Resolving power of a prism.

good, because the various rays forming a slit image are incident at varying angles, and subjected to varying deviation, and the images will therefore be smeared.

**8.7. Resolving Power of a Prism.** The *resolving* power of a prism is its capability for forming separate slit images for a small wavelength difference. The capacity of a spectroscope to form separate slit images is determined by the diffraction limit of the aperture of its lenses, and therefore the resolving power of the instrument is that wavelength difference for which the prism will give a difference of deviation equal to the angular resolving power of the aperture.

In defining the resolving power of a prism, per se, it is assumed that the full rectangular aperture is utilized and that the prism is used at minimum deviation. For this case, the sketch of Figure 8.6 can be drawn.

The effective aperture is $D$. $AA_1$ is an emergent wavefront for wavelength $\lambda$, and $AA_2$ is the wavefront for wavelength $\lambda + \delta\lambda$. The angular difference of deviation for this wavelength difference $\delta\lambda$ is therefore the angle $\delta s/D$. Now, by Fermat's principle, the optical path for all rays associated with a given wavefront are equal, hence $s_1 - s_2 = \mu s$, where $\mu$ is the index of refraction for a particular wavelength, and $s$ is the base length of the prism. The difference in air path for the two different wavelengths is $\delta s$, and the difference in optical path within the prism for the same two wavelengths is $\delta\mu\ s$. Therefore, $\delta s = \delta\mu\ s$. Thus the difference in angular deviation is $\delta\mu\, s/D$. At the limit of resolving power, this is equal to the diffraction limit of the aperture, which is $\lambda/D$ (see Section 2.69). Hence

$$\delta\mu\, s = \lambda \tag{8.9}$$

Now the definition of resolving power for a prism is $\lambda/d\lambda$. If Equation (8.9) is divided by $\delta\lambda$, it becomes

$$\frac{\lambda}{\delta\lambda} = s\,\frac{\delta\mu}{\delta\lambda} \tag{8.10}$$

and in the limit this gives

$$\frac{\lambda}{d\lambda} = s\,\frac{d\mu}{d\lambda} = \frac{2Bs}{\lambda^3} \tag{8.11}$$

the last term being given by substitution from Equation (8.8).

**8.8. Direct Vision Spectroscope.** Prisms may be placed in series to achieve double dispersion, and this is often done in spectroscopes. It is also possible to combine prisms with their bases opposite, so that the dispersion of one is opposite to that of another. In the *direct vision spectroscope* (Figure 8.7), prisms are combined so that a wavelength in the middle of the visible spectrum is undeviated by the combination; there will be one prism of flint glass (high dispersion) and two of crown glass (low dispersion) to accomplish this, or perhaps two of flint and three of crown. Wavelengths other than the undeviated wavelength will exhibit dispersion, and a spectrum will be formed. The lens system of this instrument is a simple magnifier, which focuses the slit.

**8.9. Thin Prisms—Achromatic Prisms.** For a prism whose apex angle $\theta$ is small, the equation for deviation (8.1) reduces to

$$\Delta = (\mu - 1)\theta \tag{8.12}$$

which indicates that, under the small angle approximation, the deviation is independent of the angle of incidence. Differentiating Equation (8.12) gives the dispersion for a thin prism

$$\frac{d\Delta}{d\lambda} = \theta\,\frac{d\mu}{d\lambda} \tag{8.13}$$

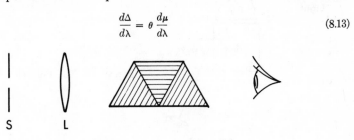

S    L

FIGURE 8.7. Direct vision spectroscope.

It is possible to combine a series of prisms so that the sum of the dispersions for a particular pair of wavelengths is zero—this combination is therefore *achromatic*. When the prisms are of different kinds of glass, the deviation will not, in general, be zero, so that an achromatic prism combination can be achieved which shows a net deviation.

Conversely, the net deviation can be made zero for a particular wavelength, and then, in general, the net dispersion will not be zero. This is the principle of the direct vision spectroscope described in the previous section, although as there described, the prisms are not thin.

**8.10. Spectroscopes, Spectrographs and Spectrometers.** There are countless varieties of instruments for the formation of and measurement of spectra,[58] and a description of even the most common of these would require more space than is available here. They are all usually known under one of the above names, with suitable modifying adjectives.

An instrument intended for visual observation is termed a *spectroscope;* if it is used to make a record of a spectrum, as for example, on a photographic plate, it becomes a *spectrograph.* If it is adapted for the actual measurement of the angles of deviation, the proper term is *spectrometer.* Spectrometers are used to measure the angles of prisms, in which case they do not form spectra at all.

**8.11. Measurement of Refractive Index.** Most instruments for the measurement of refractive index employ the arrangement of a spectrometer, by which an angle of deviation can be measured. Most of these instruments utilize the critical angle of a prism of the sample material to indicate the index of refraction (see Section 2.6). Monochromatic light must be used if an accurate measurement is to be obtained. Figure 8.8 illustrates the arrangement of the Pulfrich refractometer, which is only one of the many types available.

**8.12. Constant Deviation Spectrometers.** In the conventional spectrometer arrangement, as shown in Figure 8.4, it is necessary to rotate both

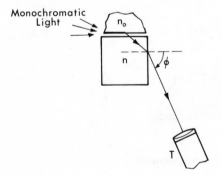

FIGURE 8.8. The Pulfrich refractometer.

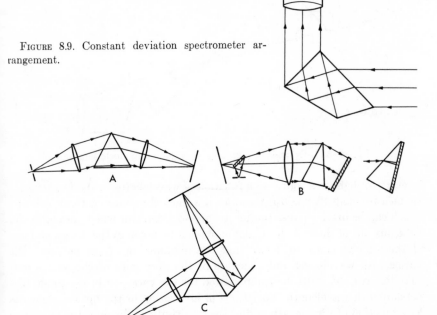

FIGURE 8.9. Constant deviation spectrometer arrangement.

FIGURE 8.10. Spectrograph arrangements.

prism and collector telescope in order to measure an angle. By using a prism design which is *constant deviation*—that is, in which the deviation is independent of the angle of incidence—an arrangement can be realized in which both collimator and telescope may remain fixed, and the prism only rotated. Figure 8.9 shows such an arrangement.

**8.13. Spectrograph Prisms and Arrangements.** Figure 8.10 shows a number of different forms of dispersing prisms and several spectrograph arrangements which are in common use.

**8.14. The Monochromator.** When a spectrometer or spectrograph is provided with an exit slit in the focal plane of the telescope or collector, it is usually termed a *monochromator*. The exit slit may be adjusted in the focal plane to isolate the light at a particular slit image, or wavelength. This instrument thus provides a source of monochromatic light, the degree of monochromaticity being determined by the dispersion of the instrument and the width of the exit and entrance slits. Monochromators may be single or double. A double monochromator arrangement is shown in Figure 8.11.

The monochromator arrangement is used to make measurements of the

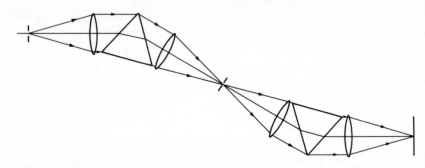

FIGURE 8.11. Optical arrangement of a double monochromator.

intensity of light in a source as a function of wavelength—a *spectrophotometric* measurement. A *spectrophotometer* is a monochromator with an exit slit which can be driven across the spectrum and a detector which measures the light flux out of the exit slit. Great care must be taken in the design and use of these instruments to insure that the illumination of the entrance slit varies with wavelength only because of the properties of the source and that the exit slit width be compensated for the variation in the prism dispersion with wavelength. Variations in absorption in the optical elements as a function of wavelength and of the sensitivity of the detector must also be compensated. Figure 8.12 shows the arrangement of a typical spectrophotometer.

## DIFFRACTION GRATINGS

**8.15. Diffraction by Multiple Apertures.** The diffraction pattern formed by multiple apertures is simply the amplitude superposition of the patterns formed by the individual apertures. In the case of multiple similar apertures, it becomes the superposition of similar patterns modified by the phase differences between the apertures. The problem can be solved by the methods described in Chapter 2.

When the multiple apertures become a series of closely spaced, equally separated slits, the arrangement becomes a *diffraction grating*,[2] and this particular array of multiple apertures is of great importance in optical technology. In the quantitative description below, it is assumed that the diffraction grating consists of a series of equally spaced slits, separated by opaque areas. In practice, a diffraction grating is rarely this, as will be seen, but the nature of the diffraction pattern is similar.

**8.16. Nature of the Diffraction Pattern.** Assume an array of equally spaced slits of width $2w$ and separation $2d$, as shown in Figure 8.13. From

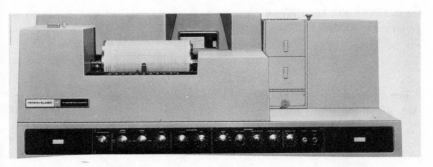

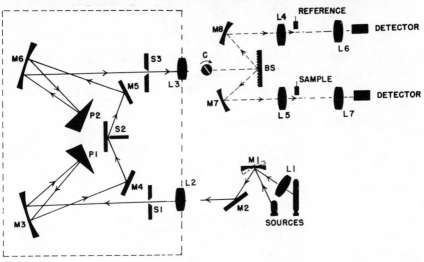

FIGURE 8.12. A spectrophotometer and a schematic optical diagram. (*Courtesy Perkin-Elmer Corp.*)

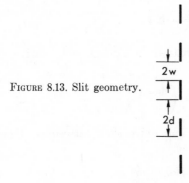

FIGURE 8.13. Slit geometry.

Equation (2.89), the diffraction pattern from a single slit was shown to be given by

$$U(P) = \mathcal{E} \int_{-a}^{a} e^{-ika p} \, dp \tag{8.14}$$

For the case of multiple slits, the complex amplitude, $\mathcal{E}$ is different for each slit; for the $m$th slit, it is

$$\mathcal{E}_m = e^{-i\delta_m} \tag{8.15}$$

where

$$\delta_m = \frac{2\pi}{\lambda} \, 2md \sin \theta \tag{8.16}$$

is the phase difference between a direction of diffraction $\theta$ and the reference direction $\theta_0$. More rigorously, $\sin \theta$ would be replaced by $(\sin \theta_1 - \sin \theta_2)$ where $\theta_1$ is the angle of incidence of the incident light and $\theta_2$ is the direction of diffraction.

Equation (8.15) therefore becomes

$$U(P) = \frac{\mathcal{E}}{2\pi} \sum_{m=1}^{N} e^{-i\delta_m} \int_{-a}^{a} e^{-ika p} \, dp \tag{8.17}$$

and it can be shown that this integral becomes

$$U(P) = \frac{\mathcal{E}}{\pi} \frac{\sin \alpha}{\alpha} \frac{\sin N\gamma}{\sin \gamma} \tag{8.18}$$

where

$$\alpha = \frac{\pi}{\lambda} \, w \sin \theta \tag{8.19}$$

$$\gamma = \frac{\pi}{\lambda} \, d \sin \theta \tag{8.20}$$

and the *intensity* of the diffraction pattern in a direction $\theta$, relative to that in the direction $\theta = 0$, is

$$I(P) = |U(P)|^2 = \left(\frac{\sin \alpha}{\alpha}\right)^2 \left(\frac{\sin N\gamma}{\sin \gamma}\right)^2 \tag{8.21}$$

**8.17. Maxima and Minima.** The diffraction pattern is, therefore, given by the product of two functions

$$I(P) = f(\alpha) \, F(N\gamma) \tag{8.22}$$

where

$$f(\alpha) = \frac{\sin^2 \alpha}{\alpha^2} \tag{8.23}$$

$$F(N\gamma) = \frac{\sin^2 N\gamma}{\sin^2 \gamma} \tag{8.24}$$

$f(\alpha)$ is the diffraction pattern for a single slit, as given in Equation (2.90). This is the *aperture shape factor*, and in the case where the actual apertures in a diffraction grating are not simple slits in an opaque screen, this factor has a different form.

$F(N\gamma)$ is the *interference factor* and represents the result of the phase differences between the individual slits. It is not affected by the nature of the slits, but it is determined only by their spacing.

$\alpha$ is the phase difference across a single slit, and $\gamma$ is the phase difference between slits.

The conditions for maxima and minima of these two functions are shown in Table 8.1.

When the pattern is plotted, as shown in Figure 8.14, it is seen that $f(\alpha)$ forms an envelope within which the maxima and minima of $F(N\gamma)$ are formed. $f(\alpha)$ has only one principal maximum, corresponding to $\theta = 0$; $F(N\gamma)$ has many principal maxima, for each of which the value of this function is unity, but the actual intensity at the maximum is controlled by the value of $f(\alpha)$ at that point. There are $n - 2$ secondary maxima and $n - 1$ minima between each principal maximum.

As the number of slits increases, the maxima become narrower, as shown in Figure 8.14.

TABLE 8.1

|  |  | Condition | Value |
|---|---|---|---|
| Principal maxima |  | $\alpha = 0$ | $f(\alpha) = 1$ |
|  |  | $\gamma = 0$ | $F(N\gamma) = 1$ |
|  | or | $\gamma = m\pi$ |  |
| Secondary maxima |  | $\alpha = \left(\dfrac{2m + 1}{2}\right) \pi$ | $f(\alpha) = \dfrac{1}{\pi^2} \left(\dfrac{2}{2m + 1}\right)^2$ |
|  |  | $\gamma = \left(\dfrac{2m + 1}{2N}\right) \pi$ | $F(N\gamma) = \dfrac{1}{N^2 \pi^2} \left(\dfrac{2}{2m + 1}\right)^2$ |
| Minima |  | $\alpha = m\pi$ | $f(\alpha) = 0$ |
|  |  | $\gamma = \dfrac{m}{N} \pi$ | $F(N\gamma) = 0$ |

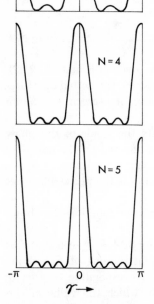

FIGURE 8.14. Diffraction pattern from a grating, showing the effect of increasing the number of lines.

**8.18. Missing Orders.** Each minimum of $f(\alpha)$ will coincide with a principal maximum of $F(N\gamma)$. When this occurs, the minimum condition will, of course, prevail, and this order will be missing. This occurs when $\gamma = m\pi$ where $m$ is the order, and at the same time $\alpha = n\pi$, where $n$ is an integer. From Equations (8.19) and (8.20) this implies that

$$\frac{m}{d} = \frac{n}{w} \tag{8.25}$$

where $w$ is ½ the width of a slit and $d$ is ½ the center-to-center distance between slits. The missing orders will be those represented by

$$m = n\frac{d}{w} \tag{8.26}$$

If the slits and spacings are equal, then $d = 2w$, and all the even orders are missing. In general, if $d = kw$, the orders $m = kn$ are missing—all orders which are integral multiples of $k$.

**8.19. Vector Diagrams.** The most convenient method for analyzing the diffraction patterns of gratings is by means of the vector diagram, which was discussed in Chapter 2. The phase shift between adjacent slits is

$$\delta = \frac{2\pi}{\lambda} d \sin \theta \tag{8.27}$$

and if it is assumed that the slits are of equal width, each incremental wave has the same amplitude. The vector diagram is therefore a series of vectors of equal length, each inclined to its predecessor by the phase angle $\delta$. For a grating of $N$ slits, there will be $N$ vectors.

When $N = 2m\pi$ these vectors form a closed circle, and the resultant amplitude is zero; this is a minimum in the diffraction pattern. When $\delta = 2n\pi$, all of the vectors are parallel, and there is a maximum. When $\delta = n\pi$, $n$ being odd, the vectors are alternately out of phase by $\pi$, and there is a minimum. The minimum is exactly zero if the number of slits is even; if the number is odd, there is a residual vector equal in length to one of the incremental vectors.

Figure 8.15 shows vector diagrams for the case of six slits for various values of $\delta$.

**8.20. The Grating Equation.** It has been shown that principal maxima occur for $\gamma = m\pi$. Putting this condition in Equation 8.20, and using the general form for an angle of incidence $I$ of the light on the grating, gives

$$d(\sin I - \sin \theta) = m\lambda \tag{8.28}$$

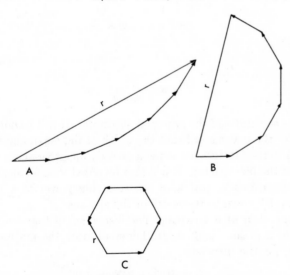

FIGURE 8.15. Vector diagrams for six slits showing effect of increasing phase angle.

This is the *grating equation*, which indicates the condition for a maximum for light of wavelength λ and slit spacing 2d.

**8.21. Formation of a Spectrum.** From the grating equation, it is evident that the location of a maximum varies with the wavelength and that, therefore, the diffraction grating forms a *spectrum*. Indeed, it forms a series of spectra—one for each value of $m$. In general, a diffraction grating forms a series of spectra of orders $m = 1, 2, 3$, etc., with some orders missing in accordance with the conditions described in Section 8.18. In comparison, a prism forms only one spectrum. As will be shown below, the dispersion of a grating increases with the order of the spectrum, so that much greater dispersion can be provided with a grating than with a prism, which is the primary reason for the preference of gratings to prisms for spectroscopy and wavelength analysis. Other advantages are that the dispersion is approximately linear and the grating can be used in reflection, so that the transparency of the material is not a problem. The principal disadvantage of "ordinary" gratings—the fact that only a small proportion of the incident light shows up in a particular spectral order—is largely overcome with the modern *blazed* gratings, the echelons, echelettes and echelles, as described below.

**8.22. Half-width of a Principal Maximum.** The increase in γ [Equation (8.20)] in going from a principal maximum to the first minimum is $\pi/N$. Equating this to the differential of γ from Equation (8.20) gives

$$\delta\gamma = \frac{\pi}{\lambda} d \cos\theta \, \delta\theta = \frac{\pi}{N} \qquad (8.29)$$

from which

$$\delta\theta = \frac{\lambda}{Nd \cos\theta} \qquad (8.30)$$

This is the *half-width* of the principal maximum. It will be noted that $Nd$ is the *width* of the grating and that the width of the maximum is inversely proportional to this. It does not depend directly on either the total number of lines or on the line spacing. It will also be noted that for small values of θ, the expression is identical with the resolving power of a rectangular aperture of width equal to the width of the grating.

**8.23. Dispersion of a Grating.** The dispersion of a grating is defined exactly as for a prism, being $d\theta/d\lambda$. Differentiating the grating Equation (8.28) gives, for the dispersion

$$\mathfrak{D} = d\theta/d\lambda = m/d \cos\theta \qquad (8.31)$$

The dispersion of a grating is therefore proportional to the spectral order.

It can be seen from the grating equation [Equation (8.28)] that for normal incidence ($I = 0$), and for small values of $\theta$ ($\sin \theta = \theta$), $\theta$ is proportional to $\lambda$. This is known as normal dispersion and is one of the desirable characteristics of a grating as compared with a prism.

It is also to be noted that the dispersion of a grating is the reverse of that for a prism—the longer wavelengths have the greater dispersion.

**8.24. Overlapping of Orders.** One of the disadvantages of a grating is that the different spectral orders overlap. Using the grating equation [Equation (8.28)], one can see that the $m$th order position for wavelength $\lambda_1$ coincides with the $(m + 1)$th order position for wavelength $\lambda_2$ when $m\lambda_1 = (m + 1)\lambda_2$. For $m + 1$, the first-order position of $\lambda_1$ coincides with the second-order position of wavelength $\lambda_1/2$. The wavelengths at the extreme ends of the visible spectrum have a ratio of very nearly 2, so that there is overlapping of the first-order extreme red end of the spectrum with the second-order violet.

As $m$ increases, the overlapping becomes more severe, so that it is necessary to suppress all but the small portion of the spectrum being examined when working in the higher orders.

**8.25. Resolving Power of a Grating.** The resolving power of a grating is defined exactly as for a prism, being $\lambda/\delta\lambda$, and the conditions are the same; the limit of resolving power is reached when the maximum for wavelength $\lambda + \delta\lambda$ falls upon the first minimum of wavelength $\lambda$. From the grating equaton [Equation (8.28)], the angle for the maximum of $\lambda + \delta\lambda$ is

$$d \sin \theta_1 = m(\lambda + \delta\lambda) \tag{8.32}$$

and the angle for the minimum of $\lambda$ is $\theta_1 + \delta\theta$, where $\delta\theta$ is given by Equation (8.30). Thus,

$$d \sin (\theta_1 + \delta\theta) = m\lambda \tag{8.33}$$

Expanding Equation (8.33) gives

$$d(\sin \theta_1 \cos \delta\theta + \sin \delta\theta \cos \theta_1) = m\lambda \tag{8.34}$$

Using the small angle approximation, $\cos \delta\theta = \cos \theta_1 = 1$ and $\sin \delta\theta = \theta$, gives

$$d \sin \theta_1 + d\delta\theta = m\lambda \tag{8.35}$$

and substituting from Equations (8.32) and (8.30) yields

$$m(\lambda + \delta\lambda) + \frac{\lambda}{N} = m\lambda \tag{8.36}$$

which reduces to the expression for the resolving power

$$\frac{\lambda}{\delta\lambda} = mN \tag{8.37}$$

showing that the resolving power is proportional to the total number of lines in the grating and to the spectral order. It is obviously a distinct advantage to work in higher spectral orders for high resolution.

**8.26. Maximum Resolving Power.** From the grating equation [Equation (8.28)] the spectral order is

$$m = \frac{d(\sin I - \sin \theta)}{\lambda} \qquad (8.38)$$

Since neither $I$ nor $\theta$ can be greater than $\pi/2$, the maximum possible value of the numerator in Equation (8.38) is 2. Thus, the maximum order possible with a given grating is

$$m_{max.} = 2d/\lambda \qquad (8.39)$$

Substituting Equation (8.39) in the equation for the resolving power [Equation (8.37)], gives

$$R_{max.} = 2Nd/\lambda \qquad (8.40)$$

for the maximum possible resolving power. It is obviously impracticable to even approach this condition in actual use.

It is interesting to note that the resolving power is equal to the number of wavelengths in the optical path difference between the extreme ends of the grating.

**8.27. Illumination.** It can be shown[3] that for a slit grating the ratio of illumination in the $m$th order to that in the zero order is $1/m^2\pi^2$. Thus, only about 10 per cent of the light appears in the first order, and about 2 per cent in the second order, while more than 80 per cent goes into the zero order, where all the wavelets are in phase and there is no spectrum. This condition makes the "ordinary" diffraction grating extremely wasteful of light.

**8.28. Production of Gratings.** Modern gratings are made by ruling with a diamond point on an evaporated aluminum film on glass. These gratings are reflection gratings, and when not "blazed" (see below), the ruled grooves either scatter light or introduce a phase shift. Thus the diffraction pattern of a single groove, which determines the envelope of the diffraction pattern of the grating, is not generally of the form shown in Equation (8.23). The interference pattern of the multiple grooves, however, is independent of the shape of the envelope.

The primary requirement for a good grating is the uniformity and the equality of spacing of the lines. Ruling engines for the manufacture of gratings are among the most carefully made machines in existence.[4] It would not be correct to call them precision machines, because they are made to produce uniformity, not to reproduce dimensions. The advance of the diamond point from stroke to stroke is controlled by a lead screw, which is made with extreme care, and lapped with its nut at great length. The advance of the nut along the lead screw for a given angular turn must be constant to a fraction of a micro-inch if the grating is to be of high quality.

Until very recently, ruling engines were made with the grating blank driven by the lead screw and the diamond mounted on a moveable carriage. This type of ruling engine was first built by Rowland and was reproduced essentially without change for more than 50 years. Shortly after World War II, Strong[5] made a careful study of the essentials of a ruling engine and built a model in which the diamond point was mounted on the lead screw and the grating blank was oscillated on a table. He also made other improvements, including different end bearings on the lead screw. Engines built according to this design have produced the finest gratings which have so far been made.

Ruling engines are made of carefully annealed and aged materials, and are usually operated in temperature-controlled rooms; often they are installed in chambers deep below the ground to avoid vibrations, although excellent gratings have been made with engines in an ordinary factory building when adequate vibration isolation has been installed.

It has been said, quite profoundly, that a ruling engine should be designed in such a way as to do its job even if made of rubber.

Excellent transmission gratings can be made from a ruled master by replication.[6]

Most diffraction gratings are made with about 15,000 lines/in. (Rowland's original gratings had 14,438 lines/in.). Gratings with about 35,000 lines/in. are also often found. The choice of the fineness of ruling is a compromise between high resolution obtained by a large $N$ and that obtained by operating in a higher spectral order. For a grating spacing of 1/15,000 inch, the third-order D-line of sodium is at a diffraction angle of approximately 90°; the entire spectrum is obtained in the first and second orders. A 35,000-line grating will give the first order only. Note that the number of orders available with a given grating becomes greater as the line spacing becomes greater, so that a finely ruled grating gives fewer orders than a coarser one.

Standard grating size is 2 x 4 inches. With a finer ruling (more total lines), the resolution is higher *in a given order*. The resolution obtainable with the grating, however, depends only on its length, as was noted above, when the observation is made in the highest available order.

**8.29. Blazing of Gratings.** If a reflection grating is ruled on a specular

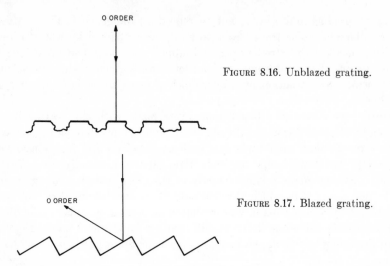

FIGURE 8.16. Unblazed grating.

FIGURE 8.17. Blazed grating.

reflecting surface, such as evaporated aluminum, in such a manner that parallel rough grooves are produced, as shown in Figure 8.16, the zero-order beam is in the direction corresponding to reflection of the incident beam from a plane mirror, and this order contains about 80 per cent of the incident light.

If, however, the grating is ruled in the form of a sawtooth, as shown in Figure 8.17, a large proportion of the light can be concentrated in the direction corresponding to specular reflection from the face of the grooves. Such gratings are now produced routinely, but it was many years before the art of ruling engine design fabrication, and use made this possible.[7] Actually, the echelon, echellette and echelle, described below, preceded the blazed grating historically.

Blazed gratings will concentrate up to 70 per cent or more of the incident light in the preferred direction; they are blazed for a particular wavelength in a particular order and are thus less efficient at other wavelengths.

**8.30. The Transmission Echelon.** As has been shown above, the resolution of a conventional grating is limited by the width of the grating, and there is no recourse in this event except to make larger gratings if extremely high resolution is to be achieved. There is a fundamental obstacle here, however, in that the diamond point wears excessively if too many lines are drawn. Very few gratings over 7 inches in width have been produced.

The resolving power, however, has an even more fundamental basis in that it is the number of wavelengths in the optical path difference between the waves from the two extremities of the grating. The order, as may be seen from the grating equation [Equation (8.28)] is the number of wave-lengths in the optical path difference between the wavelets from two ad-joining slits.

This relation was used by Michelson in proposing the *transmission echelon*[8] which achieves extremely high resolving power by operating in a very high order with a small number of "slits." The transmission echelon is shown in Figure 8.18. It consists of a series of equally thick plates placed together in a stepwise array—hence the name *echelon*.

If the thickness of each plate is $t$, then the optical path difference between light passing through $N$ plates and through $N + 1$ plates is $(\mu - 1)t$, where $\mu$ is the index of refraction. The order of interference is therefore $(\mu - 1)t/\lambda$. The optical path difference can be made thousands of wave-lengths, and therefore the interference order can be in the thousands, although there may be only a few steps in the echelon.

**8.31. The Reflecting Echelon.** The transmission echelon presents difficulties in that inhomogeneity in the material destroys its effectiveness, and it cannot, of course, be used for spectral regions where the material is not transparent. If the steps of the echelon are silvered or aluminized, however, these difficulties disappear, and at the same time the optical path difference is made about four times greater than it would otherwise be.

The reflecting echelon is more difficult to manufacture, because any dust or film between two of the plates will destroy its periodicity; this was not the case for the transmission arrangement, since the phase shift introduced affects all the beams, but Williams[9] succeeded in accomplishing the task, and reflecting echelons were in rather wide use for a time. They have now been largely replaced by the Fabry-Perot interferometer, described in the following section.

The optical path difference for the reflecting echelon is shown in Figure

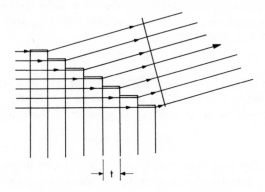

Figure 8.18. The transmission echelon.

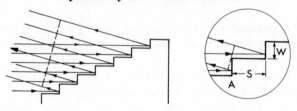

FIGURE 8.19. The reflecting echelon.

8.19. The paths of the two rays from the dotted line to the focus of the telescope are equal. The path of the upper ray from A to the dotted line is $s + s\cos\theta$, and that of the lower ray is $w\sin\theta$. For small angle $\theta$, the grating equation for the reflecting echelon becomes

$$2s - w\theta = m\lambda \tag{8.41}$$

The reflecting echelon is customarily used at a spectral order like 30,000, for which the resolving power is very large. It is of particular value in the investigation of hyperfine structure of spectral lines.

Because of the strong overlapping of orders in this region, which occurs with the echelon exactly as with conventional gratings, the available spectral band at a given setting is of the order of a fraction of an angstrom. In order to use the echelon, the spectrum must be reduced by interposing a prism or a conventional grating and/or filters in front of the echelon.

Because the available spectrum is so narrow, it is necessary to "tune" the echelon so that the desired region falls within the field of the telescope. With the transmission echelon, this can be accomplished by rotating the echelon; with the reflecting echelon, rotation may deflect all of the light out of the telescope aperture, so other means must be adopted. It is customary to mount the echelon in a sealed chamber, and vary the pressure of the air within the box, thereby introducing a slight change in its index.

For normal incidence, $\theta$ in Equation (8.41) is zero, and the condition for a maximum is, therefore

$$2s\mu = m\lambda \tag{8.42}$$

where $\mu$ is the index of refraction of the medium (air) in which the echelon is immersed. When this condition is met, there is only one spectrum, and the echelon is said to be in *single order position*. If the condition

$$2s\mu = (m + \tfrac{1}{2})\lambda \tag{8.43}$$

is met, there are two orders present, symmetrically disposed about the normal. The echelon is then said to be in *symmetrical position*. Since $m$ is very large with respect to $\lambda$, only a very small change in the air pressure is necessary to shift the wavelength for which the maximum is satisfied.

**8.32. Echelles and Echellettes.** Relatively coarse gratings with controlled groove shapes are now commonly produced, and are known under the names *echelles* and *echellettes*. The latter term was adopted by Wood in 1910[10] when he produced controlled groove gratings for infrared wavelengths with 2000 to 3000 lines/in. and an efficient blaze. Later, he extended this technique to produce the forerunners of today's blazed gratings for the visible spectrum with 15,000 lines/in. and more.

More recently, Harrison[11] and others have produced what are known as *echelles*, which are sawtooth gratings of from a few to 1000 lines/mm with groove depths up to 100 $\mu$ or more. These are really intermediate between the true echelon and the conventional plane grating, and they work in spectral orders of a few hundred.

**8.33. The Concave Grating.** By ruling a grating on a concave reflecting surface, Rowland combined the collimator and the telescope of a spectrometer in the grating itself and thus provided a tool which was independent of the transmission problems of these optical accessories to the grating. It can be shown that if the conditions shown in Figure 8.20 are satisfied, a sharply focused spectrum[12] will be obtained around the entire circle. The circle has a diameter equal to the radius of curvature of the grating, with its center halfway from this center of curvature to the surface of the grating. This is the *Rowland circle*.

**8.34. Grating Mountings.** A number of different mountings are in

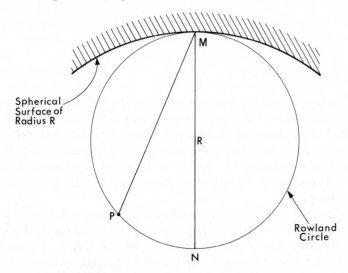

FIGURE 8.20. The Rowland circle. When the slit is located on the normal to the spherical grating surface at N, the slit images are formed on the circle.

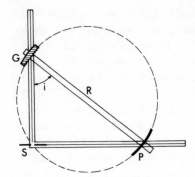

FIGURE 8.21. Rowland's girder mounting: (S) slit, (G) grating, (P) photographic plate.

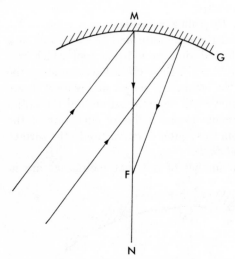

FIGURE 8.22. Wadsworth's mounting arrangement. Incident parallel light on a spherical grating gives good images of lines which focus on the meridional plane MN.

common use for grating spectrographs. For the concave grating, Rowland used a right-angle girder, in the manner shown in Figure 8.21. The slit is mounted at the intersection, and the grating and plate are connected by a beam of length equal to the diameter of the Rowland circle. As the beam slides along the arms of the girder, the Rowland circle condition is maintained. The angle of diffraction remains constant, but the angle of incidence changes.

The concave grating used in the Rowland fashion suffers from astigmatism, which is not of great concern for most work, but makes it impossible to investigate parts of a source by imaging the source on the slit. The Wadsworth[13] mounting, shown in Figure 8.22, corrects this difficulty by providing collimated light to the grating. It also makes for a more compact arrangement. By using a mirror to collimate the light from the slit, problems of glass transmission are avoided.

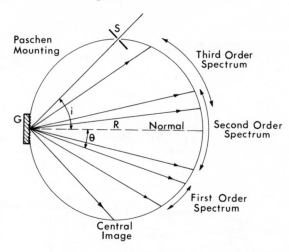

Paschen Mounting

S

Third Order
Spectrum

G

*i*

R    Normal

θ

Second Order
Spectrum

First Order
Spectrum

Central
Image

FIGURE 8.23. The Paschen mounting.

In the Paschen mounting of the concave grating, a circular track is provided, upon which the photographic plate may be mounted in a suitable position. Paschen mountings have been made in very large sizes—up to 30 feet in diameter. In such a spectrograph, with a 15,000-line/in. grating, the first-order visible spectrum is over 14 feet long. The Paschen mounting is illustrated in Figure 8.23.

It is an interesting point about the concave grating that to produce freedom from spherical aberration and coma, it is necessary to rule the grating lines equally across the *chord* of the concave surface, not equally across the *arc*. Fortunately, this is exactly the kind of spacing that the conventional ruling engine gives when it rules on a concave surface.

The other conventional mounting for the concave grating is the Eagle mounting, illustrated in Figure 8.24. The slit is located near the plate and is imaged virtually at the center of the plate. To scan the spectrum, the grating is moved along the bar, to or away from the plate, and plate and grating are rotated so as to remain on the Rowland circle.

The Littrow mounting, for plane gratings, is an *autocollimating* type, using the same optical system for both collimator and telescope. The grating is rotated until the required portion of the spectrum is returned to the vicinity of the slit, where the plate is mounted. Often, the plate and slit are displaced in a direction normal to the diagram of Figure 8.25. The Littrow mounting is by far the most common arrangement for plane gratings.

For spectral analysis in regions where glass is poorly transmitting, it is necessary to resort to reflecting systems for collimator and telescope.

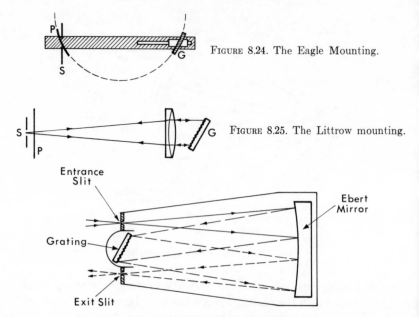

FIGURE 8.24. The Eagle Mounting.

FIGURE 8.25. The Littrow mounting.

FIGURE 8.26. The Ebert mounting.

Spherical mirrors suffer from aberrations, and paraboloids do not have a sufficient field of view to be useful for spectrographs. In the Ebert mounting, illustrated in Figure 8.26, the aberrations of a spherical mirror are compensated by using either two spherical mirrors of equal focal length, appropriately tilted, or using off-center sections of a single spherical mirror, as shown in the figure. The slits in the Ebert arrangement must be arcs of circles to provide a straight image of the slit at infinity to match the grating rulings.

**8.35. Ghosts.** Errors in the ruling of diffraction gratings cause various types of defects in their performance. Random errors in the spacing of the rulings reduce the resolving power and cause general scattering which reduces the contrast of the slit images. Progressive errors in spacing have focal properties.

By far the most serious grating errors are periodic errors, in which the spacing varies periodically across the grating, and these are the most difficult to remove in the ruling engines. Such errors cause "ghosts"—spurious spectral lines. If the periodic error is such that the grating width contains approximately one cycle, the ghosts are symmetrical about the principal maxima; they are known as *Rowland ghosts*. When there are a number of cycles of error across the grating, *Lyman ghosts* are produced; these may

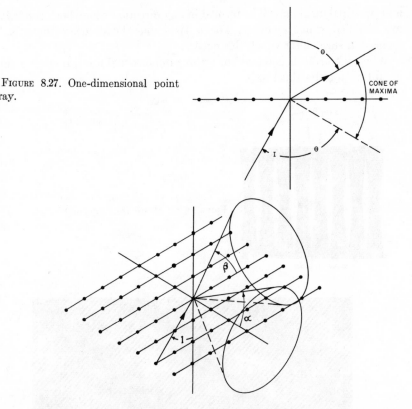

FIGURE 8.27. One-dimensional point array.

FIGURE 8.28. Two-dimensional point array.

occur at locations far from the principal maxima with which they are associated.

**8.36. Two- and Three-dimensional Gratings.** A one-dimensional array of scattering points, as shown in Figure 8.27, will act as a diffraction grating, but in this case the directions of principal maxima lie on the surface of a cone whose semi-apex angle is $\pi/2 - \theta$, where $\theta$ is the angle which would apply for a plane grating consisting of slits.

For a two-dimensional array of points, as shown in Figure 8.28, there are cones about each of the axes, with the required conditions for principal maxima:

$$s_x(\alpha - \alpha_0) = m_1\lambda \tag{8.44}$$

and

$$s_y(\beta - \beta_0) = m_2\lambda \tag{8.45}$$

and principal maxima will be formed in any direction where both conditions are satisfied simultaneously. For a two-dimensional array there is, in general, a surface for which this occurs.

When the array is extended to a three-dimensional form, there is a third condition for the third axis

$$s_z(\gamma - \gamma_0) = m_3\lambda \qquad (8.46)$$

FIGURE 8.29. Moiré fringe geometry.

FIGURE 8.29A. Moiré fringe patterns. The pattern here is for $\theta = 2°$ (see Figure 8.29); the pattern on p. 413 is for $\theta = 5°$.

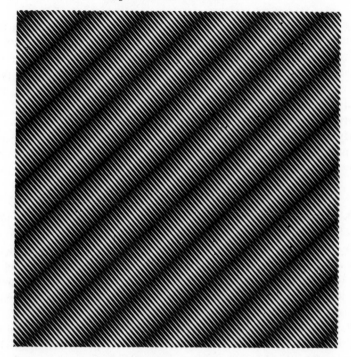

FIGURE 8.29A. *Cont'd.*

and in general all three conditions cannot simultaneously be satisfied except for specific angles of incidence of the illumination.

Three-dimensional gratings are of great interest, because natural crystals present actual examples of a three-dimensional lattice. The study of crystal structure by the diffraction of X-rays and of electrons is an active field of endeavor, whose discussion is beyond the scope of this book.

**8.37. Moiré Fringes.** The shadow fringes formed when two gratings are placed together at an angle to each other are known as Moiré fringes.[14] They are not caused by either diffraction or interference, but they have a generally similar appearance to interference fringes and are appropriately discussed here.

Figure 8.29 shows how these fringes are formed. The regions where the opaque bars of one grating overlap the transparent bars of the other cause an opaque strip to appear which is perpendicular to the grating lines.

If the gratings are moved with respect to each other in a direction normal to their rulings, the Moiré fringes appear to move in a perpendicular direction. It is readily seen that if the gratings are moved a distance $s$, the fringes will move a distance $s'$, where

$$s' = s\theta \qquad (8.47)$$

$\theta$ being the angular difference between the rulings. There is thus a magnification of $1/\theta$, and if $\theta$ is made small, this magnification can be quite large.

Moiré fringes are used in control systems to measure movements with a high degree of precision. Photodetectors are used to measure the passage of the fringes across a viewing point; these fringe passages are usually treated as pulses, and the information taken out in digital form.

Moiré fringes are also a source of annoyance in many situations, particularly in color printing, where a slight misalignment of the screens can cause prominent fringes to appear in the product.

## INTERFEROMETRY

**8.38. General.** There are dozens of types of interferometers, and hundreds of applications of them in measurement and testing; even a complete volume devoted to this subject alone could not wholly cover the field. All that is attempted here is a description of the most common types of interferometers and some explanation of their operation, together with an indication of how this technique is utilized in precision measurement and analysis.

**8.39. The Michelson Interferometer.**[15] Every textbook on optics begins its discussion of interference with a description of the Michelson interferometer; this book is no exception—the instrument was described in some detail in Section 2.51 *et seq.* since it provides a convenient tool for the explanation of the interference of beams of light.

In its original form, the Michelson interferometer is not extensively used today; in substance, however, it exists in the form of many modifications, of which the Twyman-Green (see Section 8.40) is perhaps the most often found. The advantages of the Michelson principle are that there are no multiple reflections in the instrument to produce undesirable ghosts, it is possible to adjust the optical path difference to zero (which is not possible with all types), and it is relatively easy to make the two interfering beams of equal amplitude so that the minima provide essentially zero illumination.

With the Michelson and its derivative arrangements, measurements to an accuracy of 1/20 wavelength (about 1 micro-inch) are relatively easy to make, and with special techniques, measurements as small as .001 wavelength (20 nano-inches) are possible.

Andrews has shown that, in principle, the Michelson interferometer, for optical frequencies, is identical to the Wheatstone bridge, for electrical frequencies, and that the analogy in the realm of microwave frequencies exists in the form of the "Magic T."[16]

**8.40. The Twyman-Green Interferometer.**[17] The function of the

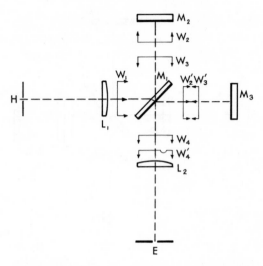

FIGURE 8.30. The Twyman-Green interferometer.

Michelson interferometer is essentially the measurement of distances, achieved by adjusting the difference in optical path of the two interfering beams and counting the fringe displacement resulting from the adjustment. Because different directions in the field of view correspond to different path lengths, due to the angle, circular fringes appear when the mirrors are parallel. The instrument is not suitable for examining the effects upon a wavefront of an object such as a prism or lens.

The *Twyman-Green interferometer* is a modification of the Michelson interferometer which adapts it to this purpose, and this instrument has become more or less standard for the testing of many forms of optical components.

The Twyman-Green interferometer is illustrated in Figure 8.30. The modification to the Michelson instrument is simply the use of a point source instead of an extended source, and the introduction of a collimating lens, $L_1$, so as to produce a coherent plane wave front at the entrance to the inteferometer. The lens $L_2$, which is used as a telescope in the Michelson instrument, is used in the Twyman Green to give a "Maxwellian view" of the instrument aperture. An arrangement wherein all of the light from an aperture which is forming a small image (usually a point) is permitted to enter the eye of the observer, so that the aperture appears fully illuminated, is called a *Maxwellian view*, after Maxwell, who described it in connection with some of his experiments. It is often used in optical testing.

If the mirrors in the Twyman-Green interferometer are parallel, the

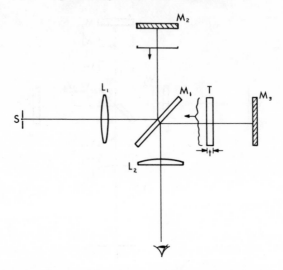

FIGURE 8.31. Test plate in a Twyman-Green interferometer.

optical path difference for the two beams is constant over the field of view
(within the limits established by the size of the source) and it appears uniformly illuminated. The intensity of the illumination will depend upon
whether the optical path difference corresponds to a maximum, a minimum,
or some intermediate point.

Now if a transparent object (such as a plane parallel plate) is introduced
into one of the arms of the instrument, as shown in Figure 8.31, the optical
path in that arm will be increased by $2(\mu - 1)t$, where $t$ is the thickness of
the plate and $\mu$ is its index of refraction. The change in optical path in units
of wavelength will be $2(\mu - 1)t/\lambda$, and when this becomes an integer, the
interference pattern will be shifted by one fringe. In general

$$2(\mu - 1)t = \delta m\lambda \qquad (8.48)$$

where $\delta m$ is the fringe shift.

In practice, a measurement of absolute fringe shift cannot be made in
the Michelson or Twyman-Green interferometers, because, for the reasons
explained in connection with the former, they must be used with monochromatic light, and with monochromatic light the fringes cannot be
individually identified. Unless the plate is very thin, the shift will be more
than one fringe, and since the introduction of the plate gives a discontinuous shift, the fringes cannot be counted.

If the shift is introduced gradually, as can be done with a gas by increasing its pressure in a sample chamber gradually, the fringes can be counted,

and thus the index of refraction of the gas can be determined from measuring $\delta m$ and $t$, knowing $\lambda$, and applying Equation 8.48.

The Twyman-Green instrument finds its usefulness in revealing differential changes in optical path caused by variations in the sample under test. If the index of refraction or the thickness of the specimen varies from point to point, there will be a shift of fringes according to Equation 8.48. The interferometer is usually adjusted so that a series of straight fringes are formed; this requires that the mirrors be tilted slightly with respect to each other. The pattern seen with the specimen in place is then a "contour map" of the specimen superimposed upon the straight slope represented by the straight fringes.

Figure 8.32 shows the Twyman-Green interferometer arranged to test a prism.

The instrument may be used to test lenses by the arrangement shown in Figure 8.33. A concave spherical mirror with its center at the focal point of the lens is used to return the "spherical" wave front formed by the lens.

This interferometer, like many others, depends upon double passage through the specimen; therefore the optical path difference is doubled, and the distance between fringes represents a difference of one-half a wavelength in the optical path. It is important to remember this, since in some interferometric arrangements, the distance between fringes may represent path differences of a whole wavelength.

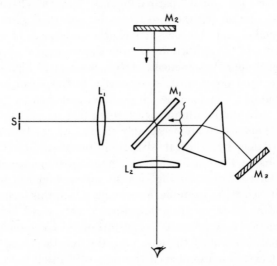

FIGURE 8.32. Testing a prism in a Twyman-Green interferometer.

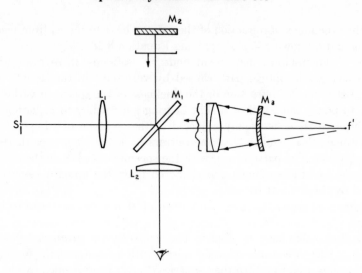

FIGURE 8.33. Testing a lens in a Twyman-Green interferometer.

The variations seen in the specimen are caused by the combination of thickness and index variations, and there is no way to separate the two with this instrument alone. The specimen may, however, be separately tested in a different type of instrument, such as the Fizeau, described below, in which the optical path difference obeys a different equation; simultaneous solution for the two measurements then gives information about both index and thickness. Thickness variations, of course, result from departures of the surface forms from the required shapes.

In the case of optical components such as prisms (see Figure 8.32) which are used in a fixed position, it is customary to test them in a Twyman-Green interferometer in their design position, and then to "work" one of the surfaces until the interferometer shows either no variations in optical path or variations which are acceptably small. One has then compensated for index variations by deliberate distortions of the surface. This is a quite satisfactory method for achieving maximum performance in an optical instrument. Of course, when the element in question has to be used in varying positions, as for example, a scanning prism, this technique for correction is not as effective. In large prisms, a very small variation in the index of refraction may cause serious distortions of the wavefront, because of the cumulative effect of the long path through the glass. With a path length of 6 inches, for example, if the wave distortion is to be less than $\lambda/10$ (which may be required in a precision instrument), the variation in index can be no greater than .0000003 (assuming the prism surfaces are

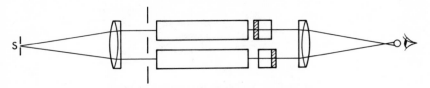

FIGURE 8.34. The Rayleigh refractometer.

perfectly flat). The best quality optical glass usually shows minimum index variations throughout a large specimen of ±.000005. To meet the above requirement, the raw optical glass would have to be at least specially selected and probably specially annealed.

The fringes seen in the Twyman-Green interferometer are Fizeau fringes, but they are not in focus on the specimen; the beams which form the individual fringes, however, are narrow, so that the eye has considerable depth of focus for them, and they may be focused simultaneously with the specimen, so that their location with respect to the specimen can be determined.

**8.41. The Rayleigh Refractometer.**[18] This instrument makes use of interference fringes to measure the refractive index of gases; it is illustrated in Figure 8.34. The two interfering beams are formed by a double slit placed in front of a collimating lens. In the upper half of the instrument, two closed tubes are provided—one for a reference and one for the sample; in the lower half of the instrument there are no tubes.

The instrument in reference condition gives the conventional interference pattern of a double slit—a series of maxima under the diffraction envelope of a single slit. When a gas is introduced into the sample tube, the difference of its index of refraction from that of the reference tube causes a shift in the diffraction pattern due to the interference of the two slits, without changing the single-slit envelope.

The lower half of the aperture provides a reference diffraction pattern, by means of which the shifts in the fringes in the upper half of the aperture can be measured. The compensating plates shown in the diagram are introduced to make the measurement easier by shifting the fringe pattern so as to bring it to a null; the fringe shift is then read from a dial attached to the compensating plates. As shown in the lower part of the Figure, the compensating plates are so mounted that rotation about the axis shown will increase one path length and decrease the other.

The Rayleigh refractometer is provided with a high-power cylindrical lens (a glass rod) as an eyepiece; this has the dual advantage of separating the upper and lower halves of the aperture and their respective fringe patterns, and of introducing a magnification perpendicular to the slit but

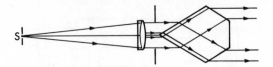

FIGURE 8.35. Williams' beam-splitting prism.

not parallel to it, thus magnifying the fringe separation with the maximum economy of light.

**8.42. Beam Separation.** It is often desired to produce two parallel, collimated beams of light for interference experiments, as in the Rayleigh refractometer. In the arrangement shown in Figure 8.34, the beams are separated by using the two extreme edges of a lens; this is not a desirable situation. A novel arrangement due to Williams is shown in Figure 8.35, in which a five-sided prism splits the beam into two parallel components. Williams found that with this arrangement, which uses the central part of the collimating lens only, a considerably wider slit could be used in the Rayleigh refractometer without decreasing its resolving power; this provides a considerable improvement in illumination in an instrument in which illumination is a serious problem.

**8.43. The Mach-Zehnder Interferometer.**[19] This instrument, illustrated in Figure 8.36, is in common use for investigating phenomena of gas flow, particularly in wind tunnels and shock tubes.

As in all division of amplitude interferometers, the incident beam, which is made parallel by a collimating lens, is divided by a beam splitter, and conducted by different paths to the viewing telescope. The sample chamber lies in one of these paths, and the interference is produced by the wave-front distortions which occur in this sample chamber.

The Mach-Zehnder interferometer has the advantage that the fringes which are observed can be localized in the region of the sample chamber, indeed the fringes can be localized anywhere within the chamber by suitable adjustment of the mirrors.

**8.44. The Wave-front Shearing Interferometer.** A number of recent developments in interferometers are adapted to the interferometry of spherical converging wave fronts, such as are obtained from ideal imaging devices, like concave mirrors and lenses. The beam-dividing element in an interferometer may be placed anywhere in the beam; with collimated light, the beam is the same size throughout its path, but in a converging spherical wave front, the beam size is quite small near the focus, and thus these interferometers can be made very small and compact and yet utilized to test very large apertures. Some of these instruments are described in the following sections.

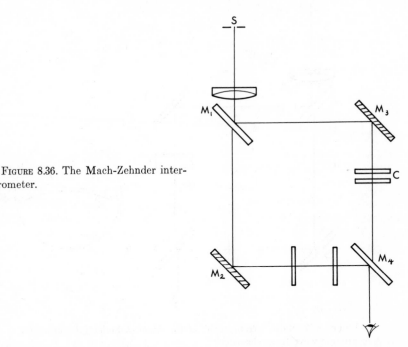

FIGURE 8.36. The Mach-Zehnder interferometer.

The forerunner of the convergent wave-front interferometers was an
arrangement of the Mach-Zehnder instrument due to Bates,[20] which is
illustrated in Figure 8.37.

The instrument is illuminated with a converging spherical wavefront,
shown at A; this is divided into two beams which eventually come to a
common focus at s. If the wave front is perfectly spherical and the mirrors
are all parallel, there will be no fringes at s, and to an eye placed there to
give the Maxwellian view, the aperture appears uniformly illuminated.

Now, let mirrors $M_2$ and $M_4$ be rotated as a unit through a small angle
about an axis parallel to BB'; the effect is to tilt the two wave fronts with
respect to each other about a horizontal axis perpendicular to BB' (Figure
8.37 is to be considered a top view). The field will now be crossed by a set
of horizontal fringes because of this tilt.

If now mirror $M_4$ is rotated slightly about a vertical axis passing through
s, the two wave fronts will be displaced horizontally, as shown in the insert. Both are still concentric about s, and there will be no change in the
pattern of fringes observed if the wave fronts are perfectly spherical.

However, any departure of the wave fronts from sphericity in a region
like x in the insert will disturb the phase relation in this region, and the

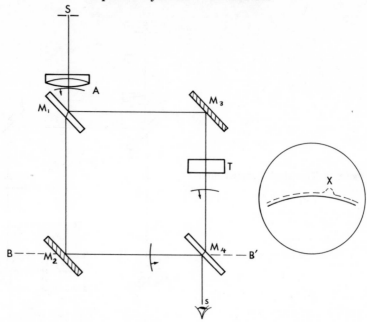

FIGURE 8.37. Bates' arrangement of the Mach-Zehnder interferometer to provide wave-front shearing.

fringes will be shifted, in the same fashion that the fringes are shifted in the Twyman-Green interferometer by variations in the optical path. The variations in sphericity of the wave fronts will be revealed in the form of a contour map of fringes superimposed upon the linear slope due to the original tilt.

It is not necessary to use an instrument the size of the Mach-Zehnder. Drew and Brown developed a compact cemented unit, shown in Figure 8.38, which was fabricated in a volume smaller than a 2-inch cube, yet could be used to test any size of objective whose relative aperture was within the limits of the device.

The device does not provide for adjustable shear and tilt. Other equally compact arrangements using the wave-front shearing principle have been constructed and used.

**8.45. Koster's Double-image Prism.**[21] The Kosters double prism, illustrated in Figure 8.39, provides another form of compact interferometer which may be used in converging spherical wave fronts from large apertures. The fringes in this device are produced by a wedge which is introduced in the manufacture, either in the prism itself, or in the cement which joins the two halves, or in both. One of the advantages of this device is that

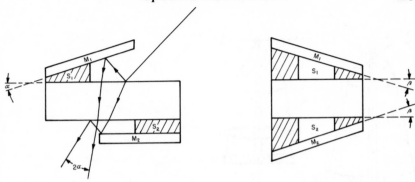

FIGURE 8.38. The interferometer of Drew and Brown.

FIGURE 8.39. Koster's prism.

with suitable choice of cement and prism wedge angle, the fringes may be made *achromatic* (two colors having the same fringe separation) so that it can be used easily with white light. Figure 8.40 shows several arrangements of the prism for testing different types of components.

A point source is used, and the emergent end of the prism can be shaped to provide a plane, converging or diverging wave front, as required for the test. For a plane wave front, of course, the addition of collimating lenses is necessary, as shown in the diagrams.

Effectively, one-half of the surface under test is compared with the other half; when the arrangement is symmetrical, as in Figure 8.40A, any wave-front distortions introduced by the test component which are symmetrical about the optical axis, such as spherical aberration, are not revealed. At first, this would appear to be a disadvantage of the arrangement, but if the device is used asymmetrically, as shown in Figure 8.40E, symmetrical aberrations will show up, so that actually the instrument provides a powerful tool for separating aberrational defects.

**8.46. The Burch Scatter-plate Interferometer.** Another extremely simple interferometer, especially well suited to the testing of large aperture optical systems is the *scatter-plate interferometer* of Burch,[22] shown in Figure 8.41.

The interference-producing device is a pair of scattering plates, $L_1$ and $L_2$ in the diagram. These plates are identical but random in structure—usually being made by drawing replicas from a single master. They are re-

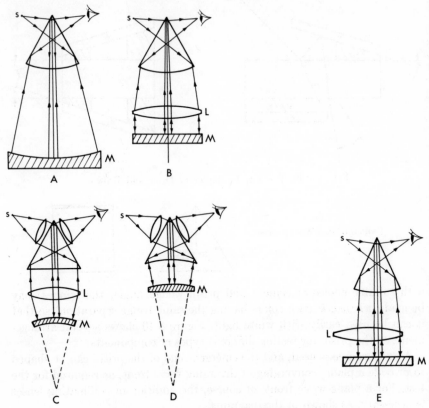

FIGURE 8.40. Applications of the Koster's prism.

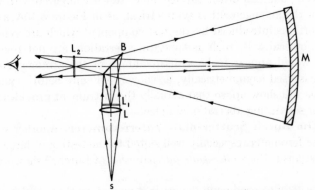

FIGURE 8.41. The scatter plate interferometer. $L_1$, $L_2$, matched scatter plates. $B$, Beam-splitter, $L$, focusing lens. $M$, mirror under test.

versed in position and placed at the center of curvature of the mirror, so that $L_1$ is imaged exactly on $L_2$ by the mirror. This is the necessary condition, and the arrangement is applicable to any other form of optical system, provided only that the two plates are at conjugate foci.

A pinhole source is used, and lens $L$ images this source on the surface of the mirror at the optical axis, whence it is returned to the focus to image $L_1$ and $L_2$. At the same time, some of the light in the converging beam just described is scattered by $L_1$ so as to fill the mirror aperture, and this light, too, is returned by the mirror to the image.

An observer looking through $L_2$ will see two superimposed fields of view, one formed by the light which passed undisturbed through $L_1$ but is scattered by $L_2$, the other by light which was scattered by $L_1$ but passes undisturbed through $L_2$. Because of the exact similarity of the scatter pattern on $L_2$ and the image of $L_1$, the two beams are nominally coherent and will produce interference fringes when the parts are adjusted so as to produce a slight tilt.

If the mirror is imperfect, however, the beam scattered by $L_1$, which fills the mirror, will show these imperfections as distortions of the wave front, while the beam which passed unscattered through $L_1$ will not show these distortions, because the area of the mirror affected, being on the axis and of small extent, is essentially aberration free.

In this interferometer, it is important that the pattern on the scatter plates be random, or patterns will be formed which interfere with the interpretation of the fringes. Also, there is usually a considerable amount of light which is not scattered by either plate, and this gives a brilliant central spot which may make it difficult to observe the fringes. This may be removed by a small central obstruction.

**8.47. Common-path Interferometers.** The scatter-plate interferometer and the Kosters double-prism interferometer are examples of a class of interferometers usually known as "common-path" instruments, because the two beams which eventually produce interference fringes traverse the same optical system throughout their full travel; this is not the case for instruments like the Twyman-Green, in which the two beams are completely separate.

The outstanding advantage of common-path interferometers is that they are immune to the dispersion of refracting elements which require interferometers with separated paths to use monochromatic light; common-path interferometers operate with white light.

Also, in most cases, these interferometers use the converging beams of the system under test, and therefore can be made small and compact. This advantage is not alone one of economy and convenience; interferometers like the Twyman-Green and the Mach-Zehnder are very sensitive to temperature, vibrations, air turbulence and many other environmental factors, which the small, compact devices avoid by reason of their being small and compact.

**8.48. Polarization Interferometers.** Several interferometers have been devised which use the properties of birefringent crystals to produce the two interfering beams; these beams are, of course, polarized at right angles when produced, but they are brought into coincidence by a $\frac{1}{4}$-wave plate. That of Dyson[23] is a typical example, as well as the use of the Savart plate as described by van Heel.[24]

**8.49. Apodization.** The shape of diffraction patterns is a function of the aperture of the optical system. The pattern formed for a point image by a circular aperture has been discussed in Section 2.71. In cases where two close objects, such as stars, which differ substantially in brightness, are required to be separated, the subsidiary maxima of the brighter object, while weak with respect to the central maximum, may still be strong enough to obscure the image of the fainter object, even when the separation is considerably greater than the resolving power of the aperture.

By properly designing the shape of the aperture, it is possible to modify the diffraction pattern so as to suppress the secondary maxima at the cost of increasing the width of the central maximum.[25] This process is called *apodization*, and it has been successful in a number of applications, particularly in astronomy.

**8.50. The Fabry-Perot Interferometer.**[26] The Fabry-Perot interferometer is the typical example of interferometers which depend upon multiple reflections within a plate; the interference conditions were discussed in Section 2.57. In the Fabry-Perot instrument, the "plate" is a pair of parallel reflecting surfaces, usually consisting of silver or aluminum films on glass or quartz plates. The condition for the interference maxima is

$$2t \sin \theta = m\lambda \tag{8.49}$$

where $t$ is the separation of the reflecting surfaces. It was shown that the intensity of the maxima and minima are given by

$$I_{max.} = \mathcal{E}^2 \tag{8.50}$$

$$I_{min.} = \frac{(1 - r)^2}{(1 + r)^2} \tag{8.51}$$

where $r$ is the reflectivity of the surfaces. The minimum approaches zero as the reflectivity approaches unity, and as the reflectivity increases, the maxima become increasingly sharp.

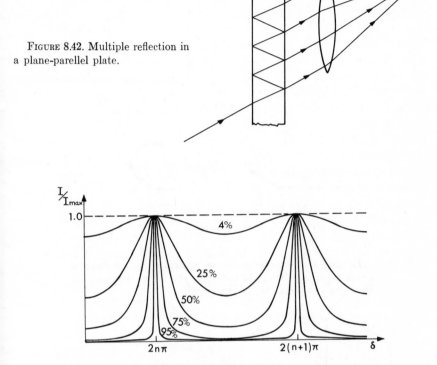

FIGURE 8.42. Multiple reflection in a plane-parellel plate.

FIGURE 8.43. Transmission *vs* wavelength for a multiply-reflecting plate.

Figure 8.42 shows the phenomenon of multiple reflections; a numerical discussion was given in Section 2.57. Figure 8.43 shows how the sharpness of the maxima increases with increasing reflectivity of the plates. An easy way to see this effect is to plot the amplitudes of the successive reflections as a vector polygon for the maxima and minima, as is done in Figure 8.44.

Figure 8.45 shows the instrumental arrangement of a Fabry-Perot interferometer. The only requirement on the source side of the instrument is that a wide beam be provided, with rays incident throughout a range of angles so that the receiving telescope can collect a sufficient number of reflections to make the conditions operate. A large diffuse source without a lens, or a small source with a collimating lens, may be used; in the latter case, the lens is located so as not to strictly collimate the light—otherwise the required range of angles of incidence would not be provided.

The fringes are Haidinger fringes, located at infinity, and they are ob-

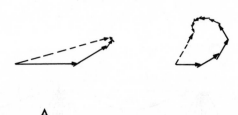

A

FIGURE 8.44. Vector polygons for maximum and minimum of transmission in a multiply reflecting plate. The diagrams are drawn for two values of the reflectivity.

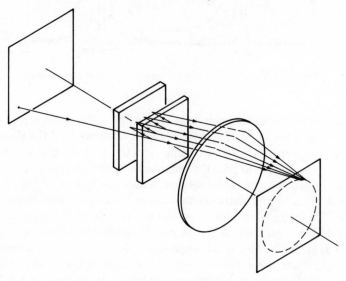

FIGURE 8.45. Arrangement of the Fabry-Perot interferometer.

served at the focal plane of a telescope. Unless the reflecting plates are very close together, a telescope is necessary to collect a sufficient number of the beams.

The Fabry-Perot interferometer is of particular interest for two reasons. It provides the highest resolving power of any available instrument for the investigation of spectra, and it is also the fundamental arrangement of the laser (see Part III), where it functions as a resonant cavity.

Equation (8.50) holds only if there is no absorption in the reflecting coatings. In practice, these coatings have significant absorption, which increases as the reflectivity increases, so that Equation (8.50) must be written

$$I_{max.} = \mathcal{E}^2 \left( 1 - \frac{\alpha}{1 - r} \right)^2 \tag{8.52}$$

and the best performance is obtained with reflecting surfaces with a reflectivity somewhat less than unity (about 90 per cent). Metal films have relatively high absorption, and it is common to use multiple dielectric films, which can provide high reflectivities with a minimum absorption.

The *half-width* of a maximum is

$$\gamma = \frac{2(1 - r)}{r^{1/2}} \tag{8.53}$$

And the *contrast factor*, or ratio of intensity at maximum and minimum, is

$$C = \left( \frac{1 + r}{1 - r} \right)^2 \tag{8.54}$$

A quantity often used in connection with the Fabry-Perot interferometer, is the *finesse*, or ratio of the separation of maxima to the half-width; this turns out to be

$$\mathfrak{F} = \frac{\pi r^{1/2}}{1 - r} \tag{8.55}$$

If a parameter, $F$ is defined

$$F = \frac{4r}{(1 - r)^2} \tag{8.56}$$

then the above three quantities can be expressed in terms of $F$ as follows:

$$\gamma = \frac{4}{\sqrt{F}} \tag{8.57}$$

$$C = 1 + F \tag{8.58}$$

$$\mathfrak{F} = \frac{\pi}{2} \sqrt{F} \tag{8.59}$$

**8.51. Fabry-Perot Interferometer and Etalons.** When the Fabry-Perot instrument is constructed with the plates adjustable for separation by means of a micrometer screw, it is usually referred to as a Fabry-Perot interferometer; when it is provided with the plates fixed at a given separation, it is referred to as a Fabry-Perot etalon. Both arrangements are used for the same purposes. The adjustable plates make a somewhat more flexible instrument, but the mechanical difficulty of construction, when the moving plates must be maintained parallel within a tolerance of a second of arc, are quite severe.

**8.52. Fabry-Perot Spectra.** The maxima in a Fabry-Perot instrument, as in any other instrument, are spread out into spectra when the incident light is not monochromatic. The situation is very like that of the echelon grating; the only difference is that there is only one step and the fringes are very sharp as a consequence of the multiple reflections. The step in the Fabry-Perot interferometer can be very large, and thus the spectral order is very high (several hundred thousand), and the resolving power is therefore correspondingly great (see below).

The overlapping of orders is naturally very severe, and the Fabry-Perot instrument would be useless as a spectrograph without auxiliary dispersion. The customary method of use of the instrument is to focus the ring system on the slit of a prism or grating spectrograph, as shown in Figure 8.46, the spectrograph slit being located as shown in the insert. The spectrograph is thus "crossed" with the etalon and will separate the orders in a direction perpendicular to the slit. The result is shown in Figure 8.47.

**8.53. Free Spectral Range.** The *free spectral range* of an instrument is

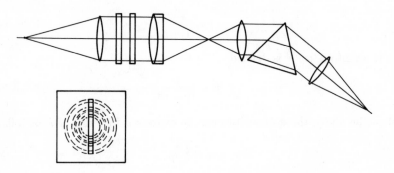

FIGURE 8.46. Prism spectrograph combined with a Fabry-Perot.

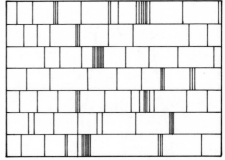

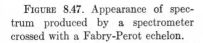
FIGURE 8.47. Appearance of spectrum produced by a spectrometer crossed with a Fabry-Perot echelon.

defined as the spectral width which can be provided without overlap. For a 15,000-line conventional diffraction grating the free spectral range just about encompasses the visible spectrum; in instruments of higher dispersion and higher resolving power, the free spectral range is reduced. In devices such as the Fabry-Perot etalon and the echelon gratings, the free spectral range may be only a fraction of an angstrom.

In such cases, it is necessary either to cross the high-resolution spectrum with another instrument of lower dispersion, to separate the orders (see Figure 8-46), or to isolate a small part of the spectrum in front of the high resolution device by means of a spectrograph or by filters.

**8.54. Energy-limited Resolving Power.** The resolving power of various spectrographic devices has been described and defined; in the case of slit instruments, the resolving power depends upon the slit width, and the definitions which have been given are valid, in many instances, only for slit widths sufficiently narrow that the slit image (which is actually the spectral line) is small with respect to the width of the associated maximum.

In many cases, it is not practicable to reduce the slit width to the degree necessary to achieve anywhere near the theoretical resolving power because this would so reduce the available light that the resulting spectral lines could not be observed or photographed or recorded by a detector. When this situation arises, and it is not at all uncommon in practice, the resolving power of the instrument is that which is established by the minimum practicable slit width. This is referred to as the *energy-limited resolving power*.

**8.55. Resolving Power of the Fabry-Perot Etalon.** With the very narrow maxima provided by the Fabry-Perot etalon, its resolving power must be defined by a criterion similar to that used for the resolving power of a telescope (see Section 6.22). The Rayleigh definition of resolving power supposes a dip in the envelope midway between the two peaks with a value of 81 per cent of the peaks, as shown in Figure 8.48.

This kind of definition lacks something in rigor, but is a satisfactory one.

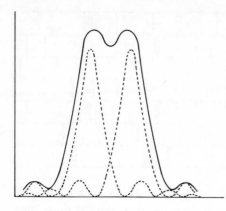

FIGURE 8.48. Diffraction pattern of two close points. The separation shown is slightly greater than that defined by the Rayleigh criterion.

Now, the general expression for the intensity in a Fabry-Perot fringe system [see Equation (2.77)] is

$$I = \frac{\mathcal{E}^2(1 - r)^2}{(1 + r^2 - 2r \cos \delta)} \tag{8.60}$$

which may be written [see (Equation 8.56)]

$$I = \frac{\mathcal{E}^2}{1 + F \sin^2 \dfrac{\delta}{2}} \tag{8.61}$$

$\delta$ being the phase difference at the position in the pattern under consideration. At a maximum, $\delta = 2m\pi$, and therefore, $I_0 = \mathcal{E}^2$. At a neighboring point (corresponding to the maximum for a wavelength $\lambda + \delta\lambda$), the intensity will be

$$I' = \frac{\mathcal{E}^2}{1 + F \sin^2 (m + \delta m)\pi} \tag{8.62}$$

For $m$ integral, this becomes

$$I' = \frac{\mathcal{E}^2}{1 + F \sin^2 \delta\, m\pi} \tag{8.63}$$

If, for a first approximation, it is assumed that the peak intensity of the envelope in Figure 8.48 is the same as the peak intensity of the maxima which lie beneath it, then the intensity at the midpoint between the maxima is 81 per cent $\times \frac{1}{2} = .405\, I_0 = .405\, \mathcal{E}^2$. Equating this value to $I'$ as given by Equation 8.63 yields

$$\sin^2 \tfrac{1}{2}\pi\, \delta m = \frac{1.469}{F} \tag{8.64}$$

the factor $\frac{1}{2}$ applying because the distance from the midpoint to a maximum is $\frac{1}{2}\delta m$. Since for the small angles involved, the angle is equal to its sign

$$\delta m = \frac{1}{1.301\sqrt{F}} \tag{8.65}$$

When the difference between the envelope and the actual value of the maxima are taken into account, this solution becomes

$$\delta m = \frac{1}{1.49\sqrt{F}} \tag{8.66}$$

At the maximum, $m\lambda = 2t$, where $t$ is the plate separation. Differentiating gives

$$\frac{\lambda}{\delta\lambda} = -\frac{m}{\delta m} \tag{8.67}$$

and thus, substituting from Equation (8.66), the *resolving power* becomes

$$\frac{\lambda}{\delta\lambda} = -1.49m\sqrt{F} \tag{8.68}$$

or

$$\frac{\lambda}{\delta\lambda} = \frac{\lambda}{2.98\ t\sqrt{F}} \tag{8.69}$$

Spectroscopists frequently talk in terms of wave number $(N = 1/\lambda)$ instead of wavelength. The resolving power in terms of the smallest difference in wave number which can be resolved is known as the *resolving limit*, and becomes

$$\delta N = \frac{1}{2.98\ t\sqrt{F}} \tag{8.70}$$

In the literature, the symbol $\delta\nu$ will often be found in reference to the resolving limit. The symbol $\nu$ usually means frequency in optical parlance. Since frequency and wave number have the same dimensions $(cm^{-1})$ and differ only by the factor $c$, in differential form they are the same, and the substitution of $\delta\nu$ for $\delta N$ in Equation (8.70) is valid. In connection with resolving limit, the term "bandwidth" is coming into general use.

**8.56. The Lummer-Gehrcke Plate.** The Lummer-Gehrcke plate[27] is a form of the Fabry-Perot etalon in which the angles of incidence are made sufficiently large that total internal reflection can be enjoyed, eliminating the need for reflective coatings. Before the development of evaporated

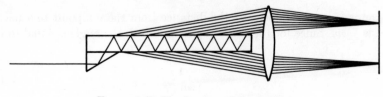

FIGURE 8.49. The Lummer-Gehrcke plate.

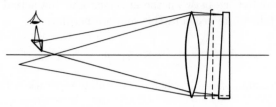

FIGURE 8.50. Optical arrangement of the Fizeau interferometer.

aluminum coatings, this technique had to be resorted to for the UV spectrum, because silver films have a poor reflectivity for ultraviolet. Figure
8.49 shows the Lummer-Gehrcke plate. The prism is provided to bring the
light in at the necessary oblique angle without suffering large losses at
the outer surface.

**8.57. The Fizeau Interferometer.**[28] An arrangement for observing
Fizeau fringes resulting from variations of index and thickness in an optical
component is shown in Figure 8.50. The interference pattern is most easily
understood if it is assumed that the instrument has a doubly reflecting
wedge to give two tilted wave fronts as shown in the insert, which interfere
and give straight fringes parallel to the apex of the wedge.

This arrangement is of particular interest because the path differences
introduced by the test specimen are governed by the condition for a maximum

$$2\mu t = m\lambda \tag{8.71}$$

where $\mu$ is the index of refraction and $t$ is the thickness. Variations in either
$\mu$ or $t$ will cause shifting of the fringes and therefore a contour map of the
variations in the specimen. Variations in $\mu$ or $t$ cannot be separated by the
measurement, but when combined with measurements in an interferometer
such as the Twyman-Green, whose governing formula is given in Equation
(8.48), a simultaneous solution of the two equations can separate the variations caused by index and those caused by thickness (surface distortions).

**8.58. The Michelson Stellar Interferometer.**[29] It is easily shown
that the maxima for the diffraction pattern of a double slit occur at loca-

tions given by

$$d \sin \theta = m\lambda \tag{8.72}$$

where $d$ is the slit separation.

For small $\theta$ the first maximum occurs at

$$\theta = \frac{\lambda}{d} \tag{8.73}$$

these maxima occurring under the envelope of the diffraction pattern of a single slit. When the slit is narrow, the diffraction envelope is quite wide, and when $d$ is large, the interference maxima given by Equation (8.71) are close together, so that they differ very little in height. In the limit, as the slit width approaches zero, the intensity curve in the focal plane approaches a simple $\cos^2$ function, as shown in Figure 8.51.

This analysis assumes a source of zero width, i.e., illumination of the slits by a plane wave front. If the source has finite width, then the maxima can be interpreted as the superposition of maxima from various parts of the slit, and the interference pattern will be spread out in the manner shown in Figure 8.52.

It is evident that a point will be approached where the minima will be filled in and the maxima disappear, and that this will occur for a definable source width. This phenomenon can be used to measure the angular size of a source or the angular separation of two close sources; it was used by Michelson in his *stellar interferometer*[30] for measuring the separation of close double stars and for measuring the angular diameter of some of the larger stars.

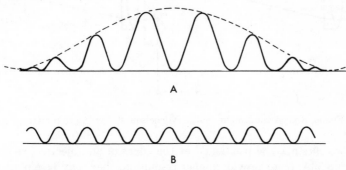

A

B

FIGURE 8.51. Diffraction pattern from a slit. At A a relatively narrow slit is assumed; the single slit envelope is quite wide, and the maxima diminish slowly in height. At B, the slit has theoretically closed to zero, and the single slit pattern becomes a horizontal line, so that all of the maxima are of equal height.

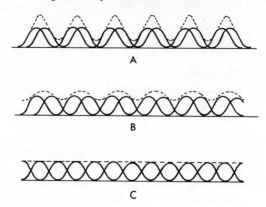

FIGURE 8.52. Effect of finite slit width. The two solid line curves represent the diffraction patterns formed by the opposite edges of the slit; the dotted curves are the result of the superposition. At A, the slit width is relatively small with respect to the separation of the maxima; at B, a wider slit reduces the amplitude of the resultant; at C, the maxima have been completely washed out.

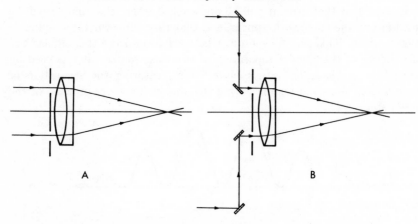

FIGURE 8.53. Arrangement of the Michelson stellar interferometer.

The two slits may be positioned at the edges of an objective, as shown in Figure 8.53A, or to provide higher resolution, they may be mounted on outriggers as shown in Figure 8.53B; the latter arrangement was used by Michelson with the 100-inch Mt. Wilson telescope, the maximum separation of the outboard mirrors being 6 meters.

The analysis of the exact conditions for disappearance of the fringes which

TABLE 8.2. RESOLVING POWER OF VARIOUS SPECTROGRAPHS

| Type of Spectrograph | Resolving Power | Resolving Limit (cm$^{-1}$) |
| --- | --- | --- |
| Ruled diffraction grating | 300,000 | .06 |
| Lummer-Gehrcke plate | 800,000 | .025 |
| Reflection echelon | 2,000,000 | .01 |
| Fabry-Perot etalon | 8,000,000 | .0025 |

are seen under high magnification at the focal plane is not carried out here. It can be shown that for a slit source, the fringes disappear when the condition of Equation (8.73) is satisfied, that is, when the angular width of the source slit $\theta$ is equal to $\lambda/d$. For a circular disc source, the contributions to the intensity from the edges is less than from the center, so that a larger angular extension is required to extinguish the fringes. For a circular disc source, the angular diameter $\theta$ at which the fringes disappear is given by

$$\theta = 1.22 \frac{\lambda}{d} \qquad (8.74)$$

It is interesting that this is exactly equal to the resolving power of a telescope aperture equal to $d$.

For two point sources, separated by an angle $\theta$, the condition for fringe disappearance is

$$\theta = \tfrac{1}{2} \frac{\lambda}{d} \qquad (8.75)$$

The principle of this technique has been adopted in radio astronomy, and the precision for both the optical and the radio case has been increased by making continuous measurements of the light from the separated mirrors and correlating the results as a function of the mirror separation.[31]

**8.59. Resolving Power of Various Spectrographs.** For comparative purposes, the resolving power and resolving limit of several different forms of spectrograph are given in the following table. These are representative only, and various arrangements in each of the categories leads to a considerable range of actual values in practice.

## INTERFEROMETRIC SPECTROSCOPY

**8.60. The Fourier Transform.** The practice of *interferometric spectroscopy* makes use of the Fourier Transform, and this is also of fundamental importance in the following chapter in connection with optical transfer functions, so that a reminder of the nature of the concept is in order.

Any function, $f(x)$ (subject to certain minor conditions as to its form) may be considered to be composed of the superposition of a series of continuous periodic functions of suitable amplitudes and frequencies. Now, a periodic function of frequency $u$ can be represented by $F(u)e^{ixu}$, so that the original function, considered as a summation of periodic functions, becomes

$$f(x) = \int_{-\infty}^{\infty} F(u)e^{ixu} \, du \tag{8.76}$$

The function

$$F(u) = \frac{1}{2\pi} \int_{-\infty}^{\infty} f(x)e^{-ixu} \, dx \tag{8.77}$$

which gives the amplitudes $F(u)$ of the periodic terms of frequency $u$, is called the *Fourier Transform* of Equation (8.76).[32] Whenever $f(x)$ or $F(u)$ can be determined, the other can be computed from the Fourier Transform relationship. This concept is of extraordinary power in many problems of analysis in communications and in optics. It is discussed at somewhat greater length in Chapter 9.

**8.61. Illumination in a Two-beam Interferometer.** Consider a two-beam interferometer (for example, a Twyman-Green or a Michelson), in which the two beams are of equal intensity (this restriction merely simplifies the mathematics). If the path difference between the two beams for the central order is $s$, then, for illumination of wavelength $\lambda$, the two beams have the amplitudes

$$\mathcal{E}_1 = \mathcal{E}_0 \, e^{-i\omega} \tag{8.78}$$

and

$$\mathcal{E}_2 = \mathcal{E}_0 \, e^{-i(\omega+\delta)} \tag{8.79}$$

where

$$\delta = \frac{2\pi s}{\lambda} \tag{8.80}$$

Adding these two amplitudes, and squaring vectorially for the intensity gives, for the combined intensity at the output of the interferometer

$$I = 2 \, \mathcal{E}_0^2 \, (1 + \cos \delta) \tag{8.81}$$

If the output of the interferometer is measured, and the path difference $s$ is varied, then the output for a particular wavelength will vary in accordance with Equation (8.81), which is seen to be a periodic function of $s$ with

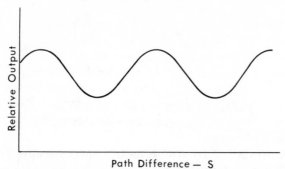

FIGURE 8.54. Output of the modulated interferometer for a monochromatic input.

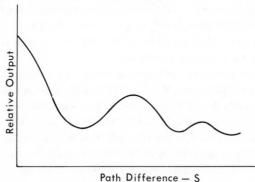

FIGURE 8.55. Modulated interferometer output for a quasimonochromatic source.

a frequency $1/\lambda$, when the definition of Equation (8.80) is used. The output, for monochromatic input, will have a form like Figure 8.54.

No light is strictly monochromatic, because its wavetrain has finite length, so that for a real input, the output function, $f(s)$, will be the composition of an infinite series of periodic terms of varying frequency, $1/\lambda$. For a quasi-monochromatic source, the output will be something like Figure 8.55.

For a heterochromatic source, the output function $f(s)$ will be more complex and will be the composition of all of the periodic functions of frequency $1/\lambda$ which make up the source radiation.

Now, this set of periodic functions is the *spectrum* of the source, and a measurement of the interferometer output, $f(s)$ permits application of the Fourier Transform relation of Equations (8.76) and (8.77) to determine the spectrum. These equations become

$$f(s) = \int_{-\infty}^{\infty} I_\lambda \, e^{jd(1/\lambda)} \, d\left(\frac{1}{\lambda}\right) \tag{8.82}$$

$$I_\lambda = \frac{1}{2\pi} \int_{-\infty}^{\infty} f(s) \, e^{-jd(1/\lambda)} \, ds \tag{8.83}$$

The intensity plots, like Figures 8.54 and 8.55 are referred to as *interferograms,* and the interferometers used in this fashion are often called *interferometer modulators.*

**8.62. Advantages of Interoferometric Spectroscopy.** The advantage of the interferogram technique for the determination of spectra lies in the fact that the detector is looking at all of the spectrum all of the time, instead of measuring the intensity of a single spectral line. In the conventional spectrograph, as the slit is made narrower to improve the attainable resolution, the illumination is reduced, and in many situations, the condition of energy limited resolution prevails. In the interferometric technique, there is no slit to limit the energy available.

The resolution is determined by the range of adjustment which is provided for the path difference. There is, of course, a resolution limit imposed by the energy available in a given spectral line, since the resolution is limited essentially by system "noise," and if the energy in a line is less than the noise which shows up in the interferogram, it will not be resolved. This is, however, a different concept from the energy-limited resolution as defined in Section 8.54; in the interferometer technique, all of the energy which can enter the aperture is utilized continuously.

There is also a gain resulting from the fact that all of the spectrum is being analyzed simultaneously, so that for a given time of observation, there is more "information" being obtained. On the basis of information theory, it can be shown that in interferometric spectroscopy there is a gain of $\frac{1}{2}\sqrt{N}$ over a conventional spectrograph, where $N$ is the number of slit widths comprising the spectral band being analyzed in the conventional spectrograph. The gain is in terms of the *signal-to-noise ratio.*

A photosensitive detector is used to measure the energy; the interferogram cannot be recorded on a photographic plate, as would the spectrum analyzed by the conventional spectrograph, since the intensity variation is a variation in time; in some respects this is a disadvantage. However, the analysis of a conventional spectrum by scanning a photosensitive detector along the focal plane is also a frequently used technique. The detectors used are usually thermal detectors, such as the Golay cell or bolometers (see Section 7.47 *et seq.*), since these detectors have a nearly flat spectral response, and less calibration is needed.

**8.63. Instrumentation for Interferometric Modulation.** The interferometer modulator requires a means for changing the optical path differ-

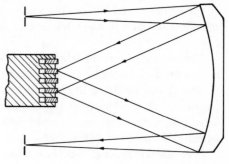

FIGURE 8.56. Lamellar grating of Strong and Vanasse.

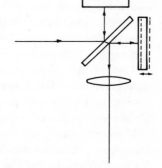

FIGURE 8.57. Michelson interferometer with oscillating mirror.

ence of the two beams as a function of time. Usually the motion is achieved by oscillation, and the output is recorded on a pen recorder or similar device. In some cases, it is displayed on an oscilloscope, where a number of cycles of oscillation can be integrated.

Figures 8.56 and 8.57 show two types of interferometer modulator. That shown in Figure 8.56 is a lamellar grating as used by Strong and Vanasse[34] to measure water vapor absorption. Alternate facets of the grating are formed on a sliding member which, in the particular device fabricated, moved a distance of 4 cm.

The instrument of Figure 8.57 is a Michelson interferometer, in which one of the mirrors is oscillated.

It is obvious that extreme care must be taken not to disturb the alignment of the mirrors during the oscillation; the surface of the moving mirror must move through exactly parallel planes (to a few seconds of arc).

## OPTICAL TESTING

**8.64. General.** Regardless of the skill and care of the designer of an optical system, its actual performance depends eventually upon the ability of the optician and the optical engineer to manufacture it to the required specifications and to assemble and adjust it to the necessary level of precision.

The nature of optical fabrication is such that the optician knows what he has produced only by the results of optical tests which he performs upon it, and it has been truthfully said that any optical surface which can be tested can be produced. In this day, with tolerances for some optical surfaces (laser windows, for example) being of the order of 1/100 of a wavelength, this is not an idle statement.

It is not surprising, therefore, that there are innumerable techniques for the testing of optical surfaces, components and systems. Even those tests which find reasonably broad use are much too numerous to describe, and there are an endless variety of special tests which have been devised for specific purposes. It is the intent here to describe only a few of the most general and most basic forms of optical test, which are universally used, and upon which most of the specific test procedures have been based.

Tests of optical components and optical systems by means of the Twyman-Green and the Kosters interferometers, and others, have been described under the sections on interferometry. Interferometric testing is in almost universal use for high performance components and systems; indeed, only interferometric testing has the necessary precision to show the deviations from perfection which occur in systems performing close to the levels set by diffraction. For the same reason, interferometers did not come into common use for optical testing until the skills of the designer and the optician had reached a level where systems performing close to the diffraction limit could be produced, and that has been in rather recent years. The tests which are described below are less sensitive than interferometry; they have been in wide use for generations and are still universally used for testing less critical systems and for bringing systems into a state of correction where interferometry can be usefully applied. An interferometer is excellent for showing departures from perfection from a fraction of a wavelength to a few wavelengths; when the departure is of the order of hundreds of wavelengths, interferometry is of little value.

The final test of any optical instrument, of course, is its performance under the design conditions of use. But it is not always convenient or practicable to simulate these conditions, and in any event it is necessary to test the separate components of the instrument before they are assembled into a complete package.

**8.65. Optical Fabrication.** The techniques of optical fabrication are not a part of the subject matter of this volume, but a brief description of the general principles will be of value in showing why optical testing is such an essential part of the fabrication procedure.

FIGURE 8.58. The spherometer.

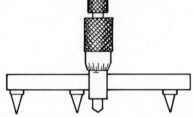

Except for a few very special problems, optical fabrication consists of producing a polished surface on glass which conforms to the size and shape specified by the designer. This is done by rubbing the surface with an abrasive, using successively finer grades, the final finishing being performed with a polishing compound, such as jeweler's rouge (iron oxide), which is really an abrasive also. The two operations of "grinding" and "polishing" are usually distinguished from each other, and in most optical shops, these two procedures are performed in separate rooms.

The abrasive or polishing compound is carried in a liquid vehicle (usually water) and is applied by means of a tool or *lap*. In grinding, the tool may be of metal, or it may be an abrasive wheel; in polishing, the tool is called a *lap*, and is composed of a semi-hard substance, such as pitch, rosin, or wax, which can be shaped to the surface by heat and pressure prior to the polishing task.

The nature of the polishing action on glass has been a subject of dispute for decades, and no really satisfactory answer is yet available; there is no general agreement as to whether the surface is worn away or is locally deformed. The shapes of surfaces may be altered significantly by appropriate distribution of the polishing action—the process is known as *figuring*. It is a required operation for the fabrication of highly precise aspheric surfaces.

**8.66. Rough Curvature Tests.** In the grinding stage of fabrication, the surfaces are tested by gages, of which the spherometer and the template are most often used. Figure 8.58 shows a typical form of *spherometer* for measuring spherical curvatures. The instrument rests upon three feet, located at the corners of an equilateral triangle, and a micrometer at the center measures the *sagitta* of the spherical surface, as shown in the insert. Measurements can be made to an accuracy of .0001 inch, although .0005 inch is more practicable.

Templates, as shown in Figure 8.59, are also in common use.

**8.67. Test Plates.** When a quantity of optical components are to be made to a given specification, it is customary to make a master *test plate*, whose surface is the inverse of the surface to be produced. The finished

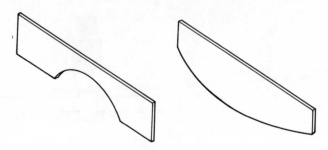

FIGURE 8.59. Templates.

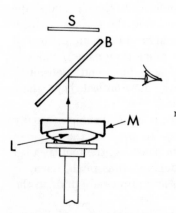

FIGURE 8.60. Testing an optical component with a master test plate.

article is then tested on this test plate by means of Fizeau interference fringes, as shown in Figure 8.60. A diffuse source of illumination is used, white light being feasible, but partially monochromatic light is better; a neon lamp is a common source for this purpose.

Fizeau fringes, as described in Sections 2.56 and 8.57, are seen in the air film between the test plate and the test piece; these represent a contour map of the surface referred to the test plate, and indicate the need, if any, for further polishing. Pressure upon one side of the air film indicates, by the direction of shift of the fringes, whether the observed contours represent "hills" or "valleys." By movement and pressure, the operator can alter the air film so as to show the desired number of fringes. Since the light traverses the air film twice, each fringe represents a change in the film thickness of $\frac{1}{2}$ wavelength. A typical fringe appearance is shown in Figure 8.61.

**8.68. Testing Objectives.** Objectives, in the form of either mirrors or lenses, are usually the components which require the most critical testing, and they are usually the largest components which are produced in the

FIGURE 8.61. Appearance of Fizeau fringes under a test plate. The photo at the left was obtained with a standard quasi-monochromatic source (sodium vapor lamp); the photo at the right was obtained with a He-Ne laser source. The improvement in the fringe contrast with the laser illumination is evident.

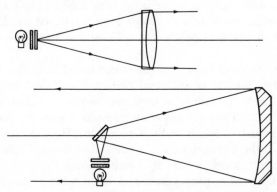

FIGURE 8.62. Optical arrangements of lens and mirror collimators.

optical shop. Almost without exception, they are designed to be used with an infinite object distance, so that their testing usually requires an arrangement which will produce *collimated* light, namely, a test object at infinity.

This is accomplished in either one of two ways. For the smaller sizes of objectives, or if a quantity is to be tested, it is usually most convenient to provide a *collimator*, which is simply a highly corrected objective with an illuminated target at its focus. Figure 8.62 shows examples of lens and mirror collimators. They must be of high quality if they are to be used to test high-quality objectives, although the fact that they are used only in the neighborhood of the axis and that they are generally of long focal length

makes a high degree of quality fairly easily obtainable. In fact, a paraboloidal mirror makes an excellent collimator for most purposes, although,
as has been previously pointed out, its useful field of view is extremely
narrow.

The collimator must be large enough to completely fill the entrance
pupil of the system under test, otherwise the test is invalid. This requirement often leads to the construction of very large diameter collimators.
It is possible to test an optical system by separately testing partial zones
of the aperture, but this is a laborious task and requires statistical analysis
of the results, so it is not generally done. In the case of the 200-inch telescope, this was done, auto-collimating against a flat as described below.
However, this was an unusual case, and the flat used was specially made
for the purpose; it was 120 inches in diameter and was itself the largest
flat which had ever been made.

It is desirable that the collimator have a focal length greater than that
of the system under test—a factor of ten is preferable. The required perfection of the collimator in terms of angle is thus reduced by this factor. To
test a system for off-axis points, the collimator is turned through the required angle.

When large diameter objectives have to be tested, it is often inconvenient
to provide a collimator of sufficient diameter and focal length, and the
technique of *auto-collimation* is used, as shown in Figure 8.63, and as
previously described and illustrated in connection with the Kosters double
prism interferometer (Section 8.45, Figure 8.40). Here the source is placed
at the focus of the test system, and a collimated beam of light is projected
onto a flat mirror, which returns the beam through the system to its focus,
where it is examined or photographed. A beam splitter is used to separate
the projected target and the returned image.

In this type of system, the error is doubled due to the double passage
of light through the system. For points which are not exactly on the optical
axis, the light path is not the same on the return as on the outward journey,
and in some cases, this effect may alter the appearance of defects.

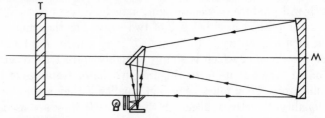

FIGURE 8.63. Mirror autocollimator. T indicates a flat being
tested.

For very high performance systems, of course, interferometric methods are to be preferred, and techniques such as the Kosters prism and the scatter plate permit such testing without large size test components. Interference methods are of value, however, only when the system is at a state of perfection which is near the limit of testing capability of the methods described here.

**8.69. Test Targets.** The most common type of test target is a simple pinhole. A great deal can be determined about the state of correction of the system by the microscopic examination of the image which it forms of a pinhole, especially if this image is examined slightly inside of and outside of focus, as well as at the focus itself. The pinhole should be of such a size that its nominal image, as formed by the system under test is approximately the diameter of the central maximum of the Airy disc. If it is too large, the diffraction image will be obscured, and if it is too small, it is almost impossible to get enough illumination. These images may, of course, be photographed and examined at greater leisure.

For the testing of photographic objectives, it is customary to use a patterned target. A target in common use is the tri-bar target illustrated in Figure 8.64; it is standard for the testing of military photographic lenses. The pattern is particularly useful for comparing resolution in two perpendicular directions—astigmatism being a matter of particular concern in photographic lenses.

Another type of test target is the Siemen's Star, illustrated in Figure 8.65. This target is very convenient for determining resolution, because, at the point where the space between the spokes equals the resolution limit, the spokes can no longer be separately defined, and there is a blur at the center of the star whose diameter is a direct measure of the resolution. The resolution is $\pi$ times the diameter divided by the number of spokes,

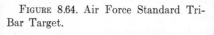

FIGURE 8.64. Air Force Standard Tri-Bar Target.

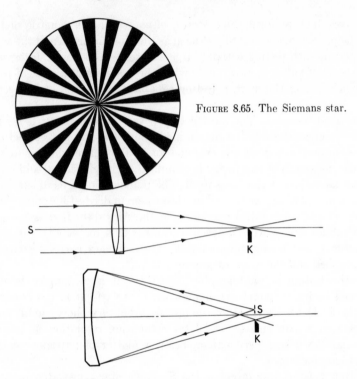

FIGURE 8.65. The Siemans star.

FIGURE 8.66. Arrangement of the Foucault test. The upper figure shows a knife-edge placed at the focus of a lens imaging a distant point source. The lower figure shows the Foucault test arrangement for a mirror tested at center of curvature.

hence to determine the resolution limit it is not necessary to measure to that degree of fineness.

**8.70. The Foucault Test.** The Foucault test[35] is perhaps the classic optical test for objectives. It is simple, reliable, fairly precise, and can be realized with very simple apparatus. Used most often for the testing of concave mirrors, for which no optical test components are required, it can also be used for testing lenses if an auxiliary flat or collimator of a diameter equal to the lens being tested is available.

The Foucault test actually plots the longitudinal spherical aberration of the component being tested. The arrangement is shown in Figure 8.66; it consists of a light source, a pinhole or slit, and a "knife-edge." A discarded razor blade makes an excellent knife edge.

Figure 8.67 shows the principle of the Foucault test. The component

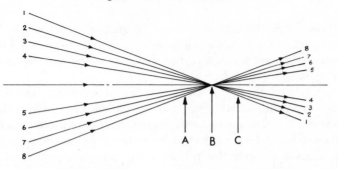

FIGURE 8.67. Principle of the Foucault test. If the knife-edge is introduced at the plane A, a shadow is seen encroaching on the mirror from below; if the knife-edge is placed at C, the direction of encroachment of the shadow is reversed. With the knife-edge in the plane B, there is uniform darkening of the mirror.

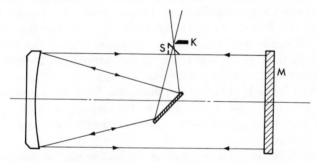

FIGURE 8.68. Foucault test of a mirror at focus, using an auxiliary flat. The source is at S; a beam-splitter permits working on axis.

under test forms an image of the pinhole, which is placed at a suitable point. If the test component is a concave mirror, the pinhole is placed at its center of curvature, and the image is then formed at the same point. A slight displacement of the pinhole off the optical axis brings the image symmetrically on the other side of the axis and does not significantly affect the results if the angular displacement is no more than a degree or so. If the component is a lens, an auxiliary flat is used, and the pinhole and image are at the focus of the lens. This arrangement is shown in Figure 8.68. A similar arrangement may be used for testing a compound telescope, such as a Cassegrainian (see Section 6.29) at focus.

If the image of the pinhole is perfect, it will have a size determined by the size of the pinhole and the diffraction image of the component, and if the knife-edge is placed at right-angles to the axis and gradually brought across this image, the illumination will be gradually blotted out. The eye is placed as shown to obtain a Maxwellian view of the mirror, and when the knife-edge is brought across a perfect image of the pinhole, the mirror will appear to darken *uniformly*.

Now, in general, the mirror will have spherical aberration. This is particularly true of a paraboloidal mirror with the pinhole and image at the center of curvature. It will be remembered that a spherical mirror forms a theoretically perfect image for an object at its center of curvature; a paraboloidal mirror forms a theoretically perfect image for an object at infinity. A spherical mirror at focus and a paraboloidal mirror at center of curvature will display considerable spherical aberration.

Figure 8.69 shows the ray structure in the neighborhood of the focus of an optical system with undercorrected spherical aberration (rays from the edge have a shorter intersection length than rays from the central zone). If the Foucault knife-edge is now brought across this bundle from the bottom, at the distance where the paraxial rays cross the axis, it will first block out the rays which come from the upper edge of the mirror, then progressively those closer and closer to the center. The observer will see a shadow coming across the mirror from the top.

If the knife-edge is placed at the distance $s$ from the mirror, where the marginal rays are in focus, the shadow will first appear on the mirror at the point B′ and will appear to move downward with increasing penetration of the knife-edge.

Thus, for different axial positions of the knife-edge, the shadow pattern which is produced upon the mirror varies. The significant point, however, is that for any position of the knife-edge along the axis, when it crosses

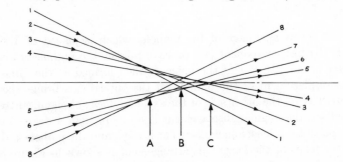

FIGURE 8.69. Ray geometry in the focal region for a case of positive spherical aberration. It can be seen that, with the knife-edge introduced in the plane B (circle of least confusion), it simultaneously cuts rays from the upper edge and the lower intermediate zone (rays 1 and 6).

the axis, it cuts the rays from the zone which has its focus at that point, and that zone on the mirror will darken simultaneously at both top and bottom.

This is the basis for the quantitative use of the Foucault test. The mirror is divided into concentric zones, and the point along the axis where each of these zones darkens uniformly is found. This point is the focus of that zone. By measuring a sufficient number of zones, the surface contour in terms of its variation in focal length is determined, and this can be compared with the theoretical variation of the required surface. It is customary to segregate the zones by means of masks, although for the experienced observer, a notched bar placed across the center of the mirror may be sufficient. In practice, the knife-edge is usually moved horizontally, rather than vertically as drawn in the illustrations. Often a slit is used to give greater illumination, since the errors in an optical surface are infrequently other than symmetrical about the axis, so that the shadows are observed across a diameter rather than over the entire aperture.

The Foucault test is particularly useful for testing aspheric surfaces, such as paraboloidal mirrors and concave mirrors of other shapes, since the test need not be made under conditions where the image is even theoretically perfect. The accuracy of focal length measurements is usually of the order of .01 inch, although with more complicated apparatus, higher accuracies can be achieved.

When the knife-edge is placed at a distance corresponding to the minimum circle of confusion, and brought to a point about midway across the light bundle, the observer sees a shadow pattern on the mirror which may be likened to a surface illuminated by a light at grazing incidence, and the shadows then give an effect of relief, with the mirror surface apparently assuming the shape which it possesses with respect to a shape which would produce a perfect image at the knife-edge. Figure 8.70 shows the appearance of a paraboloid tested at center of curvature. The "doughnut" appearance is characteristic of the paraboloid with respect to a sphere.

**8.71. The Hartmann Test.** The Hartmann test[36] is of interest because for many decades it was the standard test for astronomical objectives; it has largely been replaced by interferometric methods. In principle, it is similar to the Foucault test, but it is photographic and gives a more complete measurement of the system being tested. The arrangement is shown in Figure 8.71.

Small zones on the mirror (or lens) across a number of diameters are isolated by means of a mask, as shown in the Figure. The zones are made small enough so that there is unlikely to be any variation in the surface contour within a zone, and thus they essentially isolate rays.

FIGURE 8.70. Appearance of a paraboloid under the Foucault test at center of curvature. The surface may be compared to the contour shown below, imagined to be illuminated by light at grazing incidence from the right.

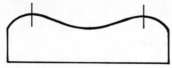

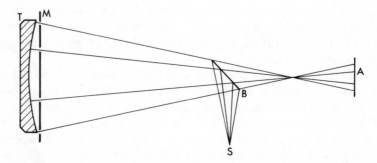

FIGURE 8.71. Arrangement for the Hartmann test: (T) test mirror, (M) zonal mask, (B) beam splitter, (A) photographic plate.

A photographic plate is exposed at varying positions along the axis, both inside and outside of focus. The intersections of the "rays" with the plane of the photographic plate at various positions are thus determined. From this information, a three-dimensional picture of the paths of the rays can thus be generated, and comparison of this picture with the theoretical ray paths for the component shows its deviations from the ideal.

**8.72. Other Tests—The Gaviola and Zernicke Tests.** The Gaviola test[37] locates the actual centers of curvature of individual zones on a mirror, as opposed to finding their axial intersections, as in the Foucault test, or their intersections in a plane, as in the Hartmann test. Its principle is illustrated for a parabola in Figure 8.72. An individual zone, s, isolated

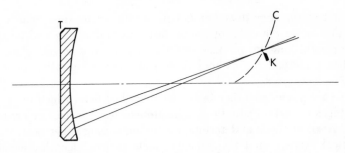

FIGURE 8.72. Arrangement for the Gaviola test. C is the caustic of the mirror. The caustic is mathematically the envelope of the normals.

as in the Hartmann test, has a focus at the point s'. The zone is considered to be spherical, and the knife-edge and pinhole are moved together, so that the "focus" being determined is the center of curvature of the zone.

The locus of the centers of curvature of zones across a diameter, as shown in the Figure, is called the *caustic* of the parabola. Mathematically, the caustic will be recognized as the envelope of the normals to the curve.

In performing the test, pinhole and knife-edge are moved together, using the beam-splitter arrangement as shown in Figure 8.66, and the rectangular coordinates of each of the centers of curvature are measured. A cross-slide mechanism to carry the pinhole and knife-edge is necessary. Thus the actual caustic is plotted and then compared with the theoretical curve.

The Gaviola test is capable of somewhat higher accuracy than the Foucault test, although it is a much more time-consuming operation. Its advantage lies in the fact that it is not restricted to mirrors of any particular relative aperture, as is the case for the Foucault test, which cannot be applied when the relative aperture of the mirror under test is too great to permit all of the light to enter the eye of the observer. The limit on relative aperture for the Foucault test is about $f/2.5$. Neither the Hartmann test nor the Gaviola test have this restriction, because they do not require the Maxwellian view.

In the Zernicke test,[38] a small phase-retarding disc is placed in the Airy disc of a selected concentric zone, and the eye is placed behind this disc for the Maxwellian view. Interference between the phase-retarded beam through the disc and the light which passes around the disc because of spherical aberration produces highly colored interference patterns which show the contours of the mirror in much the same way that the Foucault test shadows show them, but these are more readily interpretable because of the color contrasts.

The Z-discs, as they are called, must be small enough to cover the central maximum of the Airy disc, but not its secondary maxima, which means they must be on the order of .01 to .001 mm in diameter and must have the proper thickness to produce retardations of a few wavelengths. Burch describes a method for making these discs by precipitation of rosin in water.[39]

There are numerous other tests, not described here, which have special advantages in certain situations. The Ronchi test[40] in particular, is quite useful. Also, methods and techniques for measuring other characteristics of optical systems and components, such as focal lengths, location of principal planes and nodal points, magnification, and other parameters, are not described here. Details may be found in the literature.

**8.73. The Optical Bench.** The standard laboratory device for making measurements on optical systems and components of small or moderate size is the optical bench, illustrated in Figure 8.73.

The optical bench is similar to a lathe bed, the bench proper consisting of parallel sliding ways, furnished with a scale. It is a general custom to make measurements on optical systems in millimeters. Carriages are provided for light sources, for measuring devices, such as microscopes or photo detectors, and for the optical parts. Vertical, horizontal, and rotational adjustments on the carriages for the optics and the measuring devices are customary.

A common device is the *nodal slide* for the optics carriage. With this device, the lens may be translated along its axis with respect to the rotational axis of the carriage. This utilizes the principle that the image formed by a lens does not shift when the lens is rotated about an axis passing through its nodal point.

FIGURE 8.73. An Optical Bench. (*Courtesy Gaertner Scientific Corp.*)

## OPTICAL ALIGNMENT

**8.74. General.** Optical techniques are widely used for alignment, as in the erection of jigs and fixtures in the aircraft and shipbuilding industries, the alignment of rotating machinery in power plants, etc., alignment of parts in heavy machine tools, and similar applications. This area really represents a specialized application of surveying techniques, and the use of conventional surveying instruments, such as transits and levels, in these areas has been common for a long time. In recent years, however, special instruments and accessories for these tasks have been developed and are commercially available.

**8.75. The Alignment Telescope.** The basic instrument for optical alignment purposes is the *alignment telescope*, illustrated in Figure 8.74.

The special features of the alignment telescope which distinguish it from other telescopes are the provision of a light source and beam splitter for auto-collimation, a mounting which is accurately aligned to the optical axis, and frequently the provision of micrometer flats in front of the objective. All of these features are included in the instrument illustrated in Figure 8.74. The mounting is a spherical ball with its center exactly ($\pm$.0001 inch) on the optical axis. The micrometer flats are thick plane parallel plates, which can be rotated about mutually perpendicular axes. The effect of rotation is to displace the optical axis by a small distance.

**8.76. Basic Principles.** In general, the purpose of optical alignment

FIGURE 8.74. An alignment telescope. The model shown was designed primarily for aircraft tooling applications. A penta prism or "optical square" mounted in front of the objective provides a precise right-angle turn of the line of sight; behind the telescope is a typical alignment target. (*Courtesy Farrand Optical Co.*)

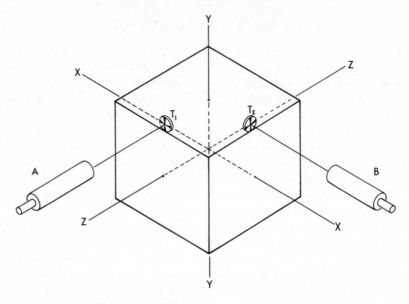

FIGURE 8.75. Optical alignment with targets.

is to locate and orient an object at a distance to a reference set of coordinates. This object has six degrees of freedom—three in translation and
three in rotation. The purpose of the optical alignment instrumentation is
to constrain the object in all six of these degrees of freedom.

Two basic techniques are used: alignment and auto-collimation. Alignment constrains the object in translation; auto-collimation constrains it
in rotation. To facilitate the application of optical instrumentation, the
object to be located is usually provided with alignment targets and auto-
collimating mirrors.

Figure 8.75 shows how translational constraint is imposed by optical
means. The object is furnished with two alignment targets, and two alignment telescopes are mounted at reference points so that their lines of sight
are perpendicular. Telescope A provides constraint on the object against
translation in $x$ and $y$; telescope B provides constraint in $y$ and $z$. Together,
they can be used to locate the object in all three translational degrees of
freedom. Actually, there is redundant constraint, since each telescope takes
care of two of the three possible degrees of freedom.

Of course, it is not necessary that the lines of sight of the two telescopes
be at right angles to each other, and in a particular application, this may
not be convenient. Any reasonably large angle will suffice, although the
accuracy of the setting will be reduced unless the angle is 90°. The usual

accuracies for optical alignment are .002 inch or 2 arc-seconds, whichever is smaller.

The micrometer flats on the alignment telescopes provide a means for measuring the actual displacement of the object from its ideal position. The lateral shift of the line of sight introduced by the flats is independent of the target distance.

In a practical application, the third degree of freedom (say $z$ in Figure 8.75) may be constrained by making a linear measurement along the $Z$-axis.

Figure 8.76 shows how auto-collimation provides constraint in rotation. The telescope is trained on a mirror mounted on the object, and the projected image of the target reticle from the telescope is returned to the telescope focal plane. The plane of the mirror is thus established normal to the telescope line of sight.

Again, two telescopes are shown, each of which provides two-axis constraint—telescope A constrains rotation about the $x$ & and $y$-axes, and telescope B constrains rotation about the $y$ and $z$-axes. As in alignment, the attainable accuracy is about 2 arc-seconds.

Figure 8.77 shows a variety of accessories which are available for optical alignment applications.

**8.77 Automatic Auto-collimators.** For special applications, photoelectric auto-collimators have been developed, of which an example is shown in Figure 8.78.

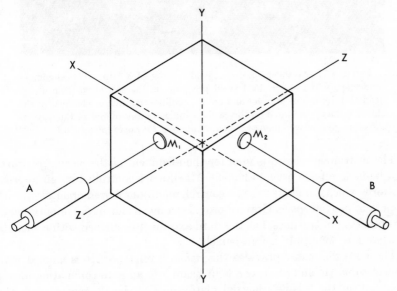

FIGURE 8.76. Optical alignment by auto-collimation.

FIGURE 8.77. Arrangement for optical trueing of a lathe. The alignment telescope (in the foreground) is set precisely on the axis of rotation of the headstock by use of a target and an auto collimating mirror clamped in the chuck. A target mounted on the carriage indicates any runout of the ways as the carriage is moved along the bed. (*Courtesy Farrand Optical Co.*)

The instrument shown is used for the alignment of the inertial platform of a ballistic missile prior to launch. Missiles are controlled by an internal platform which, under gyroscopic control, maintains a fixed orientation with respect to inertial space. Gravity provides a means for initial orientation of this platform in two axes, but the third axis must be aligned with respect to latitude and longitude before launch.

The auto-collimator provides this *azimuth* reference. It is aligned with respect to north, and projects a light beam into an auto-collimating mirror mounted on the missile's inertial platform. The signals generated in the

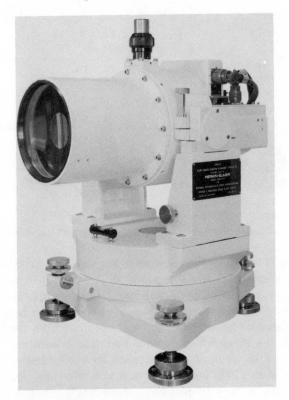

FIGURE 8.78. An automatic alignment theodelite. (*Courtesy Perkin-Elmer Corp.*)

collimator's electronic system are fed to the missile platform control to bring its mirror into precise collimation just before the missile is launched.

In the instrument shown, the measurement is made by dividing the light beam returned from the auto-collimating mirror into two parts, each of which falls upon a photodetector. When the output signals of these photodetectors are equal, the light beam is exactly on the optical axis of the instrument. Instruments for alignment about two axes are also used.

**8.78. Alignment Polarimeters.** Figure 8.79 illustrates the schematic arrangement of an *alignment polarimeter*, by means of which the orientation of a distant object with respect to rotation about the line of sight can be determined. Such an instrument, when combined with the alignment properties of an ordinary alignment telescope, makes it possible to provide constraint about three axes of rotation from a single station. Thus, addition of the polarimeter to telescope A of Figure 8.76 would eliminate the need

FIGURE 8.79. An alignment polarimeter. (*Courtesy Perkin-Elmer Corp.*)

for telescope B for rotational constraint. For translational constraint along the Z-axis, telescope B is still required as in Figure 8.75, or a means for measuring linear distance along this axis. In many applications, however, translational constraint along all three axes may not be necessary.

In the alignment polarimeter, the light returned from the target object is polarized in a plane which depends upon the orientation of the target about the line of sight. The instrument merely measures the plane of polarization of this light and compares it to a reference.

The principle is very simple; the instrumentation is not simple if high accuracy is required. A polarizing device may be used visually to determine the plane of polarization of a light beam, since when the polarizing plane of the device is at right angles to the plane of polarization of the light, the illumination is at a minimum. If the device is a perfect polarizer, and the light is completely polarized in an ideal plane, the illumination will be zero. But these ideal conditions are never met in practice, and in addition, the eye introduces an error of measurement, so that visual polarimeters are not capable of an accuracy better than about 0.1°.

In the automatic alignment polarimeter, the measurement is made electrically on the output of a rotating polarizer. This polarizer is made with high precision from highly selected polarizing materials, and the measurement is made in an electronic system which integrates many cycles of maximum and minimum illumination as the polarizer is rotated. Such instruments are capable of a precision of a few seconds of arc.

**8.79. Accuracy of Optical Measurements.** The accuracy of optical measurements is limited by the diffraction of optical apertures, which has been discussed at some length in previous chapters. For measurements made by optical instruments in combination with the eye, the angular resolution limit of $\lambda/D$ for a rectangular aperture, and $1.22\lambda/D$ for a circular aperture, essentially define the limits of precision to which measurements can be made. It is possible to approach these fundamental limits very closely in actual instrumentation.

In interferometric measurements, the fundamental limitation on precision is imposed by the degree of coherence which can be achieved in the light. Complete coherence implies an infinite wave train of infinite extent; departure from coherence is imposed by the necessarily finite length of wave trains and by the finite dimensions of apertures.

When measurements are made with photosensitive detectors, it is possible in certain applications to record the illumination in a focal plane to a resolution level finer than that of the aperture involved. *Under certain conditions*, auto-correlation and cross-correlation techniques may be applied to these recorded signals to obtain results of higher precision than could, with the same instrumentation, be achieved by visual means. An example is the photoelectric stellar interferometer mentioned in Section 8.58. It will be noted, however, that the precision is intimately associated with the separation of the two receivers and is limited by the same condition of $\lambda/D$, where $D$ is the separation. All that the technique accomplishes is to place less rigid restrictions on the individual receivers and their mechanical interconnection.

**8.80. Optical Distance Measurement.** The measurement of small distances by means of interferometry has been described earlier. Optical devices for measuring large distances have recently been developed. These are sometimes referred to as "optical radar," although the origin of the word "radar" disqualifies it for application to the optical spectrum.

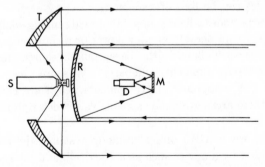

FIGURE 8.80. Arrangement of a pulse-type optical radar system: (S) pulsed light source, (T) transmitter (paraboloidal mirror), (R) receiving primary mirror, (M) secondary mirror, (D) detector.

Two methods have been applied, both of which are used in and were originally developed for, radar range-measuring systems. These may be called, to emphasize the analogy, pulse systems and continuous-wave (CW) systems.

Figure 8.80 illustrates an example of pulse-type optical ranging equipment. A short-duration pulse of light is generated in the arc lamp by capacitator discharge and is projected by the transmitter to the target. In a typical case, a pulse may have a duration of a few microseconds, and a rise time of a fraction of a microsecond, and may contain a joule of energy.

The outgoing pulse is observed by a photodetector, and electronic circuits measure the time interval between this and the return pulse from the target. This time interval, multiplied by the velocity of light, is double the range to the target. The time interval is approximately 1 $\mu$sec for each 150 meters of range. Electronic circuitry can be devised to measure time intervals of the order of a fraction of a nanosecond, so that the accuracy of the equipment is limited primarily by the shape and the repeatability of the pulses.

Electronic gating techniques are used, so that the measurement is made on the "center of gravity" of the pulse, rather than on its leading edge; accuracies of the order of one meter can be achieved.

The equipment performance in terms of maximum ranges obtainable depends upon the amount of energy which can be developed in the light pulse. Daytime ranges of several thousand meters against ordinary objects (reflectivity about five per cent) can be achieved with apertures of the order of 20 inches. Nighttime ranges are greater, because of the reduction in background noise which represents the primary performance limitation. For ranging on "friendly" objects, where retroreflectors can be used, the achievable ranges can be tens of kilometers.

The laser now provides a light source for optical ranging equipment which can give pulses of considerably greater power or a continuous output with a very narrow spectral bandwidth. Laser pulsed sources make possible improved pulse-type equipment, and laser CW sources can provide improvements in CW equipment. Developments which are currently going on in both of these areas are not yet available for description in the open literature.

In continuous wave (CW) optical ranging systems, the outgoing light beam is modulated by a device such as a Kerr cell, and the return beam is compared with the outgoing beam with respect to phase. Figure 8.81 shows a typical CW optical ranging system.

The distance measurement can be made to a fraction of a cycle of the

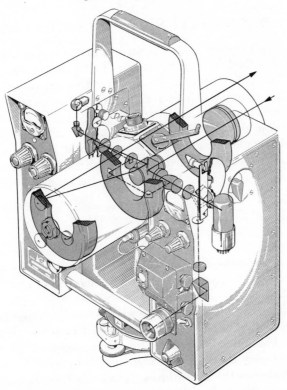

FIGURE 8.81. Schematic arrangement of the geodimeter.
(*Courtesy AGA Corp. of America*)

modulation frequency, which typically is 10 kc. To overcome the ambiguity involved in the fact that the phase difference includes an unknown number of whole cycles in addition to the fraction which is measured, an additional lower frequency is imposed on the light beam. This frequency is selected to provide a "beat" frequency whose wavelength is greater than the distance to be measured.

This type of equipment requires a continuous light source, which cannot be made as bright as the pulse sources used in the pulse type equipment; on the other hand, the "bandwidth" of the system can be very narrow and centered about the modulation frequencies to be observed. Nighttime ranges of several miles are possible with the CW equipment, and accuracies under the best conditions can be as good as a few inches. Improvement in accuracy is achieved by using relatively long times of observation, and integrating the results.

# OBSERVATIONS OF FLUID FLOW

**8.81. General.** Optical methods have contributed significantly to the investigations of fluid flow, particularly in the fields of aerodynamics and ballistics.[41] The optical systems associated with wind tunnels and shock tubes reveal the nature of shock waves, boundary layers, and other phenomena, both qualitatively and quantitatively.

Observation of details of the flow of air and other gases about a high velocity body requires making visible (or otherwise detectable) the variation of refractive index associated with the small changes of pressure created as a result of the flow. The refractive index of a gas as a function of pressure is, to a first approximation

$$\mu - 1 = k \frac{\rho}{\rho_0} \tag{8.84}$$

where $\rho/\rho_0$ is the ratio of the actual to the undisturbed density and $k$ is a constant which, for air in visible light, ranges from about .000290 to about .000298.

Light which passes through a gas in which there is a variation of density, and therefore of refractive index, is subjected to phase changes and to deflections. The optical apparatus for the examination of fluid flow is designed to display these phase changes and deflections.

**8.82. Fundamental Techniques.** There are three techniques for the optical examination of fluid flow: Schlieren methods, shadowgraph methods, and interferometer methods. These methods are complementary—each is sensitive to a different characteristic of the phenomenon, and all are required to obtain a complete picture. The Schlieren method displays the *density gradient* in the fluid stream; the shadowgraph method displays the *change* in the *density gradient;* the interferometer displays the phase changes, which are proportional to the *density ratio*. Thus, the three methods "measure" the quantity and its first and second derivatives.

The word "measure" has been included in quotations, because the three methods are not equally quantitative. It is possible to make good quantitative measurements with the interferometer; quantitative methods have been developed and are in use for Schlieren techniques,[42] but they are rather involved and are not widely used; the shadowgraph method[43] is essentially qualitative.

**8.83. The Schlieren Technique.** The Schlieren technique is usually credited to Toepler,[44] who described it in 1866; its relation to the Foucault test is readily seen.

Figure 8.82 shows the arrangement of a typical Schlieren system.[45] The

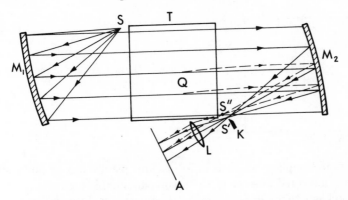

FIGURE 8.82. Functional arrangement of a Schlieren optical
system. A small source, S, is collimated by the mirror, $M_1$, and
transmitted through the test section, T. A mirror, $M_2$, reimages
the source at S′, where a knife edge, K, is placed. The lens, L,
images a plane in the test section on the screen, A, which may be
a photographic plate. A discontinuity in the refractive index in the
region Q will cause the light beam to be deflected, and the image of
the source formed at S″ instead of at S′. In this position, it is less
obscured by the knife-edge, and the illumination on the screen
is therefore increased.

two mirrors, $M_1$ and $M_2$ successively produce and refocus a parallel beam
of light from the small source s, this collimated beam passing through the
test area T.

The lens L is so located as to form an image of a plane in the test area
on the screen A. If the medium in the test area is perfectly homogeneous,
then the source will be imaged at the point S′ in front of the lens.

If, however, there is a change in refractive index in the area indicated by
Q, the portion of the beam passing through this area will be deflected by the
*gradient* in the index of refraction in this area, and will thus form a separate
image of the source at the point s″, as shown by the dotted lines in the
figure. This will not cause a deflection of the image on the screen A, because A is a conjugate image point to the plane in which Q lies.

Figure 8.82 shows the deflection grossly exaggerated; Figure 8.83 shows
how the image of the source, here drawn as a rectangular slit, might be
shifted in a typical case.

If, now, a knife-edge is placed over the normal image of the source so
as to obscure half of it, the effect of a deflection at Q will be, through the
formation of a shifted slit image, to change the *illumination* on the screen
A, in an amount proportional to the deflection.

On the screen A, therefore, appears an image of the refractive index

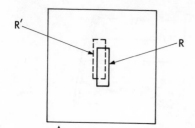

FIGURE 8.83. Displacement of the source image at the knife-edge location.

gradients in the plane which is in focus. This picture can be quite impressive, as is indicated in some of the accompanying photographs.

It is evident that the arrangement described will show gradients only in a direction normal to the knife-edge; in order to obtain the desired information, it is necessary to set the knife-edge in a direction which is appropriate for the phenomena being investigated. The direction of the deflection of the light beam is toward the higher density.

It is also evident that the deflection of the light will be the result of the integrated gradient throughout the path of the light. This fact, together with the diffraction effects introduced by the finite apertures involved and the interposition of the knife-edge, makes quantitative analysis of Schlieren photography difficult. It is not, however, impossible, and methods have been developed to correct for these and other errors.[42]

Since many of the phenomena which are being investigated in this kind of work are of very short duration, it is customary to make very short exposure photographs in Schlieren work—of the order of microseconds. To accomplish this, the light sources must be very bright; special lamps are used, usually of the arc- or spark-discharge type, fired from capacitors. Lamps which provide up to 200 joules of light energy and with flash durations of from 0.1 to 15 $\mu$sec are typical.

**8.84. Schlieren Apparatus.** A Schlieren optical system may be arranged in a number of ways. The arrangement shown in Figure 8.82, with the mirrors made as "off-axis" paraboloids, with their optical axis on the line O–O′, with equal focal lengths, and oppositely tilted as shown, is a sort of ideal system with maximum degree of optical performance. Few actual systems are made to this degree of perfection. Paraboloidal mirrors are used when the relative aperture is $f/5$ or faster; otherwise spherical mirrors give adequate performance for most purposes.

If the mirrors are of the same focal length and are oppositely tilted, so that the arrangement is similar to that of Figure 8.82, the system is free of coma. Astigmatism is always present, but when a slit is used, it may be placed at the focus which corresponds to the slit direction.

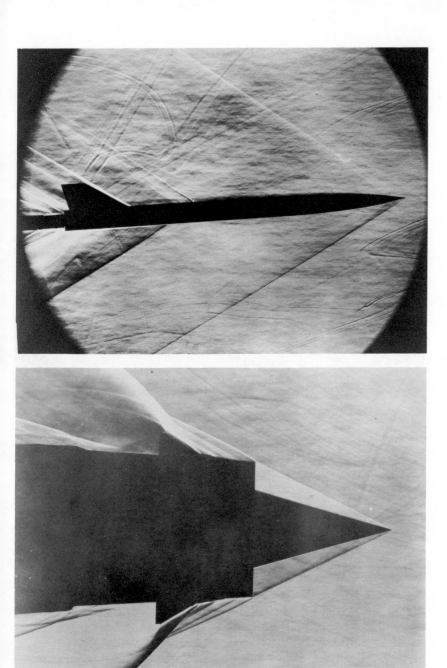

FIGURE 8.83A. Schlieren photographs. These are aircraft models in wind tunnel experiments. They are, respectively, produced at Mach 3.07, $\alpha = 0°$; Mach 3.07, $\alpha = 4.0°$; Mach 2.05, $\alpha = 4.2°$. (*Courtesy Lockheed Aircraft Corp.*)

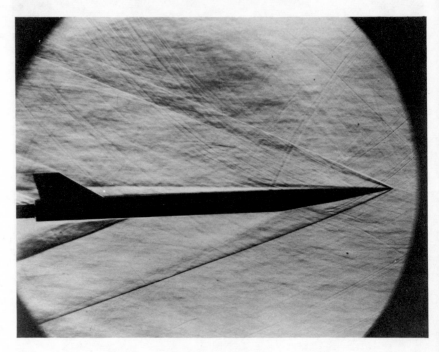

FIGURE 8.83A—*Cont'd.*

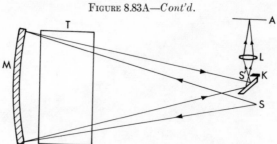

FIGURE 8.84. Single-mirror Schlieren arrangement.

Figure 8.84 shows a configuration using a single mirror, in an arrangement which may be called *autoreflective*. Slit and knife-edge are at the center of curvature of the mirror; two arrangements are possible. The arrangement shown places the slit and knife-edge slightly off axis, so that the light paths through the test area are not identical, which may introduce unwanted effects. An alternative arrangement places both slit and knife-edge on axis through the use of a beam-splitter.

Figure 8.85 shows an *auto-collimating* system, using a plane mirror be-

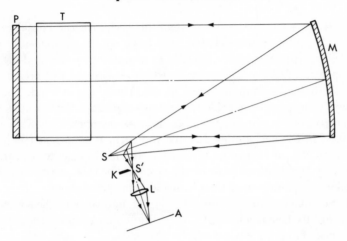

FIGURE 8.85. Auto collimating Schlieren arrangement, using an auxiliary flat mirror, P.

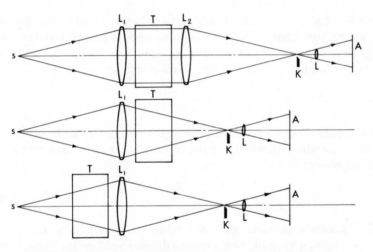

FIGURE 8.86. Three Schlieren arrangements using lenses.

hind the test area. In this system, as in the auto-reflective system, the arrangement may provide for off-axis positions of slit and knife-edge, or a beam-splitter may be used to bring both into axial coincidence.

Figure 8.86 shows three arrangements of lens systems, one with collimated light in the test chamber and two with non-collimated light.

Other arrangements are possible.

Practical Schlieren system arrangements are often dictated by available space and by economics, rather than by technological considerations. Many of the applications call for very large optical components, which would become very expensive if made to ultimate precision and arranged in the optimum fashion. The windows which enclose the test area are also part of the optical system and must be made with this in mind. The most important consideration in Schlieren systems is perhaps the homogeneity of any transparent components, such as the test chamber windows and any lenses used in the neighborhood of the test area. Inhomogeneities in such components will, of course, be revealed in the final image to a degree determined by the depth of focus of the system. For this reason, mirrors are much more frequently used than lenses in Schlieren systems.

**8.85. Sensitivity and Range.** If $B$ is the luminance of the source, and $h$ and $w$ are its height and width, then the illumination on the screen, in the absence of the knife-edge, will be

$$E = \frac{Bhw}{M^2 f_1^2} \qquad (8.85)$$

where $M$ is the magnification and $f_1$ the focal length of the first, or collimating, mirror (see Figure 8.81). If the knife-edge is placed over the source image so as to cover all but a width $w_1$, then, since the source image size will be $(f_2/f_1)h$ by $(f_2/f_1)w$, the illumination will become

$$E = \frac{Bhw_1}{M^2 f_1 f_2} \qquad (8.86)$$

If the light from an area $Q$ is deflected through the angle $\delta\epsilon$, then the source image will be displaced by the amount $f_2\delta\epsilon$, and the resulting change in illumination will be

$$\delta E = \frac{Bh \, \delta\epsilon}{M^2 f_1} \qquad (8.87)$$

The important characteristics of a Schlieren system are its contrast, its constrast sensitivity, and the maximum displacement range. These may be defined as follows:

$$\text{Contrast, } C = \frac{\delta E}{E} = \frac{f_2 \, \delta\epsilon}{a} \qquad (8.88)$$

$$\text{Contrast Sensitivity, } S_c = \frac{dC}{d\epsilon} = \frac{f_2}{a} \qquad (8.89)$$

$$\text{Maxium Displacement Range, } \overline{\delta\epsilon} = h/f_1 \qquad (8.90)$$

the latter quantity representing the fact that if the source image is displaced by half its width, it is either completely behind or completely outside of the knife-edge, and further displacement does not change the illumination.

**8.86. Special Techniques.** Various special techniques have been devised to improve the performance of Schlieren systems with respect to one or more or the characteristics defined above, or to provide additional desirable features. Some of these are described here, but space does not permit a complete review.

The range of an instrument is increased, almost indefinitely, at the cost of sensitivity, by using a graded filter[46] in place of the knife-edge. Such a filter has a maximum transmission at the center, where the undeflected source image is placed, and the transmission decreases continuously away from the center.

Occasionally anamorphic systems are used, with greater magnification in the direction of light deflection than in the perpendicular direction.

For systems in which the detector, such as the human eye or the photographic plate, have a detectivity curve which is other than linear (logarithmic for the two mentioned), an improvement in performance is obtained if the source slit is shaped so that the response of the detector is linear with respect to the deflection. For these two detectors, therefore, the slit would have a logarithmic shape.

If the knife-edge is replaced with a coarse grid,[47] whose clear spaces are equal to or slightly larger than the source image, the range is increased, and large deflections give a series of maximum and minimum illumination. If the grid is placed out of focus to the source image, fringes are formed in the field of view, and refractive index disturbances give fringe shifts which may be quantitatively analyzed.

If a prism is placed near the source slit, or color filters placed in the knife-edge position, the effect is to display the light beam displacements as changes in color.[48]

If a very narrow source slit is used, and either a narrow slit or a fine wire is inserted in the central maximum of the source image, fringes are formed in the field of view. The use of a Savart plate (see Section 8.48) at the knife-edge gives colored patterns by polarization.

Use has been made of a phase-retardation plate in the central diffraction maximum of the source image, in a manner similar to its use in the Zernicke test for mirrors (see Section 8.72). This technique and the diffraction-founded techniques described in the previous paragraph are useful for only very small light beam deflections.

Crossing of a spectrograph with the knife-edge in a Schlieren system gives information on the changes in dispersion in the gas in the test chamber, which has been found useful in investigating temperature distributions.

The standard knife-edge arrangement gives information on the density gradient in only one direction—perpendicular to the knife-edge. For obtaining two-dimensional information, techniques have been devised for obtaining cutoff of the source image in two perpendicular directions simultaneously.[49]

Another method for obtaining two-dimensional information is the use of a two-dimensional knife-edge, shaped to fit the shape of the source image, but about half its area. Both circular[50] and square[51] shapes have been used, and both apertures and opaque stops.

For quantitative investigations with Schlieren systems, it is customary to use standard objects with known deflection properties—for example, weak lenses with known inhomogeneities, bubbles, plates of glass, etc. These are known as *schlieres* and are used for calibration.

The Schlieren method has also been modified to give information on three-dimensional variations in the test chamber. Probably the best method is the stereo method,[52] illustrated in Figure 8.87.

A so-called range-finder method was used by Lamplough[53] in measuring shock fronts on aircraft in flight; a wedge is placed close to the collimating aperture, covering part of the beam. In the field of view, the shock front is displaced in the portion of the field by an amount proportional to the distance from the wedge. Kantrowitz has described a "sharp-focus" method, using an extended source, which gives a small depth of field for the system. Multiple knife-edges are used, as shown in Figure 8.88.

**8.87. The Shadowgraph Technique.**[43] If the density gradient in the test chamber which causes deflections of the light beam is not uniform, then the deflections will be different at different points across the chamber. This effect is utilized in the direct shadow method of observation, which is illustrated in Figure 8.89.

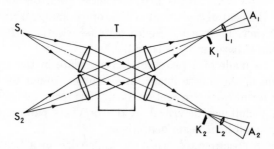

Figure 8.87. Stereo Schlieren arrangement.

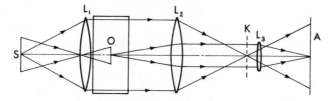

FIGURE 8.88. "Sharp-focus" Schlieren arrangement.

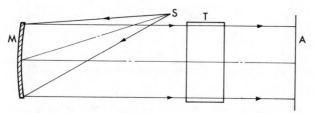

FIGURE 8.89. Shadowgraph arrangement: (M) collimating mirror, (S) source, (T) test section, (A) screen.

A photographic plate, or viewing screen, is placed in the plane P in the Figure; the dotted lines show the deflection of the light beam from a variation in the density gradient in the plane Q. This produces a change in the illumination on the screen.

This method is least capable of quantitative analysis. Its sensitivity increases with the distance of the screen from the test plane, but the illumination falls inversely as the square of this distance.

It is often inconvenient to mount a photographic plate in a position close to the test chamber exit window, so a method known as the focused direct shadow method is sometimes resorted to. The optical arrangement is that of a standard Schlieren, but the knife-edge is removed, and the camera lens (lens L in Figure 8.82) is focused upon a plane located in the position of plane P in Figure 8.88. The camera always has a considerable depth of field, so that it is not possible to focus it precisely on the desired plane, and the result is the integrated shadow pattern through the range of depth of field of the arrangement, and the images are never as sharp as in the direct shadow method itself. As mentioned above, the direct shadow method measures the second derivative of the density variations.

**8.88. Interferometer Techniques.** Most of the quantitative information in the study of fluid flow is obtained by interferometer methods. The Mach-Zehnder interferometer (see Section 8.43) is almost universally used for this purpose; indeed, it was originally developed for this application.

The interferometer measures the density variations directly, since the

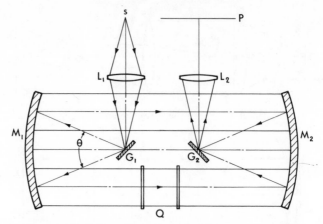

FIGURE 8.90. Diffraction grating interferometer: (S) source; (L₁) focusing lens; (G₁, G₂) gratings; (M₁, M₂) mirrors; (L₂) imaging lens; (P) observation plane, (θ) angle between zeroth- and first-order diffracted beams.

fringe contours which result are caused by the phase differences in the light, which in turn are proportional to the refractive index.

Monochromatic light is used with the interferometer, and relatively narrow spectral bands are used (typically ±100Å). The interferometer may be adjusted to provide any desired number of fringes; where the path differences are small with respect to the wavelength, an adjustment giving a very few fringes, or even only one, provides maximum sensitivity. When large path differences are involved, it is desirable to provide for a large number of fringes, so that the magnitudes of the deflections are more easily determined.

Kraushaar[54] and Sterret and Erwin[55] have described a *diffraction-grating interferometer*, illustrated in Figure 8.90.

This provides a particularly simple and effective interferometer. The source is focused on a plane diffraction grating, at G in Figure 8.90, one-half the beam being eliminated by a stop, D. The grating is oriented, and the aperture of the lens L₂ is controlled so that only the zero- and first-order beams from the grating are accepted. The zero-order beam is spectrally unresolved.

After passage through the test chamber, the beam is focused on a second, identical grating at G′, and a symmetrical stop, D′ is introduced, so that the light which reaches the screen P consists of the zero-order beam from the first grating converted to a first-order beam at the second grating, and the first-order beam from the first grating passing through the second

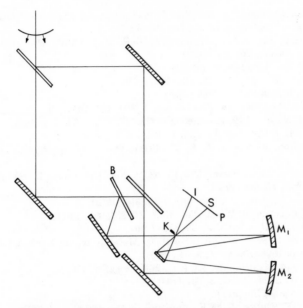

Figure 8.91. Combined Schlieren and Mach-Zehnder interferometer. The usual Mach-Zehnder arrangement uses mirror $M_2$ to obtain an interferogram at I in the observation plane, P. An additional beam-splitter, B, deflects light from the sample path to mirror $M_1$ to provide a conventional Schlieren arrangement with knife-edge K and image at S in the observation plane.

grating as its zero-order beam. These two beams have thus traversed equal optical paths and are coherent with one another.

Fringes are produced by displacing the second grating slightly from the image of the first, thus making a small angle between the two beams.

This interferometer is relatively uncomplicated and can be introduced as a temporary modification to a standard Schlieren arrangement.

Arrangements for combining interferometer and Schlieren systems to obtain simultaneous records by both techniques have been developed. Zobel[56] and Blue and Pollack[57] both describe such instruments; the latter is illustrated in Figure 8.91.

## REFERENCES

1. J. Fraunhofer, *Gilbert's Ann.*, **56,** 264 (1817).
2. J. Fraunhofer, *Densch. Akad. Wiss., Munchen*, **8,** 1 (1821–2); *Ann. Physik*, **74,** 337 (1823).

3. R. Ditchburn, "Light," p. 179, New York, Interscience Publishers, 1963.
4. J. Anderson, "Dictionary of Applied Physics."
   H. Rowland, Encyclopedia Britannica; *Phil. Mag.* **13**(5), 469 (1882); **16**, 297 (1883); Nature, **26**, 211 (1882).
5. J. Strong, *Sci. Am.*, **186**, 45 (1952).
6. R. Wallace, *Astrophys. J.*, **22**, 123 (1905).
   T. Thorp, British Patent 11460 (1899).
   T. Merton, *Proc. Roy. Soc. London Ser. A*, **201**, 187 (1950).
7. R. Wood, *Nature*, **140**, 723 (1937); *J. Opt. Soc. Am.*, **34**, 509 (1944).
   H. Babcock, *J. Opt. Soc. Am.*, **34**, 1 (1944).
8. A. Michelson, *Astrophys. J.*, **8**, 37 (1898); *Proc. Am. Acad. Arts Sci.*, **35**, 109 (1899).
9. W. Williams, British Patent 321534 (1926); *Proc. Opt. Conv.*, **2**, 982 (1926); *Proc. Phys. Soc.*, **45**, 699 (1933).
10. R. Wood, *Phil. Mag.*, **20**, 770 (1910); **23**, 310 (1912).
    A. Trowbridge and R. Wood, *Phil. Mag.*, **20**, 886, 898 (1910).
11. G. Harrison, *J. Opt. Soc. Am.*, **39**, 522 (1949).
12. F. Zernicke, P. Zeeman Verh. (Den Haag. Martenus Nijholt), p. 323, 1935.
13. F. Wadsworth, *Astrophys. J.*, **3**, 54 (1986).
14. G. Oster and Y. Nishijima, *Sci. Am.*, **208**, 54 (May, 1963).
    L. Vargedy, *Appl. Optics*, **3**, 631 (1964).
15. See reference 31, Chapter 6.
16. C. Andrews, "Optics of the Electromagnetic Spectrum," p. 155, Englewood Cliffs, N. J., Prentice-Hall, 1960.
17. F. Twyman and A. Green, British Patent 103832 (1916).
    F. Twyman, *Phil. Mag.* (6), **35**, 49 (1918); **42**, 777 (1921).
18. Lord Rayleigh, *Proc. Roy. Soc.*, **59**, 198 (1896).
19. L. Mach, "Uber ein Interferenzrefractometer," *S. B. Wien. Akad.*, **98**, 1318 (1889); *Ziets. Instkde.*, **12**, 89 (1892).
    L. Zehnder, *Zeits Instkde.*, **11**, 275 (1891).
20. G. Bates, *Proc. Roy. Soc.*, **59**, 940 (1947).
21. W. Kosters, in (E. Gehrcke, Ed.) "Handbuch der Physikalischen Optik," Vol. I, p. 484, Barth, Leipzig, 1927.
    J. Saunders, *J. Res. Natl. Bur. Std.*, **58**, 27 (1957).
22. J. Burch, *Nature*, **171**, 889 (1953).
23. J. Dyson, *Proc. Roy. Soc., London Ser. A*, **204**, 170 (1950); *J. Opt. Soc. Am.*, **47**, 557 (1957)
    M. Francon, *J. Opt. Soc. Am.*, **47**, 527 (1957).
24. M. Savart, *Ann. Physik*, **49**, 292 (1840).
    A. van Heel, in J. Strong, "Concepts in Classical Optics," p. 400, W. H. Freeman & Co., 1958.
25. G. Toraldo di Francia, *Suppl. Nuovo Cimento*, **9**, 426 (1952).
    B. Dossier, *Rev. Optique*, **33**, 57, 147, 267 (1954).
26. C. Fabry and A. Perot, *Ann. Chim. Phys.*, (7), **16**, 115 (1899).
27. O. Lummer, *Verhandl. Deutsch. Phys. Ges.*, **3**, 85 (1901).
    O. Lummer and E. Gehrcke, *Ann. Physik*, (4), **10**, 45 (1903).
28. H. Fizeau, *Ann. Chem. Phys.*, (3), **66**, 429 (1862).
29. A. Michelson, *Astrophys. J.*, **51**, 257 (1920).
    A. Michelson and F. Pease, *Astrophys. J.*, **53**, 249 (1921).
30. J. Anderson, *Astrophys. J.*, **51**, 263 (1920).

31. R. Hanbury Brown and R. Twiss, *Phil. Mag.*, (7), **45**, 663 (1954); *Nature*, **178**, 1046 (1956); *Proc. Roy. Soc., London Ser. A*, **248**, 199, 222 (1958).
    R. Hanbury Brown, *Sky & Telescope*, **28**, 64 (1964).
32. N. Weiner, "The Fourier Integral and Certain of Its Applications," Dover, 1933.
    See also T. Williams in J. Strong, "Concepts in Classical Optics," p. 616, W. H. Freeman & Co., 1958.
33. See reference 47, Chapter 7.
34. J. Strong and G. Vanasse, in "Concepts in Classical Optics," p. 419, W. H. Freeman & Co., (1958).
35. L. Foucault, *Ann. l'Observ. Imp. de Paris*, **5**, 197 (1859).
    For discussions, see:
    "Amateur Telescope Making," 4th ed., pp. 82, 96, 120, 257, 262, 281, 300, New York, Scientific American, 1945.
    E. Gaviola in "Amateur Telescope Making—Advanced," p. 76, New York, Scientific American, 1937.
36. W. Calder in "Amateur Telescope Making—Book Three," p. 109, New York, Scientific American, 1951.
37. I. Schroeder in "Amateur Telescope Making—Book Three," p. 429, New York, Scientific American, 1951.
38. F. Zernicke, *Physica*, **I**, No. 8, 689; *Monthly Notices Roy. Astron. Soc.*, **94**, 377 (1934).
    C. Burch in "Amateur Telescope Making—Advanced," p. 87, New York, Scientific American, 1937.
39. V. Ronchi, "La Provi dei Sistemi Ottica," Bologna, 1925.
    J. King, *J. Opt. Soc. Am.* (September, 1934), reprinted in "Amateur Telescope Making—Advanced," p. 104, New York, Scientific American, 1937.
40. See "Amateur Telescope Making," 4th ed., p. 264, New York, Scientific American, 1945.
41. "Modern Developments in Fluid Dynamics; High Speed Flow," (L. Haworth, Ed.) Vol. 2, Ch. 11, London, Oxford University Press. 1953.
    R. Pankhurst and D. Holder, "Wind Tunnel Technique," Pittman, 1952.
    G. Cooper and G. Rothert, Jr., "Visual Observations of the Shock Wave," NACA, RM-A.8.C.25, 1948.
    H. Townend, "On Rendering Airflow Visible by Means of Hot Wires," Brit. A.R.C., R & M 1349, 1931.
    E. Aulin, "Geometry of Wind Tunnel Optics," Rep. Lab. of Optics, No. 13, Roy. Inst. Tech., Stockholm, 1951.
    N. Barnes and S. Bellinger, *J. Opt. Soc. Am.*, **35**, 497 (1945).
    N. Barnes, *J. Soc. Motion Picture Television Engrs.*, **61**, 487 (1953).
42. H. Schardin, *V.D.I. Forschungh.*, **367**, Vol. 5 (1934).
    F. Weyl, NAVORD Rep. 211–45, 1945.
    W. Mair, *The Aero. Quar.*, **4** (August, 1952).
    H. Schafer, *J. Soc. Motion Picture Television Engrs.*, **53**, 524 (1949).
    C. Speak and D. Walter, Brit. A.R.C. No. 13066, 1950.
    L. Kean, Tech. Doc. Rep. ASD-TDR-62-924, AF Systems Command, USAF, Dec., 1962. ASTIA Document AD296979.
43. V. Dvorak, *Wiedemann's Ann. Phys. Chem.*, **9**, 502 (1880).
44. A. Toepler, *Pogg. Ann. Phys. Chem.*, **127**, 556 (1866); **128**, 126 (1866); **131**, 33, 180 (1867); **134**, 194 (1868).
45. D. Holder and R. North, Brit. A.R.C. R & M 2780, 1950.

AGARDOgraph 23, "Optical Methods for Examining the Flow in High Speed Wind Tunnels," Pt. I, Schlieren Methods, by D. Holder and R. North; Pt. II, Interferometer Methods, by G. Wood. NATO, Advisory Group for Aeronautical Res. and Dev., Paris, Nov., 1956.

46. R. North, Brit. A.R.C. No. 15099, 1952.
47. P. Darby, NAVORD Report 74-46, 1946.
48. D. Holder and R. North, *Nature*, **169**, 466 (1952).
    R. North, *Natl. Phys. Lab. Aero Note*, **266** (1954).
49. F. Barry and G. Edelman, *J. Aero. Sci.*, **15**, 364 (1948).
50. H. Taylor and J. Waldrum, *J. Sci. Inst.*, **10**, 378 (1933).
51. R. Edmonson, E. Gayhart and J. Olsen, *J Opt. Soc. Am.*, **42**, 989 (1952).
52. J. Hett, *J. Soc. Motion Picture Television Engrs.*, **56**, 214 (1951).
53. F. Lamplough, *Aero. Eng.*, (April, 1951).
54. R. Kraushaar, *J. Opt. Soc. Am.*, **40**, 480 (1950).
55. J. Sterrett and J. Erwin, NACA TN 2827, Nov., 1952.
56. T. Zobel, "Entwicklung und Bau eines Interferenzgerates zur optischen Messung von Dichtefern," Deutsche Luftfahrtforschung, Forschungsbericht Nr. 1008. (Translated in NACA TM 1184, 1947).
57. R. Blue and J. Pollack, *Rev. Sci. Inst.*, **23**, 754 (1952).
58. W. Ulrich, *Indus. Res.*, 28 (Oct., 1963).

## CHAPTER 9

# Communications Theory in Optics

**9.1. Introduction.** The performance of an optical instrument as an image-producing device is measured by the quality of the image which it produces. The desirable characteristics of this quality may vary from application to application; the spectroscopist desires sharp, readily resolvable images of spectral lines, the aerial photographer desires high contrasts and fine detail, and the general photographer desires good "tonal" quality. Geometrical optics can predict with high reliability the aberrations which an optical system will possess, and physical optics, through diffraction theory, can predict the character of the diffraction images of simple objects, such as points and lines. The limiting resolution of an aberration-free aperture is a definable quantity, as has been shown in previous chapters; in the presence of aberrations, optical spot diagrams,[23] which are calculable with the aid of computers, give information which may be used to predict the actual limiting resolution with somewhat less than satisfactory rigor.

But on the basis of topics which have so far been discussed, there is no quantitative method by which the quality of an image formed by an optical instrument may be predicted in a general way. The only recourse would seem to be to construct the instrument, test it in the manner in which it is to be used, and judge the quality of the result. Even this process is qualitative and not quantitative. Measurements of resolution by means of test charts (Section 8.69) give only the limiting resolution and tell little or nothing about the over-all image "quality."

This was the situation which prevailed until after World War II. Then, and with an increasing interest through the following decade, investigators began to apply to optical systems concepts derived from communications theory and electronics, with the result that there is now a body of analytical concepts and techniques which can treat the performance of an optical instrument in a very general way. Interestingly, in the application

479

of these concepts, use is made of mathematical descriptions which were worked out by Rayleigh, Abbe, Michelson, and others, but which had not previously been given attention.[1]

The central concepts in this area are the *optical transfer function* by means of which an optical system is treated as a *linear filter*, exactly as in the case of an electrical network, and a description of an optical image in terms of its *modulation*, this property being equivalent to the similar property of electrical signals. These methods are very powerful and have made possible the analysis of optical system performance in a manner and to a degree never before possible. They have led to a number of novel devices and techniques, some of which are described below.

**9.2. Applications of Transfer Functions.** These techniques of analysis are frequently referred to as "transfer function theory." By means of this theory, it is possible to predict with high reliability the performance which will be achieved by an optical system, using the design data alone. Many techniques for its use as a direct design tool have been developed.

One of the very important aspects of this technique is that it makes possible the assessment of the effects of external factors on the performance of an optical instrument; for example, vibration, atmospheric disturbances, image motions, thermal distortions, focus errors, to mention only a few.[2] Such factors can be treated analytically in the same manner as the optical instrument itself is treated—as linear filters—and their properties can be combined with those of the instrument to yield a quantitative description of the final image. Also, operations and devices which are interposed in a system between the optical instrument and the final presentation of the result—e.g., photographic film, photodetectors, magnetic tape, etc.—may also be quantitatively included in the analysis. In fact, it was the desire to include the camera optical system as a "black box" in the analysis of television systems that led to a considerable contribution by Schade[3] and others to the development of the analysis technique.

No attempt is made here to trace the history of these investigations and to assign credit and priority in various areas. The germ of the ideas dates back to Michelson, and even to Rayleigh and Abbe; the concepts were largely defined by Duffieux,[4] Selwyn,[5] Schade[6] and Marechal;[7] significant contributions have been made by Hopkins,[8] Fellgett and Linfoot,[9] Shack,[10] O'Neill,[11] Grey and Robinson,[12] and many others.[13]

**9.3. Image Quality.** It must not been assumed that this technique, powerful though it be, has provided a quantitative description of that elusive concept "quality." Transfer function theory provides a quantitative measure of some very general and important characteristics of an optical image; it also provides a measure of performance in terms of resolution which applies not only to limiting resolution, but to detail of all degrees of fineness—and this kind of measure has not previously been available.

There is no doubt that there is a relationship between this measure and image "quality," for instance between the *modulation function* of an aerial photograph and the amount of information which a photo interpreter can obtain from it; neither is there any doubt that when the image modulation is high, the interpreter can extract more information than when it is low. But this relationship has not yet been realistically defined in a quantitative manner.

**9.4. The Fourier Transform.** Transfer function theory is rooted in the concept of the Fourier transform, of which a brief review may be desirable. Any function, $F(x)$, may be considered to be the resultant of the summation of a set of continuous sinusoidal functions of appropriate frequency, amplitude and phase relations. This is a very general mathematical principle, and the necessary conditions that a function be representable in this way impose only minor restrictions which are not of concern in the ensuing discussion. These restrictions, together with much more rigorous and extensive treatment, are to be found in many standard mathematical treatises.

If these sinusoidal components are represented in the complex notation $ae^{j\phi}$, then the function may be written

$$F(x) = \sum_{n=1}^{\infty} a_n e^{j\phi_n} \tag{9.1}$$

If $F(x)$ is *periodic*, then it is representable as the series

$$F(x) = \sum_{n=1}^{\infty} a_n e^{2\pi n j x f} \tag{9.2}$$

[where $f$ is the frequency of the periodic function $F(x)$] that is, as the summation of harmonics of frequency $f$, $2f$, $3f \ldots nf$.

Now, it may be shown that the amplitude of the $n$th harmonic of $F(x)$ is given by

$$a_n = f \int_{-1/2f}^{1/2f} F(x) e^{-2\pi n j x f} \, dx \tag{9.3}$$

This is the *Fourier series* concept.

When $F(x)$ is *non-periodic*, then the sinusoidal components are not limited to the integral harmonics of a fundamental frequency, $f$, but comprise a continuous (nominally infinite) range of frequencies. For the general case, therefore, the summation of Equation (9.2) is replaced by the *integral* representation

$$F(x) = \int_{-\infty}^{\infty} f(u)e^{i x u}\, du \tag{9.4}$$

where $f(u)$ is the complex amplitude of a component of frequency $u$, and these amplitudes are now given by the continuous function

$$f(u) = \int_{-\infty}^{\infty} F(x)e^{-2\pi j x u}\, dx \tag{9.5}$$

Equations (9.4) and (9.5) are *Fourier transforms* of each other, and if either $F(x)$ or $f(u)$ are known, the other may be found from these relations.

$f(u)$ is the *spectrum* of $F(x)$; it is the representation of $F(x)$ as a set of frequencies.

**9.5. Imaging of a Point by an Optical Instrument.** Any object which is imaged by an optical system may be considered as an infinite set of discrete points of varying intensity, each of which is independently imaged by the optical system to constitute, by summation, the final image. Now, it is possible, at least in principle, to determine the imaging characteristics of an optical system for a discrete point. If the system is representable by an aberration-free aperture, then the complex amplitude distribution in the image plane for a point source is given by the diffraction integral for the aperture, which is derived on the assumption that the complex amplitude is uniform over the aperture; in practice, residual aberrations are always present, so that the complex amplitude distribution over the aperture is representable by a function, say $g(\beta,\gamma)$, where $\beta$, $\gamma$ are the coordinates of the aperture, expressed in angular terms as seen from the image plane, as shown in Figure 9.1.

The diffraction integral may be expressed more generally, therefore

$$U(x,y) = \iint_A g(\beta,\gamma) \exp\left[-2\pi j\left(\frac{\beta}{\lambda}x + \frac{\gamma}{\lambda}y\right)\right] d\beta\, dy \tag{9.6}$$

where $x$, $y$ are the coordinates in the image plane, and the integral is taken over the area of the aperture. This equation is equivalent to Equation (2.87), and its solution, for the case of a rectangular aperture where $g(\beta,\gamma) =$ constant, is shown in Figure 2.42. It is the familiar pattern for Fraunhofer diffraction.

Equation (9.6) is the complex amplitude of the diffraction image of a point source, and $U(x,y)$ will be called the *point image function*. $g(\beta,\gamma)$ is called the *aperture function*, or *pupil function*. For a real system, $g(\beta,\gamma)$ is determinable from optical path difference computations, or from actual interferometric test data.

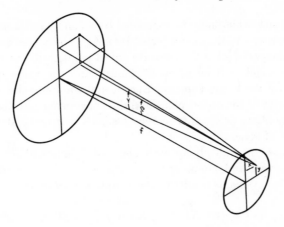

FIGURE 9.1. Geometry of the aperture.

Comparison of Equation (9.6) with Equation (9.5) shows that $U(x,y)$ satisfies the definition of a *Fourier transform* of $g(\beta,\gamma)$, and that $\beta$ and $\gamma$ are therefore to be considered as *frequencies*. However, $\beta$ and $\gamma$ are spatial coordinates of the aperture; therefore, the frequencies are *spatial frequencies* with the dimensions of cycles per unit distance.

**9.6. The Diffraction Pattern as a Spatial Spectrum.** What has been said in the previous section is of fundamental importance in transfer function theory; because it can be said so easily, its significance may be overlooked. The discussion shows very clearly that *the diffraction pattern of an aperture is the Fourier transform of the aperture function.* A plot of Equation (9.6), as presented in Figure 2.42, is not only a plot of the diffraction pattern, it is also a plot of the *spatial spectrum of the aperture.* This point is not of importance in the immediately ensuing discussion, but it will be recalled later in the chapter.

It is this property of the diffraction integral that was recognized by Rayleigh, Abbe and Michelson, and whose significance was overlooked for several decades. Rayleigh actually computed and plotted a transfer function in 1896.

It will be noted that Equation (9.6) expresses the Fourier transform in a two-dimensional domain, instead of the one-dimensional domain used in the derivation of Equation (9.5). Nothing is lost in generality by confining the treatment to one dimension, as will be done later.

**9.7. Imaging of a Scene by an Optical System.** The *intensity* distribution in the image plane for a point source is, by definition

$$E(x,y) = |U(x,y)|^2 \qquad (9.7)$$

Now, any scene being imaged by an optical system will have a distribution of intensity which may be expressed by a function $O(x,y)$, where $x$, $y$ are the coordinates in the object plane. Its image, considered as the summation of the images of all of the separate object points, will have an intensity distribution which will be given by multiplying the value of $O(x,y)$ for each point by the entire function $E(x,y)$, and summing the results. Here the coordinates of the object plane and the image plane have been assigned the same symbols $(x,y)$; this merely assumes a magnification of unity, without loss of generality.

This process of multiplying each point of a function by the whole of another function, and summing the results, is called a *convolution;* for two continuous functions, it results in the *convolution integral*[14]

$$I(x',y') = \iint_E O(x,y)E(x - x',y - y')dx\,dy \qquad (9.8)$$

where the variables $x'$, $y'$ refer to the range of the function $E(x,y)$ over which the integration is taken for each point of $O(x,y)$; $x'$, $y'$ define the same space as $x$, $y$, and are primed only for mathematical convenience.

$I(x',y')$ is the intensity function of the image. If the function $O(x,y)$ is known, then, since $E(x,y)$ is given by Equation (9.7), the intensity function of the image can be completely determined. The object function is not generally known except for rather trivial cases, in addition to which the actual computation of Equation (9.8) is not a simple task. The following discussion shows how the Fourier transform relations may be used to derive useful information in a much more simple way.

**9.8. The Optical Transfer Function.** The intensity function for a point image $E(x,y)$ is called the *point spread function*. Its one-dimensional counterpart is the *line spread function*. The previous section has shown that the intensity distribution in an image is given by the convolution of the object intensity distribution with the point spread function. If the treatment is confined to one dimension, then the convolution is with the line spread function. In the practical analysis of optical systems, a one-dimensional treatment is frequently adequate.

Now, it is a demonstrable mathematical property of functions that the *simple product* of the Fourier transforms of the two functions involved in a convolution is the Fourier transform of the result. Thus, the Fourier transform of the object intensity function, $O(x,y)$ multiplied by the Fourier transform of the point spread function, $E(x,y)$, will give the Fourier transform of the image intensity function, $I(x,y)$. These relationships are shown diagrammatically in Figure 9.2. Because of this property, *the Fourier transform of the point spread function is called the optical transfer function.* Taking the Fourier transforms transfers the problem from the *spatial*

OBJECT INTENSITY FUNCTION                    OBJECT SPECTRUM

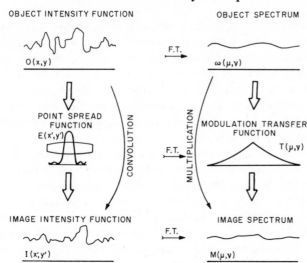

FIGURE 9.2. Functional relationships for incoherent illumination.

*domain* to the *frequency domain;* the product relationship which prevails in this domain is a consequence of the *linear* nature of an optical system; indeed, the Fourier transform treatment is valid only for *linear systems.* Some discussion of the conditions under which an optical system may be considered linear is given below. A completely rigorous discussion of this area is beyond the scope of this book.

The Fourier transform is by definition a complex function and expresses both amplitude and phase. When both phase and amplitude considerations are included in the transfer function, it is called the *optical transfer function,* and when the function is real, and there are no phase relations involved, only the *modulus* is used, and it is then called the *modulation transfer function.*[15] In situations involving incoherent illumination, it is only in very special cases that the phase relations in the object and image functions are of interest. Optical systems in general, being symmetrical in form, do not introduce strong phase shifts (the presence of unsymmetrical aberrations such as coma being an exception), so that neglecting of the phase aspects of the analysis is often justified.

**9.9. Spatial Frequency.** The Fourier transform of the object intensity function is its *spatial intensity spectrum.* It represents the object as being made up of a set of sinusoidally varying intensity patterns of different magnitudes and positions, superimposed upon each other. These components are not real in a physical sense—they are a mathematical description, in terms of the Fourier transform. It is not difficult to see how, in some cases, an object may approach, if not a sinusoid, at least a periodic pattern (fences, railroad ties, housing developments, city streets, etc.). It is important, however, to note than a specific target *object* will have a spatial spectrum which is characteristic of it; i.e., it will contain all frequencies from zero onward—usually with sharply diminished amplitudes at the higher frequencies. The Fourier sinusoidal components are, by definition, infinite in extent, whereas real objects are finite. Thus a completely pure sinusoid cannot physically exist—even a sine-wave pattern of finite extent will possess a finite *bandwidth* of frequency components. This situation was discussed in connection with spectral lines in Section 3.51.

Analogously, the Fourier transform of the image intensity function is its *spatial intensity spectrum*, expressed in terms of spatial frequencies, for which *cycles per millimeter*, or *lines per millimeter*, is the accepted dimensional unit. This tells a great deal about the nature of the image, since it describes the respective magnitudes of the frequency components, and therefore defines with how much contrast various details of the object are rendered in the final image.

An analogous term to describe a similar concept came into use before the technique of the Fourier transform was developed to its present status; this term is *contrast rendition*, and it is still to be found in the literature. The numerical relation between modulation and contrast is discussed below.

**9.10. Determination of the Transfer Function.** The transfer function has been defined as the Fourier transform of the point spread function, and if the latter is known, the transfer function is readily determined. The point spread function, however, does not emerge normally from the computations usually made in the design of an optical system. It can be inferred from a *spot diagram*, such as may be computed from ray-trace data, but spot diagrams are not customarily computed, except for special purposes such as this.

The Fourier transform relationships provide a simple means of deriving the transfer function, as is shown in Figure 9.3. The point spread function is the product of the point image function [Equation (9.6)], and its complex conjugate, as is shown in Equations (9.7) and (9.6) has been shown to be the Fourier transform of the aperture function, $g(\beta,\gamma)$. Therefore, using the identity between a convolution and a product of Fourier transforms, it is seen that the transfer function is the convolution of the aperture function with the Fourier transform of the complex conjugate of the point image function. And the latter is simply the complex conjugate of the aperture function itself, since the aperture function and the point image function stand in a Fourier transform relationship. Hence, *the transfer function is the convolution of the aperture function with its complex conjugate.*

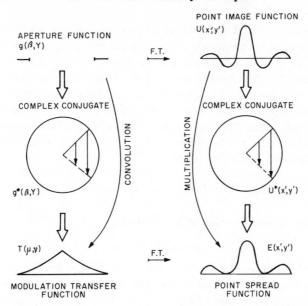

FIGURE 9.3. Functional relationships for incoherent illumination.

Therefore, when phase relations are neglected,

$$T(x,\tilde{y}) = \iint g(\beta,\gamma)g^*[(\beta - \lambda\tilde{x}),(\gamma - \lambda\tilde{y})]d\beta \, d\gamma \qquad (9.9)$$

Here, and in the ensuing discussion, the symbols $\tilde{x}$, $\tilde{y}$ have been adopted for the spatial frequencies associated with the spatial coordinates $x$, $y$, following a suggestion of Shack. Transfer function symbolism varies widely with different authors—the symbols adopted, using the tilde to indicate the frequency domain, are felt to be especially useful in associating corresponding frequency and spatial domains.

A convolution of a function with itself, as in Equation (9.9), is often referred to as an *autocorrelation function*. The significance of the terms $x$ and $y$ and the scale of the spatial frequencies $\tilde{x}$ and $\tilde{y}$ are developed in the mathematical treatment below.

**9.11. Mathematical Derivation.** The previous discussion has shown in a qualitative way that the transfer function can be derived by a convolution of the aperture function with itself. The following discussion takes the same route through the medium of equations.

The generalized point image function was given in Equation (9.6)

$$U(x,y) = \iint g(\beta,\gamma) \exp\left[-j\frac{2\pi}{\lambda}(\beta x + \gamma y)\right]d\beta \, d\gamma \qquad (9.6)$$

where $\beta$, $\gamma$ are interpreted as spatial frequencies, and the aperture function $g(\beta,\gamma)$ is the complex amplitude of the wave front emerging from the system exit pupil, or the *pupil function*. For an aberration-free aperture, its value is unity over the aperture and zero outside. It is a real function. In a practical case of a system with aberrational residuals, the pupil function is a complex function which is established by the normal optical computations for the system when these are carried out in terms of optical path differences. For this case, the treatment of Equation (9.9) is not valid.

By the Fourier transform relationship

$$g(\beta,\gamma) \;=\; \iint U(x,y)\,\exp\!\left[\,j\frac{2\pi}{\lambda}\,(\beta x + \gamma y)\right]\!dx\,dy \tag{9.10}$$

The point spread function is, by definition

$$E(x,y) \;=\; |\,U(x,y)\,|^2 \tag{9.7}$$

If the object intensity function is $O(x,y)$, then it has been shown that the image intensity function is the convolution of $O(x,y)$ with the point spread function [Equation (9.7)]:

$$I(x',y') \;=\; \iint O(x,y)E(x - x', y - y')dx\,dy \tag{9.8}$$

where, as in the previous section, the object coordinates $x$, $y$ have been set equal to the image coordinates $x$, $y$ (which merely assumes a magnification of unity) and the coordinates $x'$, $y'$ over whose range the integral is taken represent the "shift" of the coordinates involved in the convolution.

Now, the object function may be written as the Fourier integral of a set of frequency components

$$O(x,y) \;=\; \iint \omega(\tilde{x},\tilde{y})\,\exp\,[2\pi j(\tilde{x}x + \tilde{y}y)]d\tilde{x}\,d\tilde{y} \tag{9.11}$$

and its Fourier transform is

$$\omega(\tilde{x},\tilde{y}) \;=\; \iint O(x,y)\,\exp\,[-2\pi j(\tilde{x}x + \tilde{y}y)]dx\,dy \tag{9.12}$$

The optical transfer function is, by definition, the Fourier transform of the point spread function, Equation (9.7), or

$$T(\tilde{x},\tilde{y}) \;=\; \iint E(x,y)\,\exp\,[2\pi j(\tilde{x}x + \tilde{y}y)]dx\,dy \tag{9.13}$$

and the point spread function can therefore be expressed as

$$E(x,y) \;=\; \iint T(\tilde{x},\tilde{y})\,\exp\,[-2\pi j(\tilde{x}x + \tilde{y}y)]d\tilde{x}\,d\tilde{y} \tag{9.14}$$

By analogy with Equation (9.14), the second term of the convolution of Equation (9.8) becomes

$$E(x - x', y - y') = \iint T(\bar{x},\bar{y}) \exp\left[-2\pi j\{\bar{x}(x - x') + \bar{y}(y - y')\}\right]d\bar{x}\,d\bar{y} \quad (9.15)$$

Substituting Equation (9.15) in Equation (9.8) gives

$$I(x',y') = \iint O(x,y)$$

$$\cdot\left[\iint T(\bar{x},\bar{y}) \exp\left[-2\pi j\{\bar{x}(x - x') + \bar{y}(y - y')\}\right]d\bar{x}\,d\bar{y}\right]dx\,dy \quad (9.16)$$

The order of integration may be reversed, to yield

$$I(x',y') = \iint T(\bar{x},\bar{y}) \exp\left[-2\pi j(\bar{x}x' + \bar{y}y')\right]$$

$$\cdot\left[\iint O(x,y) \exp\left[-2\pi j(\bar{x}x + \bar{y}y)\right]dx\,dy\right]d\bar{x}\,d\bar{y} \quad (9.17)$$

And substituting for the bracketed term from Equation (9.12)

$$I(x',y') = \iint T(x,\bar{y})\,\omega(x,y) \exp\left[-2\pi j(xx + \bar{y}y)\right]d\bar{x}\,d\bar{y} \quad (9.18)$$

whose Fourier transform is

$$M(x,y) = T(\bar{x},\bar{y})\,\omega(\bar{x},\bar{y}) = \iint I(x',y') \exp\left[2\pi j(xx' + yy')\right]dx'\,dy' \quad (9.19)$$

which demonstrates the sequence shown at the right of Figure 9.2, namely that *the Fourier transform of the image intensity function is the product of the Fourier transform of the object intensity function and the Fourier transform of the point spread function.*

Now, using the definition of Equation (9.7), Equation (9.13) for the transfer function may be written

$$T(\bar{x},\bar{y}) = \iint U(x,y)\,U^*(x,y) \exp\left[2\pi j(\bar{x}x + \bar{y}y)\right]dx\,yy \quad (9.20)$$

and substituting for one of the factors from Equation (9.6) gives

$$T(\bar{x},\bar{y}) = \iint U(x,y) \exp\left[2\pi j(\bar{x}x + \bar{y}y)\right]$$

$$\cdot\left[\iint g(\beta,\gamma) \exp\left[-(2\pi/\lambda)j(\beta x + \gamma - y)\right]d\beta\,d\gamma\right]dx\,dy \quad (9.21)$$

Again reversing the order of the integration yields

$$T(\tilde{x},\tilde{y}) = \iint g(\beta,\gamma)$$

$$\cdot \left[ \iint U(x,y) \exp \left[-(2\pi/\lambda)j\{x(\beta - \lambda\tilde{x}) + y(\gamma - \lambda\tilde{y})\}\right]dx \, dy \right] d\beta \, d\gamma \qquad (9.22)$$

By analogy with Equation (9.10), the term in square brackets is

$$g^*[(\beta - \lambda\tilde{x}), (\gamma - \lambda\tilde{y})] \qquad (9.23)$$

and therefore, Equation (9.22) becomes

$$T(\tilde{x},\tilde{y}) = \iint g(\beta,\gamma)g^*[(\beta - \lambda\tilde{x}),(\gamma - \lambda\tilde{y})]d\beta \, d\gamma \qquad (9.9)$$

which is the expression previously given for the transfer function, and demonstrates the sequence illustrated at the left of Figure 9.3, namely that *the transfer function is the convolution of the aperture function with its complex conjugate,* or, as it is sometimes expressed, *the transfer function is the autocorrelation function of the pupil function.*

**9.12. The Convolution of the Aperture.** In the absence of aberrations, the convolution of the aperture with its complex conjugate, as expressed in Equation (9.9), is equivalent to the geometrical process of computing the area common to two similar apertures displaced by the amounts $\lambda\tilde{x}$ and $\lambda\tilde{y}$ in the two coordinates. Since the coordinates may be chosen as desired, the problem can be reduced to separate displacements in a single dimension, as illustrated in Figure 9.4.

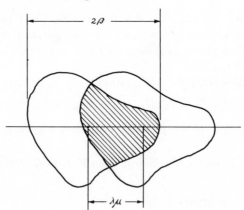

FIGURE 9.4. Geometrical equivalent of a convolution.

It will be recalled that $\beta$ and $\gamma$ were the angular coordinates of the aperture as seen from the focal plane (see Figure 9.1) and therefore that the common area in the Figure vanishes when $\lambda\tilde{x} = 2\beta_{max}$.

If $D$ is the aperture width, and $f$ the system focal length, then

$$\beta_{max.} = D/2f \qquad (2.24)$$

and therefore, the transfer function vanishes when

$$\lambda\tilde{x} = \frac{1}{N\lambda} \qquad (9.25)$$

where $N$ is the relative aperture, or $f/No$.

The limiting spatial frequency of a system, therefore, is given by Equation (9.25), which is readily interpreted as a fundamental determination of the limiting resolution of the system. The angular resolution is $1/\tilde{x}f$, where $f$ is the system focal length, and this becomes

$$\theta = \lambda/D \qquad (9.26)$$

which is identical with the limiting angular resolution of a rectangular aperture as given by diffraction theory (Section 6.22).

The limiting resolution of a circular aperture, as given in discussion of the diffraction pattern, implies a slight dip in the envelope of two close point diffraction images, in accordance with the Rayleigh criterion. The transfer function for a circular aperture, indeed for an aperture of any shape, vanishes at the spatial frequency $\tilde{x} = 1/N\lambda$.

The above treatment follows generally that given by Francon.[16]

**9.13. Use of the Transfer Function.** In most practical cases, the transfer function is treated as a one-dimensional function and is assigned the symbol $T(\tilde{x})$, where $\tilde{x}$ is the spatial frequency, for which the standardized units are cycles per millimeter or lines per millimeter.

A divergence of definition of the term "lines per millimeter" between those concerned principally with optics and those concerned principally with electro-optics (for example, television) is worthy of note. The optical definition developed from consideration of resolution in terms of two close point images, then of the resolution of two close lines, and finally of the resolution of equally spaced lines; therefore, to the optical scientist, a "line" is the spacing between two black (or white) lines, separated by a space of equal width. In television, the principal concern is the scan line on the camera or kinescope tube, and it is easy to see that to resolve two black (or white) lines separated by a space of equal width requires two scan lines on the tube. Thus, to a television scientist, a "line" is the distance between the black line and the intermediate space.

Thus there may be a difference of a factor of two between two individuals' interpretation of a situation. Figure 9.5 illustrates the distinction. The source of this misinterpretation is avoided if the term "line-pairs per millimeter" or, preferably, "cycles per millimeter" is used.

Even in the absence of aberrations, when the aperture of a system is not circular, the transfer function will be different in different directions. It is usually sufficient to analyze the case separately for only two orthogonal directions.

**9.14. Meaning of the Spatial Spectrum.** The concept under discussion interprets an object or an image as the superposition of sinusoidal intensity patterns of varying magnitude and position. The intensity pattern of a pure sinusoid varies positively and negatively around zero, as shown in Figure 9.6, and its average intensity is zero.

The minimum illumination on an actual object, however, cannot be negative, so that the sinusoidal patterns must be viewed as being superimposed on a "dc" level of some magnitude, as shown in Figure 9.7.

By analogy with communications nomenclature, the "strength" of this

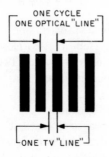

FIGURE 9.5. Relationship of optical and television parlance.

FIGURE 9.6. Normal sinusoid.

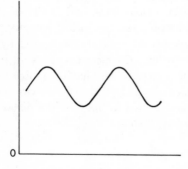

FIGURE 9.7. Sinusoid with added "dc" level.

superimposed periodic variation on the constant background level is measured by a quantity called the *modulation*, defined as

$$M = \frac{E_{\max.} - E_{\min.}}{E_{\max.} + E_{\min.}} \qquad (9.27)$$

where $E_{\max.}$ and $E_{\min.}$ are the maximum and minimum illumination levels, as shown in the figure. If the minima are zero, as in Figure 9.7B, the modulation is unity.

Now, the transfer function is concerned only with the periodic component, and describes how its amplitude is transferred from object to image; it says nothing of the "dc" background, which is transmitted by the optical system in accordance with a constant factor which expresses the reduction in background level due to absorption and scattering in the instrument and the increase in background level due to stray light from internal reflections (sometimes referred to as "veiling haze").

If it is assumed that the reduction due to absorption and scattering equally affects the dc background level and the "ac" fluctuations measured by the transfer function, and that there is no increase in the background due to stray light, then the *modulation* of the image is given by the product of the *modulation* of the object and the modulus of the transfer function, both modulations being defined as in Equation (9.27). The first assumption is generally very closely true; the second assumption is generally not true, but its effect can be taken into account by a constant term in the product which is independent of the spatial frequency.

Thus, the function $M(\tilde{x},\tilde{y})$ may be interpreted as the *modulation* of the image and the function $\omega(\tilde{x},\tilde{y})$ as the *modulation* of the object; both of these functions have values which vary from zero to unity, as does the transfer function $T(\tilde{x},\tilde{y})$.

Except for very special cases, the function $\omega(\tilde{x},\tilde{y})$ cannot be well defined for a combination of many spatial frequencies, although investigative work is currently being done in this area, especially in connection with the problems of aerial photography. It may be expected that in the not too distant future, information will be available on the distribution of frequencies and amplitudes in a general scene.

It is often possible, however, to specify the modulation of certain classes of objects of special interest; this is generally done in terms of the *contrast*.

**9.15. Contrast and Modulation.** There are varying definitions of contrast, with various authors and for various purposes. The one in most common use is

$$C = \frac{E_{\text{target}} - E_{\text{background}}}{E_{\text{background}}} \qquad (9.28)$$

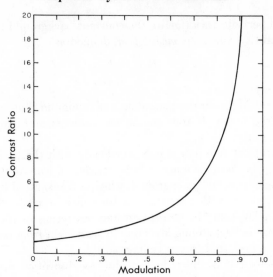

FIGURE 9.8. Contrast ratio and modulation.

This definition has developed from considerations of isolated test targets against a uniform background, and most measurements and tests of equipment and of human observers have been made on this basis.

This is an awkward kind of definition in many respects. For a bright target in a dark background, its value can vary from 0 to ∞; for a dark target in a bright background, it varies from 0 to 1. If the background is completely dark, the contrast is infinite for any target brightness.

The concept of modulation, as used with transfer function analysis, is a much more useful one. If the "background" as used in the contrast definition is identified with the "minimum" as used in the modulation definition, then the two parameters have the following relationship:

$$M = \frac{C - 1}{C + 1} \qquad C = \frac{1 + M}{1 - M} \tag{9.29}$$

Figure 9.8 shows these relationships. The value of the contrast can range from zero to infinity; the range of the modulation is from zero to unity.

In computing modulation from published data on contrast, care must be taken to analyze the contrast definition which is being used. If, in the definition of contrast, the "background" is taken to be the average over the scene, then the contrast and the modulation are numerically identical, and Equation (9.29) is not appropriate.

**9.16. Transfer Function for a Circular Aperture.** The circular aperture is the one most often encountered in practice, hence its transfer

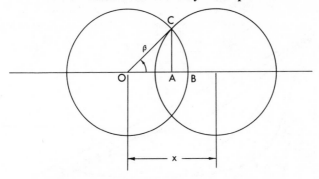

FIGURE 9.9. Convolution of a circular aperture.

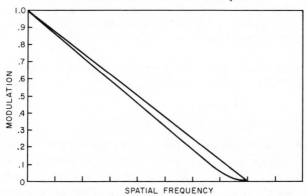

FIGURE 9.10. Modulation transfer functions for a rectangular and for a circular aperture.

function is of particular interest. This is readily derived geometrically for the aberration-free case from the procedure shown in Figure 9.4. If a circular aperture is displaced with respect to itself by the distance $x$, as shown in Figure 9.9, its radius being $\beta$, by analogy with previous discussions, then the common area is

$$A = \beta^2(2\theta - \sin 2\theta) \tag{9.30}$$

However, $\cos \theta = x/2\beta$. Also, the ratio $x/2\beta$ is the ratio of the spatial frequency to the limiting spatial frequency $\tilde{x}_0 = 1/N\lambda$, whence $x/2\beta = \tilde{x}/\tilde{x}_0$; and the transfer function is the ratio of the common area to the total area, so that the normalized expression becomes

$$T(\tilde{x}) = \frac{A}{\pi\beta^2} = \frac{2}{\pi}\left[\cos^{-1}\left(\frac{\tilde{x}}{\tilde{x}_0}\right) - \frac{\tilde{x}}{\tilde{x}_0}\sqrt{1 - \left(\frac{\tilde{x}}{x_0}\right)^2}\right] \tag{9.31}$$

This function is plotted in linear coordinates in Figure 9.10, together

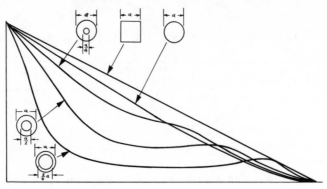

FIGURE 9.11. Modulation transfer functions for annular apertures. The curves for a rectangular and for a circular aperture are included for comparison.

with the transfer function for a rectangular aperture, in a direction parallel to one of the sides, which is seen from Figure 9.9 to be simply the straight line

$$T(\tilde{x}) = 1 - \tilde{x}/\tilde{x}_0 \tag{9.32}$$

**9.17. Annular Apertures.** The annular aperture is frequently found in optical systems, being a characteristic of reflecting and catadioptric systems which operate on axis. The transfer function for this form of aperture is readily derived by the procedure of the preceding section and is found to have the shape shown in Figure 9.11 for several obscuration ratios.

As might be expected, the performance in general deteriorates with respect to an unobscured aperture; however, for the higher frequencies, the modulation is actually improved with respect to the circular aperture, the major deterioration taking place at the lower frequencies.

This is the kind of information given by this form of analysis which would not be revealed by computations or even experimental test of limiting resolution. The frequency at which the transfer function goes to zero is the same for all *shapes* of aperture, depending only on the maximum width. The analogy with the principle of the Michelson stellar interferometer (Section 8.58) is apparent.

**9.18. Transfer Functions for Non-optical Factors.** One of the great advantages of transfer function analysis of optical systems is that factors other than the purely optical properties of the system can be taken into account by the same type of treatment. The principle that there is no optical distinction between an object and an image holds for this type of analysis as well as for geometrical optics. If a series of operations are performed upon an optical image, whose individual transfer functions are $T_1(\tilde{x})$, $T_2(\tilde{x}) \cdots T_n(\tilde{x})$, then, in general, the modulation of the final image is given by

$$M_i(\tilde{x}) = M_0(\tilde{x}) \prod_{n=1}^{n} T_n(x) \qquad (9.33)$$

This treatment is valid if, and only if, the successive operations are completely independent, and phase relations are not involved. For example, for two optical relays in series, the transfer function of the combination is not the product of the separate transfer functions, because the aberrations of the individual relays are not independent. For optical systems in series, the phase relations in each image must be destroyed (as by a diffusing screen) to make the transfer function product a valid treatment.

The operations represented by the above transfer functions $T(\tilde{x})$ may be other than image formation by an optical system, provided a transfer function can be determined. These operations might be the recording on photographic film or magnetic tape, the response of a photo-detector, vibration, image motion, atmospheric attenuation, for all of which a transfer function can be derived.

Transfer function curves are now published for photographic films. Figure 9.12 gives some typical curves for standard emulsions.

The transfer function for the human eye has also been measured by

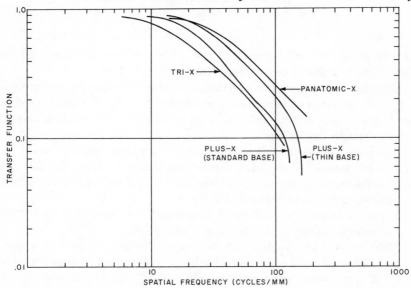

FIGURE 9.12. Typical transfer function curves for photographic emulsions.

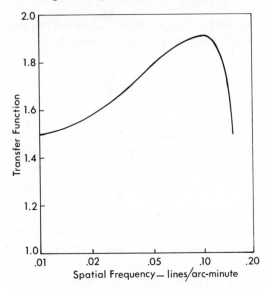

FIGURE 9.13. Approximate transfer function of
the human eye. The transfer function of the eye
varies with light level and with target contrast, so
that a single curve does not give the entire picture.
The above curve represents a general average. It is
notable that the value of the transfer function is
greater than unity, indicating that the eye enhances
the true contrast.

Ingelstam and others. Figure 9.13 shows the approximate form; details
vary slightly with different investigators.

Equation (9.13) may be used to derive a transfer function for any process
for which an image point spread function may be defined. This is the case
for image motion of various kinds, such as vibration, atmospheric seeing,
reflected target motion, etc.

Figure 9.14 shows the line spread functions for image motion caused by
sinusoidal motion (vibration), linear motion (target motion) and random
motion (atmospheric seeing) for a common value of a parameter $a$, which
has the significances indicated in the figure.

Shack has treated these effects at some length,[17] showing that the resulting transfer functions are as shown in Figure 9.15.

The necessary independence of the separate factors required for Equation (9.33) to be valid must be remembered in the case of image motions.
For example, linear image motions from several separate causes are not

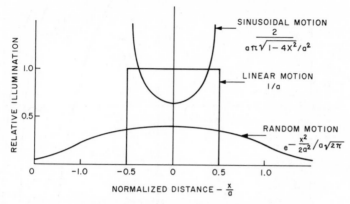

FIGURE 9.14. Line spread functions for image motions.

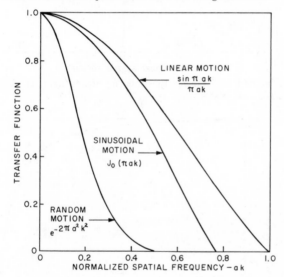

FIGURE 9.15. Modulation transfer functions for
image motions.

independent—they must be combined before the transfer function is computed.

**9.19. Log-log Plots.** It is frequently convenient to plot transfer functions in log-log coordinates on a normalized basis, as has been done in Figure 9.16. It is then possible to prepare overlays and underlays and combine the transfer functions graphically. Figures 9.16 to 9.19 show several of the functions discussed above plotted in this way.

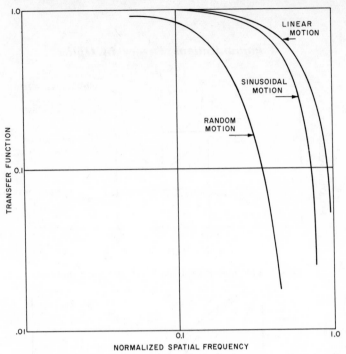

FIGURE 9.16. Transfer functions for image motions plotted on log-log coordinates.

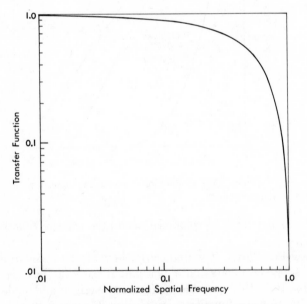

FIGURE 9.17. Modulation transfer function for a diffraction limited rectangular aperture, plotted on log-log coordinates.

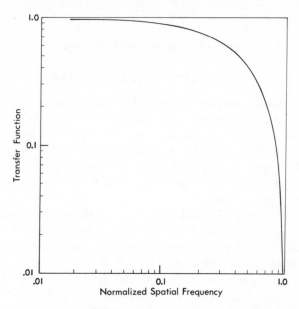

FIGURE 9.18. Modulation transfer function for a diffraction limited circular aperture, plotted on log-log coordinates.

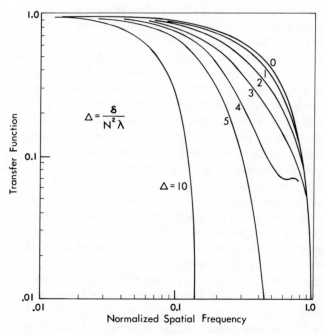

$$\Delta = \frac{\delta}{N^2 \lambda}$$

FIGURE 9.19. Modulation transfer functions for defocused circular apertures. $\delta$ is the actual amount of focus error, $N$ is the relative aperture.

501

# CONCEPT DISCUSSION

**9.20. Real and Complex Aspects.** For the case of incoherent light, it is valid to treat an optical system as a linear filter with respect to *intensity*, and the *image intensity spatial spectrum* is the *object intensity spatial spectrum* multiplied by the *modulus of the optical transfer function* (the modulation transfer function). And the OTF is the Fourier transform of the *point spread function*, where the latter represents the *intensity distribution* in the image of a point source.[18]

When aberrations are present in the system, the aperture function is no longer real, but complex, and the transfer function cannot be determined by a convolution of the aperture, but must be determined directly as the transform of the spread function. The spread function in the presence of aberrations must be either measured, computed from the optical path differences of the design data, or determined by the product of the *point spread amplitude function* and its complex conjugate.

The concept is summed up in the statement that an optical system in incoherent light is a linear system in terms of intensity if the pupil function is a real function, i.e., if the system is aberration free.

It is frequently the case in practice that systems are well enough corrected that their analysis as strictly linear systems yields a sufficiently close approximation to be entirely satisfactory for most purposes. The departure from complete rigor should, however, be kept in mind. In all cases, the image intensity function is the convolution of the point spread function with the object intensity function, as expressed in Equation (9.8).

**9.21. Effect of Aberrations.** When a system has residual aberrations, the *amplitude* of the pupil function is still constant for a point source, but there are *phase* differences, which make the pupil function complex. The point spread functions (amplitude and intensity) are not the usual diffraction patterns of a point source but are more complicated.

The case of departure from focus is a convenient one to discuss, since it is a common problem. Figure 9.20 shows the effect on the point spread function of a departure from correct focus by successively larger steps.

The function first begins to spread in the neighborhood of the maximum, and then exhibits a central depression, which leads to an apparent doubling of the image. The case of spherical aberration leads to a very similar condition, except the change is less rapid because in spherical aberration all of the zones of the aperture are not equally out of focus. The effect is readily observable in an instrument; as the image of a point is examined at a plane slightly displaced from the focus, it will appear to spread, and then to develop a dark central spot.

Figure 9.21 shows the corresponding effect on the transfer function.

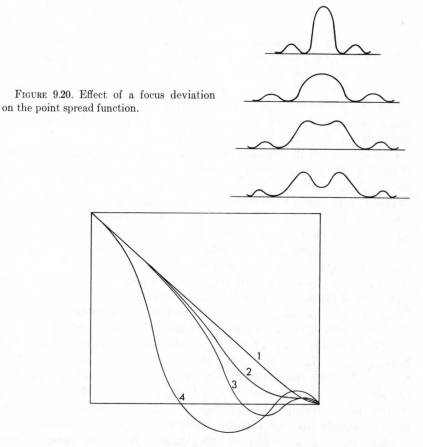

FIGURE 9.20. Effect of a focus deviation on the point spread function.

FIGURE 9.21. Effect of a focus deviation on the optical transfer function.

Those familiar with Fourier transforms will recognize the relationships. When the spread function begins to show a central dip, the transfer function begins to develop a negative lobe.

**9.22. Frequency Augmentation.** Negative lobes in the OTF indicate the condition of a multiple-peaked spread function, as well as an appearance in the image of higher spatial frequencies than those exhibited in the object. This effect was observed in imagery before its fundamental cause was understood, and at that time it acquired the unfortunate name of "spurious resolution"—unfortunate because, so far as the image is concerned it is not spurious at all, but quite real. We accordingly prefer the term *frequency augmentation*.

## COHERENT LIGHT

**9.23. Linearity Relations.** The situation for coherent light is quite different from that for incoherent light. The illumination of objects with coherent light is met with in the microscope, and the condition was discussed briefly in a qualitative way in Section 6.54, concerning Abbe's theory of microscope imagery. One can speculate that if Abbe's concepts had been followed up, the present discipline of transfer function analysis might have been available nearly a century ago.

Coherent object illumination is also met with in laboratory test conditions and is likely to become relatively common in the future with the advent of the laser as an illumination source.

The key to the difference between the situation in coherent and in incoherent light is the fundamental fact that an optical system is not a linear filter in *intensity* for coherent light, whereas it is a linear filter for *amplitude* in this case. In contradistinction, it is a linear filter in intensity but not in amplitude for incoherent light.

For the case of coherent light, the optical transfer function is the Fourier transform of the *point amplitude function*, and it relates the Fourier transforms of the *object amplitude function* and the *image amplitude function* by simple multiplication when the *pupil amplitude function* is real.

**9.24. Determination of the Optical Transfer Function for Coherent Light.** The image amplitude function, in the case of coherent light, is given by the convolution of the object amplitude function and the point amplitude function; therefore the product relation expressed in the previous paragraph is valid. However, the Fourier transform of the point amplitude function is the aperture function itself (see Section 9.6).

Figure 9.22 shows the transfer function relations for the coherent light case.

**9.25. The Aberration-free Case.** When there are no aberrations, the phase is constant across the aperture, and the aperture function, and therefore the optical transfer function, is real and is as shown in Figure 9.22. The transfer function is unity out to the limiting frequency $1/2\,N\lambda$ and zero outside. Therefore, for the case of coherent light, the limiting spatial frequency of an aberration-free system is exactly one-half that of the same system operating in incoherent light. This can be seen mathematically by noting that for coherent light, the range of the function is only over one aperture radius, whereas for incoherent light (Figure 9.10), the convolution of the aperture involved a range of *two* radii. Philosophical acceptance is perhaps not quite as easy, but this is exactly the result obtained by Abbe (see Section 6.54) and the qualitative discussion below may shed further light.

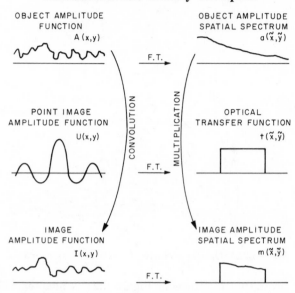

FIGURE 9.22. Functional relationships for coherent illumination.

**9.26. Partial Coherence.** There are, of course, situations which represent varying degrees of coherence, from complete incoherence to complete coherence. The rigorous analysis of such cases becomes very complex and is not discussed here. Born and Wolf give perhaps the best treatment.[19]

The case of partial coherence is not in fact an intermediate case: in the case of incoherence, the OTF is valid for expressing intensity relations between object and image; in the case of coherence, the intensity relations are not linear, and the OTF is valid for expressing amplitude relations. The condition of partial coherence is really a combination of two separate cases and is best treated as such—the analysis being carried through separately for the coherent and the incoherent parts.

## QUALITATIVE DISCUSSION

**9.27. General.** The above mathematical discussion of the diffraction theory of optical systems in terms of Fourier transform relations will satisfy those to whom visualizations come readily from mathematical equations. For those to whom such visualizations do not come so readily, a qualitative discussion may be more satisfactory. The following represents an extension of the concepts set forth originally by Abbe.

**9.28. Idealized Optical Arrangement.** To simplify the discussion,

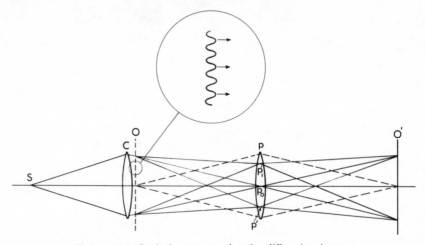

FIGURE 9.23. Optical geometry for the diffraction image.

the optical arrangement shown in Figure 9.23 is adopted. This system arrangement makes the relationships more readily understood on a qualitative basis, but it is not restrictive; the conclusions drawn are valid for any system arrangement. The system of Figure 9.23 is actually the optical system of a projector, although it resembles the compound microscope with coherent illumination, except that the imaging lens is located in the focal plane of the condenser. The system is used in exactly this way in experiments on spatial filtering, which are discussed below.

**9.29. The Coherent Light Case.** The object is assumed to be a grating with a sinusoidal amplitude distribution, shown schematically in the insert to Figure 9.23; it is an approximation to a single sinusoidal object component. The case of coherent light is discussed first, since it is simpler.

For this case, the illumination is by a single wave front of constant amplitude emerging from the condenser lens. This light may be assumed to come from a point source at S, in which case the wave front is a spherical one, converging to an image at p.

Now, the image at p is the Fraunhofer diffraction pattern of the object O, and it will be remembered that this is the Fourier transform of O (see Section 9.6). Since O is a simple sinusoid, its Fourier transform is a point, since the Fourier transform is its frequency spectrum, and it has only one frequency. The image at p is also the diffraction pattern of a grating, which will consist of a zeroth-order beam on axis and a series of maxima on each side at angles $\theta$ which satisfy the condition $s \sin \theta = \lambda$, where $s$ is the grating spacing. Since there is only one spatial frequency, there is only one maximum. By reasons of system symmetry, this maximum appears on both sides of the zeroth-order beam, the latter representing the "dc" illumination level which must be present in a real case.

The diffraction image at p, therefore, consists of a point at $p_0$, which is the zeroth-order beam, and points at $p_1$ and $p_1'$, which are the first-order maxima.

**9.30. The Diffraction Image.** The zeroth-order beam spreads out to cover the image plane at $O'$; the first-order beam is converged by the lens to also cover the same image plane. *The image is created by the interference pattern between these two beams.* When the object is made up of a super-position of sinusoidal components, each separate frequency component has its own location for the first-order image point in the lens P, the location depending upon the frequency according to the above rule for the value of $\theta$. The light from the zeroth and from the first order for each of these components will interfere in the image plane $O'$ in a location conjugate to the location in the object, and thus an image is built up.

It is again emphasized that the individual sinusoidal components which are described by the Fourier transform relationship do not really exist as independent objects in the object field. A specific object detail contains a set of frequencies. For example, a conventional diffraction grating is a "square-wave" object; its spatial frequency spectrum consists of a set of discrete harmonic frequencies. If such a grating is placed in the plane O there will be, as previously described, a series of maxima of increasing angle $\theta$ and increasing order. Each of these maxima, from the point of view of this discussion, may be considered to be a first-order beam for a specific harmonic component of the grating spatial spectrum.

**9.31. Limiting Frequency.** It is now easy to understand the limiting frequency which can be transmitted by the lens P; it is that frequency for which the first-order image $p_1$ just enters the lens at the edge of the aperture. The first-order beam for a higher frequency cannot pass the aperture and hence cannot contribute to the image formation at the image plane $O'$; the zeroth-order beams for these higher frequencies contribute only a constant light level over the whole image plane.

This limiting frequency is expressed by the angle $\theta$, which is, for small values of $\theta$

$$\theta = \lambda/2D \tag{9.34}$$

and when this is expressed in terms of spatial frequency at the image plane the coherent light limiting spatial frequency becomes $1/2N\lambda$.

**9.32. Off-axis Condition.** In the arrangement of Figure 9.23, there is a redundance in that there are two first-order images, $p_1$ and $p_1'$, which pass through the aperture, when the zeroth-order beam is imaged on the axis.

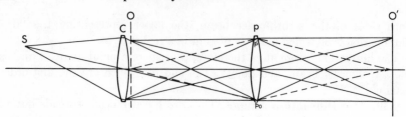

FIGURE 9.24. The diffraction image with obliquely incident light.

Only one of these beams is essential to the development of image structure in the image plane—the other contributes nothing but additional light, and a resulting improvement in contrast. To attain the limiting frequency, it would be sufficient to admit just one of these beams together with the zeroth-order beam.

If the position of the point source is changed, as shown in Figure 9.24, so that the zeroth-order beam is imaged at the edge of the aperture, then the first-order beam for a frequency twice as high as that for the axial case will be admitted, and it would seem that the limiting frequency of the lens is therefore doubled. *This is actually the case,* but there are other factors to be considered.

The drawings show the situation in only one plane—spatial frequencies in directions corresponding to a plane normal to the paper and in other planes at various angles must be considered. Actually, the spatial frequencies in a scene lie in all directions, and the first-order beams for a given frequency component will lie on a circle concentric to the zeroth-order beam.

In the axial case, all directions are equally treated by a circular aperture; in the off-axis case shown in Figure 9.24 while it is true that the aperture will accept the first-order beam corresponding to a higher spatial frequency in the direction of the off-axis shift, it reduces the spatial frequencies which are accepted in planes lying at angles to this direction, and the limiting spatial frequency in the plane orthogonal to the shift is reduced to zero.

Therefore, the image of an object under these conditions will have improved resolution in one direction, but zero resolution in a direction normal thereto. Such an image would not generally be considered acceptable.

**9.33. Incoherent Illumination.** In the arrangement of Figure 9.23, incoherent illumination is best exemplified by assuming that the source, instead of being a point, is of large extent, as shown in Figure 9.25. Each point of the object is now illuminated from a wide angle of source. The zeroth- and first-order beams from a sinusoidal component still have the same relative structure, but now there are an infinite number of such

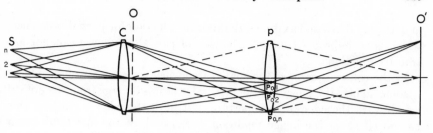

FIGURE 9.25. Incoherent illumination.

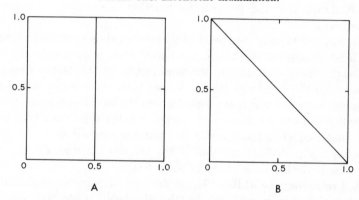

|     A     |     B     |

FIGURE 9.26. Transfer functions of a rectangular aperture for (A) coherent and for (B) incoherent light.

beams, and the zeroth order now covers the full aperture of the lens, P—each point representing a zeroth order image for a corresponding point of the source. Similarly, there will be an infinite set of first-order beams, the set covering the full area of the aperture.

The limiting frequency is now established by the highest frequency component whose first-order beam and zeroth-order beam can both pass the aperture—this is the one corresponding to a zeroth-order beam which is imaged at the edge of the aperture, as in the off-axis case in coherent light. And this is twice the limiting frequency of the on-axis coherent light case.

**9.34. Shapes of the Transfer Functions.** From the preceding discussion, it is possible to understand the difference in shape of the transfer functions for the coherent and the incoherent cases, which are reproduced for comparison in Figure 9.26. These are deliberately not drawn on the same graph, because one refers to amplitude relations and the other to intensity relations. They are sometimes drawn on the same graph, and when this is done, there is a strong tendency to interpolate between them and assume that one has drawn the transfer function for partial coherence, which is an improper concept. The case of partial coherence calls for *two* transfer functions.

In the coherent case, as the spatial frequency components of the object become higher, the images of the first-order beams diverge from the optical axis toward the edge of the aperture; but until the edge is reached, this has no effect on the image rendition, because all of the first-order beam gets through. At the edge of the aperture, however, the first-order beam suddenly disappears, and the transfer function immediately vanishes for this frequency.

In the incoherent case, each point of the source acts separately and forms, through interference in the final image plane between its zeroth- and first-order beams, its contribution to the total image. As the spatial frequency increases, and the first-order beams diverge from the zeroth-order beams, the area of the source which can contribute to the final image grows smaller and smaller, until in the limit, only one point in the source can contribute, and at that frequency the transfer function has reached zero.

The constantly decreasing value of the transfer function for the incoherent case is readily understood in these terms.

**9.35. Frequency Doubling.** If, in the case of coherent illumination, as illustrated in Figure 9.23, the zeroth-order beam is blocked, and only the two first-order beams are allowed to reach the image plane O′, interference between these beams will occur, and a sinusoidal image component will be generated, just as when the zeroth-order beam was present. But now, the angular divergence between the two interfering beams is twice as great as when the zeroth-order beam and one of the first-order beams was considered; as a result, the image component which is reproduced has *twice* the frequency of the object component. This was demonstrated by Abbe in the microscope.

**9.36. Phase Contrast.** It is now possible to shed more light on the subject of phase contrast (see Section 6.56) since this is readily understandable in the terms of the above discussion. Consider an object plane illuminated by coherent light, as shown in Figure 9.27; this object plane

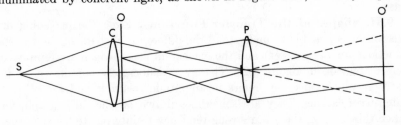

FIGURE 9.27. Geometrical principle of phase contrast.

is featureless with respect to intensity, but contains detail which affects the *phase* of the incident light. Such detail is often found in biological specimens—transparent objects which are, however, of a slightly different index of refraction than the surround. Imperfections in a polished glass surface, such as the surface of a lens, is another case in point.

Such *phase objects* give rise to a diffraction pattern, since they disturb the interference conditions which, using Huygens' construction (see Section 1.3) prevent a light beam from spreading. This diffraction pattern is shown in Figure 9.27 as a beam which fills the aperture of the lens P.

When this light is recombined in the image plane, the phase differences of the two beams are the same, and there is therefore no interference pattern produced. Suppose now, however, that a *phase plate* is placed in the path of the main beam (zeroth order) so as to introduce a phase shift of some selected amount. Now, when the light from the phase object is recombined in the image plane, a phase difference will exist, interference will occur, and there will be a variation in intensity which is observable.

By changing the retardation produced by the phase plate, the phase contrast may be made positive or negative, i.e., a phase object which retards the light can be made to appear either dark or light against the background. By introducing absorption into the phase plate, the phase contrast is enhanced (at the cost of total illumination). It is possible, in phase contrast microscopes, to make phase objects visible which change the optical path by as little as 1Å.

**9.37. Limitations on Coherence.** The discussion of Section 9.35 assumed that the illumination was coherent—from a point source. This is not a necessary restriction; the only restriction is that the image of the source formed by the condenser C be small with respect to the area covered by the diffracted light from the phase objects in the field, so that the phase plate can be made selective. It is customary to provide an annular light source of relatively small size and an annular phase plate. The phase plate must completely cover the image of the source.

**9.38. Limit of Resolution.** The transfer function concept permits a somewhat more objective determination of the limit of resolution of an optical system than the Rayleigh limit (see Section 6.22), but there is still a subjective factor involved. The spatial frequency for which the transfer function goes to zero is, as has been noted, $\bar{x}_0 = 1/N\lambda$, for which the angular subtense is $\lambda/D$. At the spatial frequency corresponding to the angular Rayleigh limit, $1.22\lambda/D$, the transfer function of an aberration-free circular aperture has a value of about .09. It can be demonstrated that the human eye can detect a modulation of about .01 or .02 in the image of a parallel-bar target, which corresponds, for a perfect aperture, to a spatial frequency higher than that given by the Rayleigh limit. Various limiting

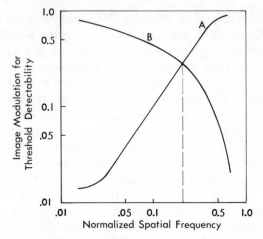

FIGURE 9.28. Determination of limiting resolution by means of the A.I.M. Curve A. A.I.M. or detectability curve. B. Transfer function of system for the aerial image at the focal plane.

values of modulation for detectability are adopted by different individuals—.04 is a fairly common value.

When photographic systems are being considered, it is possible to develop a curve which expresses the required modulation in the optical image to produce threshold detectability in the photographic material being considered. Such a curve is called an AIM (aerial image modulation) curve[22] and may be laid over the transfer function curve of a system, as shown in Figure 9.28. The intersection of the two curves then indicates the resolution limit of the system.

## OPTICAL CORRELATION AND FILTERING

**9.39. The Frequency Plane.** Referring to Figure 9.23, and the discussion in Sections 9.28 and 9.29, it was shown that the light distribution in the plane P is the Fourier transform of the light distribution in the object plane, O. Hence, the distribution of amplitude over the plane P is the *complex spatial frequency spectrum* of the object. Each point in the plane P at radius $r$ from the optical axis locates the first-order maximum corresponding to a specific spatial frequency in the object. This spatial frequency has a definite orientation (parallel to the radius to the point) and a definite value of frequency, given by the relation $\theta = d/\lambda$, where $d$ is the cyclic spacing. This situation is illustrated in Figure 9.29.

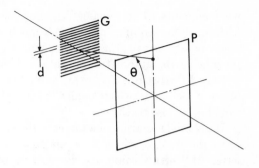

FIGURE 9.29. Location of the first order maxium. G. Idealized grating. P. Frequency plane. $\theta$ Angular position of first order maximum. d. Grating spacing.

This plane, where the spatial frequency spectrum is formed, is commonly called the *frequency plane*. In the arrangement of Figure 9.23, it is at the entrance pupil of the lens P; in the case of coherent illumination in the microscope, it is at the principal focal plane of the objective; in general, it is located at the plane where the source is imaged by the objective lens of the system.

**9.40. Spatial Filtering.** It is clear that by placing suitable masks in the frequency plane, it is possible to extract a specific spatial frequency or a desired combination of spatial frequencies and allow the image formed at $O'$ to be composed of these frequencies only. This is a powerful technique for analysis of the spatial frequency content of the object.

One particularly useful application of the technique is the identification of specific target patterns in a complex background. A particular target pattern—for example, a letter—will possess a particular spatial frequency spectrum, and if the system of Figure 9.23 is provided with a filter in the plane P which will transmit only this spectrum, the result in the image plane $O'$ will be an image of the letter only, the remainder of the information in the object field having been suppressed by the filter.

It is seen that the specific target object (the letter) will be imaged in its appropriate location in the image plane. It can be shown that no two different real objects can have identical spatial spectra, even in the limited frequency range provided by a real optical system.

**9.41. Character Recognition.** The automatic recognition of specific types of objects immersed in a complex background is a valuable technique in many areas—in aerial photo-interpretation, in microscopic examination of tissues and cells, in the photography of nuclear particle behavior, and elsewhere. A number of complex machines have been constructed to accomplish this by detailed scanning of the object photography and the application of involved mathematical computations to the derived signal. Optical spatial filtering, based upon the principle described above, offers what amounts to an "analog" method for accomplishing the same result with much less equipment and in a much shorter time. This general technique has been called *automatic character recognition*, one of its applications being the automatic translation of foreign language documents.

**9.42. Limitations.** There are two fundamental limitations to the spatial filtering technique which render it somewhat less universally useful than would otherwise be the case.

The spatial spectrum of a target in the object plane is critically dependent upon the *scale* at which it is rendered. A filter which will detect, say, a letter "L" of a certain angular size by selection of its spectrum in the frequency plane, will completely fail if the letter is presented slightly larger or slightly smaller than the size for which the filter has been prepared. In systems designed for this purpose, therefore, it is necessary to include a "scale search" over a suitable range, by varying the magnification between object and image until an exact match with the filter is obtained.

The second limitation is that of orientation, and in many cases this is even more severe than that of scale. It is often impossible to predict how the target which is to be detected will be oriented in the object; the filter, however, must be prepared for a specific orientation, since the spatial spectrum of most objects is a function of direction in the object plane. Practical systems, therefore, must have provision for testing the object complex in all possible orientations by rotation about the optical axis. Completely symmetrical objects, of course, are not subject to this limitation.

**9.43. Filter Preparation.** The obvious approach to preparation of the filter is to place a photographic plate or film in the frequency plane and expose it to a simulated target object located at the object plane O. This is the technique frequently used, but it has the restriction that the photographic plate is sensitive only to *intensity*, and therefore, *phase* information which may be present in the frequency plane is lost. This does not invalidate the procedure, but reduces its utility to a considerable extent.

**9.44. Phase Sensitization.** The system may be made phase sensitive by the adoption of a technique due to Vander Lugt[25]. If, when the filter is prepared, the frequency plane is illuminated by a beam of collimated light introduced at an angle $\phi$, as shown in Figure 9.30, then there will be superimposed upon the filter a set of parallel interference fringes, representing the interference pattern between the zero-order beam of the main system and the additional collimated beam. These fringes will be modified by the first-order beams of the object spatial spectrum. Now, however, phase differences between these beams and the collimated beam, introduced in the object, will appear as variations in intensity of the fringe system.

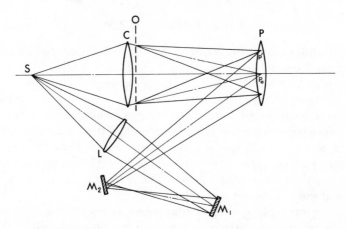

FIGURE 9.30. Arrangement for producing the reference beam.

The principle is identical to that incorporated in the phase contrast microscope described in Section 9.36.

**9.45. Phase-sensitive Projector.** When the system with a phase-sensitized filter is used as a projector, the interference fringes act as a grating in the frequency plane, and there are now three projected images—a zero-order image which contains no phase information, and two flanking images, produced by the filter grating, and containing information on phase as well as intensity.

In this system, of course, compared to the intensity system, the illumination in the final image plane is significantly reduced in the flanking images. In order to avoid over-lapping of the phase images with the zero-order image, the angle $\phi$ of introduction of the collimated beam in the preparation of the filter must be at least as great as half the angular size of the object field.

**9.46. Optical Correlation.** The method of Fourier transform analysis is applicable to many fields—particularly in many varieties of electronic signal processing applications. The use of optical systems as described above to generate the Fourier transform of an object such as a photographic transparency immediately suggests the possible application of optical systems to generate Fourier transforms for other uses.

In general, this can be done in any case where the data to be analyzed can be recorded in such a form that it introduces variations in the amplitude and/or phase of a transmitted beam of collimated light. The technique is referred to as *optical correlation*[24] and is currently undergoing an intensive development in connection with radar and other electronic systems, mostly in areas which, at this writing, are classified.

## THE HOLOGRAM

**9.47. Fundamental Principle.** If an object is illuminated by coherent light, it produces, by reflection or by refraction, a spatial distribution of light amplitudes which is characteristic of the object. If an object, A, as shown in Figure 9.31, is illuminated by coherent light, it will give rise to a set of reflected spherical waves, one corresponding to each point of the object. Since the illumination is coherent, each of these waves are mutually coherent, and hence will produce, in a remote region, P, an interference or diffraction pattern which is determined by the relative location and reflectivity of the various object points. The pattern is characteristic of the object and will be different for different objects.

The same principle applies to transparent or semitransparent objects, where the interference pattern is produced by refraction rather than by reflection.

If this amplitude pattern is recorded in a suitable fashion and the recording is subsequently illuminated by coherent light, the original amplitude distribution (within instrumental limitations) is reproduced, and an image is formed which is similar to the original object.

This is the fundamental principle of the *hologram*—although, admittedly, highly simplified. The recording of the interference pattern is usually referred to as the hologram. Apparatus for producing holograms, and subsequently producing images from them, have been constructed by a number of experimenters, and have produced striking results.[20]

**9.48. Production of the Hologram.** The most obvious way to produce a hologram is to expose a photographic plate in the region P. But the photographic plate is not sensitive to amplitude variations—only to in-

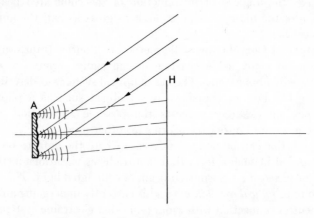

FIGURE 9.31. Production of the hologram.

tensity, and thus some means must be provided for converting the amplitude variations into intensity variations.

This is accomplished in the same fashion as described in connection with spatial filtering in Section 9.44—by introducing a reference coherent beam which has not been altered by the object.

In the original work on holograms by Gabor,[21] the reference beam was the portion of the incident beam on a transparent object which was unaffected by the object characteristics. In the more recent work of Leith and others[26], the reference beam has been introduced at an angle to the object direction, exactly as was described for phase sensitization in spatial filters. The interference between this reference beam and the amplitude pattern produced by the object provides the necessary variations in intensity for recording on a photographic plate. The arrangement is similar to that shown schematically in Figure 9.30. The reference beam must, of course, be coherent with the illuminating source and is therefore taken directly from it. A typical hologram, both with and without phase reference, is shown in Figure 9.32.

**9.49. The Reconstructed Images.** In the arrangement of Gabor, the interference pattern which is produced at the hologram represents the interference of two spherical waves (one from the object point and one constituting the reference beam). These are essentially concentric, and therefore the pattern which is produced in the hologram for a specific object point resembles a Fresnel zone plate (see Section 2.78). In the arrangement of Leith, the reference beam is introduced at an angle, and the pattern which is produced is decentered with respect to the hologram, and consists of a set of fringes.

In the reconstitution of the images, the illumination is introduced in the same direction as the reference beam, and two images are produced, one real and one virtual, as shown in Figure 9.34.

In Gabor's arrangement, these images both lie on the "axis" of the system and are therefore difficult to separate in viewing or reproduction equipment; in the arrangement of Leith, the images are angularly separated, and there is no problem of their intermixture.

**9.50. Historical.** The hologram was first proposed by Gabor[21] as a means for overcoming the severe problems of spherical aberration in electron microscopy. It is not necessary that the illumination of the original object and the illumination used in the reconstruction be of the same or even similar wavelength. The only effect of producing the hologram at one wavelength and the reconstitution at another is to introduce a change of scale. Neither is it necessary that the wave fronts be either plane or spherical—only that the shape of the wave fronts be similar for the hologram and for the reconstruction.

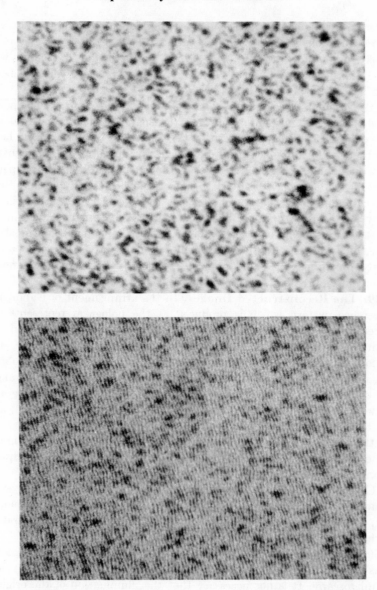

FIGURE 9.32. A typical hologram. This hologram was produced with laser beam from a U. S. Roosevelt dime. The example at the top is without phase sensitization, that at the bottom includes the phase reference beam. The area shown represents a 200× enlargement of the actual hologram; it is only a very small portion of the entire hologram. The interference fringes produced by the reference beam can be seen in the bottom picture.

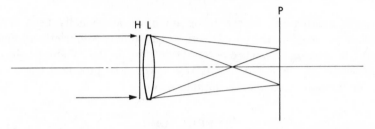

FIGURE 9.33. Projection of hologram to produce a reconstituted picture. The lens is really incidental to the phenomenon, but is useful for the collection of light.

FIGURE 9.34. Reconstituted picture from the hologram illustrated in Figure 9.33. The zero order spot and the two flanking images (real and virtual) can be seen.

It was thus proposed by Gabor that a hologram could be produced by an electron beam and reconstituted with visible light, the visible light being given spherical aberration comparable to that existing in the electron beam, which is not particularly difficult to accomplish.

Technical difficulties have so far prevented realization of this original application for the hologram.

Devices making use of the hologram have occasionally been termed "lenseless cameras" in the popular press. The term is not strictly applicable because, in general, lenses are necessary to provide the coherent light over a sufficiently large angle. Theoretically, it could be produced from a pinhole, but pinhole cameras are nothing new.

## REFERENCES

1. The backgrounds of the subject were developed in the following papers:
   E. Verdet, *Ann. Sci. l'Ecole Normale Superieure*, **2**, 291 (1865); *Lecons d'Optique Physique* (Paris, L'Imprimerie Imperiale) **1**, 106 (1869).
   A. Michelson, *Phil. Mag.*, (5), **30**, 1 (1890); **31**, 256, 338, (1891); **34**, 280 (1892); *Astrophys. J.*, **51**, 257 (1920).
   M. von Laue, *Ann. Phys.*, (4), **23**, 1 (1907).
   M. Berek, *Z. Phys.*, **36**, 675, 874 (1926); **37**, 387 (1926); **40**, 420 (1926).
   P. van Cittert, *Physica*, **1**, 201 (1934); **6**, 1129 (1939).
   F. Zernicke, *Proc. Phys. Soc.*, **61**, 158 (1948); *Physica*, **5**, 785 (1938).
   H. Hopkins, *Proc. Roy. Soc. London Ser. A*, **208**, 263 (1951); *J. Opt. Soc. Am.*, **47**, 508 (1957).
   E. Wolf, *Proc. Roy. Soc. London Ser. A*, **230**, 246 (1955); **225**, 96 (1954); *Nuovo Cimento*, **12**, 884 (1954).
   A. Blanc-Lapierre and P. Dumontet, *Rev. Opt.*, **34**, 1 (1955).
   D. Gabor, in (Z. Kopal, Ed.) "Proceedings of the Symposium on Astronomical Optics," p. 17, Amsterdam, North Holland Publishing Co., 1956; (C. Cherry, Ed.) "Proceedings of the Third Symposium on Information Theory," London, Buttersworth, 1956.
   H. Gamo, *J. Appl. Phys. Japan*, **25**, 431 (1956).
   K. Miyamoto, *J. Opt. Soc. Am.*, **48**, 57 (1958).
2. R. Scott, *Phot. Sci. Eng.*, **3**, 201 (1959).
3. O. Schade, *RCA Rev.*, **9**, Nos. 1, 2, 3, 4 (1948).
4. P. Duffieux, "L'Integral de Fourier et ses Applications a l'Optique," Besancon, Faculte des Sciences, 1946.
5. E. Selwyn, "Proceedings of the Optical Image Evaluation Symposium," 1951, Department of Commerce, National Bureau of Standards, *Natl. Bur. Std. Circ.*, **526**, 219 (1954).
6. O. Schade, *Natl. Bur. Std. Circ.*, **526**, 231 (1954); *J. Soc. Motion Picture Television Engrs.*, **56**, 137 (1951); **58**, 181 (1952).
7. A. Marechal, *J. Soc. Motion Picture Television Engrs.*, **58**, 9 (1952).
8. H. Hopkins, *Proc. Roy. Soc. London Ser. A*, **217**, 408 (1953).
9. P. Fellgett and E. Linfoot, *Phil. Trans. Roy. Soc. London Ser. A*, **247**, 367 (1955).
10. R. Shack, *J. Res. Natl. Bur. Std.*, **56**, 245 (1956); also see reference 5, p. 275.
11. E. O'Neill, *J. Opt. Soc. Am.*, **46**, 285 (1956).
12. P. Elias, D. Grey and D. Robinson, *J. Opt. Soc. Am.*, **42**, 127 (1952).
13. A. Cox, reference 5, p. 267.
    T. Cheatham and A. Kohlenberg, "Analysis and Synthesis of Optical Systems," Pt. 1, Tech. Note **84**, Boston Univ., 1952.
    M. Born and E. Wolf, "Principles of Optics," Pergamon Press, 1959, p. 479 et seq.
    E. Wolf, "Reports on Progress in Physics," XIV, 1951.

R. Lamberts, *J. Soc. Motion Picture Television Engrs.*, **71**, 635 (1962).

13. A. Cox, reference 5, p. 267.
   T. Cheathem and A. Kohlenberg, "Analysis and Synthesis of Optical Systems, Part I, *Boston Univ. Tech. Note*, **84** (1952).
   M. Born and E. Wolf, "Principles of Optics," pp. 479 et seq. New York, Pergamon Press, 1959.
   E. Wolf, *Rept. Progr. Phys.*, **14** (1951).
   R. Lamberts, *J. Soc. Motion Picture Television Engrs.*, **71**, 635 (1962).
14. R. Luneberg, "Mathematical Theory of Optics," Providence, R. I., Brown University, 1944.
15. International Commission on Optics, *Phot. Sci. Eng.*, **5**, 282 (1961).
16. M. Françon, "Modern Applications of Physical Optics," New York, Interscience Publishers, 1963.
17. R. Shack, Appl. Optics, **3**, 1171 (1964).
18. R. Jones, *J. Soc. Motion Picture Television Engrs.*, **69**, 151, 239 (1960); *J. Opt. Soc. Am.*, **48**, 487, 490 (1958); **51**, 1441 (1961).
19. M. Born and E. Wolf, "Principles of Optics," pp. 490 *et seq.*, New York, Pergamon Press, 1959.
   See also D. Gabor, reference 1.
20. W. Bragg and G. Rogers, *Nature*, **167**, 190 (1951).
   M. Haine and J. Dyson, *Nature*, **166**, 315 (1950).
   G. Rogers, *Proc. Roy. Soc. Edinburgh*, **A63**, 193, 313 (1952).
   Reference 19, pp. 452 *et seq.*
21. D. Gabor, *Nature*, **161**, 777 (1948); *Proc. Roy. Soc. London Ser. A*, **197**, 454 (1949); *Proc. Phys. Soc. B*, **64**, 449 (1951).
22. F. Scott, Proc. SPSE Conf., Cleveland, Ohio, May 17, 1964.
23. R. Heim and N. Kapany, *J. Opt. Soc. Am.*, **48**, 351 (1958).
24. L. Kovasznay and A. Arman, *Rev. Sci. Instr.*, **28**, 793 (1957).
25. A. Vander Lugt, IEEE Trans. on Information Theory, **IT-10**, 139 (1964).
26. E. Leith and J. Upatnieks, *J. Opt. Soc. Am.*, **54**, 1295 (1964); **53**, 1377 (1963).

# CHAPTER 10

# Miscellaneous Topics

**10.1. Introduction.** In this chapter, some selected topics associated to a greater or less degree with the mainstream of optical science are discussed briefly. The discussion is short and chiefly of an introductory character; no attempt is made to describe the principles or apparatus in detail. The fundamental principles involved in these areas either are adequately covered in other chapters, or are concerned with subjects such as electronics which are beyond the scope of this book.

## FIBER OPTICS

**10.2. Description.** Fiber optics[1, 2] is a development subsequent to World War II; it concerns the application of fine threads of transparent materials which are usually prepared by drawing from a heat-softened mass. Optical fibers obey all of the laws of geometrical and physical optics, but their shape and dimensions make possible certain unique applications.

There has been some misconception about the properties of optical fibers, and the term "light pipe" has been used to describe fibers, with the implication that they "conduct" light in the same way a wire conducts an electric current or a pipe conducts a fluid. When optical fibers are made in dimensions which are not large with respect to a wavelength of light, they behave as *wave guides* and must be examined theoretically by the disciplines which apply to wave guides in microwave electronics. A discussion of these principles is beyond the scope of this book, but is readily available in the literature. For this class of phenomena, the fibers must have diameters of the order of 1 to $2\mu$. Fibers of these dimensions have been made, and it is likely that they may become generally available in the not too distant future and that they may be applied to areas where their peculiar properties will be advantageous. Currently, however, reliable production of optical fibers is limited to a minimum diameter of about $5\mu$, somewhat too large for the wave-guide effects to become dominant.

**10.3. Geometrical Optics of a Long Cylinder.** An introduction to the optical behavior of fibers can be gleaned from consideration of a long straight cylinder of transparent material, with light incident at one end, as shown in Figure 10.1. If the cylinder is straight and of uniform diameter, which properties are assumed for preliminary discussion, then the diagram, which shows a meridional ray, represents the condition which gives the minimum angle of incidence at the inner surface of the cylinder. If this angle is greater than the critical angle, the light will be totally reflected internally, and the ray will be transported by multiple reflection down the cylinder to emerge at the opposite end.

Since the critical angle is given by $\sin I_c = 1/\mu$, and since, from the diagram, $\sin I_2 = \cos I_1'$, the condition for total internal reflection is

$$\cos I_1' \geq 1/\mu \tag{10.1}$$

and, when the law of refraction is applied to write the expression in terms of the original angle of incidence, $I_1$, the condition becomes

$$\mu^2 \geq \sin^2 I_1 + 1 \tag{10.2}$$

The quantity $\sin I_1$ cannot be greater than unity (for a ray at grazing incidence), hence the condition for *all* incident light to be totally reflected internally is

$$\mu \geq \sqrt{2} \tag{10.3}$$

This is true for nearly all transparent materials, and especially for glass, so that a glass rod in air will have total internal reflection for all light which enters through an end face, provided it is straight and of uniform diameter.

**10.4. Surface Losses.** Another required condition for total internal re-

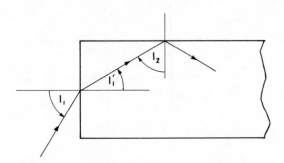

FIGURE 10.1. Light path in a dielectric cylinder

flection is that the surface of the rod be perfectly smooth and clean. Pits, digs, and scratches will, of course, cause loss of light to the outside. Also, contamination in the form of opaque material will absorb light refracted into the material, and transparent material, if it has external surfaces which are not parallel to the cylinder surface, will also cause loss of light, by reducing the critical angle at the cylinder surface, and providing faces which will permit some of this light to escape.

A layer of transparent material on an optical surface, regardless of the value of its index of refraction, will not destroy total internal reflection, provided only that its external surface is of optical quality and is parallel to the original surface. This is shown in Figure 10.2. Let $\mu_1$, $\mu_2$ and $\mu_3$ be the indices of refraction of the three media, as shown. $I_2 = I_1'$, as shown, and, by the law of refraction

$$\sin I_1' = \frac{\mu_1}{\mu_2} \sin I_1 \qquad (10.4)$$

Now, if $I_1$ is equal to the critical angle for the medium $\mu_1$ in contact with $\mu_3$ directly, then $\sin I_1 = \mu_3/\mu_1$. Substituting this in Equation (10.4) shows that for this case

$$\sin I_2 = \mu_3/\mu_2 \qquad (10.5)$$

which is the critical angle for the second surface. Therefore, while a layer of material on an optical surface will change the critical angle at that surface, the critical angle for the combination will be the same as without the layer.

**10.5. Shrouding of Fibers.** Since it is almost impossible to maintain fibers permanently in a perfectly clean condition, and further, since for many applications it is necessary to bond the fibers in some sort of matrix for mechanical reasons, it is customary to protect the optical quality of

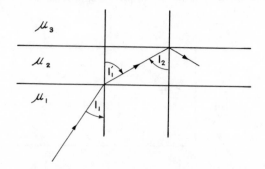

Figure 10.2. Optical effect of a surface layer

the fiber surface by shrouding or cladding the fiber with a transparent material of lower index than the fiber body itself, as shown in Figure 10.3.

The benefit of the cladding is obtained only if the total internal reflection occurs at the inner boundary between the fiber and the shroud. This places conditions upon the ratio of the refractive indices of the two materials, or it places a limitation on the maximum angle of incidence for light at the entrance end of the rod which will be transmitted by total internal reflection. If this maximum angle of incidence is expressed in the form $\mu_0 \sin \theta$, it may, by analogy with optical systems, be termed the *numerical aperture* of the rod, and it is easily shown that

$$\mu_0 \sin \theta \sqrt{\mu_1{}^2 - \mu_2{}^2} \qquad (10.6)$$

where $\mu_0$ is the index of refraction of the medium in which the rod is immersed (usually air).

Current techniques provide fibers with a minimum diameter of about $5\mu$, 10 to $12\mu$ being more common, with cladding of low index materials about 1 to $2\mu$ thick. Numerical apertures of unity have been achieved for straight fibers—all light entering the face is transmitted by total internal reflection.

**10.6. Transmission.** Light losses for ideal fibers with a numerical aperture sufficient to accept all of the light incident upon the entrance face are therefore limited to losses due to absorption within the fiber material. This is generally quite low, being less than 1 per cent per centimeter of optical path, which makes possible the use of fibers several feet in length. The extreme optical path in a fiber is $L \sec I_1'$, where $L$ is the length of the fiber. For an index of 1.6, the path is only $1.28\,L$, so that the difference in the absorption for the extreme rays and the axial ray is not great.

A light transmission factor of the order of 80 per cent per foot is typical.

**10.7. Conical Channels.** An optical fiber with diameter variations along its length is analogous to a conical rod, as illustrated in Figure 10.4. Conical rods are frequently used as light collectors, particularly in connection with photodetectors.

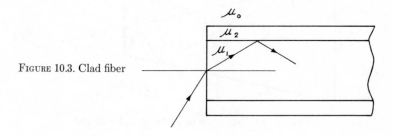

FIGURE 10.3. Clad fiber

Light which enters the large end of a conical rod is totally internally reflected. The conditions for total internal reflection are those discussed in Section 10.3. For a cone, the acceptance angle increases as the apex angle of the cone increases. For glass in air, it has been shown that the acceptance angle is a complete hemisphere even for an apex angle of zero.

In the cone, however, each succeeding angle of incidence is less than the preceding one by the apex angle of the cone, as is indicated in Figure 10.4. There will, therefore, be an incident angle for which the ray will never reach the exit face, but will return to the entrance face, if the critical angle is zero (silvered cone). With a transparent cone, even before this limiting case is reached, the critical angle condition will have been violated, and a large part of the light will escape through the walls.

Figure 10.5 shows how the limiting condition for the return of a ray to the entrance face of a conical channel can be graphically determined. The cone is graphically developed by successive 180° rotations about an edge, as shown.

All rays which intersect the developed polygon formed by the exit face of the channel will (excluding surface losses) be transmitted through the channel. Rays which do not intersect this polygon will be returned to the entrance face.

This technique of developing an optical component by successive rotations about the faces at which internal reflections occur is a useful technique for the ray tracing of prisms. Figure 10.6 shows how this technique is used to reveal the source of a ghost in a Porro prism.

The limiting condition for transmission of a ray in the conical channel shown in Figure 10.5 may be approximated by assuming the polygons formed by the entrance and exit faces to be circles with radii $R_1$ and $R_2$ respectively. Then the condition becomes

$$\sin \alpha \leq R_2/R_1 \tag{10.7}$$

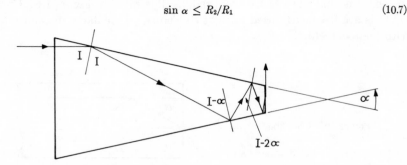

FIGURE 10.4. Refraction in a conical dielectric rod

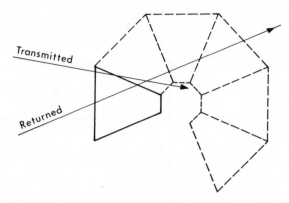

FIGURE 10.5. Limiting condition for a conical channel

where $\alpha$ is the angle of *refraction* at the entrance face. This condition is readily translated into the condition

$$E_1/E_2 \leq \mu \tag{10.8}$$

where $E_1/E_2$ is the ratio of diameter of entrance and exit faces, and $\mu$ is the index of refraction of the medium. It should be remembered that losses through the side walls and from total internal reflection at the exit face occur before the condition is approached, when the surface is not mirrored.

**10.8. Bent Fibers.** Many of the applications of fiber optics depend upon their flexibility, even in large bundles, and their ability to be bent around corners.

When the fiber is bent, as shown in Figure 10.7, the conditions derived in Section 10.3 no longer hold; the angle of incidence at the surface of the cylinder is reduced, and in general there will be a minimum radius of bend for which a particular numerical aperture can be maintained.

If the geometry is analyzed for a meridional ray, such as is shown in Figure 10.7, it will be found that the minimum radius comes out to about $R \geq 3.5d$ for an index of 1.5. This, however, is an inadequate treatment, since for a bent fiber, it is the skew rays which first begin to be lost through the surface due to failure to meet the critical angle condition. It is necessary that the radius of bend be held to a value greater than about $20d$ to avoid refractive losses through the walls for most realizable fibers. Since the dimensions of typical fibers are measured in microns, this is not a very severe restriction.

**10.9. Fiber Construction.** The usual construction technique for fibers is first to form them into bundles of up to 10,000 fibers each and then, if the application requires it, to put a number of bundles into a larger array. Figure 10.8 shows a typical bundle of fibers. The ends are packed as

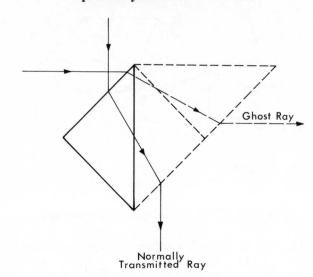

FIGURE 10.6. Ghost tracing in a Porro prism

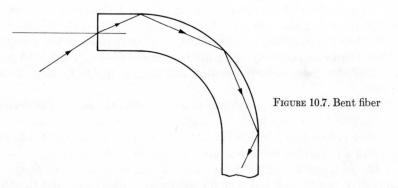

FIGURE 10.7. Bent fiber

densely together as possible, embedded in a solid matrix, and optically finished as a unit. Figure 10.9 is a microphotograph of the finished end of a fiber bundle, showing the capability of current technology to pack the fibers very close together and in a regular array.

Some of the more common applications for optical fibers are described briefly below.

**10.10. Image Transfer.** One of the most obvious and effective uses of optical fibers is the transfer of an image from one point to another, often by a circuitous path. Figure 10.10 shows a typical application of this type, in which the image geometry is maintained throughout the transfer by

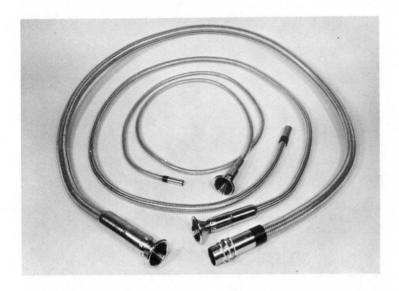

FIGURE 10.8. Fiber optics bundles. Top: Long, flexible tubes, known as fiberscopes. Bottom: Tapered bundles. (*Courtesy Space-Defense Division, American Optical Co.*)

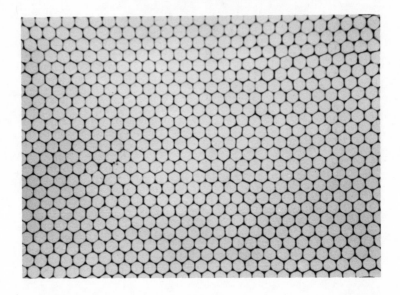

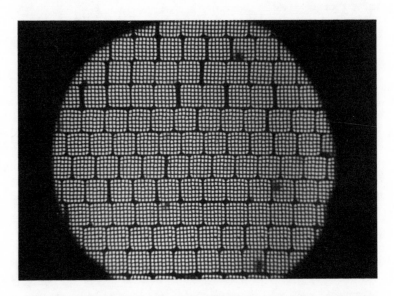

FIGURE 10.9. Microphoto cross section of fiber bundles. Top: 100-micron fibers in a solid bundle. Bottom: 10-micron fibers in an array of small bundles. (*Courtesy Space-Defense Division, American Optical Co.*)

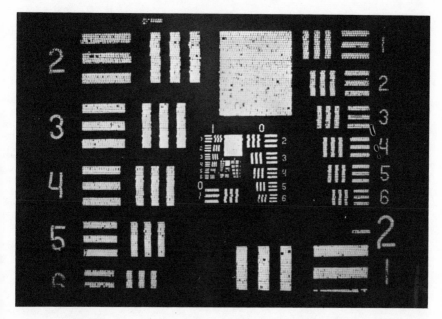

FIGURE 10.10. Resolution chart viewed through fiber bundle illustrated at top in Figure 10.9. (*Courtesy Space-Defense Division, American Optical Co.*)

packing the fibers in parallel array before any bending or twisting of the bundle takes place.

When a fiber optics bundle is used in this way, one end being placed in contact with an object, or an image formed by a conventional optical system, and the other end located wherever it is desired to view the image or to record it in some device such as a television camera or a photographic film, the resolution is limited to the spacing of the individual fibers in the bundle. The fibers do not form images of themselves, they merely collect the light from an image area which is limited by the diameter of the individual fiber, and transfer this light to the other end of the bundle where the image is reconstructed as discrete points represented by the individual fibers. Figure 10.11 shows a highly enlarged photograph of an image transmitted through a fiber bundle.

The transmission factor of a complete bundle is determined by the transmission of the individual fibers, which has been stated to be quite high, and the ratio of actual fiber core area to total area in the bundle. Typical values for this ratio are of the order of 50 to 60 per cent.

**10.11. Dynamic Scanning.** Current technology limits the resolution of

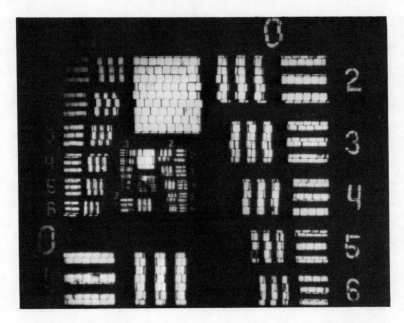

FIGURE 10.11. Resolution chart viewed through fiber bundle illustrated at bottom in Figure 10.9. (*Courtesy Space-Defense Division, American Optical Co.*)

a fiber bundle used statically in the manner described above to an element about $10\mu$ in diameter, or a resolution of 100 lines/mm. For many applications, this is an excellent order of resolution, and most optical systems are not sensibly degraded by this level of performance.

The resolution may be considerably improved, however, and image elements far below the fiber diameter may be resolved in the final image, by a technique known as *dynamic scanning*. If the fiber bundle is oscillated transversely across the field, each fiber acts as a scanning aperture, and the image is transferred in accordance with the transfer function of this aperture (see Chapter 9). This corresponds to a resolution better than the aperture size itself and improves the performance of the system. Figure 10.12 shows comparative results.

The amplitude of the oscillation need be no greater than a few fiber diameters.

**10.12. Variation of Image Geometry.** The possibility of using optical fibers to provide variations in the geometry of a transferred image is obvious. Figure 10.13 shows an example of this technique, wherein a two-dimensional image is transformed into a one-dimensional one.

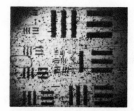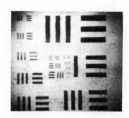

FIGURE 10.12. Dynamic scanning. Left: Image through stationary fiber bundle. Center: Image with scanner operating but slightly out of phase. Right: Image with scanner operating in phase. The scanner consisted of two identical small angle wedges, one at each end of the bundle, rotating in synchronism. Scan motion is circular, the diameter of the scan circle being about .020 inch. Choice of a fiber bundle having many broken fibers and other defects enhances the comparison. The photo at the left is not to be taken as representing typical quality. (*Courtesy Space-Defense Division, American Optical Co.*)

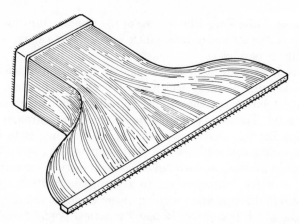

FIGURE 10.13. Fiber optics transform of two dimensions to one dimension.

One of the more intriguing possibilities which has been suggested for image geometry variation is the use of a fiber optics bundle as a coding-decoding device. If a continuous ring fiber bundle, as shown in Figure 10.14, is formed with the fibers entangled at random, and then cut in two, it will form two bundles each of which will "scramble" an image in a random way. One may be used for coding, the other for decoding. There is no record of this technique having actually been used.

Of course, a fiber optics bundle provides an excellent means for image rotation, since rotation of one end of the bundle with respect to the other rotates the image accordingly. Fiber bundles of moderate length are suf-

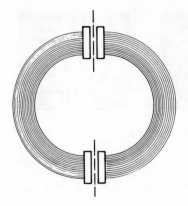

FIGURE 10.14. Random scrambling with a fiber bundle. Before cutting, the fibers are tangled at random, so that an image presented at one end of one of the halves is completely scrambled at the other end. It can be reconstituted only by means of the other half of the original bundle, if the tangling is sufficiently complex.

ficiently flexible that rotation through more than a complete circle is practicable.

**10.13. Image Tube Face Plates.** One of the common uses for fiber optics is in face plates for image tubes, such as television camera tubes and image intensifiers (see below).

When such devices are used in conjunction with conventional optical systems, the maximum energy which can be collected from an object is limited by the relative aperture of the optical system, which rarely approaches even $f/1$. The same principle applies even more strongly when an electro-optical display, as on a cathode ray oscilloscope, is to be transferred to a recording medium such as a photographic film or an image tube.

A fiber optical system can have an effective numerical aperture, as has been shown, of unity, corresponding to a geometric relative aperture of $f/0.5$. If placed in direct contact with an object or an image, it can collect all of the light which is emitted. In many practical applications, the efficiency of a fiber optics bundle, even in the face of a substantial loss in transmission, can be much higher than any practicable conventional optical arrangement.

In order to achieve its full advantage, the fiber optics bundle must be placed in direct contact with the object which is emitting light. This is accomplished in a cathode ray tube, for example, by using a fiber optics plate as the face plate, its internal surface being coated with the phosphor. Figure 10.15 shows an example of such an arrangement.

The achievable resolution, of the order of 100 lines/mm, is considerably in excess of that generally available in the electro-optical devices where this technique is used.

**10.14. Field Flatteners.** Another useful application for fiber optics is as field flatteners in conventional optical systems. It is apparent that the

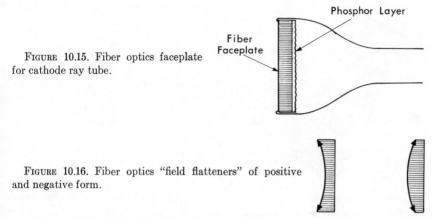

FIGURE 10.15. Fiber optics faceplate for cathode ray tube.

FIGURE 10.16. Fiber optics "field flatteners" of positive and negative form.

possible variation in image geometry which fibers can achieve extends also to variations in the image contour normal to the image plane. A fiber optics bundle may be provided with almost any desired form of surface at each of its ends, and an image which is in contact with one surface will then be transferred to the opposite surface and will fit the contour provided there.

Figure 10.16 shows how a convex or concave image surface may be made flat my means of a fiber optics plate. The freedom given an optical designer when any requirements concerning the shape of the focal plane are removed may be considerable in some applications.

**10.15. Medical Probes.** One of the most interesting of recent applications of fiber optics has been their application in medicine to the observation of internal organs in a living state.[3] A small bundle of fibers, encased in a needle similar to a hypodermic needle, can be inserted into living tissue without undue discomfort to the patient. With part of the bundle transmitting illumination from a suitable source, and the other part coupled to a microscope, the investigator can then observe the living behavior of internal organs and tissues.

While the bundle must be small, it can still contain on the order of 1000 fibers—quite sufficient to obtain a reasonably good resolution.

**10.16. Viewers.** As a final example of applications of fiber optics, their use in viewers may be mentioned. Figure 10.17 illustrates how an array of fiber optics may be interleaved to provide two, or perhaps more, displays from a single image—at the cost, of course, of dividing the available resolution elements between the several displays.

It is also possible, by varying the packing density at the two ends of the bundle, to introduce magnification—again at the cost of a spreading apart of the individual image elements.

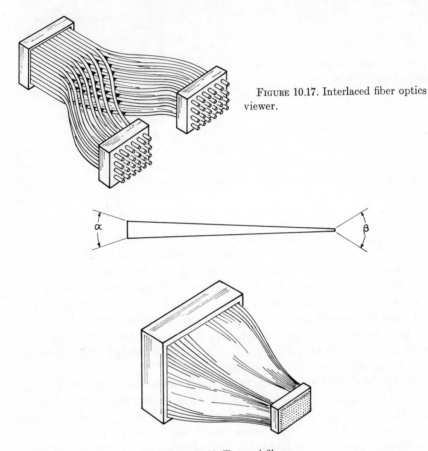

FIGURE 10.17. Interlaced fiber optics viewer.

FIGURE 10.18. Tapered fibers

The same effect can be achieved with *tapered* fibers, as shown in Figure 10.18. With a tapered fiber, if the entrance end is the large end, there is no loss in the light collection, yet the image size is reduced. The angular spread of light at the small end is greater than the acceptance angle at the large end, provided the requirements for total internal reflection are not violated.

It has been possible, through the use of tapered bundles of tapered fibers, to demagnify images to sizes which would correspond to relative apertures of the order of $f/0.6$ for a conventional optical system, in applications where it would not have been feasible to accomplish the same effect by standard optical arrangements.

## ELECTRO-OPTICAL IMAGE TUBES

**10.17. General.** The last two decades has seen a rapid development in electro-optical image tubes—making use of the external photoelectric effect to produce and intensify images in both infrared and visible light.[4] These tubes have had a twofold purpose—image intensification and the transformation of images into electrical signals for use in recording and transmission systems such as television. Television could never have become a commercial success without a means for transforming an optical image into an electrical signal at a high level of resolution and at a rate which permits its reconstruction rapidly enough to avoid the sensation of flicker.

Mechanical methods of producing the electrical representation of an image are too slow to provide an adequate transmission rate; electron beam scanning was needed to provide a sufficient information rate and a compact and reliable apparatus. The developments in image tubes which were spurred by the requirements of television have led to the creation of devices which can amplify the illumination of an optical image and are known under the name of *image intensifiers*. These are static devices and do not utilize an electron beam scan, but they are appropriately discussed as electro-optical image tubes.

**10.18. Image Scanning.** The conversion of an image into electrical signals was an accomplished fact long before the advent of television, and has been used for many years for the wire and radio transmission of pictorial information.[5] The basic principle is illustrated in Figure 10.19. In this very

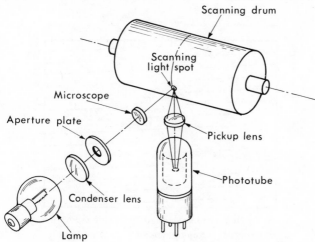

FIGURE 10.19. Schematic arrangement for facsimile scanning

simple arrangement, which has been used in some devices for *facsimile* transmission, the picture to be transmitted is mounted on a revolving drum. An optical system focuses a small spot of light on the drum; light reflected from this small area, or *element* of the picture, is collected by another optical system and focused on a phototube. As the drum rotates, the light on the phototube fluctuates in response to the reflectivity of the picture, and an electrical signal is generated which represents the density variations in the picture, element by element. This is termed a *video* signal, and the process of sequentially subdividing the picture into elements is called *scanning*. The arrangement shown in Figure 10.19 leads to the scanning pattern illustrated in Figure 10.20, which is *sequential scanning*. This is the scanning pattern most frequently used.

The effect of the finite width of the scanning aperture and the basis for determination of the required transmission frequency is shown in Figure 10.21. If the picture to be transmitted consists of a series of square "dots" as shown in the upper part of the Figure, then the electrical signal required to reproduce the pattern faithfully is the square wave shown immediately below. Such a wave would be produced in the phototube output if the width of the scanning aperture were zero and the response of the phototube were unlimited.

**10.19. Facsimile Transmission.** In practice, neither of these conditions holds true. A finite size of aperture is essential to obtain sufficient light to generate a useful signal, and the response time of the phototube has a finite magnitude; in facsimile transmission, the response time of the phototube

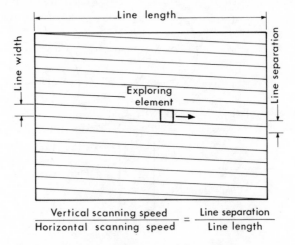

$$\frac{\text{Vertical scanning speed}}{\text{Horizontal scanning speed}} = \frac{\text{Line separation}}{\text{Line length}}$$

FIGURE 10.20. Sequential scanning

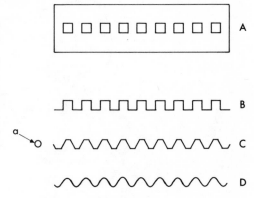

FIGURE 10.21. Scanning aperture functions. A series of targets, as shown in A, if scanned by a zero-size aperture with a detector of ideal response would yield the square wave output shown at B. A finite-size aperture, as shown at a, would yield the truncated triangular wave shown at C. Limited response of the detector will give an output similar to the sine wave shown at D.

is sufficiently fast that it is not a significant factor in the performance of the system.

If the aperture width is one-half the width of the picture "element," the electrical signal has the general form shown in C of Figure 10.21. Practical systems usually are close to this condition. It is seen that there is very little difference between this truncated triangular wave and the pure sine wave shown at D, which is the optimum form for transmission through an electrical network and is the form in which the final signal is generally developed.

The frequency of this signal is equal to the frequency with which the aperature passes over picture dots of the same color (black or white). In facsimile and television, it is customary to identify a picture *element* as a single dot—either black or white—thus the number of picture elements scanned per second is twice the corresponding frequency in the electrical signal. This situation is what has given rise to the difference of a factor of two in electrical and optical parlance, discussed in Section 9.13.

The operation at the receiving end of facsimile transmission system is shown in Figure 10.22. The received video signal is applied to a light source which is capable of modulation in intensity at the operating frequencies, and this light source is focused onto the recording material in a spot equal in size to the scanning aperture used at the "pickup" end of the system. It is clear that synchronization between the recording and pickup systems is essential to avoid picture distortion. The recording medium may be photographic film, which has the advantage of providing the most faithful recording and the maximum range of tone, but the disadvantage of requiring chemical processing before it can be read out, or it may be any one of a number of materials which have been developed for the purpose, some of which have instant readout capability.

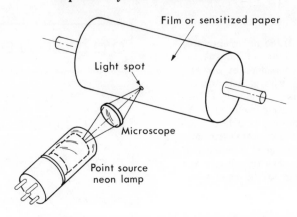

Film or sensitized paper

Light spot

Microscope

Point source
neon lamp

FIGURE 10.22. Schematic arrangement for facsimile recording.

Common dimensions used in facsimile systems include a picture element size of .01 inch; facsimile is usually carried out at unit magnification, and this resolution level provides a very satisfactory picture quality for visual observation. Scanning speeds are typically 100 lines/min. In a system with a 9-inch scan line (suitable for transmitting letter-size copy), this provides a transmission rate of 100 × 900, or 90,000 picture elements per minute— 1500 per second, and therefore a maximum video frequency of 750 cycles/ sec.

The *bandwith* required extends from this maximum frequency down to essentially zero frequency, or dc, since it is necessary to have the capability for transmitting large areas of uniform illumination. It is customary to transmit the video information by modulation of a *carrier*, whose frequency must be higher than that of the video signal itself; for rates such as the above, a carrier frequency in the audio range is adequate.

**10.20. The Flying Spot Scanner.** In facsimile transmission, the picture element transmission rate has no effect on the quality of the picture produced, so that except for reasons of convenience or equipment utilization, there is no strong need for extremely high scanning and transmission rates. In television, however, the situation is quite different.

The standard television picture contains 525 horizontal scan lines and has an aspect ratio of 4/3; therefore, the picture contains 525 × 525 × 4/3 = 367,500 picture elements. This is approximately the same number of elements as are found in a 5 × 7 inch picture at a resolution level of .01 inch, which is equivalent to a good quality halftone, such as those reproduced in this book.

To avoid noticeable "flicker" in the picture, the rate of presentation of complete "frames" must be considerably higher than the eye can detect. The standard frame rate in motion pictures is 24 per second. To make the television frame rate compatible with the standard American power frequency of 60 cycles/sec, a frame rate of 30 per second has been adopted in television. This avoids many effects which might otherwise get in from the power lines.

There are $367,500 \times 30 = 11,025,000$ picture elements per second for television, or a maximum video frequency of 5.5 Mc. In practice, to provide equal horizontal and vertical resolution and to give rigorous treatment to the "aperture function," a maximum video frequency of 4.25 Mc is found to be sufficient. The bandwidth extends from 30 cycles (the frame rate) to 4.25 Mc. The carrier frequencies necessary to transmit the information are correspondingly higher, and lie in the ultrahigh frequency range (above 40 Mc).

The scanning of pictures at these rates requires something more than the simple arrangement described for facsimile recording. The development of àdequate scanning techniques, from the early Nipkow discs to the Image Orthicons of today is a fascinating history for which, unfortunately, we have no space. The *flying spot scanner*, however, which was developed at one stage in this history, is still in use for the scanning of film recordings in many cases and is used for many other high-speed scanning purposes, including high-speed facsimile, and is therefore worthy of description.

The flying spot scanner is essentially the same as the conventional cathode ray tube and television picture tube, or *kinescope*, except that it has no requirement for modulation of the electron beam. It is illustrated in Figure 10.23.

Figure 10.23. Flying spot scanner tube

The tube consists of an electron gun and a light-emitting phosphor, as shown in Figure 10.23. The gun emits a high-velocity beam of electrons, confined by electrical means to a narrow pencil, which impinges on the phosphor at the opposite end of the evacuated tube and causes the phosphor to emit light.

Deflection plates, as shown in the Figure, are capable of deflecting this beam either vertically or horizontally, sufficiently that it may be directed to any point on the phosphor screen (which is of relatively large size). When suitable frequencies are imposed on the deflection plates, the electron beam may be made to scan a pattern on the phosphor. Conventionally, the pattern used is the sequential scan, or *rectangular raster*, shown in Figure 10.20. This device is capable of operating at deflection frequencies in the megacycle range, so that scanning at the rates required for television is no problem.

Figure 10.24 shows how the flying spot scanner may be used to scan a film transparency. The raster generated on the tube is imaged on the transparency, and the light spot which is created on the phosphor scans the picture in the desired pattern and at the desired rate. The light is collected by an optical system and focused on a phototube which then generates a video signal.

**10.21. The Photocathode in an Electric Field.** If a photocathode is mounted at one end of an evacuated tube, and a phosphor at the other, as shown in Figure 10.25, and a strong electric field is impressed between the

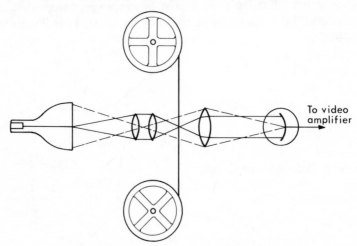

FIGURE 10.24. Application of the flying spot scanner

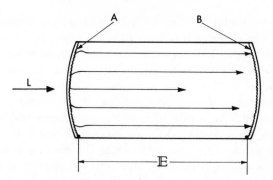

FIGURE 10.25. Fundamental elements of an
image tube: (A) photocathode, (B) phosphor,
(L) image formed by an otical system, (E)
electrostatic field.

photocathode and the phosphor, the fundamental elements of an image
tube are provided.

If an optical image is formed upon the photocathode, electrons are
emitted by reason of the external photoelectric effect (see Section 7.16).
These electrons are accelerated by the electric field and impinge upon the
phosphor, where they may be absorbed and give rise to the emission of light.

If the electron velocities created by the accelerating field are substantially greater than the randomly directed initial velocities of the ejected
electrons, then the electrons travel in the direction of the impressed field,
and the image geometry is preserved between the photocathode and the
phosphor. The result is an *image tube;* an input optical image is transformed into an electron beam, and this in turn is transformed into an output image.

The utility of such a device is not immediately evident; there are some
factors present, however, which under the proper conditions, can make
the device very useful. The intensity of the phosphor emission is dependent
upon the *kinetic energy* of the impinging electrons, and this energy is derived from the accelerating electric field and not from the energy in the
input optical image. Therefore, there is at least the theoretical possibility
of having an energy *gain* between the input and output images. In practice,
the only single-stage tubes of this type which have been made to show gain
are those in which the area of the output image is made smaller than that
of the input image by means of electron beam focusing, which is discussed
below.

The single-stage tube also has the inherent capability of producing an
output image in visible light for an input image in infrared light—limited

only by the availability of materials which exhibit the external photo-electric effect in response to infrared photon energies. This limitation, as was shown in Section 7.16, imposes a long wavelength cutoff at about $1.2\mu$.

**10.22. Electron Optics.** Direct acceleration of the electrons as illustrated in Figure 10.25 imposes a limitation on resolution caused by the velocity components of individual electrons in a direction perpendicular to the impressed field. In a tube of practical dimensions and reasonable operating voltages, the resolution limitation is of the order of a millimeter.

This effect can be overcome by focusing the electron beam in the same manner that a beam of light is focused. The behavior of an electron in an electric field is similar to the behavior of a photon in a medium of variable refractive index; in fact, the trajectories of electrons in an electric field can be analyzed by the techniques of geometrical optics. The index of refraction is equal to the square root of the electric field intensity, which of course varies from point to point depending upon the structure of the field.

Electric fields, established by suitably shaped charged electrodes, behave in a manner similar to lenses, and the photoelectron "image" at the photocathode may be imaged on the phosphor screen by the *electron optical system*. The possibilities of correction for aberrations are not as extensive as in light optics because there are limitations on the field intensity contour which can be achieved without physically blocking the electron paths, but resolutions of the order of 100 lines/mm are achievable. Similar techniques are used in the electron microscope.

The effective apertures of electron lenses are quite small, but since the equivalent wavelength of an electron is about $10^{-4}$ to $10^{-5}$ times shorter than that of light, diffraction effects do not constitute a serious problem.

Electron lenses may also be formed with magnetic fields; in a magnetic field, the effective index of refraction depends not only on the field intensity but on the direction of motion of the electron.

Figure 10.26 shows a typical electron imaging system.

**10.23. The Image Intensifier.** Image tubes in which the input image may be in infrared light and the output image is in visible light are generally known as *image converters*.[6] Tubes which have a positive gain (No. output photons/No. input photons) of as great as 100 have been developed. Because of the limitation of the wavelength to less than $1.2\mu$, these devices are not of extremely broad utility, since the normal temperature radiation of objects at ordinary temperatures lies at much longer wavelengths. In order to use these devices for night observation, it is necessary to illuminate the objects being viewed with an infrared "searchlight."

Image tubes in which the input is in visible light and the output is a brightness-amplified visible light image are known as *image intensifiers*.

This type of device has gone through a long stage of development;[7] it is now possible to build such tubes with an over-all photon gain of from 5000 to 10,000.

Figure 10.27 illustrates a typical image intensified tube. This tube contains four internal *dynodes*, at which electron multiplication occurs, in a manner similar to the action in a photomultiplier tube. The resolution in the output image is of the order of 12 lines/mm. The voltage difference between dynodes is about 4 kV, giving a total electric field strength between photocathode and phosphor of 15 kV.

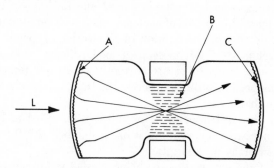

FIGURE 10.26. Typical electron imaging system: (A) photocathode, (B) electric or magnetic field, (C) phosphor, (L) image formed by an optical system.

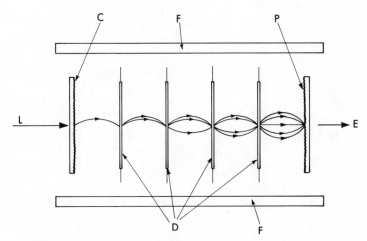

FIGURE 10.27. Image intensifier schematic: (L) image formed by an optical system, (C) photocathode, (D) dynodes (secondary electron emitters), (F) focusing coil, (P) phosphor, (E) output image.

These devices are sufficiently sensitive to record the arrival of single photons at the photocathode. Their limiting performance is set by "photon noise"—the randomness in rate of arrival of photons from the scene being viewed.

One of the common uses for this type of device is as a high-speed shutter. It is possible to "gate" the tubes by switching the accelerating voltage in times as short as 1 $\mu$sec.

**10.24. Scanning Image Tubes.** The transformation of an optical image into an electrical signal at high rates of speed is essential for the generation of signals for television systems,[8] and for high-speed recording. The required operating speeds of such devices have been discussed above.

Space does not permit description of the various types of tube which have been developed[9]—the Iconoscope,[10] the Orthicon,[11] and others. Three types of scanning image tubes are currently in use for television pickup and other high-speed recording purposes: the Image Dissector, the Vidicon, and the Image Orthicon.

**10.25. The Image Dissector.** This tube,[12] illustrated in Figure 10.28, is not widely used in television, but it has a number of other applications which make it worthy of description.

The image of the object or scene being viewed is formed by a conventional optical system on the photocathode, which gives rise to photoelectrons, these being accelerated toward the rear end of the tube by an applied electric field. At the rear of the tube, there is a small aperture and behind this, an electron collector.

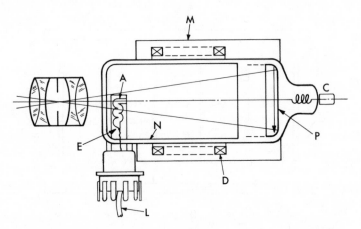

FIGURE 10.28. Image dissector schematic: (A) aperture, (E) electron multiplier, (C) cathode terminal, (D) deflecting coils, (M) magnetic focusing coil, (P) photocathode, (L) output lead.[8]

Deflection plates similar to those employed in the kinescope of the flying spot scanner deflect the entire electron beam in the desired scanning pattern—usually the rectangular raster. The effect is the same as if the aperture were caused to scan the photocathode.

**10.26. The Vidicon.** The Vidicon is widely used as a television pickup tube, especially in applications where its compactness and ruggedness are of advantage and extreme sensitivity is not required. The most publicized applications of the Vidicon have been in observation satellites, where the signals have been relayed back to earth for recording. The Vidicon is illustrated schematically in Figure 10.29.

The Vidicon is a photoconductive tube. Its photocathode is composed of a photoconductive material. Input photons alter the conductivity of the photocathode in the area where they fall.

An electron gun provides a narrow beam of electrons, which is scanned in the familiar scanning pattern over the photocathode. When this beam reaches an area where input photons have generated charge carriers, some of the electrons from the scanning beam enter the photocathode to neutralize the charge carriers, and a corresponding number of electrons flow out of the photocathode into the external circuit, generating the video signal.

The photocathode of the Vidicon is typically about ½-inch in size, and the electron beam has sufficient resolution to generate the required 525-line picture in this area. It is operable down to a light level which yields an illumination on the photocathode of 10 foot-candles or more. It is thus useful in daylight, even at rather dim levels. In this tube, as in other electro-optical image tubes, the effect of insufficient illumination is to degrade the resolution gradually.

The Vidicon and Image Orthicon obtain their primary advantage over tubes like the Image Dissector and devices which preceded them in the development process, by being *storage* tubes. The effect of the photons in the image in creating charge carriers is *cumulative* between successive scans of the electron beam, so that the effective input energy is the integral of the illumination over a frame time. In tubes like the Image Dissector, only those photons which arrive during the approximately 1/10 $\mu$sec that the appropriate part of the electron beam is over the scanning aperture can produce a signal. All of the photons which arrive during the remainder of the frame time are lost.

This storage capability in tubes like the Vidicon and the Image Orthicon means that the supply of photoelectrons available for the generation of a video signal is increased by a factor of some 250,000. This gain, of course, is partially offset by other factors.

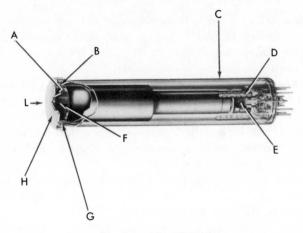

FIGURE 10.29. The Vidicon.

(A) Photoconductive-surfaces.

(B) Photoconductor mounting.

(C) Envelope.

(D) Electrode mounting.

(E) Heater.

(F) Micromesh-screens.

(G) Particle barrier.

(H) Faceplates.

(L) Image input from optical system.

(*Courtesy Radio Corp. of America*)

The limiting performance of the Vidicon is usually determined by the noise level in the amplifier which receives the signal from the photocathode. This signal is a very low-level one, and the required bandwidth of the amplifier is, as has been pointed out above, more than 4 Mc.

The Vidicon is currently provided with a cathode size of ⅜ and ¾ inch. In the smaller size, the standard 525-line television raster gives a resolution level of about 25 optical lines per mm. There is also a considerable variety of special tubes which have been developed, of both Vidicon and Image Orthicon types which have unique characteristics. Included in these developments are tubes with low target leakage, to provide for long exposures and slow scanning rates for operation at very low light levels, tubes with larger cathodes, providing operation at higher resolution levels (more lines per picture), tubes with special cathode formulations to exploit specific characteristics of the input light spectrum, and hybrid types of tubes, in which the photoconductive cathode of the Vidicon is combined with the electron multiplier operation of the Image Orthicon.

Vidicons which are sensitive in the infrared spectrum[13] have been made, the most successful being in the spectral region covered by the lead sulfide photoconductor (1 to $3\mu$), although tubes similar to the Vidicon using other photoconductors sensitive to longer wavelengths have also been made. Necessary electrical characteristics which must be provided in order to permit operation of the tube prevent the attainment of sensitivities as high as can be obtained by use of the photoconductors as non-image-forming detectors.

It is customary to rate infrared imaging devices in terms of the minimum temperature difference which can be detected in the observation of objects at ambient temperatures. A temperature sensitivity of the order of 1°C has been achieved with infrared image tubes of the Vidicon type. This compares with temperature sensitivities of the order of .01°C for highly sensitive infrared detectors used as described in Chapter 7.

**10.27. The Image Orthicon.** The Image Orthicon[14] is the most sensitive scanning image tube, and is widely used in television where the best picture reproduction is required. It gives high picture quality at a photocathode illumination level of the order of .01 foot-candle, and special modifications have made it possible to obtain pictures at scene illuminations as low as $10^{-6}$ foot-lambert with very wide aperture optical collection systems. The Image Orthicon is illustrated in Figure 10.30.

Photoelectrons emitted by the photocathode are accelerated to a target electrode by a high-potential electric field. This target electrode is composed of a secondary electron emitter material, and the impinging electrons cause secondary emission, which is collected by the screen, as shown in Figure 10.30. Thus, during the frame time, a positive charge is built up on the target, and since the target is made of high resistance, this charge persists in the pattern of the optical image on the photocathode.

The electron beam scans the target in the usual raster pattern, and the target removes electrons from the beam to neutralize its charge. The beam electrons which have not been removed by the target are collected and passed through a multistage electron multiplier, similar to that found in the photomultiplier tube. The variation in the number of electrons in the beam, as a result of the charge pattern on the target, constitutes the video signal.

The limiting performance of the Image Orthicon is determined by the "shot" noise of the electron beam—the randomness of photon distribution in the original beam, which, of course, appears like a signal to the electron

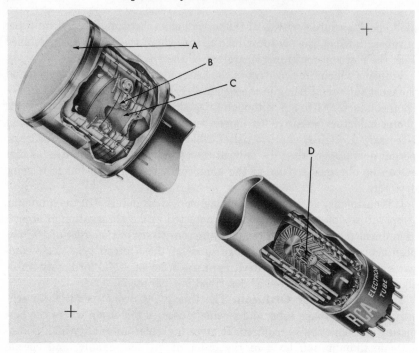

FIGURE 10.30. The Image Orthicon: (A) faceplate, (B) screen electrode, (C) target, (D) electron gun. (*Courtesy Radio Corp. of America*)

multiplier. It is necessary to set the electron beam current high enough to discharge the maximum highlight on the target at each frame; otherwise, this highlight would persist in the picture throughout several frames, even if not reinforced by the optical image. There is thus a minimum electron beam current, and therefore a minimum noise level, for a given level of illumination. When the illumination level is low, the beam current may be adjusted downward, and this possibility does much to give the Image Orthicon its very large dynamic range of performance.

The resolution of the Image Orthicon is more than adequate for conventional television applications; in fact, tubes with a resolution as high as 1000 lines in the typically 40-mm wide photocathode have been produced. The primary limitation on resolution is the structure of the screen which collects the secondary electrons from the target.

## SOLID-STATE ELECTRO-OPTICAL DEVICES

**10.28. General.** It is in very recent years that a scientific understanding of the properties and activities of matter in the solid state has begun to develop. It cannot be said that this domain of physics is yet even moderately well explored, but enough has been learned to lead to the development of a host of interesting and useful devices, utilizing properties and phenomena which a short time ago were understood imperfectly or not at all.[15]

The outstanding device to come from this field of investigation is, of course, the transistor, which has made tremendous changes in electronics. The development of infrared detectors is also an area of remarkable advancement, although it is perhaps better recognized in military than in industrial circles. Among the developments made possible by a better understanding of the solid state are many electro-optical devices, a number of which reveal for the first time the inverse of interactions between light and matter which have been known for a long time.

**10.29. Definitions and Nomenclature.** The devices to be discussed come under the heading of *electroluminescence*, and under the more general heading of *luminescence*. This is one area of optics which seems to have acquired a logical and consistent nomenclature early in its history.

The term *luminescence* refers to the emission of light for reasons other than blackbody radiation. Under this heading, the following phenomena have been identified:

*Chemiluminescence*—the emission of light by chemical reaction, as found in many animals and plants.[16] While this can rightfully be termed an optical phenomenon, we have chosen to exclude it from discussion.

*Cathodoluminescence*—this is the emission of light as a result of electron bombardment, which is the phenomenon utilized in cathode ray tubes, image tubes, kinescopes, etc. Materials which exhibit cathodoluminescence are usually termed *phosphors*,[17] which may lead to some confusion with the phenomenon of phosphorescence (see below). Most materials which exhibit one phenomenon, however, also exhibit the other.

*Fluorescence*—this term has been previously defined, and refers to the emission of light at one wavelength as a result of the absorption of light at another (shorter) wavelength.

*Phosphorescence*—this term has also been previously defined, and refers to a phenomenon exactly like fluorescence, except that there is a significant time lag between the absorption and the emission. As pointed out above, most of the materials which exhibit phosphorescence in response to the absorption of photons, also exhibit it in response to the absorption of electrons, in which case the effect is called *cathodoluminescence*.

Fluorescence and phosphorescence are combined in the term *photoluminescence*.

*Electroluminescence*—this term refers to the emission of light as a result of exposure to an electric field. Several materials have been discovered and developed which exhibit this property.

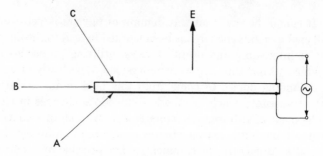

FIGURE 10.31. Electroluminescent panel: (A) opaque metallic coating, (B) electroluminescent material, (C) transparent conductor, (E) light output.

*Photo-electroluminescence*—this term refers to the modification of electroluminescence by means of an input of light.

*Electro-photoluminescence*—this term refers to the modification of photoluminescence by means of the application of an electrical input.

All of the above phenomena have been observed, investigated and made the basis for useful devices, some of which are described below.

**10.30. Electroluminescence.** Certain materials have the property of emitting light when placed in an electric field.[18] It will be recognized that this phenomenon is the inverse of the photovoltaic effect (see Section 7.32).

The most commonly used electroluminescent material is zinc sulfide, activated with impurities of various materials; the impurity materials contribute both donors and acceptors (see Chapter 7). Electroluminescence in practically every region of the visible spectrum is producible; for example, $ZnS:Cu,Cl$ yields blue and green, $ZnS:Cu,Mn,Cl$ gives yellow.

The usual method of construction is to use the electroluminescent material as the dielectric of a parallel-plate condenser (as shown in Figure 10.31) at least one of whose plates is made transparent by applying a transparent conductive coating to glass or clear plastic.

The applied electric field may be either ac or dc. Typical performance in terms of light output versus applied voltage is

100 foot-lamberts at 100 volts ac

4 foot-lamberts at 80 volts ac

$10^{-4}$ foot-lamberts at 5 volts ac

The light output-voltage curve is approximately given by

$$B = Ae^{-bV^{-1/2}} \tag{10.9}$$

where $V$ is the applied voltage and $A$ and $b$ are constants. The light output

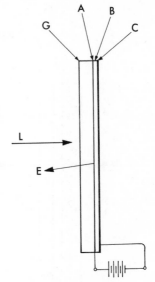

FIGURE 10.32. Single-layer light amplifier: (L) light input, (G) glass plate (A) transparent conductor, (B) electroluminescent layer, (C) metallic conductor, (E) light output.

has been made as high as 14 lumens/watt. With an applied alternating current, the output builds up to a constant value over a few cycles.

The most common use of direct electroluminescent devices has been in panels[19] for illumination. They have a life of from 1000 to 10,000 hours, and they deteriorate usually through electrolytic action in the active material.

**10.31. Electro-photoluminescence—The Single-layer Light Amplifier.** If a suitable phosphor is placed in an electric field, in the manner shown in Figure 10.31 above, under the proper conditions, the light output may be controlled by an optical image, as shown in Figure 10.32. This is the *single-layer light amplifier*.[20] The light output is greater than the light input, the energy being derived from the electric field. Energy gains of the order of 5 to 10 have been achieved, and devices have been produced in which the output light is at a shorter wavelength than the input light, making the device operable with an infrared image giving a visible light output. For this type of operation, however, useful gains have not yet been achieved.

The resolution of the device is very high—as great as 1000 lines/mm. Theoretically, it would be possible to obtain gains as high as 100 and to operate such a device at a frame rate of 20 per second, with input light levels as low as $10^{-1}$ foot-candle. Devices have not yet been produced, however, which approach this theoretical limit.

**10.32. The Double-layer Light Amplifier.** The *double-layer light am-*

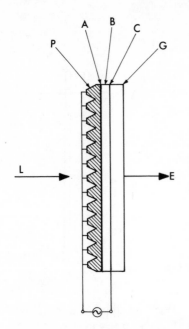

FIGURE 10.33. Double-layer light amplifier: (L) light input, (P) photoconductor, (A) metallic layer, (B) electroluminescent material, (C) transparent conductor, (G) glass plate, (E) light output.

*plifier* has had a considerably greater success.[21] This device combines a layer of a photoconductor with an electroluminescent layer between the plates of a condenser, as shown in Figure 10.33. An image falling on the photoconductor causes a decrease in resistance and consequently a greater voltage drop across the electroluminescent layer at that point and a higher light output. The photoconductive layer is usually serrated as shown in the Figure to increase its surface area, which improves the performance. The applied voltage is typically of the order of $10^5$ volts/cm.

Typical characteristics of the double-layer light amplifier are gains of 100 to 1000, a resolution of the order of 40 lines/mm, and short rise time (about a millisecond) accompanied by relatively long decay times (seconds). Input light levels from $10^{-2}$ to 1 foot-candle can be utilized. Efficiencies of current devices are from 0.2 to 0.5 of theoretical.

An interesting variation of the double-layer light amplifier has been called the electrostatic Image Converter. By providing a control grid in the photoconductive layer and two separate power supplies, a power supply phase change may be introduced which changes the output image from positive to negative.

**10.33. Storage Light Amplifiers—Optical Feedback.** In the double-layer light amplifier described above, an opaque layer between the photoconductor and the electroluminescent layer is introduced to prevent the output light from activating the photoconductor. If this layer is removed, the result is the *storage light amplifier*—a device which can be turned on upon the transient input of an image, and which will then remain on until the electric field is removed.[22]

In such devices, provision must be made to reduce the optical feedback to a limited region, therefore the photoconductor is usually deposited in the form of individual pedestals; this limits the resolution to the order of 40 elements/in.

Typical performance of such devices is an output of 0.1 foot-lambert for an applied voltage of 150 volts ac, and an input triggering signal of 1 foot-candle-second. Storage of up to 30 minutes has been achieved, being limited by transverse leakage in the feedback, which destroys the resolution in the picture. Storage which will maintain good halftone qualities is limited to a few minutes.

Applications of storage light amplifiers include logic and character displays and optical coupling[23] in electronic circuits.

**10.34. Light Emission from *p-n* Junctions.** Emission of light from *p-n* junctions has been observed (see Section 7.31), which points to radiative recombination of carriers which have been created by the injection of electrons. The effect has been observed in silicon and in gallium arsenide in particular. The emission occurs in short flashes of a duration of from $10^{-8}$ to $10^{-9}$ second at points randomly distributed over the junction.

This effect is the basis of the junction laser, discussed in following chapters.

## PROJECTION SCREENS

**10.35. General.** The projection of images on screens is a frequent requirement for optical systems; the appearance of such images depends significantly on the optical properties of the screen itself, and considerable work and ingenuity has gone into the development of screens which have desirable characteristics.

Ideally, the images should appear uniformly bright to any viewer within a prescribed angular subtense. At the same time, it is desirable that as much of the light as possible should be confined to this angular viewing region; since the usual requirement is for a relatively large horizontal spread of the light and a very small vertical spread, it is evident that ordinary materials will not be very satisfactory.

If a screen material were a perfect Lambertian diffuser, then the requirement for equal brightness at all viewing angles would be met, but the region through which the light is spread would be a complete hemisphere, and

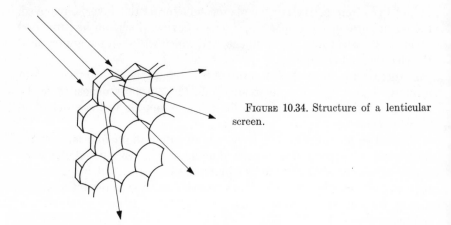

FIGURE 10.34. Structure of a lenticular screen.

most of the diffused light would be lost. Moreover, very few surfaces exhibit diffusing properties which even approach the Lambertian rule, and those which do have a relatively low reflectivity.

The light-diffusing properties which are required of screens apply both to screens on which the image is viewed by reflected light, and those which are viewed in transmission (rear projection screens). It is more difficult to meet the ideal requirements for the latter type of screen than for the former.

**10.36. The Fine-structure Screen.** The most successful screens of both front and rear projection types have been those which provide a closely packed array of tiny optical surfaces, small enough to be below the limit of resolution of the viewer. The image is therefore subdivided into individual elements, and the optical surface which represents each of these elements introduces a spread of the light beam which conforms approximately to the light distribution requirements of the application. These individual elements are essentially pupil-forming elements, and the screen becomes effectively a field lens. Figure 10.34 shows the basic principle of these *fine-structure screens*. The aperture of the projection lens is small with respect to the distance of the screen, so that the individual screen element is illuminated by essentially parallel light. It focuses this light to a point image, and the light is spread from this image into a finite angle, this angle being the relative aperture of the element. By providing the element with a larger relative aperture in the horizontal than in the vertical direction, the light spread can be independently controlled in these two directions.

A perfectly fabricated screen of this type could, of course, almost completely satisfy the ideal requirements, but since an average screen has to contain some millions of individual elements, practical difficulties preclude an ideal solution.

FIGURE 10.35. Structure of the beaded screen

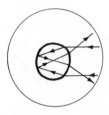

**10.37. Front Projection Screens.** The most common form of front-projection, or reflecting, screen of the fine-structure type is the *beaded screen*, which is made up of tiny glass beads embedded in a carrier, as shown schematically in Figure 10.35. The incident light is reflected internally in the beads, whose shapes closely resemble spheres, and is thus spread into a somewhat limited angle.

The beaded screen shows an equal spread in both vertical and horizontal directions and has a somewhat wider angular spread than might be considered ideal, but its efficiency with respect to simple diffusing screens is much higher.

Some screens have been constructed for the projection of motion pictures with a double layer of cylindrical elements, which provide a control of vertical versus horizontal light spread.

**10.38. Lenticulated Rear Projection Screens.** In screens for viewing by transmitted light—rear projection screens—the screen elements take the form of lenses, and the problem is compounded by the necessity for maintaining a high ratio of transmission to back reflection while at the same time providing for the required light distribution.[24]

There are two basic types of *lenticulated* rear projection screens, as illustrated in Figure 10.36. The light-distribution curves for the two types are shown in Figure 10.37, assuming spherical surfaces on the elements.

Vertical and horizontal control of the light is accomplished by using toric elements, with different curvatures in the two planes.

The screen shown at B has a more uniform light distribution and has the additional advantage that the back reflection is less than for type A. However, rear projection screens are frequently required under conditions of

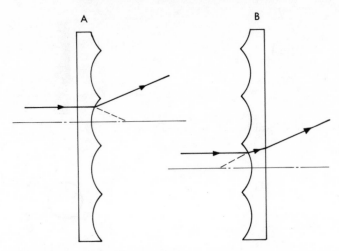

FIGURE 10.36. Two types of lenticular screen. Screens may also be made with convex lenticulations; the optical properties are the same, and the manufacture is more difficult.

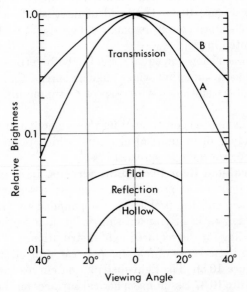

FIGURE 10.37. Transmission curves for the two types of screen shown in Figure 10.36. Back reflection from the flat and hollow sides is also shown.

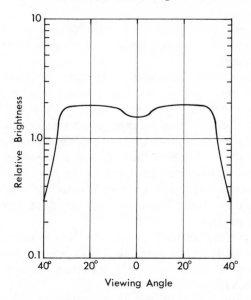

Viewing Angle

FIGURE 10.38. Transmission of an experimental lenticular screen with aspheric elements (cf. reference 24).

normal ambient illumination, in which case front reflections from the screen may reduce the contrast in the picture and must to be taken into consideration. From this point of view, type A has an advantage over type B.

Neither of these types, with spherical surfaces on the elements, comes very close to the ideal light distribution. A significant improvement is made when the elements are made with aspheric surfaces. Figure 10.38 shows the light distribution obtained with an experimental aspheric lenticulated screen.

Beaded rear projection screens are commonly found, which consist of glass beads embedded in an opaque matrix. While the light distribution leaves something to be desired, the apparent brilliance is quite high, and the screens are relatively insensitive to front reflections.

## ULTRAHIGH-SPEED PHOTOGRAPHY

**10.39. General.** Ultrahigh-speed photography is usually defined as photography at one million frames or more per second. This area of technology is replete with ingenious devices and novel methods in the continuing effort to obtain photographs of transient and rapid events.[25] At the present state of the art, it is possible to expose a photograph in so short a time period that the velocity of light determines the region which is illuminated during the exposure.

Physics is continually increasing its demands for information on high-speed processes; currently, the study of plasmas requires photography at the rate of about ten frames in 2 $\mu$sec to reveal the details of the phenomena. The technology of ultrahigh-speed photography is providing the answers.

There are three primary problems in achieving satisfactory photography at ultrahigh speed: the transporting of film at the required rate, obtaining enough illumination to record an image in the very short time intervals available, and shuttering to provide a sufficiently short exposure to "stop" motion in the object. Many ingenious ways of getting around these problems have been devised.

*Framing* (providing separate pictures in time sequence) is difficult at speeds in excess of $10^6$ frames/sec; for higher speeds, recourse is usually had to cameras which make a record of the event but do not provide separate pictures, such as the streak cameras.

Many unique types of shutters have been devised to provide extremely short exposures—many of them are such that only one picture can be taken of an event. Some of these are described below.

The illumination problem is a severe one—in fact, this is perhaps the current primary limitation to exposure speed. Light sources which emit short intense bursts of energy are the most effective; in this area, lasers have proved to be of considerable value.

**10.40. Rotating Mirror Cameras.** In the lower range of speeds in the ultrahigh-speed domain (one million to ten million frames per second) rotating mirror cameras are the type most commonly found. There are a large variety of designs, but the general operating principle is that of forming an image at the surface of a rapidly rotating mirror. The mirror sweeps the pupil of the optical system across a series of lenses, each of which takes a separate photograph. Since the image is on the surface of the mirror, it is stationary during the exposure. Figure 10.39 shows a typical design of a rotating mirror camera. Space does not permit a description of the many different arrangements of this form of camera.

**10.41. Streak Cameras.** The streak camera permits a high-speed record of an event with a very simple apparatus; its limitation is that the picture is only one dimensional in space—the other dimension in the picture represents time. This type of camera is usually provided with a rapidly rotating drum on which the film is mounted, and a slit perpendicular to the film motion where the image is formed. Figure 10.40 shows this arrangement.

A rotating mirror between the lens and the film permits the same kind of

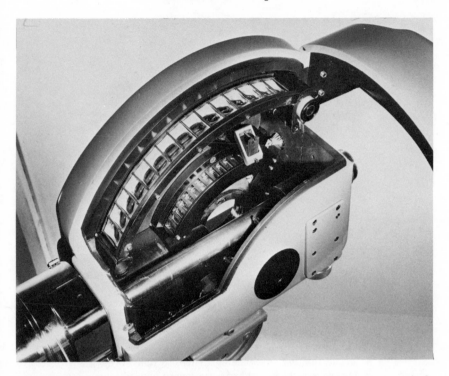

FIGURE 10.39. A rotating mirror framing camera. Rotating mirrors successively expose individual frames. Capacity of the unit shown is 15 frames at a rate of 1,300,000 frames/second. (*Courtesy Electro-Optical Instruments*)

record with a stationary drum. The time resolution of streak cameras is conventionally about 10 $\mu$sec.

**10.42. Flash Tubes and Sparks.** Flash tubes and sparks are the conventional light sources for high-speed photography. The standard form of flash tube is the xenon tube, in which a brilliant flash of short duration is generated by the break-down of a gap between electrodes in a tube containing low-pressure xenon. Other inert gases are occasionally used, but the spectrum of an arc in xenon is generally the most satisfactory for photography.

The typical flash duration for xenon arcs is 10 $\mu$sec, and powers up to several joules per flash can be obtained. With lower total energies, shorter flashes can be achieved. When the arc is formed, the gas is ionized, and a finite time is necessary after the discharge for this ionization to disappear before the next flash can be generated. This deionization time is typically 100 $\mu$sec; if a more rapid sequence of flashes is attempted, the gap break-

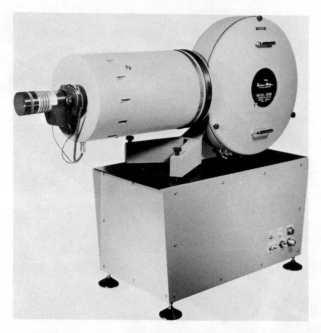

FIGURE 10.40. Streak (sweeping image) high-speed camera. A mirror, rotating at speeds up to 150,000 rpm, sweeps the image across a slit in front of a stationary film. Phenomena with durations as short as 5 n sec and with velocities of 200,000 ft/sec can be recorded. (*Courtesy Beckman & Whitley*)

down occurs at a much lower voltage, and the energy in the flash is much less. Hence, this type of illumination is not satisfactory for obtaining rapid framing.

Also, the flash has a relatively long "tail," and it is necessary to use a capping shutter to avoid image smear.

For very high illuminations, as when a large area is to be covered, explosive flash bombs are used. These generate large amounts of energy and can be operated with flash times as short as 10 to 20 $\mu$sec for the main hump of the energy curve. These also tend to have "tails," and capping shutters are usually desirable.

Electric sparks are used for shorter exposure times. It is possible to obtain fractional microsecond durations with sparks; unfortunately, they are small and do not deliver much energy. X-ray flashes can be obtained with durations of from 0.2 to 2 $\mu$sec.

**10.43. High-speed Shutters.** With continuous illumination or when the object being photographed is self-luminous, as is often the case, exposures are limited by shutters.

The fastest-acting mechanical shutters which have been devised give exposures of about 300 $\mu$sec for an aperture of the order of 5 mm. Explosive action or magnetic triggering can decrease this exposure time somewhat at the cost of less frequent operation.

The "shatter-shutter" is a glass window which is shattered by an explosive charge. This type of shutter can be closed in 2 to 3 $\mu$sec; it is usually used with a flash tube, the shutter being triggered by a photoelectric pickup from the flash tube through a suitable time delay.

Through the use of an exploding capsule of petroleum jelly and lampblack, the "scatter-shutter" can coat a window about 30 mm in diameter with an opaque film in about 50 $\mu$sec. An aluminum wire, exploded by the discharge of a high electrical current through it, can coat a window with an opaque metallic film in about 30 $\mu$sec.

**10.44. Electro-optical Shutters.** Electro-optical devices such as the Kerr cell and the Faraday cell can be operated as shutters, the latter in about 1 $\mu$sec, and the former in 5 to 10 nsec (nanoseconds). The price paid for this operational speed is a light transmission of the order of 20 per cent. These devices can be operated on and off at high frequency—to the order of 50 mc for the Kerr cell. Figure 10.41 shows an example of this type of camera.

**10.45. Image Dissection.** A method for avoiding the very high-speed motions required in framing and rotating mirror cameras is *image dissection*.[26] In this method, the image plane is subdivided into a large number of elements by means of a grid, a lenticular plate, or similar apparatus, and this dissector is then moved a relatively short distance during the exposure. The result is a series of exposures of small elements of the scene. Application of fiber optics permits very fine dissection and a rearrangement of the dissected elements into a different array, such as a single straight line from a two-dimensional image.

**10.46. Image Tubes.** Image tubes, such as the Image Orthicon, provide a means for obtaining short exposures,[27] since the accelerating voltage between the photocathode and the target can be interrupted. Exposures of the order of a microsecond are readily achievable. The illumination requirement is quite high, however, since there is no time for integration, and the quantum efficiency of the photocathodes is rather low (of the order of 10 per cent). Figure 10.42 shows a typical Image Converter camera.

**10.47. Laser Illumination.** The advent of the laser has provided ultra-

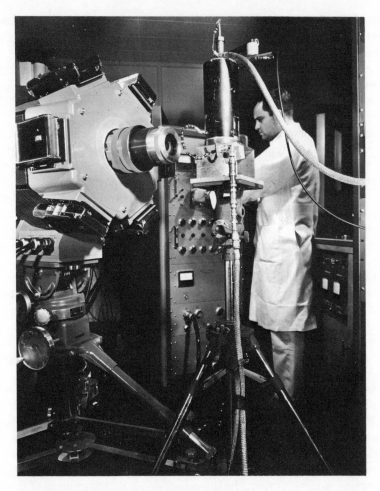

FIGURE 10.41. An ultra high-speed Kerr cell camera. This camera provides a total of 6 frames, at a rate of up to 100,000,000 frames/sec.

high-speed photography with a very useful light source, capable of flashes as short as 30 nsec, and containing a high energy. An additional advantage to laser illumination is that it is monochromatic, and thus spectral filtering can discriminate against the self-luminance of the object.

**10.48. Limitations to Ultrahigh-speed Photography.** The limitations to ultrahigh-speed photography are basically two: illumination and the velocity of light.

The number of photons per second which can be provided for a photo-

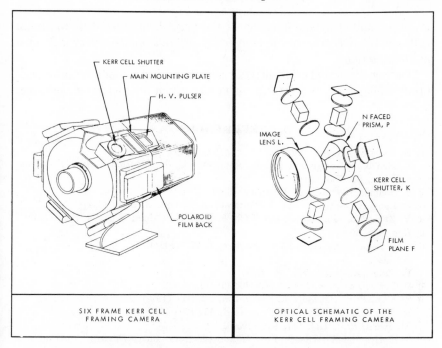

KERR CELL SHUTTER

MAIN MOUNTING PLATE

H. V. PULSER

POLAROID
FILM BACK

SIX FRAME KERR CELL
FRAMING CAMERA

N FACED
PRISM, P

IMAGE
LENS L.

KERR CELL
SHUTTER, K

FILM
PLANE F

OPTICAL SCHEMATIC OF THE
KERR CELL FRAMING CAMERA

FIGURE 10.41—cont'd. A schematic of the optical system is shown. (*Courtesy Electro-Optical Instruments*)

FIGURE 10.42. Image converter camera. (*Courtesy STL Products*)

graph is limited by the duration of the event being recorded; to obtain sufficient photons in events of nanosecond duration implies a very high level of illumination.

The velocity of light (about 1ft/nsec) introduces a fundamental uncertainty about the time sequence of events which are separated in space.

## REFERENCES

1. N. Kapany, *Sci. Am.*, **203**, 72 (November, 1960).
   L. Krolak, W. Siegmund and R. Neuhauser, *J. Soc. Motion Picture Television Engrs.*, **69**, 705 (1960).
2. J. Ballmer, *Ind. Res.*, 22 (October, 1963).
3. C. Long, A Brushenko and D. Pantarelli, *Appl. Opt.*, **3**, 1031 (1964).
4. V. Zworykin, "Photoelectricity," Ch. 9, New York, John Wiley & Sons, 1949.
5. *Ibid.*, Ch. 16.
6. First reported by Holst *et al.*, *Physica*, **1**, 297 (1934).
   See also:
   W. Kluge, *Z. Physik*, **95**, 734 (1935).
   P. Gorlich, *Z. Tech. Physik*, **18**, 460 (1947).
   S. Asao, *Proc. Phys.-Math. Soc. Japan*, **22**, 448 (1940).
   R. Wiseman and M. Klein, *Proc. IRE*, **47**, 1604 (1959).
   M. Klein, *Proc. IRE*, **47**, 904 (1959).
   J. McGee and W. Wilcock, Eds., "Photo-Electronic Image Devices," "Advances in Electronics, No. 12, New York, Academic Press, 1960.
7. M. Wachtel *et al.*, *Rev. Sci. Instr.*, **31**, 576 (1960).
   Image Intensifier Symposium, Engr. Res. & Dev. Labs., Ft. Belvoir, Oct. 6–7, 1958. ASTIA Document AD 220160
8. V. Zworykin and G. Morton, "Television," New York, John Wiley & Sons, 1954.
9. See reference 4, Ch. 17.
10. V. Zworykin, *Proc. IRE*, **22**, 16 (1934); **25**, 1071 (1937).
    H. Iams, G. Morton and V. Zworykin, *Proc. IRE*, **27**, 541 (1939).
11. A. Rose and H. Iams, *RCA Rev.*, **4**, 186 (1939).
12. P. Farnsworth, *J. Franklin Inst.*, **218**, 411 (1934).
13. G. Morton and S. Forgue, *Proc. IRE*, **47**, 1607 (1959).
    R. Redington and P. van Heerden, *J. Opt. Soc. Am.*, **49**, 997 (1959).
14. A. Rose, P. Weimer and H. Low, *Proc. IRE*, **34**, 424 (1946).
15. E. Loebner, *Proc. IRE*, **43**, 1897 (1955).
16. W. McElroy and H. Seliger, *Sci. Am.*, **207**, 76 (December, 1962).
17. B. O'Brien, *J. Opt. Soc. Am.*, **36**, 369 (1946).
    G. Fonda and F. Seitz, "Solid Luminescent Materials," New York, John Wiley & Sons, 1948.
    J. Prener and D. Sullenger, *Sci. Am.*, **191**, 62 (October, 1954).
    G. Fonda, *J. Opt. Soc. Am.*, **47**, 877 (1957).
    C. Haake, *J. Opt. Soc. Am.*, **47**, 881 (1957).
    F. Williams, *J. Opt. Soc. Am.*, **47**, 869 (1957).
    H. Ivey, *Trans. IRE, PGED*, 203 (April, 1959).
    H. Leverenz, "Luminescence of Solids," New York, John Wiley & Sons, 1960.
18. G. Destriau, *Phil. Mag.*, **38**, 700 (1947).

E. Payne, E. Mager and C. Jerome, *Illum. Eng.*, **45**, 688 (1950).

G. Destriau and H. Ivey, *Proc. IRE*, **43**, 1911 (1955).

E. Loebner, *J. Opt. Soc. Am.*, **46**, (227) 1956.

J. Welk, *Ind. Res.*, 32 (March, 1964).

19. B. Kazan and F. Nicoll, *Proc. IRE*, **43**, 1888 (1955).

A. Rose and R. Bube, *RCA Rev.*, **20**, 648 (1959).

L. Reiffel and N. Kapany, *Rev. Sci. Instr.*, **31**, 1136 (1960).

R. Windebank, *Electronics*, **34**, 53 (Dec. 8, 1961).

20. B. Kazan and F. Nicoll, *J. Opt. Soc. Am.*, **47**, 887 (1957).

R. Halsted, *J. Appl. Phys.*, **29**, 1706 (1958).

W. Thornton, *J. Appl. Phys.*, **30**, 123 (1959).

*RCA Rev.* (December, 1959) (entire issue).

21. S. Larach and R. Schrader, *RCA Rev.*, **20**, 532 (1959).

R. Orthuber and L. Ullery, *J. Opt. Soc. Am.*, **44**, 297 (1954).

B. Kazan, Paper read at Optical Society of America Meeting, March 8, 1957.

S. Roberts, *J. Opt. Soc. Am.*, **42**, 850 (1952).

22. J. Rosenthal, *Proc. IRE*, **43**, 1882 (1955).

RCA, Progress Report, Contract DA-039sc-71194, Aug. 1, 1956; ASTIA Document AD-107158.

23. M. Gilleo and J. Last, *Electronics*, 23 (Nov. 27, 1963).

24. G. Schwesinger, *Phot. Eng.*, **5**, 172 (1954).

25. K. Coleman, *Inter. Sci. & Tech.*, 40 (January, 1964).

S. Jacobs, *J. Soc. Motion Picture Television Engrs.*, **69**, 801, 808 (1960).

26. S. Provnorov *et al.*, *J. Soc. Motion Picture Television Engrs.*, **71**, 86 (1962). For a comprehensive bibliography, see J. Courtney-Pratt, *J. Soc. Motion Picture Television Engrs.*, **72**, 876 (1963).

27. A. Anderson, G. Goetze and H. Kanter, *J. Soc. Motion Picture Television Engrs.*, **70**, 440 (1961).

28. B. Vine, R. James and F. Veith, *RCA Rev.*, **13** (March, 1952).

# PART III

# Lasers

# CHAPTER 11

# Fundamentals of Lasers

**11.1. General.** The laser has opened completely new fields of development and investigation in optics. Since the first laser was operated by Maiman in 1960,[1] the magnitude and quality of scientific and engineering effort which has been devoted to this area has not been equaled since the war-inspired efforts on radar and the atomic bomb.

It is really premature to present a book on lasers—the field is too new and the depth of investigation too limited for it to be possible to make any but the most general statements of fundamentals without the risk of serious error. On the other hand, one can hardly offer a book on general optics without a discussion of this most recent and, to many, most fascinating field of activity.

The most significant property of the laser is the fact of its being a highly intense source of *coherent* light; the power levels are high enough that the light can clearly exhibit its electromagnetic character. The laser, in its present form, is essentially an electrical oscillator, no different in principle from ordinary electrical oscillators, except that it operates at frequencies of $10^{15}$ cycles/sec (1 kiloteracycle), or about a millionfold higher than the highest-frequency electrical oscillators so far produced.

With noncoherent light, only intensity can be observed; with coherent light, phase and amplitude relations are exhibited, as was seen in the discussion of interference in Chapter 2. Nearly coherent light can be produced by confining the source to a very small point—smaller than the diffraction limit of the optical system involved. With ordinary light sources, when the pinhole is made small enough to provide a high degree of coherence, the amount of light available is very small. The laser provides a source whose coherence is better than can be provided from any practicable pinhole, and at a power level, in some cases, higher than that of any blackbody source of equivalent size.

571

**11.2. Nature of the Laser.** The laser is the equivalent, at optical frequencies, of the *maser*, which operates at microwave frequencies. The maser principle was discovered by Townes,[2] and the first operating maser was completed by Gordon[3] in 1954. The possibility of operating devices at light frequencies was pointed out by Townes and Schawlow[4] in 1958, and in 1960, Maiman produced the first operating *laser*.[1]

The term *maser*[5] is derived from "*M*icrowave *A*mplification by *S*timulated *E*mission of *R*adiation"; the term *laser* merely substitutes *L*ight for *M*icrowave. Much of the literature, even at the present time (1965), uses the term *optical maser*, but *laser* seems to be becoming the accepted name.

While the maser is used widely as an *amplifier*, and indeed is extensively used this way in microwave equipment, the laser is used as an *oscillator*. Readers with electrical backgrounds will recognize that there is no essential difference in form between an amplifier and an oscillator, the latter merely being the former with positive feedback. In principle, the laser could be used as an amplifier and, in fact, has been so used; its noise level, as a result of spontaneous emission, however, is so high that it does not represent a useful amplifier at low input levels. As an oscillator, its performance rivals that of the best electronic oscillators produced.

Stimulated emission is the reverse of absorption, and the laser is simply a device which exhibits highly intense and coherent *fluorescence*. The action is in many respects similar to the chain reaction in a nuclear explosion.

Fluorescence was discussed in Chapter 3. In fluorescing, a material absorbs a photon of sufficient energy to raise the level of an atom by more than a single step; the energy then drops to an intermediate level, resulting in the emission of a photon of lower energy. The energy difference between the absorption and emission may appear as another photon, as a photon (lattice vibrational energy unit), or as heat.

The process is identical in a laser. A source of energy, which may be photons from a light source or collisions between various types of particles, raises the atoms of the active material to upper energy levels. The laser action takes place when these atoms drop to lower levels and emit photons corresponding to the intermediate energy difference. The difference between the laser action and normal fluorescence is simply that in the laser, the emission is stimulated by the emitted photons themselves and takes place in a sort of chain reaction. How this can be made to take place will become evident in the later discussion.

The term "lase" has recently been added to the language to describe the achievement of the threshold condition for this self-sustaining emission.

**11.3. Basic Properties.**[6] The basic properties of the laser, which are inherent in its mechanism, are high intensity, high monochromaticity, and directivity of the output beam.

When excited atoms are stimulated to emit, they are forced to contribute to the wave which already exists in the neighborhood, therefore they emit in phase with the existing wave, and a high degree of time coherence is maintained. The structure of the laser is that of a resonator, as will be seen below, and the frequencies which are generated are therefore confined to specific modes of the resonator, and a high degree of space coherence results. This determines the directivity of the output wave.

**11.4. Range of Wavelengths.** The wavelength of radiation from a laser is determined by the energy levels of the active material; thus a particular laser is limited to such wavelengths. However, there are a wide variety of materials which can be utilized, and the list is growing larger every day. In some instances, the energy levels can be controlled to a degree by the composition of the active material, and it would appear that eventually lasers may be provided to give emission in almost any desired spectral region from the far infrared to the ultraviolet.

**11.5. Power Levels.** The power levels of some types of lasers have been their most spectacular property. That which has been achieved to the present writing, in the very short time of development which has been available, is by no means indicative of future possibilities. Townes has estimated that laser pulses of durations of the order of .01 nsec with peak power of the order of $10^{12}$ watts (1 terawatt) are feasible and that continuous operation at power levels in the kilowatts will probably be achieved. By comparison, the sun's surface radiates about 7 kW/cm$^2$ over the entire electromagnetic spectrum.

Thus it seems possible that the laser can provide continuous *monochromatic* light sources which are equivalent to the sun in total intensity and which give an output, at the particular frequency involved, equivalent to a source that is $10^{15}$ times as bright as the sun. Operated in pulses of very short duration, this energy can be concentrated by an additional factor of about $10^9$.

The current state of the art is below these ultimates by a factor of at least $10^3$ or $10^4$.

**11.6. Bandwidth.** Much of the discussion of lasers is in terms of frequency rather than wavelength; this is convenient because of the association of frequency with atomic energy levels by the relation $h\nu = \Delta E$. Specification of the spectral location of an output, however, is conventionally stated in terms of wavelengths in angstroms. Spectral line width is often referred to in terms of wave number.

The frequency range of the visible spectrum is from $4.3 \times 10^{14}$ cycles/sec (7000Å) to $7.5 \times 10^{14}$ cycles/sec (4000Å). One angstrom, therefore, at a wavelength of 6000Å, corresponds to a frequency difference of $5 \times 10^5$ cycles, or 0.5 Mc.

Under the proper conditions, continuous-wave gas lasers can at the present time exhibit a bandwidth of less than 2 cycles/sec. This corresponds to a spectral line width of $4 \times 10^{-6}$Å, and to a frequency stability of one part in 250,000,000,000,000. The line width of the best natural optical sources do not approach this stability by a factor of $10^7$.

**11.7. Applications.** It is much too early to make any comprehensive listing of applications for lasers and laser devices, but it is immediately evident that they have unusual properties as light sources, and these very properties identify important areas of use.

Since its first development, much attention has been paid to the possible use of laser light as a communications medium. The very high frequency level ($10^{15}$ cycles/sec) would permit its use as a communications carrier with capacity for an extremely large number of channels. The bandwidth of a television channel is about 5 Mc—one laser beam could theoretically accommodate 100 million TV channels simultaneously. This is a capacity some $10^4$ times that available at the highest current microwave frequency. It is therefore not surprising that a large proportion of the effort which has been expended in laser development has come from the communications community.

Long-distance transmission of laser beams through the atmosphere is, of course, highly sensitive to weather; therefore, laser beams are not a promising means for ground communications except over short distances, although transmission through long pipelines has been seriously considered. For communications in space, however, laser light shows great promise; not only is the bandwidth capacity phenomenal, but the high directivity and intensity of the beams assures long-distance capability with moderate power levels. It has already been possible to detect a return signal from a laser beam directed at the moon.

The use of laser light in spectroscopy and in interferometry is assured; in these areas, the extremely narrow spectral bandwidth provides a new order of capability. In interferometry, where the maximum range of length measurements which may be achieved is limited by the coherence of the light source, lasers will permit measurements over distances of kilometers.

The coherent properties of laser light permit beams to be focused to very small dimensions, limited only by the diffraction of the optical elements; in such small spots, the intensity of the laser beams provides high-frequency electric and magnetic fields of hitherto unequaled intensity. Materials break down completely at the intensities presently available, and at much lower levels, many nonlinear effects are produced.

**11.8. Population Inversion.** The redistribution of atoms, raising their energy levels, which must take place as a prelude to laser action is termed *population inversion.* Under conditions of temperature equilibrium, the atoms in a material are distributed in a variety of energy levels, the numbers of atoms in each level, $n_1$, $n_2$, $n_3$ $\cdots$ $n_n$ being governed by statistical laws. If $n_1$ is the condition of lowest energy, then, in general, for atoms in equilibrium at a temperature $T$, $n_1 > n_2 > n_3 > \cdots n_n$.

Absorption and emission are continually taking place, but at rates which maintain the statistical distribution of states. If $\Delta E$ is the difference between two energy levels, say $n_1$ and $n_2$, then the absorption of a photon of the appropriate energy can raise an atom from level 1 to level 2. The wavelength of the photon will be

$$\lambda = \frac{hc}{\Delta E} = \frac{12{,}400}{\Delta E \text{ in electron volts}} \text{ angstroms} \tag{11.1}$$

The general equation for absorption is

$$I = I_0 e^{-\alpha x} \tag{11.2}$$

where $I_0$ is the incident intensity, $I$ is the transmitted intensity, $\alpha$ is the absorption coefficient, and $x$ is the path length of the radiation. Now, for absorption at a particular wavelength $\lambda$, the absorption coefficient may be written

$$\alpha = (n_1 - n_2)\sigma_\lambda \tag{11.3}$$

where $n_1$ and $n_2$ are the numbers of absorption centers (atoms) per unit volume at energy levels 1 and 2, and $\sigma_\lambda$ is the *absorption cross section,* or probability of light of $\lambda = hc/\Delta E$ being absorbed in a system which has permissible energy-level differences of $\Delta E$. Therefore, Equation (11.2) may be written

$$I = I_0 e^{-(n_1 - n_2)\sigma_\lambda x} \tag{11.4}$$

By the Boltzmann statistics,

$$\frac{n_2}{n_1} = \exp -[(\Delta E)/(kT)] = \exp -[(hc)/(\lambda kT)] \tag{11.5}$$

at thermal equilibrium, and it is seen that $n_2/n_1$ is always less than unity, unless $T$ is negative. Thus, under thermal equilibrium, there are always more atoms in a lower- than in a higher-energy state.

Now it is possible to artificially create a condition where $n_2$ exceeds $n_1$; that is, when the population of a higher-energy level exceeds that at a lower level. This can be accomplished by adding energy by absorption or by collision. This condition is termed population inversion. The absorption coefficient [Equation (11.3)] now becomes negative, and the transmitted intensity, as given by Equation (11.2), becomes greater than the incident intensity, $I_0$. This is *stimulated emission*.

The condition of population inversion, $n_2/n_1 > 1$, is often referred to as a negative temperature condition, since it leads, in Equation (11.5), to a necessarily negative value of $T$.

**11.9. Gain.** Equation (11.2) expresses the *gain* of a laser

$$G = \frac{I}{I_0} = e^{-\alpha x} \tag{11.6}$$

where $x$ is the length of the laser. When $n_2 > n_1$, $\alpha$ is negative, and the gain is greater than unity. An input signal will therefore be amplified; the analogy to a conventional electronic amplifier is evident.

If an amplifier is provided with positive feedback, its gain becomes

$$G = \frac{A}{1 - \beta A} \tag{11.7}$$

where $A$ is the gain without feedback and $\beta$ is the feedback factor. When $\beta A =$ unity, the gain is infinite, and the amplifier becomes an oscillator. In the laser, the feedback is provided by placing the active material between a pair of mirrors. Thus, the mirror reflectivity, $R$, is the feedback factor, and the path of the light through the laser becomes double its length, so that the condition for oscillation ($\beta A = 1$) becomes

$$e^{-2\alpha x} R^2 = 1 \tag{11.8}$$

since $\beta = R^2$ and $A = e^{-2\alpha x}$.

**11.10. Historical Data.** As mentioned above, the maser was developed by Townes,[2] and its first successful application was in a device constructed by Gordon[3] and reported in 1955. The application utilized the inversion frequency of ammonia gas to produce stimulated emission at a frequency of 24 gigacycles in the microwave region of the spectrum—hence the name *maser*.

Schawlow and Townes[4] suggested in 1958 that the principle was applicable at light frequencies, and the first operating *laser* was reported by Maiman in 1960.[1] The active material was pink ruby, with .05 per cent of chromium. A rod 4 cm long $\times$ $\frac{1}{2}$ cm in diameter exhibited stimulated emission at the typical fluorescence line at 6943Å.

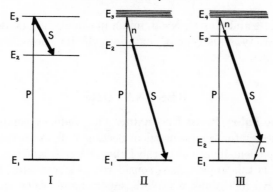

FIGURE 11.1. Three classes of lasers.

The original ruby laser exhibited its emission in short pulses. The first "continuous wave" or CW laser operation was reported for a helium-neon gas laser by Javan, Bennett, and Herriott in 1961.[7] The radiation was at $1.15\mu$ in the infrared. CW operation in the visible spectrum was achieved by White and Rigden in 1962.[8]

**11.11. Energy Levels in Laser Materials.** All lasers so far developed, with the exception of the semiconductor lasers which have a somewhat different mechanism, fall into one of three classes with respect to energy levels; these are illustrated schematically in Figure 11.1.

Classes I and II are three-level lasers; Class III is the four-level laser.

In Class I, the energy absorption, or *pumping*, raises the active atoms from a level $E_1$ to $E_3$, and the stimulated emission corresponds to the drop from level $E_3$ to an intermediate level $E_2$. An example of this type of material is atomic cesium. In this type of laser, the level $E_3$ is narrow, which is necessary if the stimulated emission is to be monochromatic; as a result, the energy quanta which "pump" the laser can only be those which have exactly the right energy—this leads to a low pumping efficiency.

In Class II materials, the pumping band is broad, i.e., the energy level is made up of many closely spaced levels. From this pumping band, the energy levels drop by spontaneous processes—which may be nonradiative —to level $E_2$, and then by stimulated emission to level $E_1$. This type of material is characterized by a relatively high pumping efficiency. Pink ruby is a typical example.

In the four-level laser (Class III), the spontaneous emission is to an intermediate level. Pumping takes place between levels $E_1$ and $E_4$, the latter being broad; spontaneous transitions drop the atoms to energy level $E_3$, which is narrow, and stimulated emission takes place between $E_3$ and $E_2$. Examples of this type of material are rare earth ions in various hosts

—crystals, glass and plastic. Neodymium in calcium tungstate is currently a common variety. This type of material exhibits a low threshold pumping power.

## RESONATORS

**11.12. The Fabry-Perot Resonator.** The feedback condition required to make an oscillator, as discussed in Section 11.9, is provided by a two-mirror arrangement identical to the Fabry-Perot Interferometer (Section 8.49 *et seq.*). If this apparatus is considered as a resonator, it is seen that when, after two reflections, a wave is superimposed upon itself, as shown in Figure 11.2, the condition for reinforcement, or oscillation, is produced.

If the mirror separation is $b$, this condition may be written

$$n\lambda = 2b \tag{11.9}$$

$n$ being integral, and since $\nu = c/\lambda$, the condition can be written in terms of frequency

$$\nu = n\frac{c}{2b} \tag{11.10}$$

When stimulated emission at a frequency $\nu$ which satisfies Equation (11.9) is generated, "lasing" will occur at this frequency provided that the gain in a single transit (back and forth) exceeds the criterion expressed in Equation (11.8).

In general, since the stimulated emission bandwidth has a finite value —i.e., the energy levels between which the stimulated transitions take place are not infinitely narrow—there will be a number of frequencies satisfying Equation (11.10) which lie within this bandwidth. The separation of these frequencies is $c/2b$. The equivalence of this frequency separation to the free spectral range of the Fabry-Perot interferometer (Section 8.52) will be readily seen.

**11.13. Q-factor.** A figure of merit known as $Q$ is a common descriptor of resonating systems and is a measure of the sharpness of the resonance peak. In electrical circuits, $Q = \omega L/R$; it is essentially a measure of the

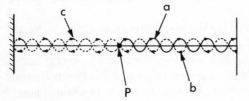

FIGURE 11.2. The Fabry-Perot Resonator. (P) Emission of a photon, (a) forward wave, (b) backward wave reflected from end mirror, (c) additional forward wave after two reflections, in phase with original wave.

ratio between the power circulating in the resonator and the power extracted. In the case of a simple Fabry-Perot resonator, the $Q$-factor[9] is closely related to the interferometer *line width* [Equation (8.52)] and is given by

$$Q = \frac{R}{1 - R} \qquad (11.11)$$

where $R$ is the mirror reflectivity. The *bandwidth* of resonance is, in terms of frequency,

$$\Delta\nu = \frac{\nu}{Q} \qquad (11.12)$$

In a laser, account must be taken of the attenuation of the beam in the material and of diffraction losses at the edges of the aperture. This may be done by writing the equation

$$Q = \frac{|R_1 R_2 e^{-2\alpha b}|}{1 - |R_1 R_1 e^{-2\alpha b}|} \qquad (11.13)$$

where $\alpha$ is the attenuation coefficient for scattering in the material, $b$ is the length of the laser, and $R_1$ and $R_2$ are the *voltage* reflection coefficients of the two mirrors; $R = (1 - \delta r - \delta d)^{1/2}$, $\delta r$ being the *amplitude* reflection loss and $\delta d$ the *amplitude* diffraction loss.

By analogy with microwave technology, the space between the mirrors in which the laser action takes place, and which contains the active material, is generally referred to as a *resonant cavity*.

**11.14. Resonant Cavity Modes.** The resonant cavity of a laser has a very close resemblance to a circular wave guide, whose theory and application have been rather thoroughly explored in microwave technology. The significant difference is that the laser is a dielectric cylinder, whereas the circular wave guide is usually a hollow tube with conductive walls. Such cavities can support patterns of standing waves, characterized by static distributions of the electric and magnetic fields; these stable patterns are known as *modes*.

Modes may be designated in two ways: by the pattern of the electric and magnetic fields, or by the frequency and direction of propagation. The former type of designation has become common because of analogy with the microwave case, although the latter would probably be more meaningful for those not having an electronics background.

The modes which can exist in a dielectric rod are those commonly designated as TEM (transverse electromagnetic) modes in a circular wave guide; these are modes in which there are no components of either electric

FIGURE 11.2A. Fabry-Perot fringes from a laser. The fine structure of the rings indicates multimode lasing. (*Courtesy Perkin-Elmer Corp.*)

or magnetic field along the axis of the cavity. They are commonly designated by subscripts ($\text{TEM}_{m,n}$) which indicate the number of nodes in the $X$- and $Y$-directions, respectively, of the cavity cross section.

Fox and Li[10] have reported a theoretical investigation of the mode patterns in dielectric rods. By digital computer techniques, they determined those electric and magnetic field distributions which reproduced themselves to develop a "steady-state" condition after many transits through the cavity. For plane-parallel end mirrors, the dominant modes were found to be those possessing even axial symmetry of the fields ($\text{TEM}_{00}$). These modes exist at a series of frequencies given by

$$\nu = m(c/2b) \tag{11.14}$$

Modes possessing odd axial symmetry ($\text{TEM}_{10}$) also exist, and these exist at a series of frequencies

$$\nu = m\,\frac{c}{2b} + \delta\nu \qquad (11.15)$$

For practicable lasers, the value of $m$ is of the order of $10^6$; the frequency separation between the members of either class of modes is $c/2b$ = 150 Mc for a 1-meter long laser. $\delta\nu$, the frequency separation between the even and odd symmetrical modes, is of the order of 1 Mc.

Fox and Li concluded that the resonant modes of a laser could be predicted with considerable accuracy from the theory of circular wave guides. The validity of their results has been demonstrated to a substantial degree with actual laser experiments.

**11.15. The Fresnel Number.** Prediction of laser modes from their treatment as circular wave guides is generally restricted to cases where the *Fresnel Number* is large—this situation holds for most lasers. The Fresnel Number is defined as

$$N = \frac{a^2}{b\lambda} \qquad (11.16)$$

where $a$ is the radius of the cavity cross section, $b$ is its length, and $\lambda$ is the wavelength of the radiation.

For large values of $N$, the diffraction losses in the dominant modes become very small and are insignificant compared to the reflection losses, which are more or less independent of modes.

**11.16. Spherical Mirror Resonators.** The first laser cavities were formed with plane-parallel end mirrors, in the arrangement of the conventional Fabry-Perot interferometer. It was soon seen, however, that arrangements using spherical mirrors would also provide a resonant cavity and that this arrangement would reduce the precision of angular adjustment required at the mirrors.

Let the radius of curvature of the mirrors (both mirrors the same) be $r$, and their separation $b$. Many relations between $r$ and $b$ will provide a resonant cavity, but there are two special configurations which have been given attention, namely the *confocal* arrangement, where the separation is equal to the radius, and therefore the paraxial foci of the two spherical mirrors are coincident ($b = r$), and the concentric arrangement, where $b = 2r$, and the centers of curvature are coincident. There is also an arrangement of a plane mirror and a spherical mirror which, when the separation is such that the center of curvature of the sphere lies on the surface of the plane, is called *hemispherical*. Figure 11.3 illustrates these three arrangements.

Resonant modes in spherical mirror cavities have been theoretically studied,[11] as have the effects of slight departures from the strict geometry.

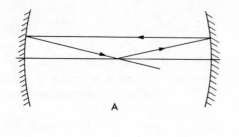

A

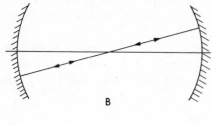

FIGURE 11.3. Spherical mirror resonators: (A) confocal, (B) concentric,
(C) hemispherical.

B

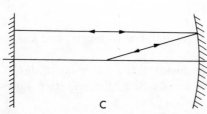

C

In principle, the mode patterns are quite similar to those for cavities with plane-parallel ends; the actual numerical values are, of course, somewhat different. For the confocal cavity, for example, the spacing between dominant $TEM_{00}$ modes is $c/4b$ instead of $c/2b$.

A large advantage is achieved in spherical mirror cavities in the control of diffraction losses; in addition, considerable relief in alignment accuracy is attained. The required accuracy of spherical mirror alignment is measured in minutes of arc—for plane-parallel mirrors, accuracy must be maintained to seconds. There is also some relief in the required optical quality of the surfaces in the case of spherical mirrors, although in high-performance lasers this is not an important factor.

**11.17. Modes in Actual Lasers.** Theoretical mode studies by Boyd and Gordon,[11] Boyd and Kogelnick,[11] and Fox and Li[10] have provided a foundation for mode studies in actual lasers. Simplifications which were adopted in these analyses cause the predictions to be somewhat different from reality, but for the most part, the departure between theory and experiment has been quite small. The analyses, in general, assumed a

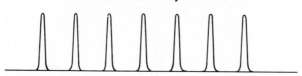

FIGURE 11.4. Dominant modes in a resonant cavity

homogeneous, lossless material—a condition which is approached in the gas laser but is considerably different from reality in the ruby and other solid-state lasers. The effect of the side walls was also ignored in the theory; this effect, although relatively small, is significant in real systems.

The frequencies in which a laser will oscillate are determined, in the first order by:

(a) The location and line width of the cavity modes.

(b) The spectrum curve of the stimulated emission energy gap.

There are, of course, many complications in higher orders of approximation.

If the stimulated emission line width is broad with respect to the frequency difference between dominant modes $(c/2b)$, there will be a number of cavity modes within this line width, and these modes will tend to oscillate at amplitudes enclosed by the envelope of the line, so that the mode oscillation will appear as shown in Figure 11.5.

The separation of these oscillations in frequency is, of course, the dominant mode frequency separation $c/2b$. In general, the oscillation will be centered on the cavity frequency.

When the fluorescent line width is of the same order as the cavity line width, the situation is more complex, and the phenomenon of "frequency pulling" may occur; the frequency of oscillation is pulled away from the cavity mode frequency toward the center of the fluorescence line.

The mode patterns in an actual laser, therefore, will depend not only on the cavity geometry, but also on the structure of the fluorescence line of the active material and on the pump power, since at a given level of pump power, the gain obtained in the lower amplitude modes will be insufficient to create oscillations.

Modes other than the dominant modes may also appear, so that the

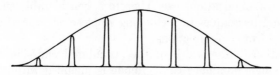

FIGURE 11.5. Dominant modes of a resonant cavity under fluorescence envelope.

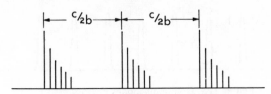

FIGURE 11.6. Transverse modes

frequency spectrum of the laser output may resemble the plot of Figure 11.6, which shows dominant mode frequencies separated by $c/2b$, together with other modes, having the same separation but differing in frequency by a constant factor.

**11.18. Thermal Effects.** Thermal conditions have a pronounced effect on the output frequency pattern of solid-state lasers.[12, 13] The most powerful effect of temperature is to change the shape of the fluorescence line, which becomes narrower as the temperature is decreased. For ruby, the stimulated emission line width decreases from 11 to 0.2 cm$^{-1}$ for a change in temperature from 20 to 77°K. At the same time, the center of the line shifts toward shorter wavelengths at lower temperatures, at a rate of about .065Å/°C.

Other temperature effects are a change in the relaxation time, changes in the optical quality of the end surfaces, and changes in optical path length due to length and refractive index change. For a 1° change in temperature, the optical path length may change in a 2.5-cm-long ruby laser rod by .05 due to change of physical length and by 0.5 due to index of refraction change.

**11.19. General Characteristics of Laser Oscillators.** Applications of lasers naturally seek to exploit their particular qualities of high power, high monochromaticity and high directivity. These properties are not inherently compatible in the laser design for present-day lasers.

The highest power output is obtained when the full width of the fluorescence line is utilized; this is inconsistent with a narrow output linewidth (monochromaticity).

Single-mode operation—to obtain maximum directivity and highest purity of output frequency—is desirable for many laser applications, particularly for communications use. Therefore, considerable effort has gone into means and techniques for achieving single-mode operation. This can be approached from two directions:

(a) Reduction in the width of the stimulated emission spectral line until only a single dominant cavity mode is included within it. This approach implies short cavities, the selection of suitable materials and/or operation at low temperatures.

(b) The provision of pump power sufficient only to create oscillation at the dominant mode of highest gain. This technique is effective, but it inherently fails to use the available power in the device.

Single-mode operation has been achieved in a number of instances by either or both of these techniques.

## REFERENCES

Bibliography for Chapters 11 to 14 will be found at the end of Chapter 14.

CHAPTER 12

# Forms and Characteristics
# of Lasers

**12.1. General.** Although only five years have elapsed since the first experimental operation of a laser was reported, there are hundreds of different materials in which laser action has been achieved. Lasers have now been constructed from solid materials, liquids and gases, and the range of frequencies covers the gamut from the far infrared to ultraviolet light. An attempt is made here to describe some of the fundamental properties of the lasers which have so far been produced—classifying them into a few basic types. The operating mechanisms are fundamental and will apply to the many new lasers which are bound to be developed in the near future—many of them, no doubt, before this book can reach a reader's eye. The general form of those described herein is likely to prevail, more or less as at present. New operating frequencies are certain to emerge rapidly.

Some discussion of power levels and quantitative characteristics is necessary; these represent the current state of the art (1964) and will very quickly become obsolete.

## THE RUBY LASER

**12.2. General Characteristics.** Ruby was the first material in which laser action was produced[1] and has received a great deal of attention because of its special properties. It is a three-level material, the energy diagram being shown in Figure 12.1. Ruby is aluminum oxide with chromium as an impurity; the emission comes from the chromium atoms. This situation, in which an impurity provides the emission, is common (but not universal) in laser materials. Ruby is characterized by a double level from

586

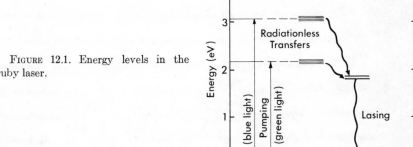

FIGURE 12.1. Energy levels in the ruby laser.

which the emission takes place. This leads to two rather close emission lines and, consequently, a complex mode situation.

The typical chromium concentration is from .05 to 0.1 per cent; this material is known as "pink" ruby. Ruby with a 1 per cent chromium concentration provides a four-level laser.

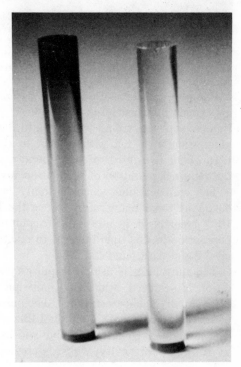

FIGURE 12.1A. Ruby laser rods. These rods, ¼-in. in diameter by 2 in. long, are of two different compositions. (*Courtesy Perkin-Elmer Corp.*)

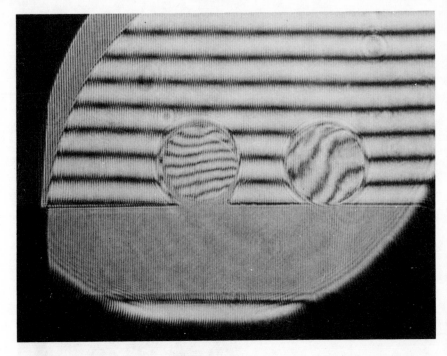

FIGURE 12.1B. Interferometric test of two ruby rods. The rods are ¼-in. in diameter and 2 in. long. Tested in a laser interferometer. (*Courtesy Perkin-Elmer Corp.*)

Pumping raises the ground-state atoms to one of two upper bands, blue and green light providing the required quanta for this excitation. Radiationless transfers from these levels to the metastable R-levels provide the population inversion with respect to the ground state, and when more than about two-thirds of the ground state population has been pumped, the required condition of population inversion is reached.

The emission line which normally lases has a central wavelength of 6943Å at room temperature. Since the lifetime in level 2 is about $5 \times 10^{-3}$ seconds, it is necessary to pump two-thirds of the ground-state population in this time interval to create a population inversion between level 2 and the ground state.

The ruby laser is usually a pulse-type laser. When the inversion condition is achieved, stimulated emission takes place, and the population ratio rapidly achieves stability. The pulse consists of multiple components of short duration, with individual line widths of the order of $4 \times 10^{-4}$Å. The actual wavelengths and line widths, of course, are largely governed by the resonant cavity, which is created by optically finishing the ends

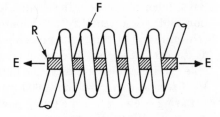

FIGURE 12.2. Schematic arrangement for an optically pumped ruby laser: (E) laser output, (R) ruby rod, (F) helical flash tube.

of a ruby rod. A typical laser rod has a diameter of 0.6 cm and a length of 5 to 10 cm. A typical pulse has about 1 joule of energy and a peak power of about 10 KW.

**12.3. Optical Pumping.** Ruby is typical of a number of laser materials in which the population inversion is created by *optical* pumping.[14, 15] A high-intensity lamp, with adequate radiation in the required blue and green spectral region, is mounted so as to concentrate its radiation in the laser rod.

In terms of total energy provided for pumping compared to laser output energy, lasers are for the most part very inefficient devices. It is the quality of the output rather than its average quantity which makes lasers worthwhile. Most of the loss in efficiency, in the case of optical pumping, occurs because most of the radiation from the source is in wavelengths other than those which are effective in producing useful atomic transitions in the laser material. There is a further substantial loss in the inefficiency of concentration of the source energy into the laser material.

Many arrangements have been devised for concentrating the light of a high-intensity lamp into a laser rod. Figure 12.2 shows a common arrangement, which consists of a high-intensity electrical flash tube wound into a helix with the laser rod in its axis. Xenon discharge tubes are customarily used. In order to provide a few tens of kilowatts of useful energy in the laser material, these lamps are operated at a few megawatts (1000 joules in a millisecond flash).

**12.4. Output Characteristics.** The output of the typical ruby laser has been shown to be an ensemble of micropulses with individual bandwidths of about 5 Mc (about .0001Å). The ruby laser characteristically oscillates in several frequencies simultaneously. Observations of interference beats between modes[16] indicate that usually the frequency differences are within a few per cent of those calculated for axial modes of the resonant cavity. In a 5-cm rod, frequency differences of a few gigacycles are typical for axial modes. Transverse modes give frequency differences in the range 30 to 300 Mc.

The available output energy of a laser is determined, in the limit, by the number of atoms in the excited level which can emit stimulated radiation and how often they participate in the emission. In ruby, a typical concentration of chromium gives about $10^{19}$ atoms/cm$^3$; if all of these were at the excited energy level, about 5 joules/cm$^3$ of energy would be available. To raise these atoms to the upper energy level in the lifetime of $5 \times 10^{-3}$ second requires about 1000 watts/cm$^3$ of pump power.

Lasing begins when the pump power is sufficient to create a population inversion. When the pump power is just above threshold, one would expect that the first dominant mode would become operative; as the pump power is increased, additional modes should appear. Total output power depends upon pump power, so that single-mode operation is obtained only at the cost of output power. In actual lasers, the situation is never quite as simple as described above, but the general nature of the process is of this form.

A phenomenon known as "hole burning" is currently an important one[17] and is not completely understood; the term refers to the depletion of available ions along a path through the laser.

**12.5. Giant Pulses.** With a technique known as "Q-spoiling" or "Q-switching," it is possible to obtain pulses of much greater intensity than in normal operation. In the usual arrangement, lasing begins as soon as the required population inversion has been achieved and before the maximum condition of inversion for the particular arrangement has been generated.

Lasing, however, depends upon the presence of the resonant cavity, and if a condition is created whereby the resonant cavity does not exist until maximum population inversion has been reached, giant pulses are produced.[18] The technique involves a rotating mirror, which is one of the end mirrors of the resonator, or a device such as a Kerr cell between the laser rod and one of the end mirrors.

The power levels in the output beam reach almost fantastic porportions compared to what could be accomplished prior to the existence of the laser. For a theoretical example, consider an output beam with a divergence of 1 mil, and a 1-cm. focal length lens concentrating the beam to a spot about .01 mm in diameter. For a pulse whose peak power (in a single mode) is a gigawatt ($10^9$ watts), the power density in the spot would be $10^{15}$ watts/cm$^2$, and the voltage gradient $10^9$ volts/cm. This is comparable to the electron binding forces in atoms. Nonlinear phenomena (see Chapter 13) are detectable at power densities of the order of $10^6$ watts/cm$^2$. Power densities even higher than those given above are quite feasible with lasers.

## THE GASEOUS LASER

**12.6. The He-Ne Laser.** Population inversions are fairly common in gas discharges, such as take place in neon tubes and fluorescent lamps; hence this kind of apparatus is a natural candidate for a laser, and a number of gas lasers have been developed.[19] A laser composed of a mixture of helium and neon at low pressure was proposed as a laser by Javan in 1959, and other mixtures were also proposed.[20] Neon has an arrangement of energy levels that provides a four-level system, as shown in Figure 12.3. The atoms are "pumped" by collisions with He atoms which are excited by the electrons accelerated by the electric field. Pumping takes place between levels 1 and 4; radiationless transitions take place between levels 4 and 3, and the emission comes from the transition to level 2. Later the atoms drop to the ground level again without radiating.

The first gas laser was an He-Ne device operated by Javan, Bennett and Herriott in 1960.[7] They obtained laser action in a transition which yielded an output wavelength of $1.15\mu$. In the following year, White and Rigden,[8] using a 10/1 mixture of helium and neon at a pressure of about 1 mm obtained a laser which gave its output at 6328Å, in the visible red. This is the transition which has been most widely exploited in the He-Ne laser so far and which is illustrated in Figure 12.3. The He-Ne laser is essentially a CW device; the four-level system, providing as it does a terminal level which is above the ground state and is therefore sparsely populated under normal conditions, needs very little pumping energy to

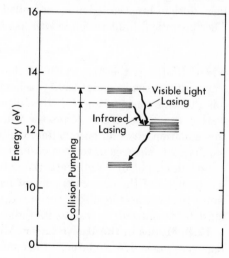

FIGURE 12.3. Energy levels in the He-Ne laser.

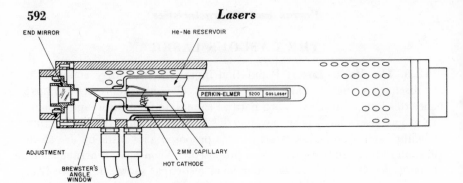

FIGURE 12.4A. Schematic diagram of a standard He-Ne laser. This laser has a rating of 0.5 milliwatts in single mode operation and over 1.5 milliwatts in multimode. (*Courtesy Perkin-Elmer Corp.*)

develop a population inversion with respect to this level. Continuous action is obtained only if the pumping can maintain the required population while the stimulated emission is going on. With present methods of pumping, this is only possible when the number of atoms to be pumped to create an inversion is relatively small.

The output of the White-Rigden laser was about 0.1 milliwatt. Similar lasers have since been developed with greatly increased outputs.

**12.7. Brightness and Line Width.** CW lasers are generally the preferred means for producing highly monochromatic and highly directional beams. Gases are less affected by temperature and, although there is line broadening in gases due to the Doppler effect, it will be recalled that the line width of laser emission is controlled primarily by the resonant cavity. The theoretical limit to line width has been given by Townes as

$$(d\omega)_{osc} = 4h\omega(d\omega)_{res}/P \tag{12.1}$$

where $(d\omega)_{osc}$ is the line width of the output; $(d\omega)_{res}$ is the theoretical line width of the resonant cavity, $\omega$ being expressed in angular frequency; $h$ is Planck's constant and $P$ is the output power. For an output of 1 milliwatt and a Fabry-Perot resonator with 99 per cent reflective end walls, this equation gives an output line width of .001 cycle/sec. Line widths as small as 2 cycles/sec have been observed.

For an output of 1 milliwatt, the actual brightness of the He-Ne laser, on the basis of the power per unit of bandwidth at the peak, is about $10^8$ times that of the sun. From the standpoint of total power, the sun's size must be considered, as well as its radiation bandwidth of $2 \times 10^{14}$ cycles.

**12.8. Modes in the He-Ne Laser.** Mode patterns have been studied extensively in the He-Ne laser;[21] the emission line is single in this laser, and the power output is lower, so that it is more amenable to quantitative study

FIGURE 12.4B. Diffraction pattern from a laser beam. This diffraction pattern, which is the Fraunhofer pattern from a crossed slit, indicates the degree of coherence which is available in a laser beam by the completeness of the fine structure of the pattern. (*Courtesy Perkin-Elmer Corp.*)

than ruby. Under normal conditions, the spontaneous emission line is approximately a gaussian curve with a half-width of about 1500 Mc. It will be recalled that the frequency difference between cavity resonances is $c/2b$, so that, for a tube ½ meter in length, the mode separation will be 300 Mc. There are therefore a number of modes under the emission curve. The cavity will sustain oscillations corresponding to $2b = n\lambda$ whenever the gain is sufficient and there are no intermode interferences. The modes which will actually oscillate will be determined by the losses, which in turn are determined by the details of the cavity and the population inversion.

The mode pattern is shown in Figure 12.5. Cavity modes appear as spikes under the gaussian emission curve. Axial modes are shown as spikes extending to the envelope; transverse modes appear as shorter spikes flanking each axial mode.

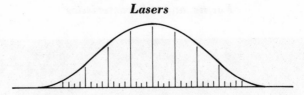

FIGURE 12.5. Modes under an emission line

With sufficient pump power, an extensive set of axial and transverse modes will oscillate. As pump power is reduced, the transverse modes disappear first, since these have higher losses than the axial modes. Further decrease in pump power causes the axial modes to disappear successively, beginning with those farthest from the center of the emission line. With pump power just above threshold, single-mode operation is obtained.

This idealized picture is usually not obtained in practice—presumably it would be attained if the geometry of the cavity was sufficiently precise and the reflectivity of the end mirrors was sufficiently high.

**12.9. Single-mode Operation.** Efforts to provide single-mode operation, which is desirable for some applications, take the following forms:

(1) Reduction of the Doppler-broadened emission line; this can be accomplished through the use of heavier atoms, or by operating under reduced temperatures.

(2) Reduction in the cavity length to increase the mode separation— this results in a loss in power because of reduced plasma volume.

(3) Optical-mode suppression. Symmetrical and unsymmetrical obstructions in the cavity can alter the mode pattern, and it is possible to eliminate some unwanted modes by these techniques. Modes with a direction of propagation not parallel to the axis can be suppressed by focusing

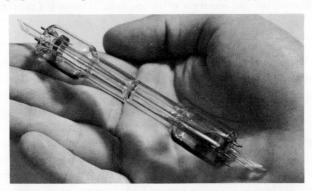

FIGURE 12.5A. A compact He-Ne laser. This laser, affectionately known as the "Pee-Wee," gives a single mode output of better than 100 microwatts. (*Courtesy Perkin-Elmer Corp.*)

FIGURE 12.6. Arrangement for
mode suppression by means of an
optical diaphragm.

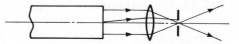

the main mode with an external lens and placing a small aperture stop
at the focus, as shown in Figure 12.6.

**12.10. Stability.** Although the frequency stability and the purity of
lasers in normal operation rival the best which can be obtained with electronic oscillators, it is often desirable to refine the performance to the
maximum extent possible. Vibration and temperature variations are
sources of frequency variation and "mode-hopping." Unstable excitation
power is another cause. For maximum stability, the power supply to the
excitation source must be well regulated, and the laser must be maintained at constant temperature and isolated against vibration. Two He-Ne
lasers under carefully controlled conditions have been observed to maintain relative frequency stability to about 20 cycles/sec.

Techniques have been developed for servo systems which adjust the
mirror spacing to maintain the output frequency. The required movement
of the mirrors is of the order of a fraction of a wavelength; piezoelectric
techniques have usually been used.

FIGURE 12.6A. An experimental 100-milliwatt He-Ne laser. (*Courtesy Perkin-
Elmer Corp.*)

**12.11. Pulse Operation.** Just as the ruby laser, which is inherently a pulsing device, has been operated as a CW laser,[22] so the He-Ne laser has been operated as a pulsing device. A 50/1 mixture of He-Ne in a 3-inch diameter tube, 130 cm long, has been operated to give $\frac{1}{2}$-$\mu$sec pulses at a rate of 2000 per second. Peak power output was about 100 watts, and average power was 100 milliwatts at the 1.15$\mu$ wavelength of neon.

## SEMICONDUCTOR LASERS

**12.12. The GaAs Laser.** Late in 1962, it was reported that stimulated emission had been obtained in a gallium arsenide $n$-type semiconductor diode;[23] these reports ushered in the currently very active area of semiconductor lasers, which are rather different in nature from the lasers discussed above and which have some unusual properties.

In most lasers, as mentioned previously, the stimulated emission is generated by the atoms of an impurity material or, as in the case of the He-Ne laser, by a material which is present in minor quantities. In semiconductor lasers, the stimulated emission arises from the host material itself, and therefore the concentration of active material is substantially higher.

Light emission from semiconductors as a result of recombination of electrons and holes in the form of incoherent radiation from randomly distributed spots is a common occurrence; it has been mentioned in a previous chapter. *Stimulated* emission from the same type of mechanism is a new phenomenon.

**12.13. Mechanism.** Lasing semiconductors are characterized by the energy-level diagram shown in Figure 12.7. The $p$-$n$ junction, with no ap-

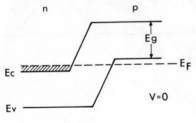

FIGURE 12.7. Energy levels for semiconductor lasers.

plied voltage, is as shown in A. The junction is *degenerate*—the Fermi energy line is above the conduction band on the $n$-side of the junction and below the valence band on the $p$-side.

When a forward bias voltage is applied, the barrier voltage is reduced—electrons are ejected from the $n$-region into the $p$-region, where they combine with holes to produce photons with energy $h\nu$. If the applied voltage is sufficiently high that $eV > h\nu$, there is a narrow region near the junction where population inversion is produced; in this region, the recombination photons can cause stimulated recombination and therefore laser action.

Lasing semiconductors are direct semiconductors; in these, an electron excited to the conduction band can combine directly with a hole and emit radiation. In indirect semiconductors, simultaneous emission of a photon and a phonon are required for recombination, therefore the stimulation is weak.

**12.14. Structure.** The region in which stimulated emission can take place is very thin—of the order of $10^{-4}$ cm. This is at the $p$-$n$ junction, and therefore normally takes the form of a thin plane. Light propagated in this plane is the most amplified because it has the longest path in the active material. The laser structure normally takes the form of a Fabry-Perot resonator: two faces normal to the plane of the junction are cleaved or polished, the other faces of the block are sawed or ground. Figure 12.8 shows a typical structure. The dimensions are of the order of 0.1 to 1.0 mm.

Figure 12.9 shows another structure which has been effectively used. Performance is improved if the laser is operated at low temperature, and this structure provides for close coupling to a cryostat. The junction in the case of this structure has an area of about $10^{-3}$ cm$^2$.

**12.15. Mode Behavior.** GaAs is currently the best-known semiconduc-

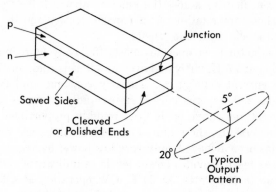

FIGURE 12.8. Typical structure and output pattern for the GaAs laser.

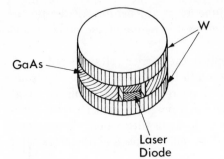

W

GaAs

Laser
Diode

FIGURE 12.9. A suggested structure for semiconductor laser. The lasing diode is surrounded by a semi-insulating ring of GaAs and placed between two tungsten plates which act as heat sinks.

tor laser material. The energy gap for this material is 1.47 eV, which corresponds to a wavelength of 8400Å. The width of the energy gap is about .02 eV, or about 100Å. Since the mode separation in a 1-mm long cavity is about 3Å, many modes are possible within the gap. Line widths in individual modes of much less than 300 Mc have been measured. Rise times of a few nanoseconds are typical.

**12.16. Efficiency.** A quantity called the *external quantum efficiency* is defined for the semiconductor laser ($n_{\text{ext}}$) as the ratio of the number of photons in the output per electron crossing the junction. Values of $n_{\text{ext}}$ as high as 60 per cent have been obtained at liquid helium temperature, with 40 per cent a typical value for operation at 77°K. At room temperature, $n_{\text{ext}}$ is of the order of 15 per cent.

The efficiency of the semiconductor (injection) laser in terms of radiation output versus dc electrical input is about 10 per cent at 77°K. This is greatly above the efficiencies which can be obtained with other types of lasers.

**12.17. Characteristics.** The semiconductor laser is characterized by a threshold current density across the junction at which lasing takes place. Figure 12.10 shows the relation of the current density and the output. The point $j_t$ is the threshold current density.

The semiconductor laser operates most effectively at reduced temperatures; operation at 77°K, 20°K and even at 4.2°K is common. Below 20°K, the threshold current density, $j_t$, is nearly constant, and for GaAs has a value of about 200 amperes/cm². It rises rapidly at higher temperatures, and for temperatures above 60°K, it is roughly proportional to $T^3$.

At room temperature, the required current densities are very high, and while lasing has been achieved, only very low power has been produced. At 77°K, the GaAs laser provides power levels in milliwatts and pulses with peak powers up to 100 watts. At 20°K, CW operation at a level above 1 watt has been achieved. Heating is a difficult problem at high power

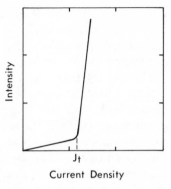

FIGURE 12.10. Relation of output intensity to current density.

levels, and pulsed operation is utilized primarily to reduce the average power and prevent overheating of the active material.

**12.18. Tunable Lasers.** The discussion above refers mainly to the gallium arsenide semiconductor laser with zinc doping. There are a large number of varieties of gallium arsenide with different dopings—especially phosphorus, and a wide variety of other materials with similar properties. Together, these materials provide a large array of possible output wavelengths, extending from 6500Å to above $5.2\mu$.

In some of the materials, particularly an alloy of phosphorus and gallium arsenide, it is possible to control the wavelength of emission through a continuous range by controlling the proportion of phosphorus. This provides a capability for producing a laser with any desired emission wavelength within the available range. The advantages of this freedom for applications such as spectroscopy are apparent.

It is also possible to *tune* a given semiconductor laser over a small range of wavelength by the application of a magnetic field, by pressure, and by temperature.

**12.19. Types of Semiconductor Lasers.** There are three types of semiconductor lasers,[24] only one of which has at this writing been realized in a working device. A further possible type has been suggested.

The first of the three basic types is the direct transition type, of which GaAs and some other extrinsic semiconductors are examples. The mechanism of this type has been described above.

The second has been called the two-boson type of laser.[25] This kind is derived from the intrinsic, or indirect, semiconductors, in which the normal recombination mechanism which involves both a photon and a phonon, as described above, can lead to laser action. Because of the necessity for both of these particles to cooperate in the downward transition of an electron which leads to the emission of the stimulated photon, the transition probability is less than in the case of the direct semiconductor, such as GaAs. The possibility of providing stimulated emission at otherwise unavailable wavelengths makes the two-boson laser a device worth experimentation. At this writing, the device has not been realized in practice.

The third type of semiconductor laser makes use of a high-strength magnetic field, and for this reason, it has been called the cyclotron resonance laser,[26] or the magnetic-optical laser. Under the influence of a strong magnetic field, the energy levels in the conduction band of a semiconductor are separated; this leads to the possibility of stimulated emission corresponding to a downward transition within this band. The energy-level differences are relatively small and thus would lead to emission in the infrared or even the microwave spectrum.

The attractiveness of this type of laser is the fact that the energy difference between the magnetically induced levels is proportional to the magnetic field, and thus the laser would be continuously tunable—a very valuable property in applications where modulation of the output is required.

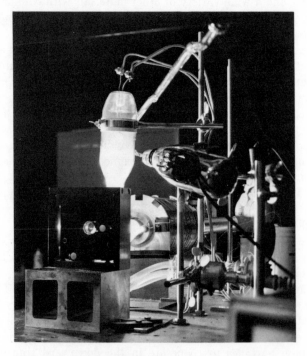

FIGURE 12.10A. Experimental argon gas laser. This laser gives an output in the visible green.

A fourth type of possible semiconductor laser is one in which the stimulated transitions take place in the impurity atoms; this would be a semiconductor (solid-state) laser with a mechanism precisely like that of the He-Ne and ruby lasers.

## OTHER TYPES OF LASERS

**12.20. Doped Glasses and Crystals.** A number of lasers have been produced through the doping of glasses and crystals with various elements. These include neodymium[27] in ordinary glass and in calcium tungstate, and trivalent uranium $(U^{3+})$[28] and samarium $(Sm^{2+})$[29] in calcium fluoride. These are all four-level materials. Neodymium in calcium tungstate was the first solid-state material to show CW laser action.

Fiber optics have been suggested as laser structures, and some experiments have been carried out with them. Because of their small dimensions, there should be a limited number of possible modes.

**12.21. Chelate Lasers.** A recent development has been the production of laser action in a number of rare earth chelates,[30] carried in plastic hosts. These materials are easily pumped optically, have a high quantum efficiency and narrow emission lines, and provide output wavelengths from about 1 mm to the ultraviolet region.

A typical example is europium benzoacetanate.[31] Operated at 77°K it has an output wavelength of 6130Å and a 15-Ångstrom line width. Threshold pumping energy is .01 joule, and the quantum efficiency of the material is quoted at 0.8.

Laser action has also been observed in liquids such as naphthalene.

A number of lasers are possible with divalent rare earth elements with materials like calcium fluorite as a host; these lasers have natural fluorescent line widths generally smaller than the cavity mode spacing. In such cases, modulation may be produced by a magnetic field, which, through the Zeeman effect, changes the position of the emission lines.

**12.22. Chelate Laser Mechanism.** In the chelate lasers, which are made of materials whose molecules are a combination of organic and inorganic parts, the energy absorption takes place in the organic part of the molecule and is efficiently transferred to the inorganic (rare earth) part.[32] This provides an unusually broad pumping band and hence a relatively efficient laser. Plastics, organic solutions and glasses provide material for the host.

# CHAPTER 13

# New Optical Phenomena

**13.1. New Fields of Exploration.** The laser is something more than an interesting optical device; it is not simply a more intense, more monochromatic and more coherent light source than was previously available. The laser has demanded a completely different point of view on many factors.

This new viewpoint has developed in two primary areas. The intensity of the laser beam creates an electromagnetic field incomparably stronger than it has hitherto been possible to produce; moreover, this field is highly coherent and oscillates at a frequency about a million times higher than coherent electromagnetic fields produced by any other means. The effects of this high-intensity, high-frequency field on materials have brought to light many new phenomena.

The second area is that of the treatment of the optical spectrum in a manner hitherto available only in a much lower range of frequencies, e.g., modulation and demodulation, frequency mixing, heterodyning, etc.

**13.2. Power Levels in Laser Beams.** A typical pulsed ruby laser at the current state of the art has the following characteristics:

| | |
|---|---|
| Output per pulse | 4 joules |
| Peak power | 8 kW |
| Pulse width | 500 $\mu$sec |
| Dimensions | $\frac{1}{4}$ inch diameter $\times$ 3 inch long |
| Pump input | 4000 joules |

The intensity of the peak output from the end of the ruby rod is, if uniform over the face, about 25 kW/cm². This beam may be focused by a lens to a small spot. If the laser output had perfect spatial coherence and the lens was diffraction limited and had a relative aperture of $f/2.8$, the size of the focused spot would be .00016 cm in diameter. A practical size of focused spot from a laser beam is .01 cm in diameter.

602

A little calculation yields the following comparisons:

(1) For the diffraction-limited focused spot:

(a) The intensity is 70,000 times that of the surface of the sun.

(b) The intensity is about 100 million times that which can be achieved by focusing an image of the sun.

(c) The intensity corresponds to that produced by a blackbody at a temperature of 90,000°K—16 times the temperature of the sun and 3 times the temperature of the hottest known stars.

(2) For the now attainable .01-cm diameter spot:

(a) The intensity is about 15 times that of the surface of the sun.

(b) The intensity is about 30,000 times that which can be achieved by focusing an image of the sun.

It must be borne in mind that this is the case for a typical state-of-the-art ruby laser in an ordinary pulse mode. In Q-switch operation, peak power outputs some four to five orders of magnitude greater can be achieved. It must also be remembered that these conditions persist for only a few microseconds, at most.

For the above case, the intensity in the focused spot (.01 cm) is nearly $10^8$ watts/cm$^2$, and the electric field is about $10^5$ volts/cm. The intensity of the magnetic field is about 3000 oersteds.

Highly unusual effects occur in dielectric materials at field intensities considerably less than those quoted above. At field strengths which are attainable with Q-switch techniques, many materials will show complete breakdown. The electrical breakdown of air in a Q-switched laser beam has been observed, and it has been computed that the maximum power density which can be transmitted on a continuous basis through air is $7 \times 10^{11}$ watts/cm$^2$ at all pressures for which the mean free path is small compared to the diameter of the beam.

## NONLINEAR PHENOMENA IN DIELECTRICS

**13.3. Dielectric Crystals in an Electric Field.** When an electric field is applied in a dielectric crystal, the valence electrons in the material are subject to the field and are pulled or pushed from their equilibrium positions in response to it. If the field is an oscillating one, then the electrons will oscillate.

Light is an oscillating electromagnetic field, and consequently it generates an oscillation of the valence electrons in materials through which it is being propagated. This phenomenon is the polarization of the medium, which was discussed in a previous chapter. For small fields, such as exist for all light beams which it was possible to produce before the advent of the laser, the electrons merely oscillate with very small amplitude, and the only result is a weak alternating current in the medium which occurs at the frequency of the incident light and is responsible for refraction and dispersion, as discussed previously.

The electric fields which exist locally in the crystal and which are responsible for maintenance of the crystal bond have strengths of the order of $10^8$ to $10^{10}$ volts/cm. The field strength in a beam of ordinary sunlight is about 10 volts/cm. Such fields are tiny compared to the crystal fields, and only minor effects occur, such as dispersion. This situation is recognized in the statement of the polarization of the medium [Equation (3.1)] as being linearly proportional to the electric field strength.

The field strength of a focused laser beam, however, is comparable to, and may even exceed, the local fields in the crystal, and therefore the linearity relation expressed in Equation (3.1) may be expected to become invalid. Under the influence of these very high field strengths, massive redistribution of the electrons occurs, and the material may even break down.

**13.4. Nonlinear Polarization.** More rigorously, the displacement of a valence electron in the crystal is given by a power series expansion of the electric field, of the form

$$P = x_{ij}E_j + d_{ijk}E_jE_k + \cdots \qquad (13.1)$$

where $d_{ijk}$, and similar operators following, are tensors. It is beyond the scope of this discussion to venture into tensor analysis; in simplification, it may be said that the successive terms of the expansion become rapidly smaller, so that higher and higher intensities are required to observe the effects of the successive terms.

Various terms may be shown to be related to known optical effects, such as the Kerr effect, the Faraday effect, etc.; other terms relate to the generation of harmonics of the incident light frequency. Effects associated with many of the terms of the expansion have been observed in crystals irradiated with laser beams. Blooembergen and others[33] have given a theoretical treatment of this subject.

**13.5. Polarization Wave in Nonsymmetric Crystals.** The nonlinear effect results in the propagation, in the crystal, of a *polarization wave*, which travels with the velocity of the incident light and is the sum of three components:

(a) a wave at the fundamental frequency of the incident light;

(b) a wave at twice the incident light frequency;

(c) a dc component.

These are the components of the polarization wave in crystals which do not have a center of symmetry, and in which, therefore, the amplitudes of the oscillating valence electrons are not purely sinusoidal in response to a sinusoidal input oscillation. Such crystals show piezoelectric properties, and in the present early stages of investigation of nonlinear phenomena, they have naturally come in for the major share of attention, since nonlinear effects are most easily achieved with them.

**13.6. Second Harmonic Generation.** The component of the polarization wave which has the frequency $2v$, where $v$ is the frequency of the incident light, generates a second harmonic optical beam. There is a slight difference of velocity between this optical second harmonic and the second harmonic component of the polarization wave which causes them to interfere and cancel out at multiples of their mutual coherence length, which is of the order of $10^{-3}$ cm.

In order to observe the second harmonic generation of light, special techniques to avoid this cancellation must be employed. Two methods have been used: double refraction in crystals so oriented that the velocity of the second harmonic is made equal to the corresponding component of the polarization wave (as applied by Terhune at Ford and Giordmaine[34] at Bell Laboratories) and the use of crystal laminates which reverse the phase of the generated second harmonic in alternate lamina (as applied with barium titanate by Miller at Bell Laboratories and by Franken[35] *et al.* at the University of Michigan, using stacked quartz plates). Franken's team has detected the dc component of the polarization wave with the quartz plate technique.

**13.7. Polarization Wave in Symmetric Crystals.** All materials exhibit nonlinear polarization effects for sufficiently intense light beams, but the effects are much weaker in symmetric crystals and in isotropic materials such as glass.

In such materials, the polarization wave is not skewed as in the case of nonsymmetric crystals, but the displacements are not linearly proportional to the applied field and hence nonlinear effects appear. The principal component of the polarization wave in these materials, aside from the fundamental, is a weak third harmonic. Third harmonic generation has been observed for Q-switched ruby beams in KDP.

**13.8. Experiments in Second Harmonic Generation.** Numerous experiments in second harmonic generation have been carried out with various types of lasers. This effect has been produced in quartz, zinc sulfide, ADP (ammonium dihydrogen phosphate), EDP (ethylene diamine tartrate), barium titanate, KDP (potassium dihydrogen phosphate), and in 20 to 30 other materials. The conversion of fundamental to second harmonic has been as high as 22 per cent.

Second harmonic generation has also been observed in semiconductors

(GaAs), both as a surface reflection from an incident laser beam and as internally self-induced in the lasing action.

**13.9. Other Nonlinear Phenomena.** Many other unusual effects have been observed in materials irradiated with intense laser beams; these are generally discussed under the title of "nonlinear" effects, although the name may not be strictly appropriate in all cases.

Changes in the absorption and transmission properties of materials under the intense fields induced by laser beams have been reported in a number of instances. Ducuing and Blooembergen have observed harmonic generation on reflection from crystals such as tellurium that are normally opaque to both the fundamental and the second harmonic. Blooembergen and Pershan have shown that the laws of reflection and refraction must be generalized to include harmonic generation at surfaces.

Opacity has been observed to be induced in normally transparent materials under laser illumination.

Absorption of laser light in material that normally absorbs only at twice the frequency has been shown by Kaiser and Garrett. This phenomenon implies that two photons in the incident beam have combined to produce a single atomic transition. This highly unusual effect was predicted theoretically by Maria Goeppert Mayer in 1931.

**13.10. Beat Frequencies.** It has become almost an axiom in optics that two light beams which cross each other do not produce any observable effect.

This is a first-order condition and is not rigorously true when effects such as those expressed in Equation (13.1) are taken into account. Theoretically, two light beams can interact even in empty space,[36] although the effects are so small that it is unlikely that they will be observed in the foreseeable future. In dielectric materials, however, in the presence of nonlinear conditions induced by the high electric field intensities of laser beams, the interaction of crossing light beams in producing "beat" frequencies can be and has been observed.

**13.11. The Moiré Beat Pattern.** The creation of sum and difference frequencies in the crossing of light beams is most readily illustrated by the Moiré pattern shown in Figure 13.1. The intersections of wave fronts which give rise to the Moiré fringes can be seen to represent two new loci of maxima and minima which therefore define two new sets of wave fronts. The frequency of these two new sets of waves are respectively the sum and difference of the two original beams, and their directions of propagation are different from either of the incident beams.

**13.12. Quantum Explanation of Light Beats.** The occurrence of the sum frequency is explained without much difficulty in terms of the quantum

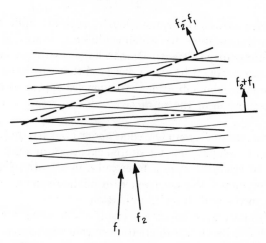

FIGURE 13.1. Mixing of two light waves. The dotted lines show the wave fronts for the harmonic and subharmonic resultants and their direction of propagation.

theory as the combination of two photons, one from each of the incident beams, to produce a single photon with an energy equal to the sum of the energies of the two original photons. Energy and momentum conservation are both preserved in this type of interaction.

The production of the difference frequency is not quite so easily explained, since this requires the production of a photon with an energy less than either of the original photons. The following interaction is postulated: If the original photons are $p_1$ and $p_2$, in the interaction to produce the photon $p_3$, whose energy is $p_1 - p_2$, $p_1$ is annihilated. Two new photons are produced, one is identical to $p_2$, and the other is $p_3$, which takes on the energy difference. The effect is to produce not only some light at the frequency corresponding to $p_3$, but also an increase in the light of frequency corresponding to $p_2$. The postulation has not been experimentally confirmed.

**13.13. Raman Spectra.** In 1962, in experiments with a 1-megawatt ruby laser, Woodbury and Ng, passing the laser beam through nitrobenzene, found that about 10 per cent of the light was converted into a coherent beam at a wavelength of 7660Å. The frequency difference between this beam and the incident beam is $4 \times 10^{13}$ cycles/sec, which was immediately recognized as a characteristic vibration frequency of the nitrobenzene molecule. Here then was *Raman emission*, discussed in Section 3.12, in which some of the energy in an incident light beam is absorbed in molecular vibrational frequencies and the remainder is emitted.

Raman spectra are, however, notoriously weak and difficult to observe, yet here was a Raman intensity which could be measured in kilowatts.

**13.14. Enhancement Effects.** Raman light is strongly enhanced when coupled to a laser beam. It has been observed that side bands at both plus and minus the molecular vibrational frequencies appear as a result of the very strong oscillation of the refractive index in response to the induced electric field.

The enhancement of Raman emission under laser irradiation is striking. Raman spectra which previously required exposures of a minute to an hour to record can be recorded from a laser pulse in a tenth of a microsecond. Townes has predicted the occurrence of high-frequency sound from a Raman-like process with laser illumination.

A secondary but highly important result of the discovery of stimulated Raman emission is its ability to create new coherent sources at new wavelengths. At present, more than 100 new coherent wavelengths have been generated through stimulated Raman emission. The coupling of these through sum and difference effects can result in 5000 different sources.

## ELECTRONICS IN THE OPTICAL SPECTRUM

**13.15. Photomixing.**[37] Photodetectors, such as phototubes, phototransistors, and the like, are *square law* detectors; i.e., their response is proportional to the square of the incident amplitude, or

$$i = \alpha_0 + \alpha_1 E^2 \tag{13.2}$$

If, then, two coherent plane waves are incident upon such a detector, the output will be, ignoring the constant term, which is a dc component,

$$\begin{aligned} i &= \alpha_1 (E_1 \sin \omega_1 t + E_2 \sin \omega_2 t)^2 \\ &= \alpha_1 (E_1{}^2 \sin^2 \omega_1 t + E_2{}^2 \sin^2 \omega_2 t + 2E_1 E_2 \sin \omega_1 t \sin \omega_2 t) \end{aligned} \tag{13.3}$$

which consists of a term at twice the frequency of each of the incident beams and a combination term. If the frequency difference $\omega_1 - \omega_2$ is small with respect to either of the incident frequencies, then the combination term is a low-frequency term with the frequency $\omega_1 - \omega_2$.

The response time of a photodetector, which is of the order of $10^{-8}$ second, is long with respect to optical frequencies, so that there is an *averaging* of the oscillations at the incident light frequencies and certainly at the double frequencies; but the term at the difference frequency may well have a sufficiently low rate of oscillation for it to be observed in the photodetector output.

This phenomenon was first observed by Forrester in 1955 and has become a commonplace with the advent of the laser.

It has been widely used to detect beat frequencies between different modes in laser beams and, thereby, to measure the frequencies and mode behavior. It has also been used to detect high-frequency modulation of laser beams.

In order to produce successful photomixing, it is important that the phase difference of the two incident beams be constant over the sensitive area of the photodetector; this implies a high directivity in the input beams and input directions parallel to each other—conditions readily achieved with laser beams.

**13.16. Optical Heterodyning.**[38] Anyone familiar with radio will immediately note that the phenomenon of photomixing makes possible heterodyning at optical frequencies. In a heterodyne radio circuit, an oscillator in the receiver beats with the input signal to produce an *intermediate frequency* which is the difference between the two. This technique leads to a very high frequency selectivity and high background signal suppression.

In the optical case, a laser provides an ideal local oscillator, and a photodetector provides the frequency mixing which generates the intermediate frequency. In conventional radio technology, it is customary to tune the local oscillator so that the intermediate frequency is always the same, regardless of the signal frequency. This permits an advantage in the amplifying stages of the receiver.

Lasers, at the present state of the art, are essentially constant-frequency devices, so that the optical heterodyne arrangement creates a variable intermediate frequency; this is not a fundamental limitation. With the promise of tunable lasers in the not too distant future, the optical heterodyne may assume the standard radio form.

Figure 13.2 shows schematically the arrangement for the optical heterodyne. Such devices have been used by a number of experimenters in the megacycle and gigacycle range.

**13.17. Optical Amplification.** It has been pointed out that the *maser*, operating at microwave frequencies, is often employed as an *amplifier*. An input signal provides the stimulation to create stimulated emission, which is amplified. It was also noted that the *laser*, although identical in its mech-

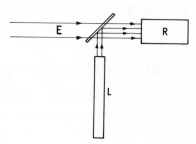

FIGURE 13.2. Schematic arrangement for optical heterodyning: (E) input light, (L) laser, (R) receiver.

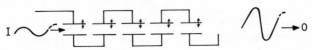

FIGURE 13.3. Schematic of mechanical amplifier

anism, is customarily employed as an *oscillator*, and that it is unsuitable as an amplifier.

The suitability of an amplifier of any kind, aside from the existence of useful gain, lies in the magnitude of internally generated noise. Noise in electronic amplifiers arises from such sources as thermal noise in resistive elements, random electron emission from the cathodes of electronic tubes, recombination noise in transistors, etc. Noise in a laser arises from spontaneous emission.

The spontaneous emission in a laser is not insignificant with respect to the stimulated emission; the spontaneous emission noise in a laser used as an amplifier of weak signals would completely swamp any input signal which it was desired to amplify.

This situation does not, however, eliminate the possibility of the laser as a *large-signal amplifier*. Experiments along these lines have been conducted by several workers, using a laser as a signal input to a second laser. In ruby, it has required kilowatts of signal input to produce measurable amplification. With neodymium glass lasers used in series, amplification of 7 decibels has been produced. Suggestions have been made for the use of lasers as pumping sources for other lasers.

**13.18. Optical Voltage Amplification.** A mechanical amplifier can be constructed, as shown in Figure 13.3, with a series of condensers. If an alternating current flows through the condensers, and the plates are mechanically pulled apart at the time a voltage peak occurs and returned to normal position at instants of zero voltage, amplification will be obtained, the amplified wave having the frequency $f$. It is also possible to produce an amplified wave with frequency $f_1 + f_2$ where $f_1$ is the frequency of the input voltage and $f_2$ is the frequency of the mechanical plate oscillation.

A similar principle can be applied to a laser beam, with the mechanical motion substituted by a change in the dielectric constant of the condenser dielectric. Experiments are under way for the production of pairs of infrared wavelengths by this technique.

## PHOTODETECTORS FOR LASER APPLICATIONS

**13.19. Requirements.** Measurements and experiments with lasers and some laser applications require the use of photodetectors applied in a man-

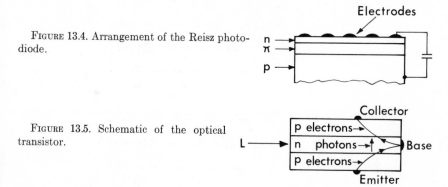

FIGURE 13.4. Arrangement of the Reisz photo-diode.

FIGURE 13.5. Schematic of the optical transistor.

ner not typical of their usual uses. In particular, the new type of use involves photomixing, as described above. As a result of the new requirements, some new types of photodetectors have been developed, and improvements have been made to existing types. In particular, the photodetectors which have been primarily involved in laser work have been the photodiode, the optical transistor, and the traveling-wave phototube.

**13.20. Photodiodes.** The photodiode is a semiconductor junction in which the necessary injection of electrons to produce conduction is provided by radiant energy falling on the junction. Figure 13.4 shows, schematically, the photodiode developed by Riesz.[39] In common with all photodiodes, it consists fundamentally of a $p$-$n$ junction separated by a relatively thick epitaxial layer. Typically these regions have the thicknesses shown in the diagram. Contact to the $n$-layer is provided by strip electrodes, joined by a contact ring. Germanium and silicon are typical materials for this device.

Values of the quantum efficiency as high as 40 per cent have been reported for practical devices of this type, which are available commercially. Demodulation at frequencies up to 20 gigacycles and frequency bandwidth of 5 gigacycles has been achieved.

**13.21. The Optical Transistor.** A transistor which operates with optical effects has been recently announced. It consists of an $n$-$p$-$n$ junction, as shown in Figure 13.5. Part of the emitter signal produces photons, which are absorbed at the base-collector junction, releasing electrons to the collector.

**13.22. The Traveling-wave Phototube.**[40] Two types of traveling-wave phototubes have been developed for use in modulation and demodulation of laser beams. These two types, which differ only in mechanical arrangement, are shown in Figure 13.6.

The principle is the same as for the microwave traveling-wave amplifier.

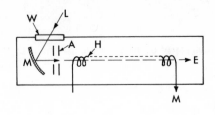

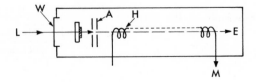

FIGURE 13.6. Two arrangements of the traveling-wave phototube.

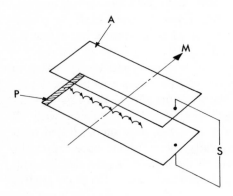

FIGURE 13.7. Schematic of the electrostatic multiplier phototube.

The beam of photoelectrons produced at the photoemissive cathode travels along the helix of a microwave conductor. The pitch of the helix is dimensioned to that the component of the microwave velocity along the axis of the helix is equal to the velocity of the photoelectron beam. Any modulation in the electron beam is transferred by induction to the microwave current at each turn, resulting in an amplified signal at the microwave output.

**13.23. Electrostatic Multiplier Phototube.**[41] A device similar in principle but different in construction from the traveling-wave tube is the electrostatic multiplier phototube of Gaddy and Holshouser, illustrated in Figure 13.7.

In this device, the photoelectron beam "skips" down the tube with multiple contacts on a continuous secondary emitter, the skipping being caused by the impression of a magnetic field across the tube. A close parallel plate microwave current conductor provides inductive coupling of a microwave current to the electron beam. The effect is a compound amplification, both from the electron multiplication by secondary emission and from the multiple coupling to the microwave current.

## REFERENCES

Bibliography for Chapters 13 to 14 will be found at the end of Chapter 14.

CHAPTER 14

# Laser Applications

**14.1. General.** The intense interest which has been shown in lasers since their first successful operation in 1960 has, of course, been partly due to the optical phenomena which they have revealed and the new areas of investigation which have been opened. The economic support which laser investigation has received, however, could not have been generated by mere scientific curiosity; it has been due to the wide field of applications which became evident immediately.

It is quite premature to discuss specific applications in great detail; only a very few have so far been actually realized with practical instrumentation, and even these are destined to be modified and improved very rapidly as the technology advances. Many general areas of application which lasers open to possible exploitation are readily defined, however. Some reasonable conclusions can be drawn as to the possibilities which lie in these areas, and it would be improper not to include some discussion of these.

**14.2. Properties of Lasers.** The specific properties of lasers which set them apart from techniques and devices which have previously been available are monochromaticity, time coherence, space coherence, and power level. Each of these properties points the way to particular applications of great interest and importance.

## COMMUNICATIONS

**14.3. Communications.** One of the most promising areas for application of lasers is in communications—to the extent that a large share of the economic support which laser development has received has come from organizations and agencies interested primarily in communications.

The reason for this interest is easy to see. Communications has come, in the modern world, to depend more and more on electromagnetic radiation. From radio to radar, the electromagnetic frequency spectrum from a few kilocycles to a few hundred gigacycles (10 to $10^{11}$ cycles), covering wavelengths from a millimeter to thousands of meters, has been exploited to the point where hardly a region can be found which is not being used by various communications equipment. Demands for greater and greater capacity mount exponentially.

The *capacity* of a communications channel is determined by its *bandwidth*—the range of frequencies which it is possible to impose upon it. A television channel, for example, typically utilizes a *carrier* frequency of, say, 200 Mc. This carrier is *modulated* by the information which must be conveyed, and this information, typically, requires a range of frequencies of about 5 Mc. Whether amplitude or frequency is employed, the effect of the modulation is to spread the frequency content of the modulated carrier over the band reaching from 197.5 to 202.5 Mc. To avoid interference, a different television station must be assigned a carrier frequency at least 5 megacycles away from the first. There is thus only a limited amount of room in the spectrum band assigned to television.

Lasers provide a carrier frequency of the order of $10^{14}$ cycles; if it is assumed that the upper limit of present communication frequencies is $10^{11}$ cycles, then lasers provide for an increase in the available frequency range by a factor of 1000. In the interval between $10^{11}$ cycles and $10^{14}$ cycles, there is 1000 times as much room as exists in the entire band from zero to $10^{11}$ cycles. With the present crowding in available channels, this provides an area worth exploiting.

Transmission and detection of a television program transmitted at 3 gigacycles over a laser beam has already been demonstrated over a short path length.

**14.4. Limitations.** Laser beams are severely affected by the atmosphere; ground-to-ground communications by means of lasers would be limited to rather short paths and would be at the mercy of weather conditions, unless enclosed pipelines were used. There is no such limitation, however, in space, and with the new space era opening up, the possibilities of lasers for interspace communication are very promising.[42] There are also promising possibilities for applications at very high altitudes, above the regions of clouds and haze.

**14.5. Modulation.**[43] The primary requirement for the use of a laser beam for communication is a means for modulation of the beam so that it may carry information. Modulation may be in frequency, amplitude or phase.

There are two methods of approach to the problem of modulating a laser beam—internal and external modulation. In internal modulation, the modulating signal is applied to the cavity, so that the emitted beam is modulated; in external modulation, the emitted beam is passed through a modulating element. Both types of modulation have been applied in experimental work.

**14.6. Internal Modulation.**[44] A mode frequency of a cavity is determined by the relation $2b = N\lambda$, where $b$ is the cavity length. Changing $b$ changes the mode frequency, and if this is done by an input signal, the output will be frequency modulated.

Changing the length of the cavity by half a wavelength ($2.5 \times 10^{-5}$ cm) changes the resonant frequency in a typical laser by about 150 Mc, so that the input modulating signal does not have to introduce a great change. Changes in an end-mirror location by application of the piezoelectric effect are adequate. The technique has also been used to stabilize the cavity frequency, as described in a previous section.

Other possible methods of internal modulation have been mentioned, including the variation of energy level values in the magnetic-optical laser and Zeeman tuning in the divalent rare earths.

**14.7. External Modulation.**[45] External modulation has been most energetically explored, most of the schemes depending upon polarization and birefringence effects in crystals. Most used has been the Pockels Effect (see Section 3.32) in which the polarization of the incident light beam is altered upon passing through the crystal, the effect being proportional to an electric field applied across the crystal. Typical crystals showing this effect are KDP (potassium dihydrogen phosphate) and ADP (ammonium dihydrogen phosphate).

**14.8. Pockels Effect Modulation.** Figure 14.1 shows an arrangement used to achieve microwave modulation of a laser beam.

The modulator crystal (KDP or ADP) is enclosed in a microwave cavity and shrouded in a plastic bed. The variations in the microwave field act upon the crystal, which in turn modulates the laser beam.

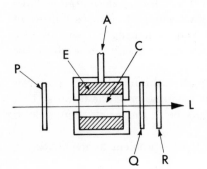

FIGURE 14.1. Schematic arrangement for optical modulation: (A) microwave modulating input, (P) polarizer, (E) plastic embedment, (C) piezoelectric crystal, (Q) quarter-wave plate, (R) analyzer, (L) light output.

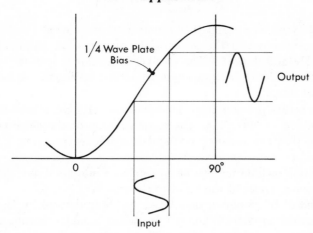

FIGURE 14.2. Output signal from modulator

The arrangement shown in the Figure includes a polarizer at the input to the modulator; many lasers are provided with Brewster-angle windows which provide a polarized output from the laser—the losses being low only for light which is polarized in the plane corresponding to Brewster's angle —and when this type of laser is used, the polarizer shown in the Figure is not required.

Figure 14.2 shows the analyzer output as modulated by the input signal. The ¼-wave plate which is shown in the Figure displaces the output to a region of the curve which provides more efficient modulation, as the comparative graphs show.

This arrangement provides *amplitude modulation* of the beam; bandwidths of the order of 10 Mc have been provided at a modulating frequency of 0.5 to 2 gigacycles. Pockels effect modulators in this operating range are now available as standard products; they require 2 to 10 watts of modulation input.

**14.9. Polarization Modulation.** It is also possible to apply this method of modulation and directly transmit the output of the modulator (after the ¼-wave plate). The beam, which is now polarization modulated, would then be converted to amplitude modulation at the receiver, which would have an analyzer at its input end.

**14.10. Dual Modulation.** The dual transverse linear electro-optical effect provides a means for imposing two independent modulating signals on the transmitted beam. Cubic crystals, for example zinc sulfide (ZnS) and cuprous chloride (CuCl), can be modulated independently in mutually perpendicular planes, both transverse to the beam. The output consists of two independent beams, polarized in mutually perpendicular planes, each modulated by its own signal. The signal is recoverable at the receiver by detectors responding to the appropriate directions of polarization.

**14.11. Demodulation.**[46] The receiver of a communications system includes a *demodulator*, with the function of responding to the modulation in the input signal.

Photodetectors provide good demodulators for light beams for modulation frequencies lower than the response time of the detectors, which means that they can respond to modulation frequencies up to a few gigacycles.

Polarization modulation can be transformed into amplitude modulation by a polarizing device at the input to the receiver.

A method of frequency demodulation has been devised by Harris, who used two calcite crystals to convert frequency modulation into amplitude modulation over a frequency range of about 2:1.

**14.12. Magneto-optic Kerr Effect.** The magneto-optic Kerr effect (see Section 3.37), in which a polarization effect is observed in light reflected from a surface subjected to a magnetic field, has been used as a modulation device. In this scheme, thin magnetic films are used.

**14.13. Laser Stability.** One of the practical problems in the adaptation of lasers to communications through the use of modulated beams is maintaining laser frequency and amplitude stability to a satisfactory degree. Since movements of the end mirrors of the resonant cavity by fractions of a wavelength can introduce a major degree of frequency modulation, instabilities are readily caused by vibration. Longer-term frequency changes are caused by temperature variations, and "mode-hopping" is a result of instability in the excitation power.

The control of cavity length through feedback to a piezoelectric crystal controlling the end-mirror position has been mentioned as a technique for frequency stabilization of laser output.

## MONOCHROMATICITY AND COHERENCE

**14.14. Interferometry.**[47] Prior to the laser, much effort had been spent in searching for and developing sources of narrow bandwidth for interferometric applications and for wavelength standards. For many years (since 1927), the red cadmium line at 6438Å has been the international standard wavelength in the visible spectrum for spectrographic calibration. Early in the 1950's the emission at 5461Å from the $Hg^{198}$ isotope of mercury was proposed as a new standard, since it has a narrower bandwidth. With this line, interference fringes of order about 500,000 can be observed. For the sodium D-lines, by comparison, about 50,000 orders of interference can be observed.

FIGURE 14.2A. Twyman-Green interferometer with laser source. (*Courtesy Perkin-Elmer Corp.*)

In terms of the coherence length, as defined by Wolf[48]

$$L = \bar{\lambda}^2/\Delta\lambda \qquad (14.1)$$

the coherence length of the sodium D-lines is about 6 cm and that of the Hg[198] line about 60 cm, its width being of the order of .005Å.

Laser emission, as has been indicated, has shown line widths as narrow as 2 cycles/sec, or about $2 \times 10^{-11}$Å. The corresponding coherence length is about 50,000 miles, which implies the possibility of interference to about $10^{13}$ orders.

It is highly probable that a laser source will eventually be adopted as a

FIGURE 14.2B. Interference fringes with a Herriott multiple beam interferometer. The path difference between fringes is .03 wavelength [see D. Herriott, *J. Opt. Soc. Am., 52, 1142 (1962)*]. (*Courtesy Perkin-Elmer Corp.*)

wavelength standard; this adoption, however, must wait for the development of techniques to stabilize wavelengths and to specify conditions under which the emission is constant and repeatable. The above computations, based upon a frequency bandwidth of 2 cycles/sec, represent a theoretical situation, not a practical one at the present state of the art. While line widths of this order have been observed, they do not remain stable long enough to be relied upon for interferometric work. However, one would be quite satisfied with a line width of the order of 3 Mc (coherence length 100 meters), and this is quite possible at the present time.

The effect of the laser on interferometry, therefore, has been essentially to remove the problem of coherence length and to permit observation of high-contrast fringes over almost any desired path difference.

**14.15. Metrology.** In recent years, there have been a number of applications of interference to the direct measurement of length, through the technique of fringe counting as the separation between two mirrors is varied. It has been used for the measurement of the stylus advance of ruling engines, for the checking of mechanical gage blocks, for the measurement of star and missile images on photographic plates, and for other purposes.

One of the limitations on this type of measurement has been the visibility of fringes due to limited coherence lengths in available light sources. The almost unlimited coherence lengths characteristic of the laser will provide a new freedom in the application of fringe counting to direct distance measurement. It is theoretically possible, with laser beams which can now be produced, to measure distances of several miles to an accuracy of a micro-inch.

One quickly discovers, when techniques for very precise distance measurement become available, that distances do not "stay put" to these kind of accuracies.

**14.16. Lasers in Spectroscopy.** The laser provides a new tool of great power for spectroscopy and spectrography. There are at least four areas of application in this field in which the characteristics of the laser provide a new dimension.

With the strong monochromatic source which a laser provides, it is possible to induce specific excitation in various materials which it was not previously possible to do. At the beginning of laser development, it appeared that the very few specific wavelengths which were available (ruby, He-Ne, Nd-glass and a few others) would severely limit this kind of application. However, recent developments of literally hundreds of different wavelengths from different intrinsic materials, from Raman-effect stimulation, from the tunable characteristics of semiconductor lasers, and from harmonic generation, have made it clear that there will be no shortage of available wavelengths for almost any desired experiment.

The high electrical and magnetic field strengths which are obtained with focused laser beams has opened a new field of investigation into the nature and structure of materials, and the interaction of radiation and matter. Current interest has been largely concentrated on the inducing of nonlinear effects, such as those discussed in the previous chapter; these constitute only one facet of the interaction domain, and there are innumerable other areas awaiting exploration. The controllable aspect of laser beams provides a tremendous advantage in this type of investigation.

A third characteristic is also of considerable interest: the ability to concentrate a large amount of heat energy in a small volume with a focused laser beam. By this means, phenomena which take place only under conditions such as are found in the stars can be induced in the laboratory on a scale small enough for them to be carefully examined.

Finally, the ability to produce interaction phenomena associated with very high energy levels on a highly transient basis with the extremely fast pulses possible with laser beams is another useful characteristic.

For these applications which utilize highly localized concentrations of energy, frequency and amplitude stabilization are not important, and lasers in their present form provide tremendously powerful tools which are only now beginning to be utilized. The results which will be achieved with these new tools will continue to be felt for decades to come.

## OTHER APPLICATIONS

**14.17. Direction and Ranging.** In many ways, the laser is very like a radar system; it produces high-energy, highly coherent electromagnetic radiation on either a pulse or a continuous-wave basis. It can, therefore, in principle be applied to the same problems to which radar is applied. This includes tracking, ranging and scanning applications.

Currently, laser beam powers do not compare with those which can be produced with microwave equipment, but this is a temporary situation, and the present-day laboratory-size lasers are being compared with very large microwave installations. A disadvantage of the laser with respect to microwave radar lies in the high level of scattering of visible and infrared wavelengths in the atmosphere. But, as has been pointed out before, we are in the process of emerging from the atmosphere into space, and in this domain the laser will be highly useful for these types of application.

One of the great advantages of the laser in radar-like applications lies in its very narrow beam width. The beam spread of microwave radiation is limited primarily by diffraction effects—the angular spread being given by the now familiar ratio, $\lambda/D$. For this reason, radar systems with high pointing accuracy require very large antennas—in some cases hundreds of feet.

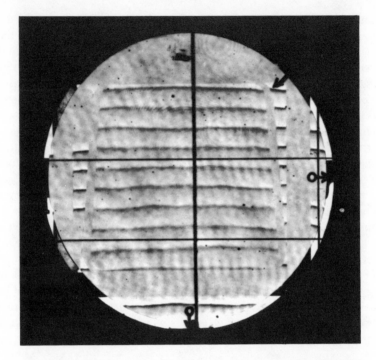

FIGURE 14.2C. Test of a plane-parallel window in a laser interferometer. The dark lines crossing the field are strings stretched across the aperture for reference. Portions of the interferometer background fringes can be seen through apertures in the mounting. (*Photo courtesy Perkin-Elmer Corp.*)

The diffraction limit for a given aperture in the case of radiation at laser wavelengths is some $10^4$ times smaller, so that a one-inch laser beam without any additional optics has a beam width smaller than radar equipment using a 50-foot antenna.

It is possible, by special techniques involving phase comparisons, to obtain angular resolutions with microwave equipment to angles which are orders of magnitude smaller than the diffraction-limited beam width of the apparatus; these techniques are also theoretically possible with laser beams, since they show a similar, if not a superior, degree of coherence. However, these techniques imply detectors which will respond to phase as well as amplitude, and these are not currently available for operation at light frequencies.

Also, in the case of microwaves, although special techniques avoid the limitation on *resolution* imposed by diffraction, there is no way to avoid the energy loss associated with a beam which is much wider than it needs to be.

**14.18. Project Luna See.** A laser beam reflected from the surface of the moon has already been detected, in an experiment by Smullin and Fiocco[49] in 1963. Using a giant-pulse ruby laser, they were able to obtain a return of about 12 photons per pulse on the receiving detector which could be statistically shown to be due to the laser beam. A 12-inch diameter Cassegrainian telescope was used in the experiment.

**14.19. Methods of Producing Giant Pulses.** Hellwarth and McClung used a Kerr cell in producing their giant pulses from ruby. This arrangement does not provide an *absolute* shutter, in that it does not completely prevent oscillations when the shutter is closed; it merely raises the threshold for oscillations sufficiently to produce less frequent and therefore larger pulses (about 3 orders of magnitude higher than normal). The addition of a polarizing device, such as a Glan-Thompson prism, in front of the Kerr cell would provide an absolute shutter.

Stitch *et al.*, have produced large pulses by a method known as the "hair-trigger" method. The laser is pumped nearly to threshold by conventional means, and the large pulse is initiated by flashing a second pumping lamp. which raises the laser suddenly above threshold.

DeMaria and Gagosz[17] have utilized an ultrasonic cell in the resonant cavity of a laser to produce a controlled pulse repetition rate. Light is scattered from the standing waves produced by an ultrasonic generator in the cell, in a manner similar to scattering from a diffraction grating. The deflection follows the generation of the ultrasonic wave in time, and is zero when the wave amplitude is zero; thus the favored condition for pulsing occurs at twice the ultrasonic frequency.

**14.20. The Ring Laser.** If two light beams travel in opposite directions around a path which is a closed loop, then if the loop is rotating around an axis normal to its plane, the two light beams will show a relative phase shift upon return to the starting point. If the source of the light is outside the loop and does not take part in the rotation, the fringe shift is due to a path difference in the coordinate system containing the source; if the source is within the loop and takes part in the rotation, then the fringe shift is due to a frequency difference beween the two beams.

An experiment of this type was performed by Sagnac in 1913, using a light source outside the loop; he was able to detect a rotation rate of 120 rpm.

The sensitivity of the experiment is dependent upon the line width of the source and the area of the loop, the fringe shift being proportional to the area. The narrow line width of a laser beam permits detection of very small

FIGURE 14.2D. Laser beam refracted through a prism. This illustration gives an indication of the very narrow beam width obtained with lasers. (*Courtesy Perkin-Elmer Corp.*)

fringe shifts. The experiment has been repeated by Macek *et al.*[50] At Sperry Rand in 1962, and rotational rates as low as 2 deg/min were observed, with a loop in the form of a square four feet on a side.

The ring laser has also been called a *laser gyro*, because in detecting rotation rates it performs the same function as a gyroscope. It is theoretically possible to construct such a device which would compete in accuracy with the best mechanical gyros.

**14.21. Applications in Biology and Chemistry.**[51] Focused laser beams can create localized high-intensity effects which will be useful in investigations in chemistry and biology. Already laser beams have been used for microsurgery, especially in the retina for operations in the surgically difficult treatment of the "detached retina." Thermal coagulation in tiny areas with a focused laser beam has been very successful in correcting this condition.

The ability of a focused laser beam to create thermal coagulation, cauterization and tissue destruction in highly localized areas points the way to many new treatments in surgery and many new experiments in biology.

Specific thermal effects which may be created on a small scale can initiate physicochemical effects, such as changes in osmosis, which will be of

FIGURE 14.2E. Damage to glass surfaces by a laser beam. (*Courtesy Perkin-Elmer Corp.*)

FIGURE 14.2F. Laser beam penetrating a glass block. The beam is causing breakdown of the glass at various "hot spots" along the beam. (*Courtesy Perkin-Elmer Corp.*)

great value in biological studies. The very high-intensity electric fields which can be created in tissues and in materials by laser beams will make possible numerous types of investigations which were not practicable previously. For example, it is now possible to put a potential of hundreds of volts across a red blood corpuscle or across a nerve synapse.

**14.22. Microforming.** Focused laser beams are powerful enough to vaporize metal, thus providing a cutting tool of very small dimensions. Laser beams have already been used for fusing electrical connections in microcircuitry, and many other new and useful applications are forecast.

## REFERENCES

Note: The following references for Part 3 are presented as an aid to the reader in pursuing more detailed discussion of the various areas involved. This is by no means a comprehensive bibliography on laser literature, and no particular attempt has been made to include all significant contributions or to exclude contributions of little value. Neither is there any historical significance to be attached to the listings.

1. T. Maiman, *Nature*, **187**, 498 (1960).
   T. Maiman, R. Hoskins, I. D'Haenens, C. Asawa and V. Evtuhov, *Phys. Rev.*, **123**, 1151 (1961).
2. J. Gordon, H. Zieger and C. Townes, *Phys. Rev.*, **95**, 282 (1954).
3. J. Gordon, H. Zieger and C. Townes, *Phys. Rev.*, **99**, 1264 (1955).
4. A. Schwalow and C. Townes, *Phys. Rev.*, **112**, 1940 (1958).
5. J. Gordon, *Sci. Am.* (December 1958).
6. I. D'Haenens and D. Buddenhagen, *J. Soc. Motion Picture Television Engrs.*, **71**, 828 (1962).
   A. Schwalow, *Sci. Am.* (June 1961).
   B. Lengyel, "Lasers," New York, John Wiley & Sons, 1962.
   G. Birnbaum, "Optical Masers," New York, Academic Press, 1963.
   A. Schwalow, *Phys. Today*, **17**, 28 (1964).
   W. Wagner and G. Birnbaum, *J. Appl. Phys.*, **32**, 1185 (1961).
7. A. Javan, W. Bennett and D. Herriott, *Phys. Rev. Letters*, **6**, 106 (1961).
8. A. White and J. Rigden, *Proc. IRE*, **50**, 1697 (1962).
9. E. Ballik, Proceedings of Symposium on Optical Masses, p. 231, Brooklyn, N.Y., Polytechnic Press, 1963.
10. A. Fox and T. Li, *Bell System Tech. J.*, **40**, 453 (1961).
11. D. Herriott, H. Kogelnik and R. Kompfer, *Appl. Opt.*, **3**, 523 (1964).
    P. Connes, *Rev. d'Opt.*, **35**, 37 (1956).
    G. Boyd and J. Gordon, *Bell System Tech. J.*, **40**, 489 (1961).
    G. Boyd and H. Kogelnik, *Bell System Tech. J.*, **41**, 1347 (1962).
    J. Pierce, "Theory and Design of Electron Beams," p. 194, Princeton, N. J., D. Van Nostrand, 1954.
12. A. Blume and K. Tittel, *Appl. Opt.*, **3**, 527 (1964).
13. I. Abella and H. Cummins, *J. Appl. Phys.*, **32**, 1177 (1961).
14. O. Svelto, *Appl. Opt.*, **1**, 745 (1962).
15. R. Kaplan, Proceedings of Symposium on Optical Masers, p. 211, Brooklyn, N.Y., 1963.

16. M. Silver, R. Witte and C. York, *Appl. Opt.*, **3**, 539 (1964).
17. T. Hughes, *Nature*, **195**, 325 (1962).
    A. DeMaria and R. Gagosz, *Appl. Opt.*, **2**, 807 (1963).
    W. Bennett, *Phys. Rev.*, **126**, 580 (1962).
18. F. McClung and R. Hellwarth, *J. Appl. Phys.*, **33**, 828 (1962).
19. W. Bennett, *Appl. Opt. Suppl.*, 24 (1962).
20. A. Prokhorov, *Zh. Eksperim. i Teor. Fiz.*, **34**, 1658 (1958); *Soviet Phys.—JETP*, **7**, 1140 (1958).
21. T. Polanyi and W. Watson, *J. Opt. Soc. Am.*, **54**, 449 (1964).
    D. Herriott, *J. Opt. Soc. Am.*, **52**, 131 (1962).
    W. Rigrod et al., *J. Appl. Phys.*, **33**, 743 (1962).
    W. Rigrod and H. Kogelnik, *Proc. IRE*, **50**, 220 (1962).
    W. Rigrod, *J. Appl. Phys. Letters*, **2**, 3 (1963).
    T. Polanyi and W. Watson, *J. Appl. Phys.*, **34**, 553 (1963).
22. D. Nelson and W. Boyle, *Appl. Opt.*, **1**, 181 (1962).
23. R. Hall et al., *Phys. Rev. Letters*, **9**, 366 (1962).
    M. Nathan et al., *Appl. Phys. Letters*, **1**, 62 (1962).
    T. Quist et al., *Appl. Phys. Letters*, **1**, 91 (1962).
24. B. Lax, Proceedings of Symposium on Optical Masses, p. 119, Brooklyn, N.Y., Polytechnic Press, 1963.
25. P. Aigrain, *Intern. Conf. Solid State Physics, Brussels* (1958); 3d *Quantum Electron. Conf., Paris* (1963).
26. B. Lax, in (Townes, C., Ed.) "Quantum Electronics," New York, Columbia University Press, 1960.
27. L. Johnson and K. Nassau, *Proc. IRE*, **49**, 1704 (1961).
    L. Johnson, *J. Appl. Phys.*, **34**, 897 (1963).
28. P. Sorokin and M. Stevenson, *Phys. Rev. Letters*, **5**, 557 (1960).
29. P. Sorokin and M. Stevenson, *IBM J. Res. Develop.*, **5**, 56 (January 1961).
30. G. Crosby and R. Whan, *J. Mol. Spectry.*, **8**, 315 (1962).
    E. Schmitschek and E. Schwarz, *Nature*, **196**, 832 (1962).
31. A. Lempicki and H. Samuelson, *Phys. Rev. Letters*, **4**, 133 (1963).
32. G. Crosby et al., *J. Chem. Phys.*, **34**, 743 (1961).
33. J. Armstrong, N. Blooembergen, J. Ducuing and P. Pershan, *Phys. Rev.*, **127**, 1918 (1962).
    N. Blooembergen and P. Pershan, *Phys. Rev.*, **128**, 606 (1962).
    J. Kleinman, *Phys. Rev.*, **128**, 1761 (1962).
    N. Blooembergen, *Proc. IEEE*, **51**, 124 (1963).
    P. Franken and J. Ward, *Rev. Mod. Phys.*, **35**, 23 (1963).
    N. Blooembergen, Proceedings of Symposium on Optical Masses, p. 13, Brooklyn, N.Y., Polytechnic Press, 1963.
34. J. Giordmaine, *Phys. Rev. Letters*, **8**, 19 (1962).
35. P. Franken et al., *Phys. Rev. Letters*, **7**, 118 (1961).
    P. Maker et al., *Phys. Rev. Letters*, **8**, 21 (1962).
36. J. Giordmaine, *Sci. Am.* (April 1964).
37. B. McMurtry, *Appl. Opt.*, **2**, 767 (1963).
    B. McMurtry and A. Siegman, *Appl. Opt.*, **1**, 51 (1962).
    A. Forrester, *J. Opt. Soc. Am.*, **51**, 253 (1961).
    A. Forrester, R. Gudmundsen and P. Johnson, *Phys. Rev.*, **99**, 1691 (1955).
    P. Pershan and N. Blooembergen, *Appl. Phys. Letters*, **2**, 117 (1963).

L. Anderson, Proceedings of Symposium on Optical Masses, p. 549, Brooklyn, N.Y., Polytechnic Press, 1963.

38. H. Cummins, N. Knable and Y. Yeh, *Appl. Opt.*, **2**, 823 (1963).
    A. Seigman and S. Harris, Proceedings of Symposium on Optical Masses, p. 511, Brooklyn, N.Y., Polytechnic Press, 1963.
39. R. Reisz, *Rev. Sci. Instr.*, **33**, 994 (1962).
40. B. McMurtry and A. Siegman, *Appl. Opt.*, **1**, 51 (1962).
41. A. Gaddy and D. Holshouser, *Proc. IEEE*, **51**, 153 (1963).
42. R. Schwartz and C. Townes, *Nature*, **190**, 205 (1961).
43. C. Buhrer, L. Bloom and D. Baird, *Appl. Opt.*, **2**, 839 (1963).
44. I. Kaminow, *Phys. Rev. Letters*, **6**, 528 (1961).
    R. Blumenthal, *Proc. IRE*, **50**, 452 (1962).
    E. Gordon and J. Rigden, *Bell System Tech. J.*, **42**, 155 (1963).
45. B. Seraphin *et al.*, Proceedings of Symposium on Optical Masses, p. 635, Brooklyn, N.Y., Polytechnic Press, 1963.
46. S. Harris, *Appl. Phys. Letters*, **2**, 47 (1963).
    S. Harris *et al.*, *Appl. Phys. Letters*, **1**, 37 (1962).
    See also reference 38.
47. H. Moos *et al.*, *Appl. Opt.*, **2**, 817 (1963).
48. E. Wolf, *Proc. Roy. Soc., London Ser. A*, **239**, 246 (1955); A**225**, 96 (1954); *Proc. Symp. Optical Masers*, 29 (1963).
49. L. Smullin and G. Fiocco, *Proc. IRE*, **50**, 1703 (1962).
50. W. Macek *et al.*, Proceedings of Symposium on Optical Masses, p. 199, Brooklyn, N.Y., Polytechnic Press, 1963.
51. V. Tomberg, Proceedings of Symposium on Optical Masses, p. 505, Brooklyn, N.Y., Polytechnic Press, 1963.

# Index

# Index